# AFRICA'S LANDS AND NATIONS

**McGRAW-HILL BOOK COMPANY**
NEW YORK • ST. LOUIS • SAN FRANCISCO
TORONTO • LONDON • SYDNEY

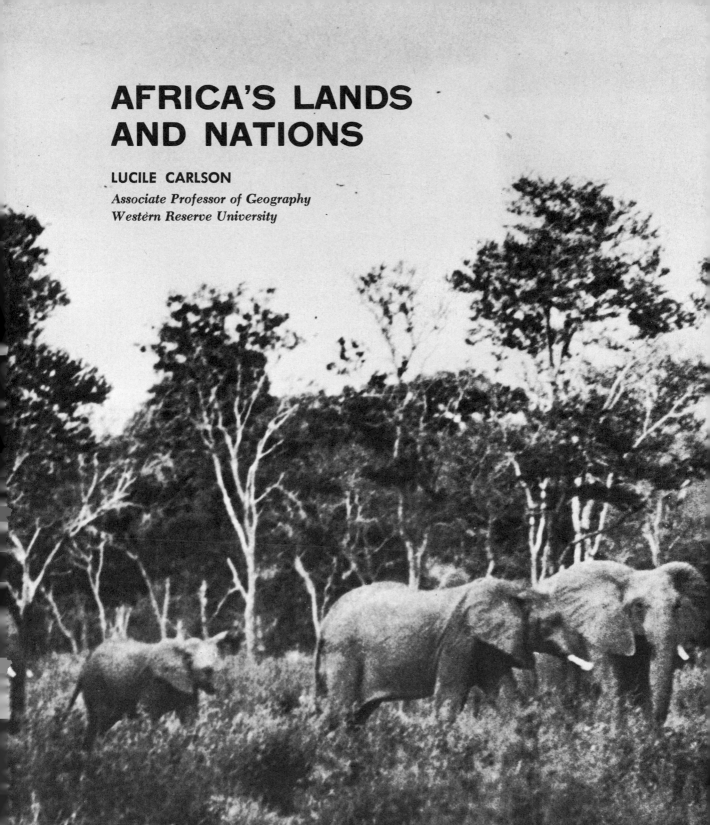

# AFRICA'S LANDS AND NATIONS

**LUCILE CARLSON**

*Associate Professor of Geography*
*Western Reserve University*

**McGRAW-HILL SERIES IN GEOGRAPHY**
John C. Weaver, *Consulting Editor*

Vernor C. Finch was Consulting Editor of this series
from its inception in 1934 to 1951.

**AFRICA'S LANDS AND NATIONS**

1234567890 HD 7432106987

## CREDITS FOR CHAPTER-OPENING PHOTOGRAPHS

**FIGURE 1.1** The Sphinx at Giza. (*Photograph by C. Zachary. Courtesy Egyptian State Tourist Administration.*)

**FIGURE 2.1** Ruins of a Roman aqueduct, Tunisia. (*Courtesy Embassy of Tunisia.*)

**FIGURE 3.1** Mosque, Morocco. (*Courtesy French Information Service.*)

**FIGURE 4.1** Bou Saada, Algeria. (*Photograph by Gzindat. Courtesy French Information Service, Algiers.*)

**FIGURE 5.1** Ruins at Leptis Magna, Libya. (*From The Lamp. Courtesy The Standard Oil Company of New Jersey.*)

**FIGURE 6.1** Ripon Falls, the source of the Nile, now disappeared as a result of the Owen Falls Dam. (*Courtesy Department of Information, Uganda.*)

**FIGURE 7.1** Airview of the pyramids at Giza. (*Photograph by C. Zachary. Courtesy Egyptian State Tourist Administration.*)

**FIGURE 8.1** Where the waters of the Blue and White Niles merge. (*Photograph by writer.*)

**FIGURE 9.1** Caravaneers and their camels, Niger. (*From Le Niger en Marche, first-anniversary booklet of the Republic of the Niger. Courtesy, Embassy of the Niger Republic.*)

**FIGURE 10.1** Silhouette of the Sahara. (*Courtesy Service de l'Information, AOF.*)

**FIGURE 11.1** The stilt-rooted mangrove grows thickly in many places along the West African shore—in the mud flats and up the river mouths. (*Photograph by writer.*)

**FIGURE 12.1** Fishing in the lagoon at Abidjan. (*Courtesy Service de l'Information, AOF.*)

**FIGURE 13.1** The African elephant has never been successfully domesticated to hard labor as has the Asian. However, attempts at domestication were made with some success at Gangala Na Bodio, Oriental Province, The Congo, by the Service of Water and Forests. In this photograph, domesticated African elephants are bathing in the Epulu River at Gangala Na Bodio. (*Courtesy Belgian Information Services.*)

**FIGURE 14.1** Boma, Congo. Tropical woods are one of the important resources of Africa's equatorial lands. Boma on the north bank of the Congo estuary, like Port Gentil on the Gabon coast, is a major lumber shipping point. (*Photograph C. Lamote, Congopresse.*)

**FIGURE 15.1** Lioness and her kill. (*Courtesy Information Service, Nairobi.*)

**FIGURE 16.1** Cape Peninsula with Cape Town in foreground. (*Courtesy South African Information Service, Pretoria.*)

**FIGURE 17.1** Study of an old African, Rhodesia. (*Courtesy Federal Information Department, Rhodesia.*)

**FIGURE 18.1** Zambezi River view, Mozambique. (*Courtesy Portuguese Embassy.*)

**FIGURE 19.1** Johannesburg, city of the Rand and industrial giant of South Africa. (*Courtesy P. G. Higgins.*)

**FIGURE 20.1** A view across the Great Rift Valley in Kenya. (*Courtesy Kenya Information Service.*)

**FIGURE 21.1** Flamingos wading in Lake Nakuru, Kenya. (*Courtesy Department of Information, Nairobi.*)

**FIGURE 22.1** A view of the magnificent Blue Nile Falls in Ethiopia showing, in part, the tumultuous descent of the river from the high Ethiopian plateau, where the Blue Nile has its source in Lake Tana, to the African lowlands. Here, near Bahar Dar, on the south shore of Lake Tana, the Blue Nile (here known as the Abbai River) plunges more than 150 feet over the famed Tisisat Falls, one of the most spectacular in the world. (*Courtesy of Ethiopian Airlines, through Trans World Airlines.*)

**FIGURE 23.1** Market scene, Tananarive. (*Photograph by Leavitt Morris, travel editor, The Christian Science Monitor. Courtesy The Christian Science Monitor.*)

**FIGURE 24.1** The old and the new mingle everywhere in Africa: Archaic dhows on the Nile sway in silhouette against modern, storied buildings along the river bank. (*Courtesy Pan American Airways.*)

IN MEMORY OF MY DEAR FATHER

# PREFACE

Physically, Africa is one continent, but historically, ethnically, and racially it is a part of at least two worlds, not one. A great divide occurs along the southern edges of the Sahara. It is a zone that stretches irregularly from the mouth of the Senegal River to the confluence of the White and Blue Niles, and then slips along the base of the Ethiopian plateau to pass to the eastern edge of the continent along the lower course of the Juba River. North of this zone is a generally Caucasian-Moslem world; to the south of it lies much of black Africa, where Christian or native religions are generally followed.

Africa also divides into realms. There is the realm of the Maghrib in the Northwest in many ways unlike the lands dependent on the Nile; there is West Africa, very different from the eastern plateaus; and there is the equatorial heart (so long unknown) and southern Africa, still largely ruled by Europeans.

Africa needs treatment from several points of view. This book presents only the regional. Other approaches are expected to follow; one at present in the writing stage. The regional pattern has been set against the background of the realities noted above. It is hoped that the overviews provided by the "realm" concept will help to minimize the effect of fragmentation resulting from the great number of political units into which the continent divides.

# ACKNOWLEDGMENTS

In writing this book, there has been an attempt to strip down details and superficialities and look at the basics of African geography—the distinctiveness that is Africa and its character as different from that of every other continent.

Every book is written in time and space. So is this one—in time, it is set in the beginning of the era of great changeover in Africa. To present this view, it has been necessary to look back to the past and partially to anticipate the future, for the present lies between; Africa is a continent in transition. Perhaps a century from now, when the Africa of the past and the present have been blurred by progress and the passage of time, someone will leaf through this book in the same curious and absorbed fashion with which the writer has turned the pages of the volumes of the great explorers of Africa of a hundred years ago, and it may help toward an understanding of the Africa of that future day.

*Africa's Lands and Nations* is written as a university textbook. Every textbook should be like a springboard, should project the student into further reading and knowledge on a particular subject. It is the hope that this book will thus stimulate the interest of the reader in the old-new continent that is Africa, and lead him into further understanding.

The writing of this book would not have been possible without the assistance of many. I extend my gratitude to the scores of friends, scholars, and strangers, at home and in the field, who extended their hospitality, help, and guidance to me, and to missionaries, to corporations and their representatives, to research institutes, and to government officials, agencies, and departments, American and foreign. The number of individuals who have lent assistance are too numerous to list, but I am especially indebted to Mr. C. F. Mason and Mr. G. B. Longan of the Firestone International Company, to Dr. James P. Chapin of The American Museum of Natural History in New York, and to Mr. Arthur G. Fetzer, General Secretary of the Baptist Mid-Missions, for the many contacts and opportunities that they opened up for me in Africa.

The writer of any book draws on the research and writing of people who have gone before him. In this way the work of hundreds of individuals is represented here. Space does not allow a complete bibliography; it is, rather, a selected bibliography that includes some of the books that were most useful to the writer. Few specific articles from journals are separately listed; instead, scholarly and professional societies, whose journals the writer referred to frequently, are named.

For the field research that the preparation of this book required, I was granted two sabbatical leaves by Western Reserve University, the many months of which were all spent in Africa. This assistance is gratefully acknowledged. I also wish to express my deep appreciation for the artistic and excellent photographic work done for me by Mr. George LeMaster, now deceased. Because of his technical assistance, I have been able to use many of my own photographs.

*Lucile Carlson*

# CONTENTS

# 1 AFRICAN LANDSCAPES

*And yet may Africa have a Prerogative in Rarities,
and some seeming incredibilities be true.*

CAPT. JOHN SMITH

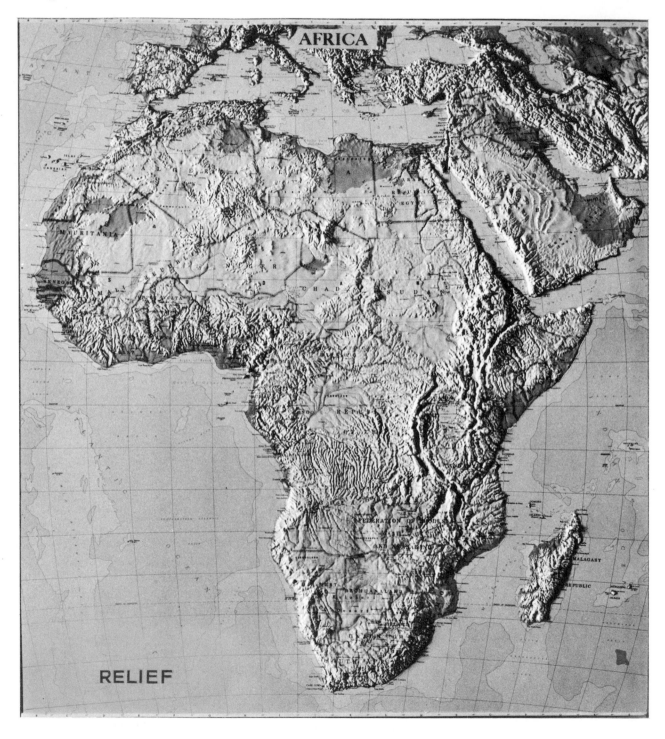

**FIGURE 1.2   Relief map of Africa. (Courtesy Aero Service Corporation.)**

Africa is the second largest continent in the world, 11,635,000 square miles in area. It straddles four hemispheres, for both the Prime Meridian and the Equator pass over it. In the Gulf of Guinea, below the great African hump, the two lines cross, the Prime Meridian bisecting the bulge, the Equator the continent. Africa extends 37°N and 35°S of the Equator and is the most tropical of the continents.

It is a part of the great "World Island," that vast block of land made up of Eurasia and Africa, and is barely separated from Europe at Gibralter, and from Asia at Suez. In fact, Africa and Asia were joined by the thread of land across which the Suez Canal now passes until the canal was dug and opened in A.D. 1869. Because of this, Africa is a part of three worlds —Middle Eastern, Mediterranean, and African.

Its interior is difficult of access. Littoral plains abut against plateaus onto which there are no easy routes because the rivers fall to the sea, or the plains merge into the immensity of the Sahara. Once the interior has been attained, it is still a hard land that repulses conquest—hot and humid, or hot and dry, or swinging climatically from extremes of drought to equal extremes of moisture. Huge rifts rend the surface, forming a system of valleys that cuts across well over half of the north-south length of the continent: East Africa was almost split apart from the rest of the continent in the geologic past (Figure 1.2).

There are mountains in Africa that are capped with eternal snow, one (Mount Kenya) whose flanks touch the Equator. The climates of Africa, therefore, range from some of the hottest on earth to some that, because of altitude, are polar in character. It holds the world's greatest desert, and the most impenetrable swamp. Henry M. Stanley opened up the unknown interior of "Darkest Africa," by tracing the course of the Congo River, less than 4 decades before Robert Falcon Scott was pushing across the snows toward the South Pole in Antarctica.

## Patterns of Relief and Rivers

Africa is a block plateau of notable extent, with edging escarpments whose abrupt fronts, dissected by streams and notched with ravines, resemble angular mountains when viewed from the sea. Once the summits of the escarpments are reached, broad and relatively flat uplands stretch away in many directions. Prominences rise upon the plateau surface, some very high. These are apt to be volcanic in structure or capped by lava. Notable among the interior mountains of nonvolcanic origin, however, is Mount Ruwenzori lying along the rift valley (see Glossary). Some are more like hills, and are likely to be remnants left during periods of intense erosion.

The African plateau has several times been lifted en masse, and as often undergone peneplanation (see Glossary, peneplain). It is a very rigid piece of the earth's crust on which tectonic forces have had little effect. The relatively flat lying rock strata that form the basement of the continent are, therefore, little crumpled. Only in the extreme northwest in the Atlas Mountains, and in the extreme south in the Cape highlands has extensive folding occurred. In some places warping has left gently undulating surfaces, as in parts of the Sahara; volcanic activity, fairly widespread and yet extremely localized, has constructed mountains whose bold features stand out conspicuously within the landscape. Lava flows were associated with the formation of the central Saharan domes, and the resistant igneous rocks that represent the formerly molten deposits stand up as grotesque and tortured landforms in this arid region. Volcanic activity was associated with the rifting of the East African plateau (see Glossary). The volcanoes thus formed rise as majestic mountains—Kilimanjaro, Kenya, Elgon, the Mufumbiro cluster, and others; a double range of volcanoes forms the linear highlands that run diagonally southwest-northeast through the Cameroons.

The plateau extends without interruption from the bounding escarpments of South Africa northward to the northern Sahara, and from the Guinea coast to Somaliland. The folded regions in the south and northwest lie outside of the plateau.

Since Africa is a plateau, the continent generally stands high with the margins dropping as escarpments to the sea. Some of the most rugged mountains in Africa mark the plateau or rift edges, such as the Drakensberg and Ruwenzori. In general, the plateau rises from the west and north toward the east and south. The eastern and southern portions of the upland stand highest—Abyssinia and northward along the Red Sea coast and south, and all of the plateau south of the Congo basin; portions of the ranges of the Guinea lands and the central Saharan massifs also rise high in parts.

Between and among the higher blocks lie wide basins. The central portion of the plateau, cradling the Congo basin, is one such depression. It is separated from the basinlike surface of South Africa by the Benguela swell; in the north, the Congo and Chad basins are separated by the Ubangi-Chari upland, the water divide between Congo and Chad drainage.

## THE SAHARA

The Ubangi-Chari swell slopes northward into the Sahara, a vast desert that persists without interruption from one side of the continent to the other through a band of 20° of latitude. It stretches away, a remarkably flat surface averaging from 600 to 2,000 feet in elevation but with mountainlike masses rising above the plateau platform here and there, and basins occurring as shallow, intervening lowlands. Underneath lies the African shield, as rigid and resistant here as elsewhere.

Relief in the Sahara has been controlled both by tectonic and erosion factors, and by the rigidity of the rock base. The mountains—Ahaggar, Tibesti, Ouenat, Aïr, Adrar des Iforas—are structural domes, formed by a combination of warping and symmetrical local uplift due to pressure, and volcanic activity. The latter was particularly important, and the rocks testify that these massifs are essentially eroded lava plateaus; volcanic necks, lava flows, and craters crown the domed surfaces of the ancient structures. Subsequent erosion carved the broad slopes into series of wide encircling lowlands and inward-facing scarps and plateaus rimming the domes, and of barren and forbidding sandstone and rock plateaus that sweep, in places, nearly to the base of the Sahara Atlas. The massifs and their "halos" of erosional forms make up the principal features of the central Sahara. The Tibesti plateau rises the highest; its greatest eminence, Emi Kusi, a still active volcano, mounts to over 11,000 feet elevation.

Surrounding and separating the domes are the *ergs* and *regs* (see Glossary), the sand and gravel surfaces that cover a large part of the central Sahara. The greatest of the sand deserts, the Oriental and Occidental *ergs*, are the immense alluvial fans of rivers: the Grand Erg Oriental of the ancient Irharhar River that flowed northward from the Ahaggar to lose itself in the depression of the shotts (see Glossary) Melghir and Djerid, the Grand Erg Occidental of the several rivers that flow down the slopes of the Southern Atlas, jointly depositing their alluviums in a series of fans that together form the huge western dune desert of the Erg Occidental, the Erg Iguidi formed by the Daoura River, and the *ergs* Raoui and Chech deposited by the Saoura River (Figure 1.3).

FIGURE 1.3 Airview of an oasis along the meander of a wadi in a sandy desert, or erg. Notice how the gardens and villages lie beside, not in the wadi. The effectiveness of the infrequent rains is revealed in the gully erosion along the left side of the photogaph. *(Courtesy French Information Service.)*

More forbidding and less known than the central portions, the western Sahara is an immense waste where few transportation lines cross and few oases are found. Structurally it is simple, dominated by the northeast-southwest trending arch of the Yetti-Eglab that is bounded, as in the case of the central Saharan plateaus, by the eroded slopes of the dome. Broad lowlands and rugged escarpments face toward the anticline (see Glossary). At the base of these eroded slopes are two longitudinal synclines (see Glossary), the Tindouf lowland between the Yetti-Eglab arch and the arch of the Anti-Atlas, and the broad depression of the Djouf that blends into the flat and barren Azaouad and Tanezrouft. To the south and east of this syncline lie the Aouker dome and the Adrar des Iforas. The Yetti-Eglab arch stretches westward, as the Mauritanian upland, to the borders of the Atlantic.

Like the western portion of the desert, the eastern Sahara, extending from the Tibesti to the Red Sea ranges, is an immense, little traveled waste except where the Nile River makes possible the long oasis confined within the valley bottom. The strata here are generally flat lying, with slight uplift toward the east in the Arabian-Nubian deserts beyond the Nile; northward, from the Ouenat dome, the Libyan desert slopes gradually down toward the Mediterranean so that eroded scarps face inward and south. In the far north, the scarps of Marmarica mark the edge of the Libyan plateau and, at the foot of the escarpment, lie the Quattara depression and the famed oasis and desert entrepôt (see Glossary) of Siwa.

## THE GREAT RIFT VALLEY

More spectacular, possibly, than any of the foregoing features are those associated with the eastern plateau, namely, the great rift valleys with their elongate grabens (see Glossary) and associated lofty mountains and volcanoes, and the sagging plateau that lies between the western and eastern rifts and within which lies equatorial Lake Victoria (see Glossary).

The upland surface of East Africa is high, edged by escarpments that may present long slopes or resemble bold, serrate mountains. The upland is a broad, level to undulating plateau interrupted here and there by hills and volcanoes, the latter isolated and impressive features. Deep ravines slash through the whole.

Horizontal force of one kind or another caused the formation of the East African rifts, which are a part of a greater rift system with links continuous in a generally north-south direction, across one-sixth of the earth's circumference from the Sea of Galilee–Jordan River–Red Sea depression to and beyond the coastline of Mozambique.

The rift occupied by the Red Sea is intermediary between the Asian and African sectors, and represents a faulted block of the earth's crust. It is bordered by the steep escarpments of the Arabian plateau on the east, and the edges of the Nubian and Abyssinian plateaus on the west. In the north, the Red Sea rift divides to send spurs along the two sides of Sinai Peninsula; in the south, also, it bifurcates, one stem being represented in the southwest-northeast trench of the Gulf of Aden, which is depressed between the precipitous plateau margins of southern Arabia and northern Somalia, the second and more impressive branch striking south and slightly to the west. The latter begins as a wide funnel top between the bisected parts of the Ethiopian massif and narrows to a furrowlike graben about halfway through the massif. The main strike of fracture faulting continues, interruptedly and generally southward, as an eastern branch across the uplands of Kenya and into Tanganyika. In Tanganyika the clear trace of rifting becomes partially lost, but is picked up again somewhat farther south as it recurves to meet the western rift. The latter arcuately outlines the western margin of the Nyanza basin, which therefore occupies a cradled position between the eastern and western rifts. Lake Victoria lies in a gentle dip in the center of this saucerlike upland.

South of the point of juncture the line of faulting passes south to southeast through the cleft of the Lake Nyasa graben, across Malawi and Mozambique to disappear under the ocean waters.

## Patterning of Climate, Vegetation, and Soils

Every day of the year, the vertical rays of the sun fall on some part of Africa. There is no landmass on earth that proportionately receives an equivalent amount of sunshine because there is no other continent that is so "symmetrically located"[1] relative to latitude. Most of Africa lies within the tropics; only the extreme northern and southern tips are extratropical. These sectors, subtropical, extend poleward from the Equator far enough to come under the influence of the westerly winds and their accompanying disturbances during the low sun period.

As Africa is a plateau standing moderately above sea level, altitude introduces modifications: the equatorial African lands that lie over and near the Equator, averaging generally between 1,000 and 2,000 feet elevation, are neither so hot nor so humid as are the South American tropics with comparable distances from the Equator. However, where mountains stand athwart winds that are drawn in from the sea onto the continent, as along the Guinea coast, rainfall averages are so high that South America can show no equivalent readings. In South America the equatorial basin lowlands are the wettest lands; in Africa, coasts backed by mountainous highlands receive the highest rainfall. Great mountain systems, that act so effectively as climatic divides in North and South America and in Eurasia, are absent in Africa, and transitional zones of climate are characteristic.

## PRESSURE, WIND, AND CLIMATE: MECHANICS OF SEASONALITY

Night is the "winter" of tropical Africa. In other words, diurnal ranges of temperature are greater than seasonal ranges. Temperatures are warm the year around, and except as elevations intervene or cold currents send in cooling effects to produce asymmetry, temperatures vary smoothly and transitionally across Africa from the Equator north and south. Belts of climate likewise match outward from the Equator (except in East Africa), the equatorial rainy zone merging into wet and dry tropics which in turn pass into tropical deserts, dry subtropics, and in the southeast, humid subtropics. The basic character of African climate is derived from latitude; varying elevation and trend of the landforms, differentials in continental

bulk, proximity to Eurasia, and ocean currents impose the modifications.

The year-round high incidence of sunshine, low pressures, and vigorous convection make the equatorial zone hot and humid. Contrariwise, because the anticyclonic effects of the subtropical high pressure belts north and south of the equatorial areas likewise persist the year around, extensive areas of Africa both north and south of the Equator are desert. Africa is the only continent that feels the effects of the subtropical anticyclonic, high pressure belts in both hemispheres. Transitional between the belts of moisture and drought are the tropical wet and dry lands, or the tropical savannas whose climates derive from the movement inward of the bordering belts at reciprocal seasons: during the high sun period, when the humid equatorial zone with its organized disturbances and high humidity is pulled in, these tropics are wet; they are dry when the sun, shining vertically in the opposite hemisphere, pulls the desert across the land. The alternating seasons are as absolute in character as are the migrating belts that set the climatic frame.

The trade winds, or the tropical easterlies, blow toward the Equator out of the subtropical high pressure belts. Anticyclonic in their source regions, warm, and blowing toward equatorial lands, they are by nature drying winds. Poleward out of the subtropical highs move the westerlies, away from warm tropical regions toward cooler zones, by their very nature moist winds. Dominating a zone 30° or more of latitude in width in each hemisphere, the westerlies alternate their influence seasonally with the arid tropics over intervening areas, producing another wet and dry climate known as the dry subtropical or Mediterranean. In Africa this occurs in the extreme northwest and southwest. The alternating wet and dry periods of these subtropics occur at seasons directly opposite to those of the tropical wet and dry lands, so that the Mediterranean lands have wet winters and dry summers.

## GRADATIONS OF TEMPERATURE

Plotting actual seasonal temperatures on maps will bring out several significant factors. It is notable that in the broad belt between 10°S and 23½°N, there are no stations that record average monthly tempera-

---

[1] Glenn T. Trewartha, *The Earth's Problem Climates,* Madison, Wis.: The University of Wisconsin Press, 1961, p. 91.

tures below 64.4°F except on the East African plateaus. Nairobi, Kenya (altitude 5,450 feet, latitude 1.17°S) may be taken as a typical plateau station. Here, in July and August, the average temperature falls to 62.9 and 63.7°F respectively; on the Abyssinian plateau where elevations reach to above 8,000 feet, the whole temperature curve is thrown several degrees lower than in a lowland area in the same latitude.

North and south of this middle, high temperature zone there are no cold seasons, although both the deserts and uplands have weather during the low sun period that can be called cool. Winters throughout Africa, if the term winter can be applied here as distinct from summers (the high sun period), are to be defined in terms of moisture, not temperature, although with distance from the Equator seasonal temperature differences become greater. Contrasts in temperature between the daylight and nighttime hours may make sensible temperatures (see Glossary) seem extreme: in humid lands the diurnal range, although normally low, can be greater than the annual; in dry lands temperatures tend to drop rapidly at night due to radiation cooling, sometimes many degrees within a short time.

These effects of changing humidity conditions, elevation and trend of uplands, situation—marine or inland, windward or leeward—and currents bring an asymmetry into thermal and other elements of climatic distribution in Africa. The contrary effects of cold and warm currents produce a lower thermal curve on west side littorals, where cold currents moving toward the Equator lower temperatures in all months of the year, than on the East coast, where equatorial currents are warming and moistening. The effects of currents upon temperatures are most noticeable right along the coast and in latitudes where cold currents parallel the shore; inland, after a distance of a few miles, the influence of the currents plays out. Warm currents touching warm coasts have only slight temperature effects in tropical lands.

Temperature contrasts between lowlands and uplands in those regions of Africa that have humid climates are sharp and considerable, with consequent greater periodicity of seasons and lower humidity on the plateaus. The Lake Victoria plateau, bisected by the Equator, is equatorial in neither temperature nor

moisture; it falls within the wet and dry climate, and the drought-resistant character of the acacia grass and bush savannas reflect the semiaridity and lowered temperatures. This contrasts sharply with conditions throughout most of the Congo basin and the Guinea coast in like latitudes; desert laps along all sides of the green-crested Ethiopian plateau.

Generalized maps bring out only the broad thermal contrasts between the equatorial and tropical lowlands and the uplands of the same latitudes. They do not show the gradations that occur with ascent, as along the slopes of Ruwenzori, Kenya, Kilimanjaro (Figure 1.4), and Elgon where climates pass from equatorial or tropical through a series that terminates in polarlike zones of bare rock and sometimes glaciers. Nor do generalized maps define the pattern of windward, rainy slopes and semiarid to arid lee slopes that occurs in crossing some mountains, as the Atlas from the seaward north to the Saharan south. Such maps do not prepare one for the quick appearance of semiarid vegetation as one departs from the equatorial Congo River basin, as at Yangambi or Kisangani and drives by car, north and east, into the bush savanna of Parc de la Garamba. The savanna seems to appear too soon and too close to the Equator. One is unprepared, after studying a generalized climatic map, for the chill and gusty winds that blow across the plateau veld of South Africa in July and August,

FIGURE 1.4 Eastern face of Mount Kibo, snow-covered, highest peak of Kilimanjaro, 3°E. (Photograph from R. U. Light, Focus on Africa.)

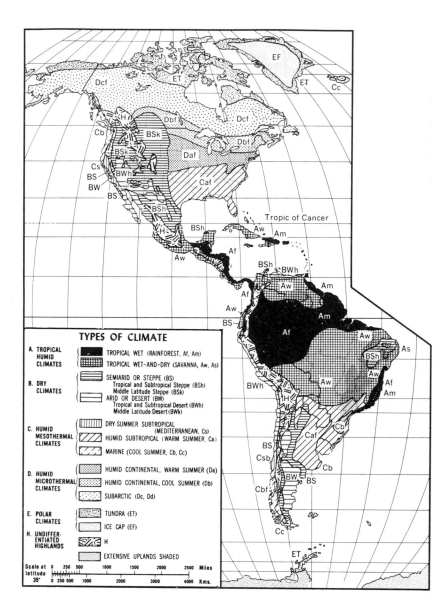

**FIGURE 1.5 Climates of the world.** *(After Glenn T. Trewartha, An Introduction to Climate, 3d ed., New York: McGraw-Hill Book Company, 1954. Courtesy McGraw-Hill Book Company.)*

at latitudes just beyond the Tropic of Capricorn. One expects the Congo basin to be distressingly hot and humid at all times; but such is not the case because the plateau character of the basin, lifting the basin to a 1,000 to 2,000 foot elevation, ameliorates the equatorial effects. Also not discernible on these maps are the contrasts in daytime temperatures between the equatorial and desert lands: daytime temperatures in the rainy tropics are not so high as are those of the central Sahara, 15 or 20° from the Equator, where, in the afternoon, the mercury can climb to 122°F in the shade, and where average daytime temperatures

are not much below this extreme figure. By contrast, people have perished in snowstorms on the Algerian plateaus just north of the Sahara.

## PATTERNS OF MOISTURE DISTRIBUTION

Humidity and precipitation follow conditions of temperature, pressure, and winds.

The trade winds are the most persistent winds of Africa. Blowing diagonally from the northeast and southeast out of the cells of subtropical high pressure toward the low pressure belt engirdling the Equator,

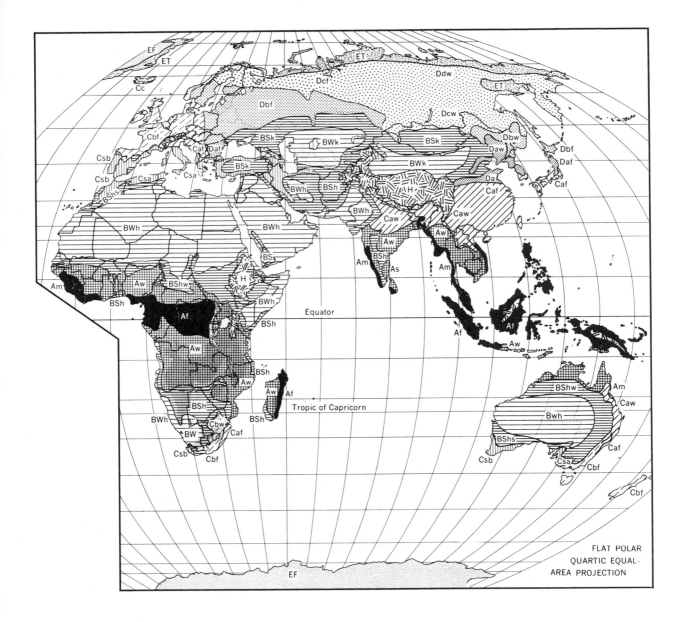

FLAT POLAR
QUARTIC EQUAL-
AREA PROJECTION

the trades help to sustain the great tropical deserts that cover a good two-fifths of the continent. Meager rainfall, excessive aridity of the air, and excessive evapotranspiration are characteristic. There is no rainfall in the Sahara except from passing storms, always unpredictable in time, which may drop abundant showers occasionally over limited localities. There is no season of rainfall, no assurance even that rain will fall during the course of a given year except along the fringes where traces of rain may be seasonally predicted at the height of the rainy periods in the adjacent wet and dry lands. There are desert stations that record the passage of several years without rainfall; whatever falls is negligible. It is the heights that draw most of the moisture from the atmosphere in the deserts. But even this usually fails, and desert rivers are ephemeral in the extreme, some merely leaving scars from the past to recall a former more humid era. Such a river is the Irharhar.

Evaporation is high, because in addition to great heat, relative humidity is low. At Tamanrasset in the Ahaggar, relative humidity varies between 4 and 21 percent; while in contrast, relative humidity in New York City varies between 65 and 72 percent.

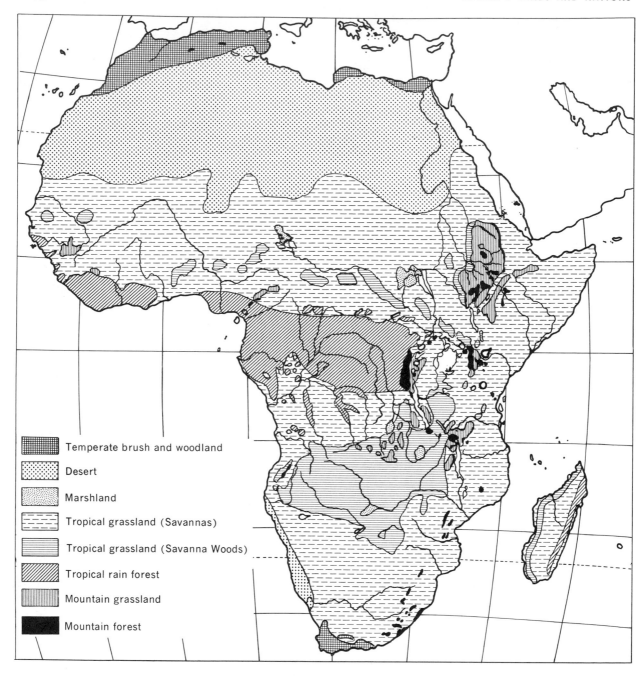

Temperate brush and woodland

Desert

Marshland

Tropical grassland (Savannas)

Tropical grassland (Savanna Woods)

Tropical rain forest

Mountain grassland

Mountain forest

## CLIMATIC PATTERN

The realm of the rainy tropics extends across a belt that is irregular and asymmetric (Figures 1.5 and 1.6) and varies in width from about 4 to 10° of latitude on either side of the Equator; outliers extend along sections of the Guinea coast. Within the basin of the Congo River, the ever near vertical rays of the sun, heating the earth, creating low pressures, and generating convection provide the requisites for intensified moisture conditions despite the small frontage on the ocean. Heat, high humidity, and year-round rainfall obtain across wide sectors, giving rise to an abundant verdure in most places where conditions of equatoriality occur. These are the equatorial rain forests. The rainy tropics are nature's greenhouse. Although rainfall in central Africa does not compare with the amounts spilled seasonally upon sections of the monsoon lands of Asia, nevertheless the constancy of precipitation and the conditions of high humidity create an environment that is "conservatory" in character. The warm humid air has an earthy scent (Figure 1.7).

The equatorial climate terminates abruptly in the east along the base of the East African plateau, and is almost absent in East Africa even along the low coast. Only on the lowlands of the eastern Madagascar shore does the wet tropical climate really prevail. West of the East African plateau, the symmetry of the equatorial belt of the interior becomes less marked as the Atlantic shore is approached: the equatorial zone recedes toward the north, especially along the south and markedly along the coast, compressing the span of tropical wet climate to about half the width that it had in the interior basin. The isohyets (see Glossary) bend northward so that along the Gulf of

Guinea the sectors of heaviest rainfall and the most marked development of equatorial climate occur north of the Equator. This is Africa's rainiest sector (Figure 1.8).

The rainfall of the tropical wet regions results less from the mechanics of local heating and convection, however, than from winds that originate outside of but penetrate into the equatorial zones. Two circulations of air of contrasting characteristics dominate the Congo basin. One is a southwesterly flow of surface air, present at all seasons, that originates over the South Atlantic Ocean and above the cool Benguela Current off the southwestern coast of Africa. Maritime in its source, it is a humid air current about 3,000 to 4,500 feet in depth that flows into the equatorial zone of low pressure with relative ease. Above these southwesterly maritime air masses blow the tropical easterlies, both from the southeast and the northeast, the latter affecting especially the lands lying in the latitudes north of 5°N. These trades extend down to the surface of the earth, where they flow contrary to the movement of air currents from the southwest along a zone of convergence that fluctuates greatly, changing its position not only with the seasons but "aperiodically as well. Seemingly, the stream of southwesterly

FIGURE 1.6 (left) Vegetation. (From James P. Chapin, Birds of the Belgian Congo. Courtesy The American Museum of Natural History, New York.)

FIGURE 1.7 (right) Equatorial scene, Congo. (Photograph by writer.)

maritime air varies considerably in thickness and also in vertical structure, and as a consequence its weather does as well."

There is a wide divergence of opinion as to the functions of the easterly and westerly circulations in Congo weather and also of the relative significance of the Atlantic and Indian Oceans

> as moisture sources of this region . . . . Jeandidier and Rainteau . . . look upon the southwesterlies as providing much the greater part of the precipitable moisture, [and state the view that] weather in the Congo Basin depends largely upon the vertical depth and the extent of penetration by the southwest current. Even as far east as Uganda on the East African Plateau the equatorial westerlies appear to play an important role in the precipitation processes. . . . When the westerly flow is weak or absent, rainfall on the western part of the East African Plateau in equatorial latitudes is below normal.

According to Rainteau, the eastern plateau and associated mountains exert a blocking effect upon the southeast trades so that there is no significant contribution of moisture to the Congo basin from the Indian Ocean except "along the corridor" between the Ethiopian and Kenyan highlands, along which small amounts are carried to the interior. Locally the tropical southeasterlies are called monsoons.[2]

Despite the constant high humidity, rainfall in most areas is relatively moderate, although torrential in character. However, where elevations stand in the path of winds drawn in from the sea, as in the Gulf of Guinea, rainfall may exceed (Figure 1.9) 400 inches a year, as in the Cameroon Mountains; Monrovia averages 198.48 inches annually. In these and other instances, topography puts the "orographic squeeze"[3] (see Glossary) on the humid monsoonal air masses, causing excessive amounts of moisture to fall.

As distance from the equator increases, marked periodicity of rainfall sets in, and the climate becomes tropical wet and dry. Because these tropics merge on one side with rainy, forested lands and on the other

[2] *Ibid.*, pp. 111–112.
[3] Joseph E. Spencer, *Asia, East by South,* New York: John Wiley & Sons, Inc., 1954, p. 49.

**FIGURE 1.8   (right) Moisture regions of Africa. (From Glenn T. Trewartha, The Earth's Problem Climates, Madison, Wis.: The University of Wisconsin Press, 1961. Courtesy The University of Wisconsin Press.)**

with arid, barren lands, conditions within the realm are transitional. The rainfall pattern ranges from a wet and dry cycle that does not have a really dry season but only one that is less wet and is therefore modified wet tropical as at Lagos, to one where seasons are nearly equal in length as at Kano, to near desert as at Timbuktu, where for 5 months no rain falls and for 4 more months only traces of rain appear. In the southern part of the continent the pattern is much the same, going from a long rainy and short dry season on the equatorial side to a long dry and short rainy season on the desert margin. The belt from Bujumbura to Elizabethville to Bulawayo might be taken as illustrative. The extreme conditions of the two bordering climates typify the seasons in the wet and dry regions: during the months of drought, desert conditions obtain and out of the Sahara the harmattan blows; during the wet period, humid heat and rain are characteristic. Colors change from brown to green, and back to brown with the seasons.

These are the savanna lands. Except along streams, the dry period impairs the growth of tree vegetation other than such drought resistant types as acacias and bush savanna. Tropical grass is characteristic of this zone. It varies from thick elephant grass that grows to heights of 10 and 12 feet on the equatorial edges to low clump steppe along the dry side.

These lands of varying savannas stretch in a horseshoe-shaped belt across what are known as the Sudan, the plateau of East Africa, and, southward, the veld, a broad but ill-defined and irregular region extending almost from sea to sea along the southern side of the equatorial rain forests. The zone of savanna is broader in the south than in the north, the more rapid advance toward aridity along the north being due to the greater bulk of the African continent here.

Outward from the deserts and their poleward steppelike fringes are the dry subtropical, or Mediter-

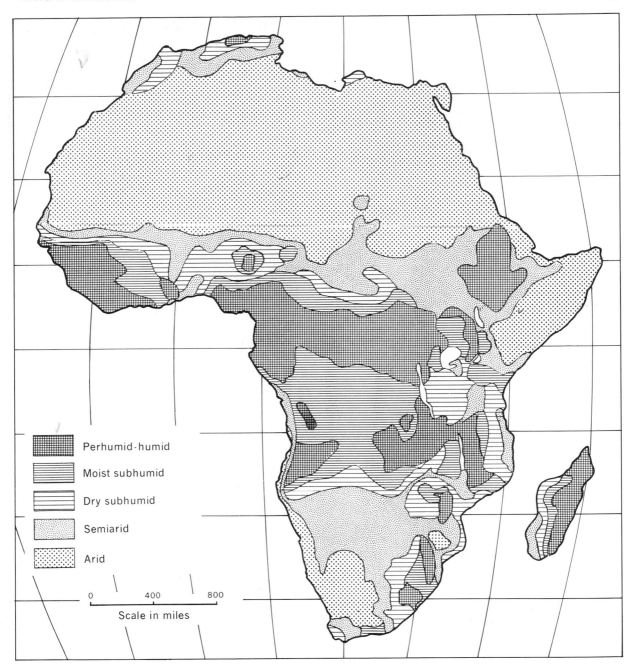

Perhumid-humid

Moist subhumid

Dry subhumid

Semiarid

Arid

0        400        800

Scale in miles

ranean lands, like the wet and dry tropics intermediate between arid and humid belts, the latter in this case being that of the westerlies. Since the Mediterranean lands partake of the characteristics of the bordering zones at alternate seasons, summers are clear, bright,

and dry as the desert takes over while winters bring rain as the fringes of the moist westerlies drop across the area.

Only two small sectors of Africa are dry subtropical, the tip of Cape Province in the southwest, and

**FIGURE 1.9** Left is an airview of Liberian rain forest. Above is a closeup of the fluted bases typical of a number of trees in the African equatorial forests. *(Photographs by writer.)*

the coastal sectors of the Atlas lands in the northwest. Vegetation is drought resistant because it must endure through a long dry period: the olive tree with its deep taproot, the cork oak with its evaporation resistant bark, and bush (known as maqui and including a large group of sagelike and dwarf plants) live through the dry seasons.

Winters are cool, not cold, and as might be expected, temperature contrasts heighten inland with cooler winter and warmer summer temperatures. Rainfall is moderate, ranging from about 15 to 27 inches. The rainfall pattern is typified in the regimes of Cape Town and Casablanca, at opposite ends of Africa and in different hemispheres and therefore with the wet season in one coming at the time of the dry season in the other.

Most of South Africa, except the southwest corner of Mediterranean climate and the humid Southeast, is steppe or desert. The humid eastern coast of the south (the Natal coast) comprises the African humid

subtropics. The warm Mozambique Current washes along this shore, reflecting its influence in both temperature and moisture. Rainfall, while not excessively high, is enough to support a tropical palm and bush vegetation, and this subtropical Natal coast is sometimes called "the palm belt" in South Africa.

The eastern side of the plateau of the south is more moist than the western two-thirds of the upland in the same latitude, owing to the indrawn humid air from the Indian Ocean. Although the veld lands show the same seasonality in rainfall as do those of the Natal coast, year-round precipitation with a summer maximum, the plateau is semicontinental in climate and vegetation. This means that winters are colder and drier, summers are warm, and temperature ranges are greater than along the coast. This semicontinentality becomes more marked westward as aridity increases.

One other feature of African climate should be mentioned before leaving moisture. This is the effect of the monsoon control upon winds and rainfall in certain parts of Africa. By the monsoon effect is meant that alternation of wind direction controlled by the differential pressures set up seasonally on land and over adjacent seas: during the low sun period north of the Equator, a high pressure center that represents a movement inward of the permanent high pressure belt found in the southern part of the North Atlantic forms over the northern desert and fends off moisture-laden winds from the sea; at the same season, a large center of low pressure forms from approximately the Equator southward. Air moves from the northern high, which is most pronounced in the northwest, mostly

south across the Sahara, pulled into the areas of lower pressures off the coast of Guinea and Africa south of the Equator. This southward pull of air across the desert from the dominant high in the north is responsible for the disagreeable harmattans, previously referred to—hot, searing, dusty winds that blow out of the Sahara southward.

During the northern high sun period, opposite conditions of pressure obtain across the northern half of Africa: the dominant Asian low, centered over the Indus valley, extends westward into northern Africa. The effect is to accentuate, along those areas where indrawn winds flow across the coast, the humid condi-

FIGURE 1.10    (a) Approximate locations and boundaries of West Africa's five weather zones; (b) structure of the ITC in Africa north of the Equator in summer: hot, dry easterly winds from the Sahara overrun humid and less hot southwesterly winds from the sea along a very gently sloping surface of discontinuity. (After Glenn T. Trewartha, The Earth's Problem Climates, Madison, Wis.: The University of Wisconsin Press, 1961. Courtesy The University of Wisconsin Press.)

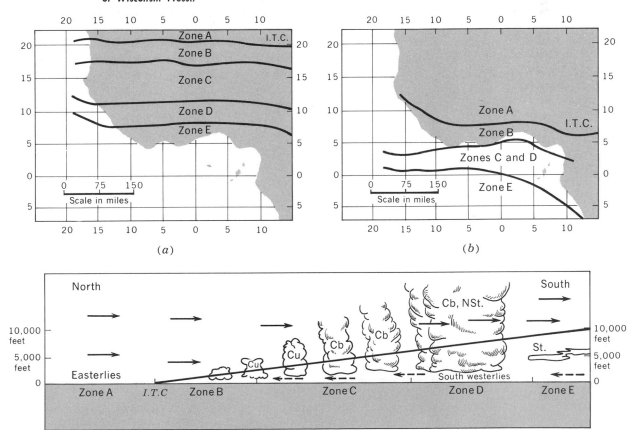

(a)

(b)

tions brought on by the movement inward of the equatorial belt with its convectional rains. The Guinea coast and the Ethiopian highlands feel strong effects from this summer monsoon.

Preliminary to an analysis of the causes for excessive or meager rainfall we must bear in mind the seasonal patterns of atmospheric circulation over Africa. Except in southern Africa a "marked seasonal reversal of surface winds is conspicuous"—southerly winds when the sun is in the Northern Hemisphere, northerly winds when the sun is south of the Equator. Locally these are called the northeast and the southeast monsoons. "However, the seasonal wind reversal is scarcely the result of differential heating of land and water, but instead represents only a normal migration of pressure and wind systems following the course of the sun. The somewhat elusive and diffuse zone of wind discontinuity and confluence separating the two monsoons is the well-known ITC"[4] (see Glossary).

The major controls of climate in West Africa are the seasonal movements of two air masses: tropical continental (Figure 1.10 *a* and *b*) air that moves down from the Sahara between November and late April, reaching its most southerly extent (5 to 7°N) in January; and tropical maritime air that migrates inland from the west and southwest, beginning in May, to about 17°N along the coast and 21°N inland at the time of its greatest extent (in July or August). Since during the winter months highest pressures lie over the northern Sahara and decrease southward across West Africa, the winds are out of the Sahara, northeasterly or easterly, and are warm and dry. During the summer season the opposite condition obtains: highest pressures are offshore and along the shores, and decrease toward the interior of the desert. Winds drawn in from the sea bring moisture.

The two air masses meet along a front, the maritime air, because of its cooler temperatures and greater density, wedging under the continental air. Rains occur where the wedge of moist maritime air reaches heights of 3,000 feet or more. The front migrates—advances or retreats—with the seasons, and also with daily variations in the depth of the wedge; precipitation seems to be related to these diurnal and seasonal changes. Because dry air overlies the moist,

the front itself is not a rain producer; rather, a belt of doldrums develops, the weather is clear with few clouds, and winds are persistently gentle. (See Figure 1.10 *b*.) Thus in West Africa the front acts to screen out rain rather than to generate it. The tropical easterlies, which originate in the Indian Ocean and most of the time overlie the two alternating air masses discussed above, may at times produce line squalls because they are moist.

Orographic precipitation is particularly heavy where uplands run athwart the winds from the sea. This accounts for the excessive rainfall averages in the southwest (Guinea, Sierra Leone, and Liberia especially), and in southeast Nigeria and the highlands of the Cameroons. On the other hand, those lands that lie in the rain shadow of the uplands are drier than would otherwise be the case, as in central Ivory Coast and the coastal sectors of eastern Ghana, Togo, and Dahomey. A further effect of the highlands upon climate is to decrease the overall average temperatures in the upland areas and to increase the daily temperature ranges.

In East Africa "the northerly flow is made up of two unlike air streams, a drier one that has traveled across Egypt and the Sudan, and a more humid one originating in much the same region but which in moving around the eastern side of the Arabian high has had a sea track of modest length. In the equinoctial transition seasons, between the retreat of one monsoon and the advance of the other, winds are fickle and more easterly. Above the surface monsoons the winds of higher altitudes are dominantly from the east (Figure 1.11 *a* and *b*).

"In addition to the northerly and southerly surface currents there are also occasional invasions of moist unstable westerlies representing Congo air which probably originated in the South Atlantic" (see beginning of section on Climatic Pattern earlier in this chapter).

Over most of East Africa there is a deficiency of rainfall despite the incidence of the two monsoons. Reasons for this differ among East African meteorologists, but most agree that the origin of the water deficiency is found in not one but several causes. "There is general agreement that both monsoons are divergent and subsident over extensive areas; . . . the surface air flow . . . likewise is not of great depth," in

[4] Trewartha, *op. cit.*, pp. 123–124.

places "too shallow to surmount the escarpment and reach the plateau. . . . In addition, these shallow monsoon currents are capped by another current moving from a somewhat different direction, usually easterly, in which moisture content is low but variable and lapse rates weak and even inverted" in consequence of which, if clouds do form in the lower moister air strata they are "unable to develop and expand in the dry and stable easterly air aloft."

A further element conducive to moderate rainfall in East Africa, states Trewartha:

is the strongly meridional flow characteristic of both monsoons over the land. The southeasterly current, the moister of the two, has had a long trajectory across the Indian Ocean before reaching the African coast, but the drier northerly monsoon has a much more meridional than zonal track both over the ocean and the adjoining land. But along the coast and over the land the southerly monsoon likewise becomes strongly meridional, so that at times it is nearly parallel to the coast or even offshore. The result is a much smaller transport of moisture from ocean to land than would be true if the air flow were more nearly normal to the

**FIGURE 1.11**  Mean circulation at lower levels for South and East Africa (a) in July and (b) in January. The vertical cross section is taken along line AB. (After Glenn T. Trewartha, *The Earth's Problem Climates,* Madison, Wis.: The University of Wisconsin Press, 1961. Courtesy The University of Wisconsin Press.)

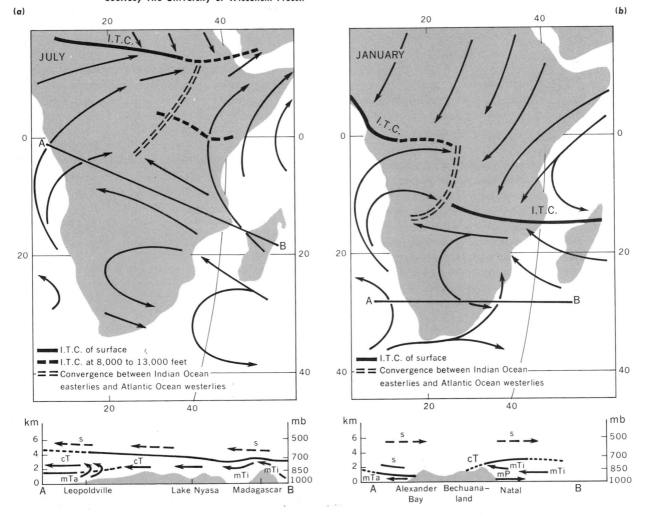

coast while the lifting effect of the eastward-facing plateau escarpment is greatly minimized. It is significant in this respect that it is during the transition seasons between the two monsoons, when the air movement is more zonal and from the east, that rainfall reaches its maximum.[5]

In southern Africa climates and seasons reflect the controls imposed by the great planetary pressure and wind belts except as relief and altitude introduce modifications. Isohyets representing annual rainfall, from the Equator to about 20°S latitude, trend generally east and west; precipitation is greater near the Equator and declines southward, and shows a high maximum during the high sun period. "This expresses the operation of latitudinally migrating zonal controls such as the ITC wind systems, and associated disturbance belts." South of about 20°S the trend of the isohyets is transverse to the east-west direction farther north, running generally north-south and parallel with the coast. Rainfall decreases from east to west, the 16-inch isohyet approximately bisecting the southern sector.

This contrasting meridional alignment of the isohyets south of about 20°S reflects the waning effect on rainfall of zonal tropical controls, and the rapid taking over of subtropical anticyclones and westerly flow, with drought-producing controls in the form of a stable anticyclone and cold waters prevailing on the west side, and weaker subsidence, a warm current and more numerous disturbances, chiefly of westerly origin, on the east. An exception to the prevailing aridity on the west side is to be found in the extreme southwest, where, in the vicinity of the elevated Cape, cold-season cyclonic-orographic rains produce a limited area of Mediterranean climate.[6]

## AFRICA'S WATER PROBLEMS

Water problems in Africa swing to extremes, regionally and seasonally, from excess water owing to too persistent rainfall and high humidity, or the flooding of rivers to too little water as a result of low rainfall and high evaporation, to a harsh swinging from one extreme to the other, seasonally, in the wet and dry lands. Only in the humid and dry subtropical parts can the continent be described as not being plagued by a water problem, and even in the Mediterranean lands, irrigation is a necessity for the most part, so the water problem is not absent. (See Figure 1.12 *a* to *c*.)

In places where subsurface conditions, aridity, and excessive evaporation have caused salts to accumulate in the upper layers of the soil, a region may have not only the problem of irrigating the land but, because of irrigation, also that of drawing off the salty vadose (see Glossary) waters at depths so that they will not accumulate. In parts of North Africa, for example, impervious layers of subsurface clay cause water to be retained at depths varying from 8 to 10 feet. Deep drainage ditches must be dug to draw off these salt-impregnated waters, at the same time that irrigation water is needed to provide moisture at the surface. Nature is lavish—and harsh—in Africa and often both at one and the same time and place. These two features of irrigation and drainage in the African environment accentuate the difficulty of development.

Although swamps undoubtedly cover far wider regions and a greater proportion of the equatorial lands in South America than they do in Africa, along riverine areas of equatorial Africa where lowlands extend away from stream edges, swamps nevertheless stretch outward for miles and miles beneath the tree vegetation. Such inundated lands are a major problem along sections of the Nile River, in the upper Niger delta, and along the Congo River and its tributary streams and lakes. Only fishing peoples occupy these wetlands in the Congo basin: their houses stand precariously along the riverfront, hemmed in on three sides by marshes, on tiny islets of moist land standing but slightly above the water in the midst of these murky swamps. The all-pervading humidity and heat, the ever-present moisture underfoot, and the thick dark drapery of vegetation overhead and all around make these swamp forests extremely dismal and unhealthful. Mangrove swamps make useless large sections of the Guinea coast and the delta lands that build up along the sea, as in the delta area between Port Harcourt and the historic old slaving port of Bonny.

At the opposite extreme are the dry lands. It has already been noted that deserts alone cover two-fifths

[5] *Ibid.,* pp. 124–126.
[6] *Ibid.,* p. 138.

(b)

(c)

FIGURE 1.12 Water stored by perennial irrigation schemes is transferred from the dammed lake through smaller and smaller channels until at last run onto the fields. (a) Im Fout barrage on the Oum er Rbia; (b) a broad, concrete-lined channel carries the water from the lake; (c) raised canals. (a, courtesy of Service Général de l'Information, Morocco; b and c by the writer.)

FIGURE 1.13 Water is always a problem in Northern Province, Masailand. Thorn brush savanna. (Courtesy Public Relations Department, Tanganyika.)

of Africa, and if the steppelands are included in these water-starved lands, three-fifths of the continent is arid to semiarid (Figure 1.13). The problem here is to find enough water to irrigate the land, to grow pastures, and to support life. Where rivers like the Nile send their waters from equatorial headstreams across the width of the desert, or, like the Niger, intrude along the arid fringe, or like the Atlas streams rush, short but swiftly, down the Saharan side from moister heights to water the thirsty land, or where man-made pipes conduct water across miles of arid surface to irrigate such garden spots as Marrakech watered from the distant Atlas, the land is blessed, and with painstaking work flowers and produces.

Where such obvious means are absent, where will the water be obtained to sustain life?

It may be concealed in the porous dunes of sand that billow across the surfaces of the *ergs*, to be tapped by plant roots or by shallow digging, as in the Saharan Suf. Or it may lie deep beneath the surface in the rocks, to be laboriously drawn up from 50 to 100 or more feet by rope and leather bucket, by man or animal or, if modern technology has reached the reservoir, by diesel motor from thousands of feet below the surface. This is occurring in some places in both the Algerian and Libyan deserts in association with oil development. Or water may be trapped between layers of rock—porous rocks that make good reservoirs when resting on impervious layers—and seep out as springs at the base of the reservoir; then oases will be found along the base of the rocks adjacent to the springs, as at Egyptian Siwa situated at the foot of the Marmarica escarpment. Or diligent, persevering men may hollow out cisterns on the surface, the rocks to serve as catchments for the rain that occasionally may fall, or build barrages across wadis to dam the waters of flash floods originating farther upstream. The Algerian Mozabites do this.

Man taxes his ingenuity to meet the challenge of sustaining life in the midst of aridity. A look at the map of the deserts, however, indicates the measure of success that man has had in his efforts to conquer the arid places. The oases are few, far between, and small. Each green spot, set alone and apart, is a haven of security against the cruel lack or insufficiency of water and a harsh, relentless sun. Entire caravans have been known to perish for lack of water.

Modern science and engineering are trying to utilize a small fraction of the desert by impounding water that originates outside of the desert, as in the case of the High and Sennar dams on the Nile, or along the Orange and other rivers. But were the acres reclaimed by such perennial irrigation projects plotted on the breadth of the African arid and semi-desert lands, they would look minute in contrast to the area of the water-deficient expanses of the Sahara, the Namib and Kalahari deserts, and the steppes. Their importance, however, can scarcely be calculated.

*Water Balance.* The amount of rain that falls is not the sole determinant of how well the water needs of any given region are being met. Also involved is the area's potential rate of evapotranspiration: by placing one against the other, a "water balance" is determined from which the water needs can be calculated. This is not a direct or simple process.

Thornthwaite introduced the idea of potential evapotranspiration as a method of climatic classification; from his studies, others have followed. He defined evapotranspiration as "the combined evaporation from the soil surfaces and transpiration from plants," therefore "the reserve of precipitation." The process of evapotranspiration is accomplished by the combination of vaporization by the sun and of the "sink strength (attractive power)" of the atmosphere. The effect of the sun upon vaporization is translated through insolation (sunshine), length of the daylight period, and temperature; that of atmosphere in wind and atmospheric turbulence, and relative humidity. The effectiveness of evapotranspiration depends upon the completeness or incompleteness of the vegetation cover, and upon the moisture that is available.[7]

On the basis of water balance, a possible 36 percent of Africa may be characterized as humid; of the remainder, about 16 percent is true desert, 26 percent arid, and 22 percent semiarid. In other words, nearly two-thirds of Africa is plagued during all or part of the year by a moisture deficiency. Where seasons are based on moisture variation, as throughout most of

[7] C. W. Thornthwaite, "An Approach toward a Rational Classification of Climate," *Geographical Review,* vol. XXXVIII, no. 1, p. 55, January, 1948.

Africa, the seasonal distribution sets limits on the crops that can be cultivated: those plants that require a growing period that is longer than the season of rains can be cultivated only under irrigation. Where seasonal changes are marked not only by moisture differences but also by temperature change and by a winter maximum of precipitation, as in the northern and southern Mediterranean extremities, evaporation is less critical, and the rainfall, although less than in the tropical lands, will be more effective. In other words, it requires less rain to grow crops in lands of winter rain than in those where rain falls during the warm season and consequently have a higher evaporation rate.

The cultivation mosaic that prevails is greatly influenced by natural conditions of the habitat, reflecting in no small measure the precipitation-evapotranspiration factor. New techniques of cultivation and the stabilization of the water supply through irrigation can, in places and at times, better the water balance even as poor methods may accentuate the rate of moisture loss. How best to procure the maximum good out of this coefficient is a problem for scientific agriculture to solve. In the extensive regions where a deficiency of water exists, there is also greater variability and seasonal fluctuation. Since an accentuation of low moisture conditions in these normally moisture-deficient regions is almost invariably accompanied by high temperatures, thereby raising the rate of evapotranspiration, crop yields show a like fluctuation. Only where irrigation is practiced on a broad scale, as in the Nile valley, can crop yields be held steady in the arid and semiarid lands; only then will yields consistently rise to above continental averages.

## SOILS

African soils generally show a remarkably belted distribution closely coincident with climatic and vegetation belts. Since climate, vegetation, and soil impact upon each other, and in the case of soil and vegetation, are basically interdependent, our study of African soils will be largely an interpretation of soils from this viewpoint. This means that we will be speaking largely in generalizations that hold for wide sweeps of territory. As soon as one begins to do detailed soil analyses within small areas, however, this method will break down, because in addition to climate and vegetation, a number of other things such as topography, use and misuse by man, drainage conditions, parent rock material, insects, and animal life have their effects and often create wide soil differences within small areas. Leaching is another basic process, operative especially in humid areas, that affects the soil horizons. In some climates it operates slowly, in others rapidly, but in all places it has a similar effect—soaking out the mineral substances and leaving the soil more or less infertile depending upon the amount, rate, and continuousness of the leaching process. And yet a comparison of the climatic, vegetation, and soil maps of Africa will reveal that vegetation follows climate, and soil follows vegetation (and climate). The process of soil formation is slow. It has operated under all conditions of climate, and throughout all eras of time.

Laterization, which sometimes is applied blanket-like to all humid soils from the equator into the humid subtropics, is by no means so generally prevalent as this. Laterites develop under conditions of tropically hot temperatures and high rainfall, as do also red loams. Both have their red color because of a residual iron constituent. This characteristic of color is so widespread and striking that it has been accepted as "a universal and essential characteristic of laterites. It is always present (also) in red loams."[8] Both soil types occur in Africa. It is perhaps unwise to say, therefore, that the laterites are the soils of the tropical and equatorial zones of Africa. Rather it is better to use terms cautiously, and to speak of characteristics, instead, until further research clarifies the exact types.

Most tropical soils, although deep, wear out rapidly, losing both fertility and structure when continuously cultivated, because cultivation places a greater strain upon soil than does natural growth, luxuriant though the latter may be. Even where tropical lands have a profuse floral complex, and much humus is therefore added to the soil, soils are leached and infertile because the rapidity of decomposition, caused by the persistency of the rains and heat, does not permit the humus to accumulate in the surface horizon. If the

[8] H. L. Shantz and C. F. Marbut, *The Vegetation and Soils of Africa*, New York: American Geophysical Society, Res. Series 13, 1923, pp. 125–126.

organic material could remain for a long time undisturbed, and if the profuse plant association persisted, the soils would be rich because the plants would so continuously feed a supply of organic materials into the soil that they would maintain a supply of the soluble elements, and also support bacteria. However, once the plant cover is removed by burning and clearing for cultivation, the meager residue of organic and inorganic solubles depletes much more rapidly than it does in temperate latitudes. It takes only a few years for a soil that formerly supported a towering three-storied rain forest, whose highest species may have reached 175 to 200 feet, to become exhausted.

Across all the equatorial and wet and dry tropical lands of Africa, the problem of how to preserve soil fertility and structure is insistent. The Africans solved it by engaging in a type of shifting cultivation that is an excellent adaptation to soil conditions as they naturally exist. Two years of cultivation (generally four croppings) will wear out a tropical soil and break down the structure. To counter this, the migratory cultivators practice long periods of fallowing—to restore a vegetation cover that will once more provide humus, and that can be burned to contribute potash,

FIGURE 1.14  Soil erosion, Cape Province, South Africa. Small reeds have been planted in attempts at revegetation so as to cut down the washing away of the soil. (*Courtesy South African Information Service, Pretoria.*)

at the beginning at least. The long fallow also allows the roots of trees time to penetrate deeply into the soil and bring up fertilizing chemicals from the zones of alluviation. Shifting cultivation is practiced throughout all of the equatorial and wet and dry tropical lands of Africa. Although a soil preserving technique, it is highly destructive of vegetation.

Overlooking the wasteful aspects of vegetation destruction and/or deterioration, the method of migratory cultivation is suitable where population pressure is not great; but when large populations begin to press on the land, making impossible the long fallow and continuous clearing of new lands, the system becomes impractical and precarious. Cultivation techniques whereby fertility is maintained or restored by shorter periods of fallowing, or fertilization must then be substituted. Fertilization comprises the use of commercial fertilizers, composting, green or animal manuring, cover cropping, crop rotation, or the adoption of integrated farming that involves animal rearing as well as cultivation. Most humid African soils need to be protected and restored.

To prescribe and to practice are, however, two different things, because success depends also upon the solution of many other problems. Plant a leguminous fallow (green manure) and permit animals to graze upon this land? In many parts of the continent animal rearing awaits control of the tsetse fly, a scourge across hundreds of thousands of square miles of African savannas and forests where other environmental conditions would favor animal keeping. Add commercial fertilizer? It is too expensive for most small cultivators.

All African soils are good for short periods of cultivation and long fallow, but as agriculture intensifies, soil analyses and changed techniques are needed. Not only must a right system be used, but also the right soil for the right plant culture. It is a slow process to experiment with soil usage under varying conditions of climate, cropping, and fallowing. In central Africa alone hundreds of tests have been concurrently and constantly carried out under the guidance and financing of Europeans. It is likely that integrated farming, with animals and the restorative manures, in combination with other remedies will be needed to provide the answer to this problem of soil and agriculture in tropical and equatorial Africa.

The problems incident to soils in arid and semi-arid lands are completely different from those of the humid hot lands. In deserts, the first need is to obtain water to use the soil at all. Generally, desert soils are relatively rich in inorganic minerals because scant moisture and high evaporation tend to concentrate salts near the surface. An excess of these chemicals may even be harmful. Humus is low, and absent in many parts. Erosion, both by running water and wind, is another problem of immense proportions (Figure 1.14). When soil and water are properly handled, however, the deserts produce abundantly.

## Natural Fauna

Africa has the greatest and most varied reserve of natural fauna on earth, and the combination of African wildlife and the untamed environment that is their habitat leaves an impression of immensity and grandeur. The setting is primeval, and everything is on a grand scale: the animals graze across the vast plains of the savannas, in the valleys of the mighty rifts, up the slopes of mountains and rock faults—profuse in variety and numerous.

A century ago extratropical America was also a vast natural conservatory of wildlife, but with the filling in of the land by humans and with man's encroachment upon the haunts of the wildlife, the picture changed. The herds of bison that had thundered over the plains, supplying meat and furs and horns for the Indians without diminishment, disappeared almost to the point of extinction.

But for the setting aside of reserves for the preservation of the fauna, decades ago Africa would have followed the same way to the near extinction of the faunal species. The wanton killing began later in Africa because the European hunter with his gun did not get into the interior of the continent until the latter years of the nineteenth century, or the destruction of game would have been greater. However, in those parts where he did penetrate Africa at an earlier date, the indigenous animal life was all but exterminated, as in the Maghrib where the Romans wiped out the animals of Mediterranean lands, and when no more were available there, transported wild beasts from below the Sahara for the spectacles in the arenas. The pressure of the native Africans upon faunal life before the advent of the European (as in America) was not so great but that natural replacement was sufficient to replenish the herds; but as "the great hunters" and traders began their trophy killing, hunting by Africans—who wanted to get in on the profits that this rich booty brought—also increased.

Although game reserves and "controlled areas" have been set aside, they have not eliminated illegal hunting and poaching; both are problems. The two most serious forms of poaching are the killing of animals for the traffic in trophies such as ivory, rhino horn, and leopard skins, and commercialized meat hunting. Whereas petty poaching makes only small inroads on the game because the number killed is small, poaching for trophies and commercial meat constitutes a genuine threat to faunal populations. Further, the practice of trophy-hunting takes the "trophy," and leaves the carcass of the animal to rot where it was killed—or, possibly, leaves the animal to die a slow, agonizing death. The circling of vultures indicates the spot of such killings. Clearing of the land for safe occupation, especially in the past, also made great inroads on the reserves of wildlife.

Why is man so destructive of this treasury of wildlife that is so quickly destroyed, so difficult to replenish, and impossible to replace once it is gone? The above is only one side of the wildlife picture; crop damage and conveying contagion are another. Intruding on the farmlands, trampling and tearing up their crops, killing and carrying off their livestock, spreading disease, the natural fauna represent a destructive force that must be held in check. Crop destruction by some marauding mammals, such as elephants and hippos, is considerable; elephants are particularly destructive. Plundering by lions results in considerable loss of livestock; baboons and monkeys are pests.

The wild game are also carriers of disease, the herds constituting "reservoirs of infection"; in the various stages of development of ticks and insects, birds, bats, animals, reptiles, and even amphibians play host to many species of these arachnids (see Glossary) and insects that infest extensive areas of Africa and to a greater degree than on any other continent; various sorts of tick fever result from the bite. The fur, feathers, and hides of the wild creatures

**FIGURE 1.15 Game rescue and marking on Lake Kariba.
When Kariba Dam was built on the Zambezi, thousands of
acres of grazing lands for wild fauna were flooded by the
impounded water; hence, a game rescue mission on a vast
scale was implemented. Each of the animals rescued was
marked so it could later be identified. (Courtesy Federal Information Department, Rhodesia.)**

serve as admirable places for germ carriers to hide
and be transported, and the arachnids and insects
thus transferred may communicate diseases not only
to other animals but also to human beings.

Thus, although the wildlife in their natural habitat
may create scenes of haunting beauty, men, cohabit-
ing Africa with the animals, must protect themselves
and their property from them.

Nevertheless, this rich faunal heritage should be
preserved (Figure 1.15). Some species are already
extinct; some strains have been so decimated that
extinction is a possibility; all African wildlife has
numerically declined as compared with the prolific
populations that existed a century and a half ago,
and as the balance that nature created is upset by
further changes in the proportions of the faunal population and in the vegetation, the imbalance thus induced may lead naturally to an ungovernable decima-
tion of some species and the ungovernable multiplication of others. Out of this an entirely new faunal
complex could emerge. Sanctuaries where the fauna
are allowed to live unrestricted and unmolested
within an environment natural to their habits are now
the only means by which the complex developed by
Nature can be maintained; control over population
numbers and ratios is also affected by the setting up
of reserves.

# 2 THE AFRICANS

*As for man, his days are as grass:*
*as a flower of the field, so he*
*flourisheth. For the wind passeth*
*over it, and it is gone; and the*
*place thereof shall know it no more.*

PSALM 103:15

## Migration and Mixing of the Races

The ethnohistory of Africa is obscure during most of the period of prehistory. Not until the indwellers of the continent had settled down with some degree of continuous occupance does there emerge any sort of picture of the way in which men were spatially and racially arranged. It has been surmised what this distribution was about 7,000 years ago: Caucasians occupied the north, Negroes inhabited West Africa and the Sahara, Pygmoids the central forest regions, and Bushmanoids spread from the plateau of East Africa widely across the rest of the continent southward.

This disposition was transformed into a mosaic of a different pattern when the Bantu began their series of migrations east and south from southeast Nigeria. They confined the Pygmoids into a small eastern sector of the Congo basin, and drove the Bushmanoids south until they were compressed into the southwestern lands of South Africa.

Invasions by Arabs and subsequent advances of the proselytizing Moslems, and the advent of Europeans brought about another transposition, equally as drastic as that wrought by the Bantu. In the Maghrib, Arabs drove the resident Berbers from the lowlands into mountain and valley recesses, and deeper into the desert; the Saharan Negro was largely displaced by Caucasians from the north; the Bushmanoids were pressed farther inward into ever more marginal zones until they occupied only the arid and semiarid lands of the southwest. In those places where Europeans found environments healthful and developable, African Negroes were pushed into reserves or had their lands alienated in other ways as they were forced to compete with the more advanced Europeans for living space. Only a few parts of inhabited Africa remained relatively uncolonized by Europeans, namely, the Nile valley, Ethiopia, and parts of Somaliland.

These spatial modifications of African populations were attended by racial and cultural transmutations resulting from the migrations and invasions, and the subsequent blood mixing that took place as wanderers, invaders, and conquerors diffused outward from their primary centers of origin into new territories. As the varied types migrated between lands, crossed trails, took root in new environments, and cohabited regions with other peoples, original types were modified or swallowed up in the large scale alloying of one blood type and culture with another, or with two or three other blood types and cultures. Thus, the composition of African population is varied—varied to such a degree that race and color and other biological characteristics have less validity in associating people with people than do the cultural traits of language, tradition, religion, and the artifacts of man's inventions in music, painting, carving, agriculture, and the like. There is still much to be learned about migrations and supposed migrations and about the racial and cultural mixing that occurred as a result.

Nevertheless, there is a line (more accurately, a zone) that represents an outstanding cultural division in Africa—and there is validity to the idea that this line is also a racial divider. It runs between arid Africa, largely peopled by Caucasoids who are either nomadic herders or oasis-irrigation cultivators, and the humid lands of black Africa to the south, where people tend to be sedentary, and are either pastoralists or cultivators who may or may not supplement their farming with animal rearing (Figure 2.2). This boundary, one of the major cultural dividers in the world, runs approximately from the mouth of the Senegal River eastward through Timbuktu, Lake Chad, and Khartoum, dipping southward along the western frontier of Ethiopia, and from there cutting southeastward toward the mouth of the Juba River. North of the line pastoral pursuits, nomads' tents, and irrigated oasis agriculture dominate the cultures; south of the line, patch agriculture—varying according to the limitations imposed by climate, and vegetation, and the level of progress—and permanent to semipermanent huts and houses, characterize traditional ways of living. Animal industries are carried on in places in the southern portion but always from semipermanent bases. Even among peoples who are solely animal keepers, like the Masai, the home is a hut or a house, and agricultural items are produced, although by a serf group. The hunting and gathering Bushmen comprise a disparate enclave within an area of sedentary habitation.

FIGURE 2.2　(right) Indigenous cultural-geographic regions of Africa.

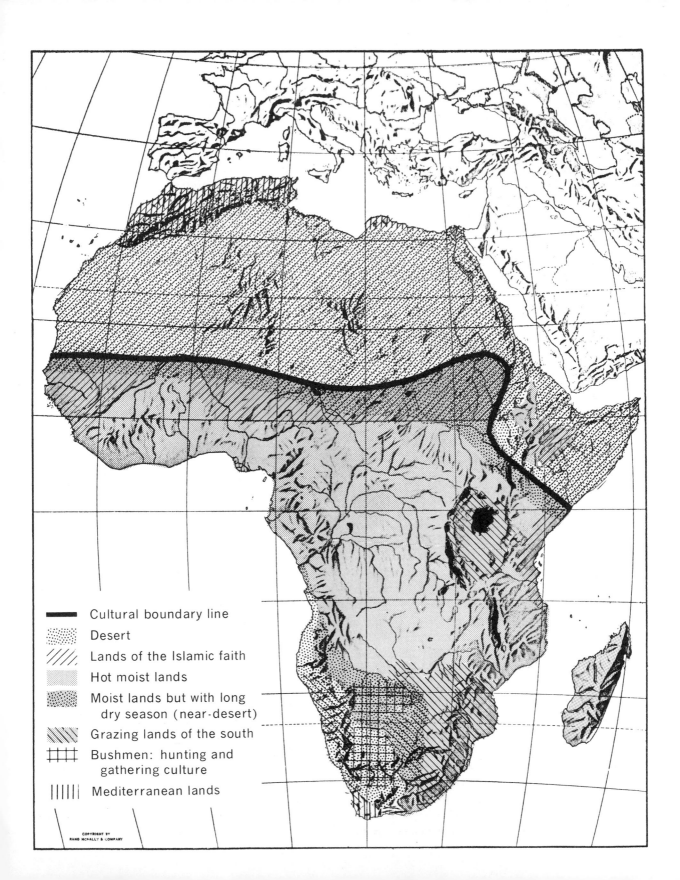

Cultural boundary line

Desert

Lands of the Islamic faith

Hot moist lands

Moist lands but with long
dry season (near-desert)

Grazing lands of the south

Bushmen: hunting and
gathering culture

Mediterranean lands

Compare the dividing line with the advance front of Islam in Africa, and the two will prove to coincide with little deviation. This line separates not only cultural areas, but literally culture worlds: arid North Africa is an intimate and indivisible part of the desert Moslem culture world that spreads across southern Asia from the shores of the Mediterranean to the eastern borders of West Pakistan with outliers farther east; the culture world of humid Africa, savanna and forest, finds a counterpart in that of peoples living in other equatorial forest and tropical savannas in other parts of the world, for environments permit and restrict, and hence persuade primitive peoples to make certain types of adjustment within particular natural habitats. In other words, aboriginal cultures respond to and reflect the nature of their homelands. The more primitive the group, the more distinguishable is the relationship. Indigenous African cultures, because they still closely approximate the adjustments of primordial societies, display this intimate association between man and nature.

## Patterns of Cultural Distribution

### LANGUAGE

Language may have no relation to race. In Africa, however, a language map bears some relationship to racial distribution. To some extent it also reflects the movements and blending of the racial stocks.

Figure 2.3 presents a complicated pattern of hundreds of languages and dialects. Mixtures are generally found along contact zones between language groups, as along the east, where Arab and Indonesian infiltrations have modified both race and language; as along the upper Nile, a contact zone between Egypt and black Africa; or as along the northern Sudan, where Moslem influence has modified at least ritualistic language and religion and thus caused culture to change, although it still contains strong elements of pre-Islamic traditions.

The purely African languages, namely, the tribal tongues of the Sahara and Africa south of the Sahara, show the same effects of change through contact and mixing. There has been a noticeable alteration in the structure and vocabularies of certain tongues as the

users migrated or made contacts, for long or brief periods, with peoples of other languages. As a result certain language families stand out as dominant, others as less dominant; some languages have become recessive, i.e., spoken archaically by a small group or dying out. The living reality of language is change, and a recognition of this is necessary to any classification of African languages.

Bantu-speaking people (Benue-Congo, according to Greenberg[1]) occupy all of Africa south of an irregular line that (Figure 2.3) extends from southeast Nigeria and Cameroon east to the Indian Ocean coast approximately along the border between eastern Somalia and Kenya. The only interruptions to Bantu (always a linguistic designation) are found in the large enclave of the Click, or Khoisan languages in the southwest, tiny outliers of Click and/or Hamitic on the plateau, and in coastal Angola. There is a "very obvious unity" among all of the Bantu dialects: Bantu forms a subgroup of the Niger-Congo, "an already established genetic subfamily" according to Greenberg's revised classification.

North of the large zone of Bantu-speaking peoples lies the Sudan, a geographical area that is characterized by a vast diversity of tongues. West of Nigeria, the languages are clearly interrelated, and form what are called the Congo-Kordofanian group. The eastern languages are remotely related, if at all. They belong both to the Congo-Kordofanian and the Nilo-Saharan families (Figure 2.3), and comprise an interrupted sector, Nilo-Saharan-speaking peoples alternating with those linguistically Kordofanian and even Afro-Asian. North and east, from here and the Niger-Congo belt, stretches a vast area inhabited by peoples who are linguistically Afro-Asian. All of North Africa, from the western Sahara through to and across the Horn, fall within this belt which reaches south to approximately middle Sudan (the country) with two major interruptions, namely, much of the central Sahara and the Nile valley of the Nubian desert; here the people speak Eastern Sudanic of the Nilo-Saharan language family. The lands of the upper Nile are Nilo-Saharan, and an extension of this group spreads down centrally across the East African plateau into Tanganyika.

[1] Joseph H. Greenberg, *The Languages of Africa,* Bloomington, Ind.: University of Indiana, 1963.

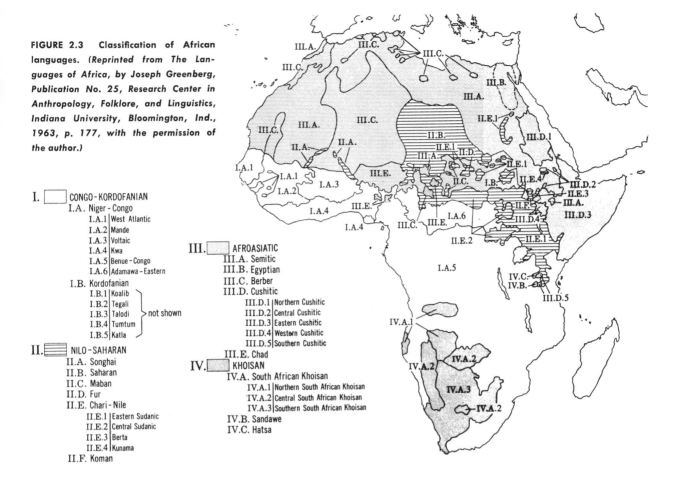

**FIGURE 2.3** Classification of African languages. (Reprinted from The Languages of Africa, by Joseph Greenberg, Publication No. 25, Research Center in Anthropology, Folklore, and Linguistics, Indiana University, Bloomington, Ind., 1963, p. 177, with the permission of the author.)

I. ☐ CONGO-KORDOFANIAN
    I.A. Niger-Congo
        I.A.1 | West Atlantic
        I.A.2 | Mande
        I.A.3 | Voltaic
        I.A.4 | Kwa
        I.A.5 | Benue-Congo
        I.A.6 | Adamawa-Eastern
    I.B. Kordofanian
        I.B.1 | Koalib
        I.B.2 | Tegali
        I.B.3 | Talodi  } not shown
        I.B.4 | Tumtum
        I.B.5 | Katla

II. ☰ NILO-SAHARAN
    II.A. Songhai
    II.B. Saharan
    II.C. Maban
    II.D. Fur
    II.E. Chari-Nile
        II.E.1 | Eastern Sudanic
        II.E.2 | Central Sudanic
        II.E.3 | Berta
        II.E.4 | Kunama
    II.F. Koman

III. ▦ AFROASIATIC
    III.A. Semitic
    III.B. Egyptian
    III.C. Berber
    III.D. Cushitic
        III.D.1 | Northern Cushitic
        III.D.2 | Central Cushitic
        III.D.3 | Eastern Cushitic
        III.D.4 | Western Cushitic
        III.D.5 | Southern Cushitic
    III.E. Chad

IV. ▦ KHOISAN
    IV.A. South African Khoisan
        IV.A.1 | Northern South African Khoisan
        IV.A.2 | Central South African Khoisan
        IV.A.3 | Southern South African Khoisan
    IV.B. Sandawe
    IV.C. Hatsa

The map portrays the sector of the continent that is linguistically Afro-Asian. The language family thus designated by Greenberg is that traditionally referred to as Hamito-Semitic or simply Hamitic, and has five coordinate subfamilies: Ancient Egyptian, Semite, Berber, Cushite, and Chad. Greenberg substitutes the term "Afroasiatic" for Hamitic because of the loose fashion in which the word Hamite, a linguistic connotation, is used.

The terms Hamite and Semite are from a common source, likely, for they derive from the names of the sons of Noah (Ham and Shem). Hence, the Hamitic-Semitic family. The separation of the common mother tongue into the African Hamitic and the Asiatic Semitic divisions must have occurred in very ancient times. North Africa was at one time Hamitic, but in the past 1,000 years Hamitic has yielded ground before Semitic, owing to the spread of Arabic in Moslem Africa.

The Click languages constitute three subfamilies—Khoisan, Sandawe, and Hatsa. The Khoisan cultures are those of the Hottentots and Bushmen, and the word Khoisan is compounded from Khoi-Khoin, the term used by the Hottentots to designate themselves, and San, Hottentot name for the Bushmen. Khoisan was taken by Greenberg "to refer to the group of physically, culturally, and linguistically distinctive peoples which, formerly at least, occupied all of the southern portion of the continent." Except for language, however, culturally the two Khoisan groups are quite distinct, because the Hottentots are cattle keepers whose society is characterized by a rather complex political organization and a strong "sense of ethnic distinctness" while the Bushmen are hunters and food gatherers. "Both of these peoples speak languages whose most conspicuous feature is the presence of the Click sounds. These sounds are also found in the neighboring Bantu language of the Zulu and southern Suto where their presence is the result of borrowing from the languages of the Khoisan peoples. In addition, two languages of East Africa . . . —Sandawe and Hatsa—contain clicks. These sounds are not known to occur anywhere in the world outside of this African area."[2] The Sandawe, hunters and, to some extent, cultivators and animal keepers, inhabit a small section of Tanganyika.

Greenberg's map shows that even linguistically Africa divides closely along the culture line previously delineated; outliers lie largely just above or below the boundary zone.

## RELIGION

Credence in the supernatural is everywhere present in Africa, these beliefs extending deeply into the past. The two maps of R. Mauny portray the distribution and changing patterns of religion over the first half of this century. Before the periods represented native religions, usually animistic in form, prevailed in most parts of Black Africa. Islam began to be felt for the first time, in the North, in the seventh century of the Christian era, where it swiftly replaced Christianity and most forms of native religion (Figure 2.4 *a* and *b*).

Among Africans, religions have operated as strong forces in shaping cultures. Every religion has its body of beliefs, rituals, and symbols. These not only take hold on the minds and motivate the customs of the group that originates the beliefs; they may become one with the culture because religious beliefs, in their developing stages, are inspired by and derived from the habitat even as are other features of culture. Religious rituals and symbols are, at least in their beginnings, the rituals and symbols of everyday living.

When a religion washes over, or is carried into an environment of a different character than that from which it sprang, the ritualistic dogmas and practices generally become altered to accommodate to the new setting. The more absolutely a religion regulates the behavior of a group, the more closely will religious areas coincide with cultural areas. When a religion is alien to a region or people, religious and cultural areas will tend to be disparate, and worship is likely to be a thing apart from the rest of living. Under these circumstances it lacks dynamic force, being unconformable to the rest of the culture. In such instances the exotic religion, accepted on the surface, will be corrupted by beliefs, rituals, and symbols of old native beliefs, and religion will cross culture lines.

Primitive tribal animism characterizes the religions that were native to Africa. These locally inspired beliefs have not acted as reservoirs from which impressive organized religions have sprung; the great religions of modern Africa, those with converts across wide areas, are imports. However, only where the imports have conquered the whole way of life, as in Moslem Africa, have the traditional tribal beliefs and symbols been superseded and not always entirely even then. It is interesting to note that the Moslem faith, a product of the desert, has had widest acceptance among the desert and near desert dwellers of Africa: North Africa, down into the semiarid lands of the Sudan south of the Sahara, is almost solidly Islamic; elsewhere in Africa, the Moslem faith has taken hold only spottily aside from the East African coast where it is more prevalent. These outliers are in the main outposts of Islam's frontal attempts at proselytization.

Nowhere in Africa has Christianity taken hold over the lives of its converts as has the Moslem faith in the regions of its acceptance. One of the reasons for this disparity of impression between Christianity and Islam undoubtedly is to be found in the symbolism of the two faiths: both religions, desert-born, speak in the symbols of desert lands. Proselytization by Moslems has been concentrated in arid and semiarid Africa where it has taken a deep hold on the minds of people; Christian missionary effort, on the other hand, has focused on the moist lands of Africa where the symbolisms of Christianity are foreign to the thinking of the people. However, possibly far more important than symbolism is polygamy as a favorable factor for Islam. The distribution of missionary effort in Africa is a complex subject only now being studied.

[2] Joseph H. Greenberg, "Studies in African Linguistic Classification: "VI. The Click Languages," *Southwestern Journal of Anthropology*, vol. VI, no. 3, p. 223, Autumn, 1950.

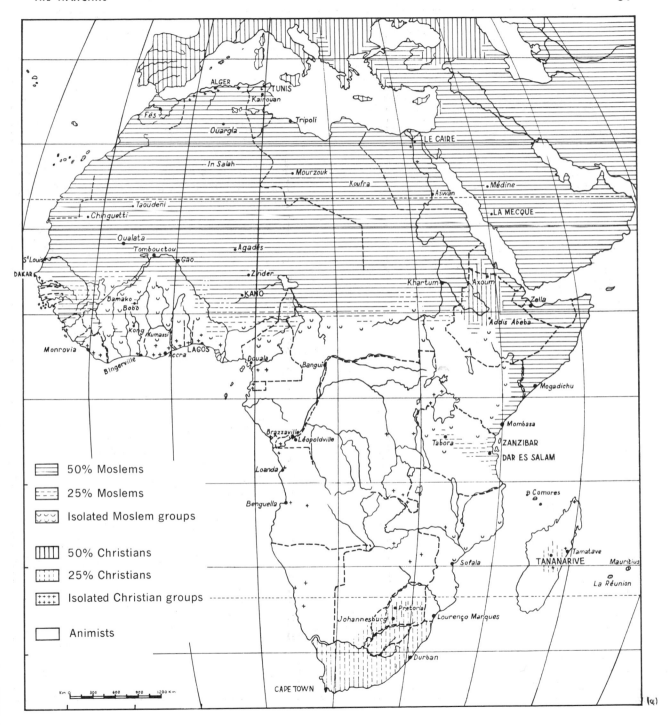

**FIGURE 2.4** Religions in Africa (a) 1900 and (b, next page) 1955. (By R. Mauny, Director, L'Institut l'Afrique Noire Française, Dakar. Courtesy R. Mauny.)

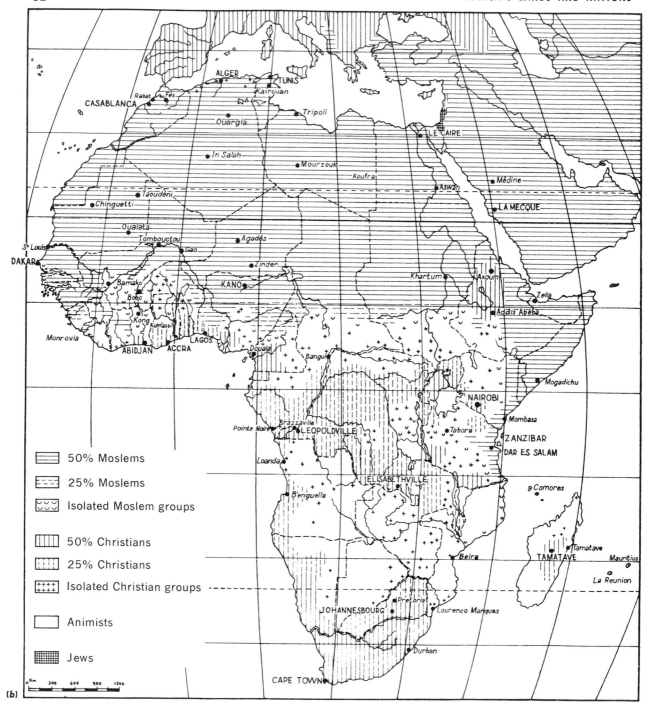

50% Moslems
25% Moslems
Isolated Moslem groups

50% Christians
25% Christians
Isolated Christian groups

Animists

Jews

(b)

**FIGURE 2.4** (b above) **Religions in Africa, 1955. Data for 1900 are on page 31. (By R. Mauny, Director, L'Institut l'Afrique Noire Française, Dakar. Courtesy S. Mauny.)**

**FIGURE 2.5** (right) **Population density. (After Goode's World Atlas, Edward B. Espenstrade, ed., Chicago: Rand McNally & Company, 1964.)**

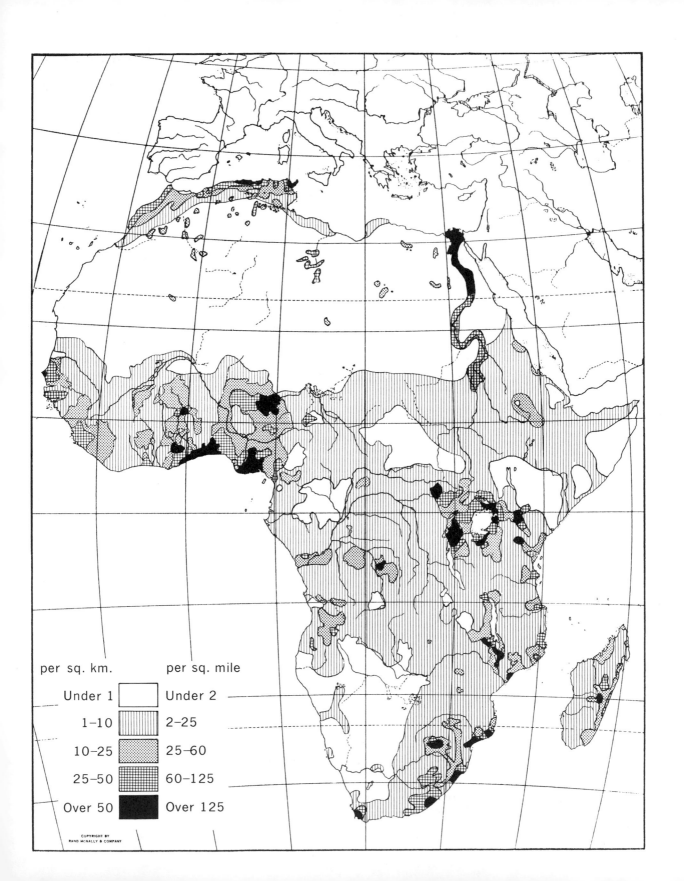

| per sq. km. | | per sq. mile |
|---|---|---|
| Under 1 | | Under 2 |
| 1–10 | | 2–25 |
| 10–25 | | 25–60 |
| 25–50 | | 60–125 |
| Over 50 | | Over 125 |

## Population Patterns

Africa is one of the sparsely populated parts of the world. The Africans are spread unevenly over the continent, some areas having hundreds living and subsisting upon each square mile of territory, whereas across immense stretches there may not be one sedentary inhabitant in hundreds, or even thousands of square miles. The Nile valley of Egypt and particularly the river delta is one of the most heavily peopled regions on the globe; conversely, the Libyan Desert of Egypt and great portions of the Mauritanian deserts are almost empty quarters (Figure 2.5).

Over 305 million people live in the continent. Compare this with the over 3,160 million for the world and it will be seen that Africa, second largest landmass (with over one-fifth of the world's land area), has less than 10 percent of the world's people.

Growth appears to have been relatively static in Africa over many centuries, although as was true in other parts of the world, there were periods of increase and decline throughout the continent. Evidence seems to indicate that the rise and decline of African populations in early eras became closely adjusted to the food-producing capacity of the land. Emergence from hunting-and-gathering economies to cultures based on agrarian activities undoubtedly gave impetus to an increase in population because it provided a more abundant and steadier food supply.

The cessation of slave trading may have effected the first big increase in modern times. This took place between the middle of the nineteenth and the beginning of the twenties centuries. It is likely, however, that some of the beneficial effects of colonialism also began to affect the birth-death ratio, as population more than doubled in the last 100 years. Before Europeans came on the African scene, population growth was almost static; today Africa has one of the highest rates of increase among the continents, second only to Latin America. (Percentage annual increase, 1960 to 1963: world, 1.9; Latin America, 2.9; Africa, 2.5; South Asia, 2.4; Oceania, 2.3; North America, 1.5; East Asia, 1.5; Europe, 0.9.)

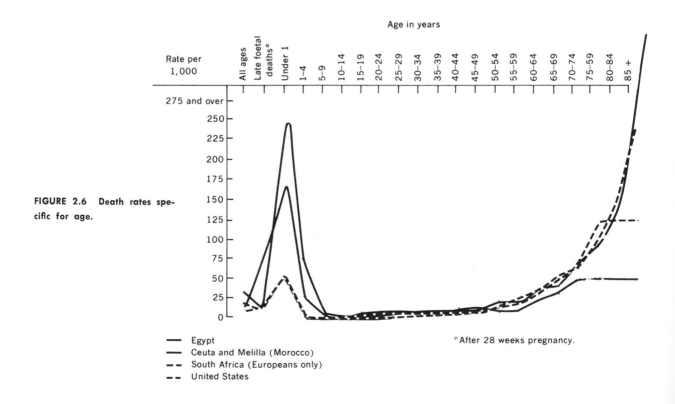

FIGURE 2.6  Death rates specific for age.

Egypt
Ceuta and Melilla (Morocco)
South Africa (Europeans only)
United States

*After 28 weeks pregnancy.

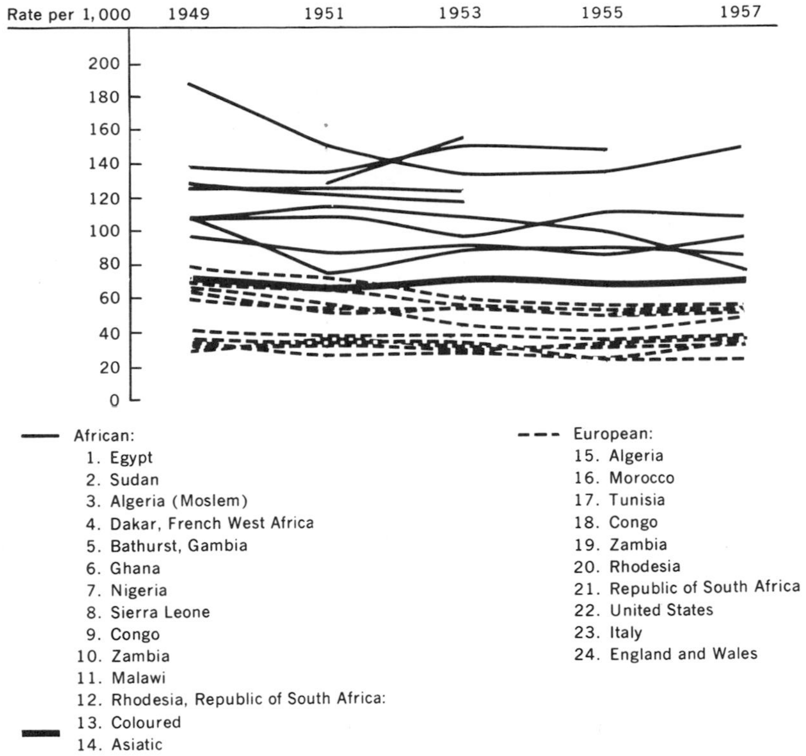

Rate per 1,000    1949          1951          1953          1955          1957

FIGURE 2.7 Infant mortality rates per 1,000 live births, 1949 to 1957.

African:
1. Egypt
2. Sudan
3. Algeria (Moslem)
4. Dakar, French West Africa
5. Bathurst, Gambia
6. Ghana
7. Nigeria
8. Sierra Leone
9. Congo
10. Zambia
11. Malawi
12. Rhodesia, Republic of South Africa:
13. Coloured
14. Asiatic

European:
15. Algeria
16. Morocco
17. Tunisia
18. Congo
19. Zambia
20. Rhodesia
21. Republic of South Africa
22. United States
23. Italy
24. England and Wales

Demographic conditions vary across the continent. While average densities are highest in West and East Africa, rates of increase are highest in the North and West, and there are centers of excessively high density: Zanzibar, Rwanda, Burundi, and Nigeria, as countries,[3] have the highest densities, but the Nile valley in Egypt exceeds 1,800 per square mile with rural densities not uncommonly exceeding 2,500 per square mile. According to Hance,[4] 28 percent of Africa is likely overpopulated, and 38 percent of the Africans live in overpopulated areas.

Africa and Asia have the highest mortality rates in the world—and also the highest fertility rates. These facts are significant in view of the improving socioeconomic conditions that appear imminent in Africa: death rates should lower, and, unless planned or unplanned conditions reduce the birthrate, African populations are likely to rise markedly. The significant data in Figure 2.6 are apparent, namely, the preponderant number of deaths during the first year of life, and between years 1 and 4 among Africans (Egyptians and Moroccans) as contrasted to mortality rates among European South Africans and Americans. The wastage of life in infancy among African peoples is marked. The graph also shows, however, that, if a child survives the first 4 years of life, he has a fair chance of living to quite an advanced age. Figure 2.7 presents essentially the same thing, although not comparatively: it consistently bears out the higher mortality rates for infants in backward societies and among underprivileged groups than among Europeans, and even Indians, in Africa. Figure 2.8 reveals in a startling manner the effect of high infant mortality on life expectancy.

What causes this high toll among infants in Africa, and among Africans in general? Figure 2.9 presents, for very limited areas, death by cause. An interesting feature is the coincidence of peaks and depressions among Africans, and among Europeans whether living

[3] *1964 United Nations Statistical Yearbook.*
[4] William A. Hance, *Geography of Modern Africa*, New York: Columbia University Press, 1964, p. 52.

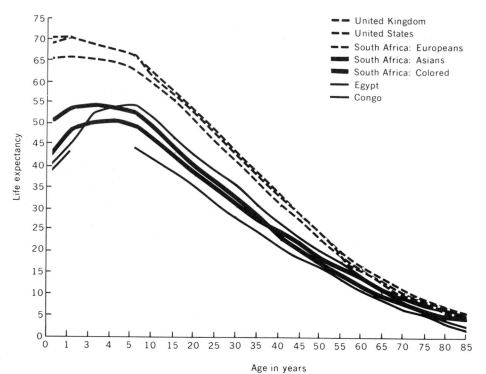

**FIGURE 2.8 Expectation of life at specific ages.**

Life expectancy (y-axis)
Age in years (x-axis)

Legend:
- United Kingdom
- United States
- South Africa: Europeans
- South Africa: Asians
- South Africa: Colored
- Egypt
- Congo

**FIGURE 2.9 Death rates by cause for specified countries.**

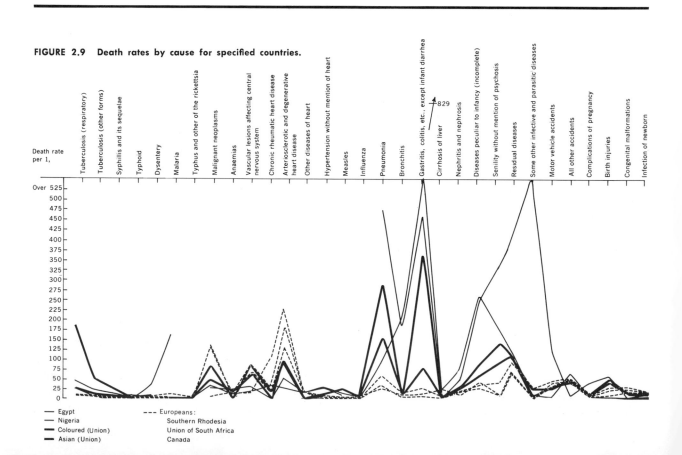

Death rate per 1,

Causes (column headers):
Tuberculosis (respiratory), Tuberculosis (other forms), Syphilis and its sequelae, Typhoid, Dysentery, Malaria, Typhus and other of the rickettsia, Malignant neoplasms, Anaemias, Vascular lesions affecting central nervous system, Chronic rheumatic heart disease, Arteriosclerotic and degenerative heart disease, Other diseases of heart, Hypertension without mention of heart, Measles, Influenza, Pneumonia, Bronchitis, Gastritis, colitis, etc., except infant diarrhea, Cirrhosis of liver, Nephritis and nephrosis, Diseases peculiar to infancy (incomplete), Senility without mention of psychosis, Residual diseases, Some other infective and parasitic diseases, Motor vehicle accidents, All other accidents, Complications of pregnancy, Birth injuries, Congenital malformations, Infection of newborn

829

Legend:
- Egypt
- Nigeria
- Coloured (Union)
- Asian (Union)
- Europeans:
  Southern Rhodesia
  Union of South Africa
  Canada

in or out of Africa: all sectors of each group conform to their own group. Malignant neoplasms and heart diseases cause the greatest number of deaths among Europeans whereas among all the Africans lung diseases, diseases of infancy and old age, and infective and parasitic diseases are very prevalent.

## The Geography of Health, Energy, and Disease

### THE MEASURE OF DISEASE

The majority of Africans live all their lives with debilitating ailments. The fittest survive, and hence the Africans that live to adulthood are probably the healthiest that were born or the luckiest. Disease and malnutrition are two of the great problems and frustrations of Africa. Tropical medicine has made great progress: Vaccinations and inoculations provide almost sure protection against many of the former killers; several very effective suppressives and even cures are available for malaria while medicines for dysentery, powders for heat rash, and vitamins to guard against physical rundown remove many of the dangers and discomforts of these afflictions. Nonetheless, disease eradication will not be fast all over Africa for several reasons, one being the immensity of the problem, another the scattered nature of population distribution. It will be difficult to carry medical and hospital facilities to all the people, to villages and outdistricts, and even more difficult to supply all parts of the continent with sanitary water supplies. Over large areas, therefore, population likely will be held down for quite some time, it would seem, by a not much lower mortality rate than before.

Despite the progress in tropical medicine, there is much that is not known about tropical disease and about such attendant factors as germ carriers and hosts (see Glossary), the effects of African climates upon the human body and health, and the best means of germ eradication. Accentuating the problem is the fact that Africa is one of the most effective natural incubators in the world for breeding the microorganisms of disease, germ carriers, and the hosts for the carriers. Vegetation complements heat and moisture in disease propagation and spread, while the importance of flies, mosquitoes, ticks, and other insects in the transmission of disease is incalculable.

The high incidence of disease and the high death rate among Africans, a condition that prevails from the Atlas and Nile lands to the Cape, are in part the result of custom and culture and attitudes held by Africans; diet and clothing, abetted by climate, also play their part. Africans are generally undernourished because most of them know little about nutrition; starches make up the bulk of the diet, and protein is deficient for the majority in great parts of the continent. Almost everywhere one is impressed by the small number of children where one expects to see many: they die of dysentery in summer and of pneumonia in winter; in the tropical and equatorial zones, lung diseases are contracted at night because, although the temperature-drop may not be extreme, inadequate covering gives poor protection from the dampness. Clothing too is generally inadequate for the young. In the bush country of black Africa, many of the children wear no clothing at all.

Customs that induce, and attitudes towards syphilis and the other venereal diseases have made these ailments widely prevalent. Venereal diseases are one of the curses of Africa, and they are almost impossible to treat, partly because of their wide social acceptance. The sanitary habits of most Africans also contribute to the spread of disease: drinking and cooking water are not uncommonly drawn from the same streams or pools in which people bathe; these water sources may also be their latrines.

It can be seen that health problems are not merely those of research, or of making health and medical facilities available, but also of converting Africans to seek (or even accept) medical aid, and of changing centuries of habits.

There are many knotty problems yet to be solved before the many threats to health in Africa will be eliminated, but the means of preserving and extending life are slowly unfolding and spreading. It has also become apparent that any race is subject to the same laws of health and disease as are all others living under similar conditions, including conditions of sanitation, nutrition, and the like. In spite of differences in resistance or susceptibility to disease among Africans and people from outside Africa, these differences can be equalized by medicine, proper sanitation, pure water, and diet.

Different parts of Africa differ in the degree of healthfulness and energy they conduce. The humid equatorial areas of central Africa and the Guinea coast are enervating because humid heat generally drains energy more than does dry heat. On the other hand, in the wet and dry tropics of West Africa, the extreme drought and the associated desiccating, dusty winds of the dry period are more uncomfortable and physically distressing than is the heat of the humid season. The uplands are more invigorating than the lowlands. The Atlas lands, with seasonal changes in both temperature and humidity, are climatically healthful lands but here, as in Egypt, habits of unsanitary living, dark houses, and poverty encourage insects and microorganisms.

## THE GENESIS OF DISEASE

The factors to be taken into account in considering the genesis of disease in Africa are multiple. Among the most important are the environment of disease, the disease itself, the infecting microorganisms, the carriers and vectors (see Glossary), the hosts, and epidemics and plagues. In Africa, nature—climate, vegetation, fauna—conduces to create an environment highly favorable to the breeding of microorganisms and vectors while, as noted, the habits of culture and living, superstition, and a lack of knowledge produce conditions that are advantageous to the spread and devastation of disease.

The roles of climate and culture are well known. Not so well understood are the other integrants of the genesis of African disease. The continent is large, and the variety of disease and the contributing accomplices—vectors, carriers, and hosts—is numerous. Study and research in Africa, although intense in many places, is young, and so knowledge is short of what is needed. There is so much that is not yet known about some of the greatest killers and enervators.

The genesis of any disease involves its identification, distribution, hosts, biology, disease relations, and control. Where does the disease occur? Is it native to a region, or was it introduced? Is the disease, within a given area, of major or minor proportions? Is it endemic or epidemic in its occurrence?

Identification, meaning the key characteristics as well as the diagnostic criteria, must be made of all the integrants, and even of the disease itself. This involves an often difficult isolating of germs, vectors, hosts, and carriers. What bacteria cause the disease? Have the microorganisms been fully identified? What are the relationships of the germs to the environment, to their hosts, to the carriers, to the disease? Have hosts, vectors, and carriers been identified?

Control of the disease is another problem. Is there a preventive? In attempting to conquer and eradicate the disease, is it best to attack the disease itself, the hosts, the germ, the vectors, the environment, or all? Is is curable? Should the patient be isolated? How does the disease spread, and the carriers? How do the vectors travel—are they transported, or do they have a wide range of movement, by flight or otherwise? What causes epidemics and plagues?

The problems involved in analyzing disease are seemingly endless. The foregoing paragraphs give some indication of the needed scope of investigation, and from this brief view, the reader will at least not be misled into believing that the subjects of health and disease in Africa are simple.

*Infectious and Parasitic Diseases: Diseases Spread by Insects.* Many of the maladies prevalent across much of the continent are spread by insects and other arthropods acting as vectors. Of these, malaria is the most widespread. Although distributed across many degrees of latitude, extending as far poleward as 65°N, malaria occurs most abundantly in warm countries and headed the list, for long years, as the "most formidable of tropical diseases." It is spread by the *Anopheles* mosquito. Among indigenous Africans, who generally have been exposed to it for centuries, malaria acts very differently from the way it does among those with no immunity. Because the African is laid open repeatedly to its infection, acute malaria among these people is almost entirely a disease of infancy and early childhood. The high rate of mortality during the early years of life must be attributed to the malignant complications of malaria, which include cerebral malaria. However, with increased age those Africans living in an endemic area gradually acquire

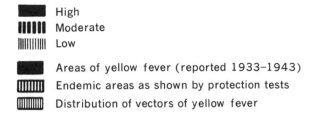

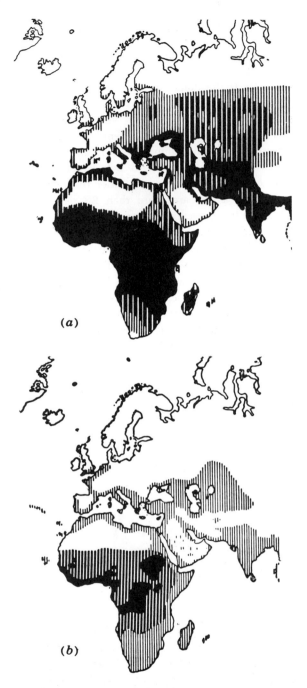

(a)

(b)

(c)

**FIGURE 2.10** (a) Malaria; (b) yellow fever; (c) filariasis. (a and b courtesy of American Registry of Pathology of the U.S. Armed Forces Institute of Pathology; c from Philip Manson-Bahr's Manson's Tropical Diseases. Courtesy Cassel & Co., Ltd.)

a relative immunity, and even when they do have an attack of malaria, it is likely to be mild. However, the individual remains a host to the malaria parasite for all of his life—in other words, his blood, fed on by the mosquito, provides the microorganism that will cause others to contract malaria if the mosquito bites them. The cycle is man—mosquito—man.

In the past there was no cure for malaria; there were only suppressives, that is, drugs that help to hold the disease in control, below the threshold of an attack. Today there are a number of synthetic arrestives, but for about 300 years the universal counteractant was quinine, a remedy that has had an unprecedented life among medicines. Although quinine was known and used for a long time, it was only around 1860 that it began to be used as a preventive rather than as a curative medicine. Only in the last 30 years has it largely been superseded by the synthetics.

The only means of malaria eradication over wide areas is through the destruction of the *Anopheles* mosquito (Figure 2.10 *a*).

Yellow fever is endemic across a broad band of middle Africa that reaches from about 15°N to 10°S, with some outliers. The vector for this disease is also a mosquito, *Aedes aegypti*. Since the *Aedes aegypti* is much more widely spread than the belt delimited on the map, there is always a danger of new regions becoming infected (Figure 2.10 *b*). It has been suggested that the dominant cycle here is not always man—mosquito—man: in some places, as in Sudan, there may be an important vertebrate reservoir in nature in the small, large-eyed primates known as "the bushbabies of galagoes."

The mosquito is the intermediary host also for the *Filariae* (worms) (Figure 2.10*c*). The insect feeds on the blood of one human and transfers the parasite to another human through its bite.

Flies also spread disease in Africa, especially in the north where the fly is "the most pestiferous, assaulting, clinging, and numerous of his breed anywhere in the world. His medical and economic importance is incalculable." It is a completely different species from the tsetse, found south of the Sahara and carrier of sleeping sickness. In the tropics flies abound the year around, but in North Africa they reach peak populations in the spring and fall. Through their various contacts they spread a variety of diseases, especially the enteric illnesses and blindness (trachoma and other eye ailments).

"Flies constitute one of the major health hazards (especially) in Egypt. . . ." The Egyptian fly is particularly pestiferous, swarming over the meat, bread, and fruit in the open markets and in eating places, breeding in the cesspools and disposal dumps, darting always at the faces of humans to infest the eyes, noses, and mouths of countless children and adults,[5]

[5] Report of the U.S. Naval Medical Research Unit No. 3, Cairo, Egypt, March, 1958, p. 4. Also observed by the writer.

transmitting virus and bacteria causing blindness (Figure 2.11).

Baffling as is the domestic fly, there is another fly that creates even greater devastation across wide parts of Africa. This is the tsetse, vector of sleeping sickness (trypanosomiasis). Different species carry the disease to man and animals. Nearly all the continent between 15°N and 20°S—a belt larger in area than the entire United States—is under the blight of this destroyer. There are more than 20 recognized species of the tsetse, each with its own special requirements in food and in the type of country and climate it needs to live in; each has its own particular pattern of behavior by which it succeeds in finding the right conditions for existence and survival. Within the lands infested with the tsetse, countless multitudes of humans have wasted away into emaciation, coma, and eventual death; great herds of animals have been destroyed; vast reaches of farm and ranchland have

FIGURE 2.11  Flies cluster in moist places and are important vectors of disease. (Courtesy Public Relations Department, Tanganyika.)

been surrendered back to nature, and even mineral fields have remained untouched because of this insect. In parts of tropical Africa, the tsetse fly has been the greatest single barrier to development.

Trypanosomiasis can be attacked in two ways, either by trying to eradicate the insect or by attempting to find a cure for the disease; both are being pursued. Three techniques are employed in the attempted extermination of the tsetse fly: the destruction of the animal hosts, the clearing (by cutting and burning) of the infested bush and river-fringing forests, and spraying. The first and last methods are the least effective, the latter because the tsetse can develop a resistance to insecticides. An antitrypanosomiasis serum is available for cattle and hogs, and serums to prevent human infection have been developed, but the inoculation of humans is still considered dangerous.

Ticks, mites, fleas, and lice are likewise vectors of disease. Cosmopolitan and distributed over most parts of Africa, they transmit a variety of maladies to animals and man, such as tick and Q fever, relapsing fever, tick paralysis, tick typhus (tick-bite fever), and skin irritations and sores.

***Diseases Spread from Human to Human.*** For some diseases man, and man alone, is the vector, carrier, and host. Infection comes through contact, as in the case of yaws and the venereal diseases, skin infections, respiratory ailments, and leprosy (Figure 2.12). Trachoma, while spread from human to human by contact, is also disseminated by flies. It occurs throughout Africa, but is more prevalent among sedentary, agglomerated populations than among nomadic peoples because of the infectious nature of the disease and the way it is transferred. For these reasons incidence also increases along trade routes. In the area of Africa lying north of about 10°N, it is more common than elsewhere on the continent. Here, from 40 to 90 percent of the sedentary populations may be infected.

The abdominal killers, cholera and dysentery, move from man to man. "*Cholera* follows the great trade routes of human intercourse and is conveyed by man —probably in its principal extensions, by man alone— from place to place. Widely prevalent throughout the tropics, subtropics, and even into the midlatitudes, all of Africa except Cape Province and West Africa

FIGURE 2.12  Liberian leper village. Notice the effects of leprosy: deformation of the hands and the loss of the little finger on the right hand and the way the disease is spreading over the body. *(Photograph by writer.)*

are afflicted." From remotest antiquity it has prevailed in lower Bengal and central China, and probably radiated outward from there. An epidemic can usually be predicted, and the season when and areas where cholera is at its highest are those with high temperatures accompanied by high relative humidity and intermittent rains: the "presence of endemic centers" from which outbreaks can germinate "at any time must be accepted. . . . The death rate is always high—still about 20–30 per cent (formerly as high as 70 per cent), . . . and prognosis is [especially] unfavorable in those over 50 and under five."[6]

[6] Sir Philip H. Manson-Bahr, *Manson's Tropical Diseases,* 13th ed., Baltimore: Williams & Wilkins Company, 1950, pp. 478–495.

Dysentery has a like distribution, but whereas cholera breaks out in epidemic form, dysentery is a constant companion of man in tropical Africa and, in places, in the subtropics. Unsanitary living conditions and the contamination of food by the carriers (man) are thought to constitute the most important means of spread in urban communities, but flies and polluted water supplies are frequently implicated in rural areas. Both cholera and dysentery are body dehydrators. Among the very young, fatality from dysentery is extremely high; in those of more advanced age, it may give rise to an anemic state of debilitation with attendant symptoms of dietary deficiencies.

*Schistosomiasis.* Among the infectious diseases of Africa, the most rapidly spreading and one of the most dangerous is schistosomiasis, also known as bilharzia. It is contracted by wading in fresh water in which the cercariae of the disease live. This disease cannot be transmitted from man to man; a snail, in which the cercariae breed and develop, is the necessary intermediary. It is not a new disease in Africa. It has

been known for a few decades in some places, over 100 years in others, and in Egypt for perhaps 5,000 years. It is widespread throughout the continent wherever freshwater bodies, including rivers, are found (Figure 2.13).

Schistosomiasis can both be prevented and controlled. Prevention depends on any practical means by which the human and the cercariae are kept out of contact, in other words, through the destruction of the snails and the cercariae, and the purification of the water supplies. However, where primitive water sources are used, contamination is inevitable and the infection will go on. Bilharzia is a growing problem; it is difficult to treat and difficult to prevent. Although important advances have been made in the control of some parasitic diseases in Africa, this is not the case with schistosomiasis.

An enigmatic aspect of the disease is that as development of lands advances through the impounding of waters and irrigation schemes, the spread of schistosomiasis is accelerated. The following quotation will indicate a measure of the very large scope of this problem.

> The entire Nile Valley is the most heavily infected area in the continent. In this context it should be noted that the vast irrigation network supplied by the Nile is responsible for the millions of cases seen annually, and not the Nile River itself.
>
> There is much to be learnt from the Sudan, which is a semiarid, almost desert country, except along its big rivers and its irrigation schemes. Its areas of greatest prevalence were, until recently, along the Blue, White, and Main Niles, with perhaps the heaviest infections occurring in the north, near the Egyptian border. The advent of the big Gezira irrigation project has changed the picture completely in the last 20 years, even though the authorities realized the danger inherent in such a scheme. In the formerly arid Gezira, infection rates have risen year by year from the previously unimportant few per cent. The position here is not helped by an annual influx of migrant labourers, many of whom are infected.[7]

FIGURE 2.13    Schistosomiasis. *(Courtesy U.S. Army Medical Museum.)*

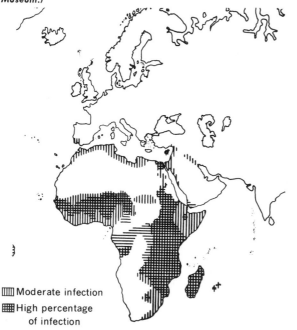

▦ Moderate infection
▦ High percentage
   of infection

[7] William Alves, "The Challenge of Bilharzia in Developing Africa," *Optima*, vol. VIII, no. 3, pp. 139–146, September, 1958.

*Noninfectious and Nonparasitic Diseases.* The infectious and parasitic ailments are not the totality of African disease. There is a noninfectious and nonparasitic morbidity that is peculiarly associated with the tropics. Among the more important are the nutritional diseases. Protein starvation, or kwashiorkor, is now recognized as a disease. Its symptoms include malignant malnutrition, Gillian's edema (in Africa), peculiar changes in the skin and hair making them turn a reddish or muddyish color, and fatty degeneration of the liver. It is widely prevalent throughout tropical and equatorial Africa. The "red boy" indicates the presence of kwashiorkor. In early stages it can be controlled by means of well-balanced diets.

## THE PROBLEMS OF DISEASE AND HEALTH

As everywhere in the world, the problems of health in Africa are part of a complex made up of numerous intermingling forces. It is not possible to dissociate health from any of the other elements that form a part of the structure of life of the peoples. The study of disease in Africa has both exciting and depressing facets, but any true conception of disease and health in this tropical continent entails not only a knowledge of the physical elements of the habitats but of the sociological, economic, and educational conditions as well. The spread of disease is contingent upon many factors. It has already been noted that the critical problem of disease spread was found to be intimately and adversely associated with progress in irrigation extension; and that diseases travel along the routes of trade. The wanderers—the migrant peoples—may infect, or reinfect areas once cleared, if they carry with them in their baggage, or on their persons or animals, the vectors or parasites of disease. The vast seasonal migrations, therefore, constitute a problem which requires more careful attention.

In some respects, factors of the habitat have a more direct bearing upon the health of primitive people than of more advanced groups. The inadequate supply of water over wide regions, erosion, the loss of soil fertility through certain practices of cultivation and grazing, the dense populations within limited areas such as the valley of the Nile, the Lake Victoria region, Rwanda and Burundi and sections of the Guinea coast, and the relatively sparse populations in almost all other parts of the continent are problems that are inseparable from health and disease, and economic and social well-being. Diet, ignorance, and in the north, poverty among the Africans bear directly upon the disease and death rates in the different regions. Further, the spread and course of a disease are frequently more rapid under tropical conditions (as in the case of tuberculosis and pneumonia), the climate acting to accelerate the multiplication of parasites and vectors, but being depressive to the human. Malnutrition and the likely enervation from other ailments accentuate these effects.

In Africa, the interrelation of social and health problems is in places many times magnified because of customs or conditions peculiar to certain peoples or groups. Between industrial centers and native areas there is a constant large movement of laborers, inter- and intranational in character, and at times over long distances. There are many tribal groups whose habits of living keep them almost constantly on the march, and among the Moslems, there is the deep-felt urge to make the pilgrimage to Mecca. All of these migrant folk are "potential smugglers" of parasites and vectors into the areas into which, or between which, they move. Whereas within large urban or industrial centers organized health services are able to reach many people, outlying districts are almost unserved, and the migrants largely uncontrolled and uncontrollable. Disease in Africa must be treated as a health problem rather than a curative, although the two processes go hand in hand.

Africa is not one place, but many places, and the epidemiology of disease, "whether of man or animals, will vary considerably in detail as one goes a thousand miles one way or a thousand miles the other, or climbs from sea level to 6,000 feet above, or surveys the scene in the relatively uniform warm and moist climate . . . , or in many areas where a hot, dry season lasting several months intervenes between the rains."[8] Differential planning and treatment must, therefore, be carried out between places.

[8] D. G. Davey, "Human and Animal Trypanosomiasis in Africa," *American Journal of Tropical Medicine and Hygiene,* vol. VII, no. 5, pp. 546–553, September, 1958.

# 3 THE MAGHRIB

*Like trees, great historical events
spring from a soil enriched by
the remains of earlier growths.*

PARKER THOMAS MOON

## The Realm of the Barbary States

The word "Barbary" comes from the name of the original inhabitants of the region, the Barbars—or Berbers, as the word is more commonly spelled. Arab geographers called these lands Djezira-el-Maghrib, meaning "Western Isle." The name is appropriate because there is no region in Africa that stands so distinctly apart from the rest of the continent as the Northwest. Facing Europe and turning its back on Africa, the Maghrib seems more of an adjunct to Africa than a part of it, a sort of Africa Minor.

The Barbary states are five—Morocco, Algeria, Tunisia, Libya, and Mauritania. As states, territories with political identity, some are historically old; approximately the present frontiers have existed from the time of the Turkish conquests, some 400 years ago, for the three easternmost territories. Previous to French and Spanish control, Morocco was for more than a millennium an independent state while Tunisia, except for interruptions of which the 600-year Roman rule was the longest, has existed as the center of independent or virtually independent governments since Carthage was founded, over 800 years before the Christian era. Also included in the Northwest realm are the Spanish Sahara and the Spanish enclaves of Ifni along the Atlantic coast, and Ceuta and Melilla along the Mediterranean Sea.

Since 1950 all but the Spanish territories have gained independence. The status of some parts of the Northwest are still disputed by Morocco, namely, the Spanish Sahara and enclaves, and independent Mauritania. Morocco maintains that for historic reasons, Mauritania should be united with her domain: it was Mauritanians who first organized Moroccan tribes into political unity. Portions of the Algerian-Moroccan boundary also are contested, particularly in the vicinity of Tindouf in Algeria.

Northwest Africa spreads across more than 2½ million square miles of territory, covering an area over half as great as that of the United States and reaching from the western borders of Egypt and Sudan to the Atlantic Ocean. On the north it is limited by the Mediterranean; along the south and east it merges from desert into desert, while to the west lies the ocean. Geographic barriers therefore set it apart from other populated areas.

Nonetheless, geography and history relate the Maghrib with all regions across the barriers, especially Europe and the Middle East. Like the narrows of the Dardanelles and Bosporus, the Strait of Gibraltar has been not only a water passage dividing continents but a connection between them as well. Carthaginians and Moslems used this route to go from the Maghrib to Iberia; car travel today between Europe and Africa is heavily by way of Gibraltar, and plans are under consideration for the construction of an underwater tunnel, from Africa to Europe. From the East religion, language, and culture have permeated the Maghrib making the Atlas Mountains and Saharan lands, along with Egypt, a part of the Arab world.

There are associations southward with and across the Sahara as well. Connections with the Sahara are ancient. Across the desert, caravan trade wrought tenuous links between North Africa and the Sudan until European ships turned the commerce from the desert trails to the sea-lanes. The Almoravids, who established the first of the great Moroccan dynasties, were Saharan nomads from Mauritania who invaded the Moroccan plateau through passes in the Atlas. In reverse, Berbers from the Maghrib fled into the fastnesses of some of the Saharan uplands to escape the invasions of Moslems from Arabia. The Sahara, barrier that it is, is nevertheless a sort of marchland, a mixing zone for black people from the humid lands of west and equatorial Africa and the Berbers of the north. Black Africans at one time had spread so far northward that they inhabited portions of the northern fringes of the desert; Berbers and black Africans cohabit the interior massifs. The people of the Maghrib range from very black to blond, Scandinavianlike types with variations in between, indicative of the interpenetrations of the races.

In general, however, the Northwest realm looks north and east, and away from Africa—north because the mountains, more sparsely inhabited than the Atlantic and Mediterranean-facing plateaus and plains, are like a wall shutting out the rest of the continent; east because culture, religion, and language relate them to the Arabic-speaking people and the rest of Islam.

Within the Maghrib, there is a geographic, historic, and ethnic coherence. These lands are Moslem, a part of that great world of Islam that extends outward

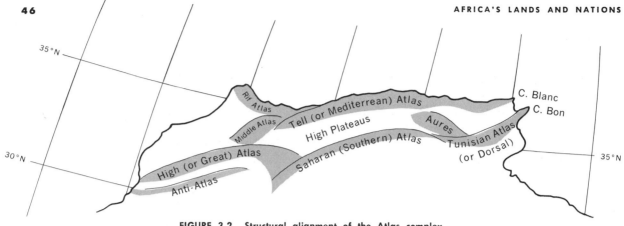

**FIGURE 3.2   Structural alignment of the Atlas complex.**

from its center in the Middle East, eastward across southern Asia to and beyond Pakistan, westward across all of northern Africa. Climatically, they are all lands of variable rainfall with extensive deserts and steppes. Relief also unites, at the same time that it separates, the states of the Northwest because the topographic alignment runs generally east-west; political boundaries cut across the relief structure. Plant, animal, and human migrations have followed the grain of the mountain system so that the dispersal of like influences throughout the whole of the area is remarkable.

Striking contrasts characterize the Maghrib, however, for physically the environment is one of great variety. In the broadest view, the realm is composed of three regions: the coasts, the mountains, and the desert.

The great alpine system of the Atlas is so prominent a part of the habitat that the three northwestern states of the Maghrib are often referred to as "the Atlas lands." The Atlas are a great upland block trending northeast-southwest, and comprised of three parts that run more or less parallel with each other: the folded structures of the Mediterranean and Sahara Atlas, and the high plateaus that lie in between. (See Figure 3.2.) Essentially this mountain block, about 1,500 miles long, is a plateau buttressed along the north and south by lofty folded ranges.

The Mediterranean Atlas, comprised of many individual ranges and block plateaus separated from each other by valleys, extend from the Rif Mountains at Gibraltar through the Tell Atlas of Algeria into Tu-

nisia, playing out in the tip of the promontory of Cape Blanc. The ranges generally parallel the coast. At times they rise abruptly as rocky headlands out of the sea; in places they are fringed with narrow coastal plains that sometimes penetrate inland as slender river valleys between mountains. The most important sown areas are found in these longitudinal lowlands, surrounded on three sides by great heights and opening to the sea.

The Southern Atlas stretch from the Atlantic Ocean near Agadir, where they project into the sea as a steep and hilly coast, eastward as the High and Anti-Atlas of Morocco, the Sahara Atlas of Algeria, and the Tunisian Dorsal that ends in Cape Bon, the latter the longest eastward trajectory of the Atlas system. The desert laps at the base of the mountains, licking up the slopes, and occupying the southern portions of all of these countries—southern and southeastern Morocco, most of Algeria, large portions of Tunisia, all of Mauritania, and almost all of Libya. Except for tiny coastal fringes, Libya is desert from the Mediterranean Sea inland for about 900 miles to its frontiers with Niger and Chad, and east and west in its full extent. The high plateaus are semiarid steppelands as are also the plateaus that front the mountains toward the Atlantic (Figure 3.3).

The regions of heavy population in the Maghrib are spotty, like islands of habitation that lie in the desert, or between sea and desert, or between sea and mountains. Aside from the scattered oases south of the Atlas, population concentrates in a long thin line bordering the shore, densest between the moun-

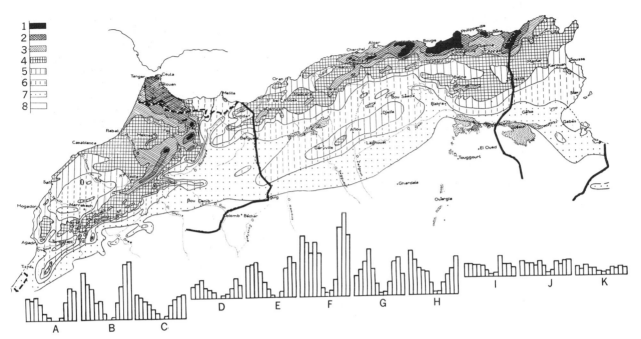

**FIGURE 3.3   Climate: Rainfall (1) above 40 inches; (2) 30—40 inches; (3) 20—30 inches; (4) 15—20 inches; (5) 12—15 inches; (6) 8—12 inches; (7) 4—8 inches; (8) below 4 inches. Casablanca (A) and Algiers (B) are maritime stations, Tunis (C) lies in the proximity of the sea. Meknes (E) at an altitude of about 1,740 feet, Constantine (H) at 2,165 feet, Kairouan (I) at 164 feet, Marrakech (D) at 1,542 feet, Djelfa (J) at about 3,610 feet, and Gafsa (K) at about 1,132 feet are stations of the Mediterranean-type climate. Ifran (F) in the Middle Atlas (at about 5,413 feet) and Agaïour (G) (at over 5,905 feet) are mountain stations. (Map after Capot-Rey. Graphs after Despois.)**

tains and the coast, in a belt that stretches for about 2,600 miles from Cyrenaica to the Spanish Sahara, but seldom more than 50 to 100 miles deep. This most densely populated sector runs generally east and west, fronting on the sea and backing into the Atlas complex and the desert.

Uninterrupted expanses of cultivation are rare. The foremost are the fertile plains that occur interruptedly along the seaboard, wedged in like the population between the sea and the mountains, and sometimes extending inland between the ranges of rugged uplands. Usually the green of fields or orchards stands out sharply against rocky hills and mountains, or within arid wastes, often ending abruptly at a confining wall or where irrigation stops. However, in winter even the hills may be covered for wide spaces with cultivated green. The contrasts are particularly

striking in the desert, or as one comes from the barren south or rugged interior onto a vantage point that looks down upon such a garden as the Fez-Meknes lowland.

Except in alluvial lowlands and in the desert oases, fields are rocky and the soils poor. Rocks are continuously gathered from the sown plots, and often disposed of by building stone fences. The Berbers say that "the stones grow" in their land, so persistently do the rocks rise to the surface, time after time, after fields have been cleared.

Water is the chief problem throughout all of this realm. Even along the coasts where the Mediterranean climate prevails, summer crops require irrigation although winter crops grow on the winter rains. Elsewhere irrigation must be depended upon to supply the deficit of moisture, and the farther south one goes

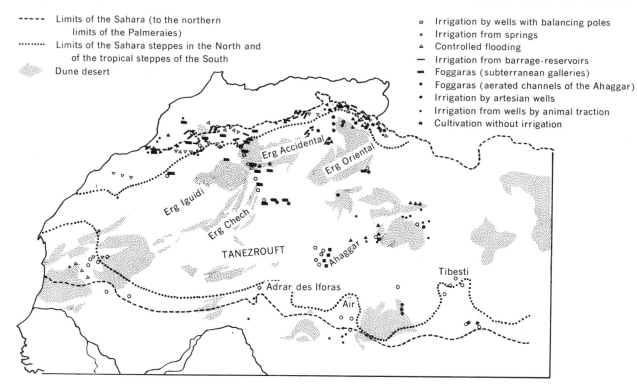

- - - - -  Limits of the Sahara (to the northern
           limits of the Palmeraies)
· · · · · ·  Limits of the Sahara steppes in the North and
           of the tropical steppes of the South
           Dune desert

o   Irrigation by wells with balancing poles
▲   Irrigation from springs
△   Controlled flooding
—   Irrigation from barrage-reservoirs
▬   Foggaras (subterranean galleries)
•   Foggaras (aerated channels of the Ahaggar)
•   Irrigation by artesian wells
•   Irrigation from wells by animal traction
*   Cultivation without irrigation

**FIGURE 3.4   Systems of irrigation. (After Capot-Rey.)**

the greater the need becomes. Perennial irrigation works provide some of the water, and in places irrigation constructions are very old, as in the case of the system that carries water from the Atlas to Marrakech and its *palmeraies* (see Glossary); the ruins of aqueducts and foggaras built by the Romans, still more ancient, attest to the need for water even along the Tell. (See Figure 3.4.) Some of these ancient systems of foggaras are still in use in the Maghrib. The foggaras are peculiar constructions that correspond to the *karez* of Afghanistan and the *kanez* of Iran. They employ a system of draining water from alluvial fans, and conducting it through subterranean conduits that slope gently toward a lower area where the water will be used for irrigation. They are built by sinking a number of vertical holes into water-bearing sands, and connecting the shafts at the bottom by channels that have just the right degree of slope, a highly skilled as well as difficult operation. The vertical shafts become wells from which water may be drawn, manually or by animals.

In many places, and across wide expanses, very simple methods of irrigation still are employed. Men or animals laboriously raise water from wells in small buckets which are emptied into channels that carry the water to the gardens. Water for household use sometimes must be carried great distances and not infrequently across rugged terrain, in earthen jugs on the heads of women, or in leather bags or drums on the backs of animals.

Predictable rainfall is concentrated in the winter months, with scattered showers in the spring and fall; summers are dry. This is what is known as the Mediterranean regime. But the places in the Maghrib where rainfall can be reasonably predicted are confined to the north, to regions that face on coasts and to the mountains, particularly the Mediterranean and Middle Atlas. Most of the Maghrib receives less than 10 inches of precipitation.

Latitude, exposure, and altitude cause important differences in the amount of rainfall received and determine the vegetation zones. Thus, with sufficient

49

FIGURE 3.5 (right) Winter snow in the Moroccan Atlas. *(Courtesy French Information Service.)*

FIGURE 3.6 (below) Rainfall regimes within the confines of the Sahara. (1) Autumn maximum of precipitation (September, October, November); (2) summer maximum (June, July August); (3) spring maximum (March, April, May); (4) winter maximum, December, January, February); (5) a secondary season of maximum rainfall in autumn, winter, or spring.

In the northern Sahara and Atlas lands maximum rains fall during the cool seasons of the year, whereas in the southern Sahara maximum precipitation falls during the summer season. Note the simplicity of the rainfall pattern in the south and the complexity of secondary maximums along the edges of northern and western Sahara. *(After Capot-Rey, Le Sahara Français.)*

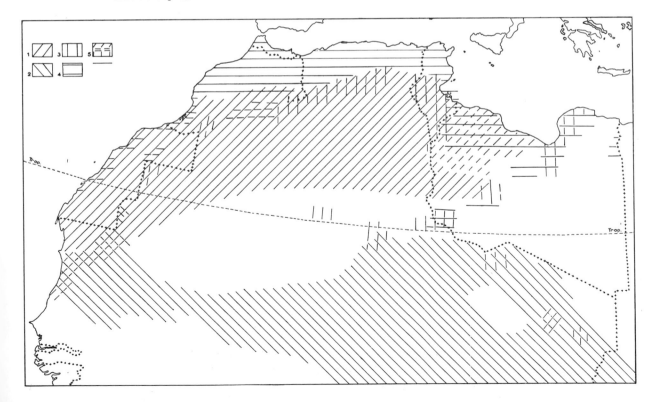

altitude and exposure, some mountain slopes have forests, or are green with meadows; one of the reasons for the semiarid character of the high plateaus is found in the fact that they lie behind mountains that act as barriers shutting out rain-bearing winds. The Mediterranean Atlas are snow covered in winter (Figure 3.5), but the snow generally melts during the dry summer; only the highest parts of the Grand Atlas carry snow the year around, and even this is rare; in the Sahara Atlas, snow seldom falls. The south facing slopes of these Southern Atlas and their intermontane valleys, and the lands along the south base of the Atlas massif range from semi-Saharan to Saharan. Topographic influences and exposure are at least as important as latitude in the Atlas lands in determining the absolute amounts of moisture that fall.

The rainfall regime (see Glossary) of the Mediterranean lands is to be explained as follows: during the low sun period when the sun is in the Southern Hemisphere, the belt of the northern westerlies, with their cyclonic storms, moves down from central Europe across the Mediterranean and the fringes of northern Africa. During this period, rain-bearing low pressure centers occasionally advance into the northernmost sectors of the Northwest. They are, however, erratic in their occurrence, and vary greatly in size and in their capacity to produce moisture. During the summer, the cyclonic belt lies considerably farther north, and in its place a semipermanent high takes hold in Northwest Africa. Associated with the high pressure are descending currents of dry air and the surface movement, out of the high, of desiccating winds, including the warming trades that blow toward the Equator. Thus, with distance inland, except for the extra moisture that the mountain elevations may wring out, rainfall declines and aridity increases (Figure 3.6).

Nevertheless, even on the desert side of the Southern Atlas, there are some rivers that flow down the slopes, the water coming from the rains of winter and the melting snows of spring. The steep slopes and abrupt break to the desert have led to the development of enormous alluvial fans which have become the locale of important oases. Most of these rivers lose themselves in the interior of the Sahara, some in great playa basins such as the Shotts Melghir and Djerid. Most, however, simply disappear in the sands,

their waters exhausted by irrigation, evaporation, and seepage. At the western end, some of the intermittent streams from the Saharan slopes have outlets to the ocean. Of these, the Dra is the most important.

## Patterns of Land and People

Crops more or less follow climate because agricultural conditions are dominated above all else by the volume of rainfall, or, in the desert, aside from drought by the occurrence of subterranean water reserves. In the northern part of the Atlas lands rainfall is sufficient to grow crops without irrigation, although variability of rainfall from year to year constitutes a problem that irrigation would eliminate; also, the seasonal character of the rainfall, which comes between November and May, means that without irrigation the land must lie idle for half the year. In the southern half of the Atlas lands and across all of the Saharan sector, rainfall is insufficient for the growth of crops without irrigation. In general, therefore, cultivation is carried on without irrigation in the north Atlas lands, with irrigation in all of the areas southward. Wheat, barley, vines, citrus, and olives grow on most of the unirrigated Mediterranean lands; vegetables become important where irrigation water is available. In the semiarid rocky *bled* (see Glossary and Figure 3.7) the Barbary fig is constantly in view, grown as a hedge or in rocky enclosures, and eaten as a fruit. As aridity increases, the olive disappears and the date comes in.

Throughout the Maghrib, primitive and modern agriculture are practiced side by side. Most of the Berber population lives off the land, tilling the soil and/or keeping animals. In mountainous and plateau regions they are likely to do both because fields are small and production poor; in the valleys and on the lowlands they only farm. Much of the agriculture is still primitive in all these countries: donkeys, horses, and camels still draw wooden homemade plows; in the mountains, stone casbahs stand beside plots of stony ground out of which tiny fields have been wrested, barricaded against intruders with walls of stone and brush, buttressed against slope erosion by terraces that are often bulwarked with stone.

The general aspect of agriculture varies considerably depending on whether it is practiced according to the traditional methods used by the great mass of the Berber farmers, or with the modern techniques and equipment used by large landowners who have sufficient land and capital. It is not difficult to distinguish between the fields of the traditional small farmer and those of wealthy landowners, because the small Berber cultivator has had to be content with the most marginal lands on the plateaus and lowlands (Figure 3.7) or has had to withdraw to isolated regions to cultivate the soil—into the high mountain valleys, or the semiarid intermontane valleys that are near Saharan, such as the Dra and the Sous.

Livestock, along with agricultural products, are among the chief sources of wealth in the Maghrib. The various regions, however, are not all equally suited to the raising of all types of livestock. The major portion of the realm consists of mountains and plateaus with harsh climates or of deserts. Pastures are essentially poor and seasonal. Above all, therefore, the three Atlas countries are lands of sheep and goats; and as pasture deteriorates and aridity increases, camels become important. The coastal plains, especially those facing the Atlantic and the Mediterranean Sea, with a heavier rainfall and richer pasture, are better suited to raising cattle and horses. Consequently, such regions as the Gharb in Morocco and the plains along the north coast raise quite large numbers. Donkeys are important throughout the Maghrib as beasts of burden, even in the desert, where they are burden bearers around the oases.

Over three-fourths of the population are still rural—sedentary cultivators living in oases, nomadic tent dwellers who are pastoralists and traders, or seminomadic peoples such as the inhabitants of the Aurès Mountains, who both cultivate the land and keep animals by herding them on natural pastures. On the high plateaus great numbers of sheep and goats and some camels graze; in the desert, as among the Tuareg of the Ahaggar and in the Tassili, camels are relatively more important (Figure 3.8).

Although change is slow and by no means a new phenomenon, nomadism is gradually declining and giving way to sedentary living. The shift to the sedentary mode of life normally takes years, sometimes decades, as a group passes from herding to cultivating, and from tent to permanent dwelling. Generally for a long time the two ways of life are

FIGURE 3.7  Plowing in the *bled*. Strangely paired animals, and even humans, often draw the crude wooden plows. (Photograph by J. Belin.)

FIGURE 3.8  Camel market at Goulimine, Morocco, casbah of the "blue people" lying at the northern edge of the Sahara. (Courtesy Service Général de l'Information, Morocco.)

simultaneously practiced; it is usual, when such a transition is occurring, for tent and house to stand side by side, with the family at first continuing to live in the tent, and using the permanent structure for storage.

More and more people from the countryside are being drawn to the cities looking for work, driven from the *bled* by impoverished conditions, attracted by supposed opportunities in industrial centers. Outside of all the large cities of the North, shantytowns (*bidonvilles,* in French—see Glossary) have grown up, giving rise to conditions that normally are far worse than those that the people left in the country. The filth and disease associated with these crowded slums, where none of the amenities of modern living are found, have been added to the problems that the people came with; and there is not the industry to accommodate more than a small part of those who have been drawn in. The *bidonville* of Algiers harbors about 40,000 people from the *bled,* that of Oran even more.

These sociological problems of change are found in all of the countries of the Maghrib, but in Algeria they are more pronounced because of the long period of French tenure, the policies of land appropriation and economic discrimination against the Algerians, and the revolutionary war.

## People and History, Then and Now

About 28 million people live in the Maghrib. Of these, perhaps 1 million inhabit the Sahara. Aside from the few Christian Europeans that still remain in these lands since independence and except for perhaps ½ million Jews, the population is Arabized Berbers (called Kabyles in Algeria) or North African Arabs.

The Northwest was one of the earliest parts of Africa known to the outside world, and many waves of foreigners have impacted upon the Maghrib. The people called "indigenous" are themselves not native to this area but were immigrants.[1] They are the Berbers, but who they are and where they came from are unknown. They are, however, likely related to Mediterranean peoples, south European or Middle Eastern. Whatever their origin, they were in the Maghrib and firmly established when other peoples began to invade.

As early as the twelfth century B.C. Phoenicians were colonizing these shores, and their inheritors, the maritime Carthaginians, not only established many ports of trade along the North African coasts and controlled the western basin of the Mediterranean Sea, but they are thought to have navigated as well along the coast of West Africa as far as the Gulf of Guinea. The Carthaginian state, centered in what is now northern Tunisia, extended westward beyond Bône and Constantine and east to include the coast of Tripoli. The sea, not the land, was their empire, and it was by maritime commerce that they increased their wealth. Carthage, founded in 814 B.C. by Phoenicians from Tyre, became the most illustrious of the port cities of the ancient era. From here the Carthaginians, heirs of the Phoenicians in the Maghrib, spread their domination over the western Mediterranean, fighting for Sicily and engaging in bitter wars with Rome.

The defeat of Carthage by Rome in 146 B.C. led to Roman domination in North Africa. From the conquered base of Carthage they extended their domain eastward across all of North Africa, including Egypt and the Nile basin up to the cataracts. Relics of the Romans rise across the Maghrib in skeletal ruins—coliseums greater than the one in Rome, aqueducts, foggaras, and colonnaded cities. It was they who first applied the term Africa to a part of the continent, calling the former Carthaginian lands "Proconsular Africa" (Province of Africa). The name was perpetuated in the Arabic *Ifriqiya* and later changed to its present form. Roman rule lasted about 640 years. Theirs was a land empire that developed agriculture to help support Rome with needed grain. They exploited other natural resources, also, such as the then abundant wildlife of the Maghrib for the arena. Before Roman rule, wild animals had been a threat and hindrance to those who tried to farm; but long before the Roman era ended, the big game had been wiped out.

[1] Carleton S. Coon, *Origin of Races,* New York: Alfred A. Knopf, Inc., 1962, p. 588.

During their era of dominance the Romans set out to convert the people of the Maghrib to the Christian faith, and by the end of the Roman period Christianity prevailed rather widely among the Berbers. However, it did not survive here as it did among some of the indigenous groups in southwest Asia, but died out completely as Islam took over. Scarcely a trace remains except in symbolic designs here and there.

Vandals and Byzantines successively followed the Romans, controlling the Maghrib for brief periods. The Byzantines were in turn displaced by Moslem Arabs, who first appeared in Libya in A.D. 642, less than a decade after Mohammed's death. Whereas the Arab victory over the Byzantine rulers was swift, it required nearly a century to conquer the Berbers. Even then the conquest was less political than spiritual and cultural: the people of the Maghrib accepted the Moslem faith, and adopted the Arabic language and culture.

Moslem influence became very strong throughout the Atlas lands, which were ruled from then on by a succession of Islamic dynasties—the Abbasids, Fatimids, and the Almohads (who held power until A.D. 1230) and others. Sometimes North Africa was ruled as a unit under a caliphate from Asia; at times there were several centers of political control. It was during the latter periods that the great Moroccan dynasties came to the fore, extending their power even across much of Spain.

Although much that was brilliant in Arab civilization developed in Asia, the Moslem Maghrib also had its periods of splendor. Islam spread forcefully across North Africa, but nowhere was the vigor of its diffusion more clearly visible than in the city of Kairouan, established as the Holy City for the Maghrib, a center from which the light of the Islamic religion, learning, and law should "shine like a beacon." For centuries the main school of Islamic law was here. Today the city is badly deteriorated, and its importance as a center of religion and learning has been superseded by other African cities, such as Cairo, Fez, and Tunis.

The Moorish conquest of Spain by the Almoravids of Morocco is another chapter in Islam's splendid history in Africa. But later on came the Turks to a part of the Maghrib, and then the West Europeans.

Today the Maghrib's magnificent mosques and universities show physical decay, and the retardation of culture that has characterized all of the Moslem world in the last centuries is found also in Africa's "Western Isle." But a thousand years ago Islam was pressing against Christendom, and was culturally more advanced. Signs of a renascence are strong in North Africa in the present era, stronger here than elsewhere within the realm of Islam.

The common Islamic-Arabic social, religious, and language structure has tended to unify the states of the Maghrib, for few factors are so binding among peoples as language and religion, and when social structure and culture are dictated by religion, the ties are even stronger. History also has united these lands because, generally speaking, a common history has affected them all, even up to independence. A revived expression of the ancient union is found in the recent reluctance of any of the states to join with other African or Arab groups in economic or political associations before the Maghrib first has united.

Within the unity, however, distinct national characteristics have developed in the several states; further, despite the homogeneity of language, the Maghrib presents a sort of linguistic mosaic. In the broad view, people speak Arabic or Berber, and the proportion is about 3 to 1. Washed over this, especially among the upper and middle classes in Tunisia, Algeria, and Morocco is French; in the Rif, and to a degree in Oran Province in Algeria, Spanish is spoken; many Libyans use Italian; and a number of Libyans, and Tunisians as well, have a knowledge of English. This multilingual character is the result of the domination, in modern times, of different portions of these territories by various European nations.

Nationalism in recent decades has been vigorous, and within the states, minority groups are locally active. Political rivalry within countries often represents tribal expression, as instanced in the strong suppression of El Glaoui and his followers in Morocco during the period immediately following independence, and in the later opposition of the Algerian Kabyles to the Boumedienne regime in that country. These in no sense represent separationist movements, however, although tribalism does die hard.

## Geostrategy

At Gibraltar, the Barbary states hold the southern control point of the western entrance to the Mediterranean Sea, the dominant passageway between Africa and Europe; Spain is only 8 miles away. The Maghrib occupies a similar position at the narrows between the eastern and western basins of the Mediterranean. Although Malta has generally been regarded as the "key" here, geography gave Tunisia a situation that has made it important in maritime and Mediterranean affairs for a long time: it lies midway along the northern coast of Africa between Gibraltar and Suez, and its coast forms a right angle that projects into the Mediterranean across from Sicily, dividing that strategic inland water body into two vast basins. While France held Tunisia, Bizerte, on Cape Blanc and with a fine natural harbor, was France's leading North African naval base. During World War II Tunisia was the point from which Sicily and Italy were invaded by the Allies.

From Phoenician times the Tunisian coasts have attracted outsiders—conquerors who sought to hold the important control point at the narrows, merchants who used the shallow but good harbors along the Tunisian shore for trade. Even the structure orients the country toward the sea and away from the other lands of the Atlas: westward, the Aurès Mountains and the prohibitive plateaus exert a blocking effect; eastward the mountains and the country open wide to the Mediterranean.

Most of the southern shore of the Mediterranean Sea, that "middle sea" that is one of the most important links in the second greatest ocean tradeway in the world, is held by the states of the Maghrib. It was from the southern Mediterranean coasts that the Barbary pirates harassed Mediterranean shipping for many centuries. However, in a nuclear and space age,

FIGURE 3.9  Sheep grazing among the ruins of ancient Cyrene, Libya. This city was colonized by Greeks in 630 B.C. (Photograph from The Lamp. Courtesy Standard Oil Company of New Jersey.)

this geographical position becomes less important, at least in time of war.

The realm has important resources. Although its oil fields may not equal those of the Persian Gulf basin, they are great and the associated gas is perhaps equally significant. Phosphates, lead, zinc, iron, and manganese are among other mineral resources that are known and produced.

As a part of the Moslem world the Maghrib is also of great importance. It feels akin to the rest of Islam, which is spreading its doctrines southward across Africa faster than any other religion. It has washed across the Sahara and northern Sudan, regions with physical characteristics similar to those within which this religion developed, and it is even taking hold in regions that are physically dissimilar.

## The Imprint of History

The lands of the Maghrib still bear "the scars of a tormented past" where several cultures have clashed and mingled. Vestiges of successive colonizations and invasions linger—in the rubble of Carthage; in the ruins of Roman cities, astonishing to us today for their sites and size, made possible by the construction of aqueducts, cisterns, and dams by engineers from Rome; in the methods of planting, irrigation, and piping that made the Tell a breadbasket of the ancient world. Sometimes no traces remain of magnificent structures except those that are contained in the composition of certain mosques, as the great one at Kairouan which embodies 300 columns from Roman and Byzantine buildings no longer extant.

Time itself is a despoiler (see Figure 3.9), but more important were the Beni Hilal, nomadic Arabs who in the eleventh century poured westward out of Egypt, destroying everything in their path—cities, towns, villages, aqueducts, bridges, cisterns, dams, fields. They overgrazed the pastures as they moved across with their herds so that the desert crept in onto tracts formerly grasslands or cultivated. Even forests contracted against the consuming advance of the Hilalian Arabs. The coastal dwelling Berbers fled from the littoral plains into the fastness of the mountains, sometimes even into the desert.

Although the Beni Hilal were the most destructive of the Arab invaders, they were not the first Moslems from the east to enter the Maghrib. Earlier waves had conquered the lands and proselyted the people. Although different parts of North Africa preserved different traditions, modifying the coherence that Islam imposed upon the cultures, the general acceptance of Islam more or less unified the way of life.

Later came the modern European, accomplishing remarkable achievements but still unable to erase all of the devastation of the Beni Hilal or to change in any great degree the cultural landscape wrought by Berber and Moslem Arab, except along the coasts and in some of the cities.

Although the countries of the Maghrib are politically new states, the "new" is found merely in the recovered sovereignty, and in the modernization and revitalization of the economies. These nations are among the oldest inhabited lands in the world, their histories dating back to the earliest manifestations of settled life along the Mediterranean. Side by side stand the new and the old, each with its particular value and flavor, the new often resting inconformably upon or beside the ancient. The blending can be seen in the country—the *bled*. But in the *bled* people are conservative and change is slow, so it is in the cities that change is most readily accepted, and there one finds in most pronounced degree the ancient and modern existing in juxtaposition.

The cities, villages, and towns also reflect better than elsewhere the changes of history because except for nomad groups, Berbers and Arabs habitually live in agglomerated settlements. In addition, the most varied mixing has occurred along the coasts and in the ports; here the modern and traditional stand side by side, or are interwoven. A European-style city stands beside the old casbah, or apart by ½ mile or more; sometimes the new city encircles the casbah; sometimes the casbah stands alone. In places, old casbahs are being torn out and modern versions, patterned somewhat along customary ways of casbah living, are being built. The farther one passes from the coast, the more traditional the casbah becomes— towns shrouded in ramparts, windowless walls toward the streets, courtyards hidden and secret from the outsider. In these inland centers in the *bled* one senses deeply the old customs, ways, and arts of the Maghrib, and the casbah remains almost unchanged.

# 4 THE ATLAS LANDS

*There is a splendid formality about
the sharp line of masonry where the
city ends at a stroke, and the open
country spreads up to its very feet;—*

ANN BRIDGE

## The Facades

In the northwest sector of the Maghrib are the lands of the Atlas Mountains complex, bounded on two edges by seas, wrapped along the continental sides by the Sahara. Although divided among Morocco, Algeria, and Tunisia they are a coherent geographic unit by virtue of the embracing barriers, and their common sharing of the mountain complex.

The frontiers are inhospitable. Along the 620-mile coast that faces on the Atlantic, natural shelters are lacking and the continental edge is pounded by a surf that makes the western shore resemble a great breakwater. Because of its inhospitable character this long ocean facade has had less significance than might have been expected. Almost as difficult is the northern coast facing Gibraltar and the Mediterranean Sea. Here the Rif, Tell, and Tunisia Atlas drop in almost sheer abruptness to the water. The coastal inaccessibility is paralleled by land barriers facing interior Africa. In the south not only mountains but deserts buttress the countries, and in great depth.

There are breaches through the barriers, however, and through the openings peoples have poured in and out. The Taza corridor between the Rif and Middle Atlas is one such gateway; Saharan movement has followed along the base of the mountains and through wadi valleys; Tangier and Ceuta are ports facing Europe on opposite sides of the Jebel Musa, one of the two Pillars of Hercules, at the eastern end of the Strait of Gibraltar across from the Rock of Gibraltar. Gateways across the Atlas give access between the inner and outer belts.

The terms "inner" and "outer" are interesting. Although the concept has been applied to Morocco, it applies equally well in all three states: "Inner" Morocco is that portion of the country that looks toward the sea and away from the continent (see Figure 4.2), while "outer" Morocco is that part of the land that is south of the mountains. Long ago Arabian historians distinguished between these two zones. Although the usage of the terms is almost unique (China has always called "Outer Mongolia" that part of Mongolia which is farthest from Peking, the capital, though it is closer the center of the Asian landmass than Inner Mongolia), the contradiction represents the true nature of the Atlas countries, for the cores

of the states are along the coast while the lands across the mountains are the nations' backyards. Since space does not allow a separate analysis of all countries in these terms, let us look at inner, outer and mountain Morocco, and hope that similarities in the physical aspects of all three states will allow us to transfer the ideas, with some small modifications, to Algeria and Tunisia.

### THE CHARACTER OF THE THREE MOROCCOS

Inner Morocco faces the seas, and is Atlantic-Mediterranean in climate; in relief it is a series of lowlands and plateaus that open to the shore. Climate, relief, and soil make it the most easily worked; transportation and communication are also easy, and it is the agricultural and industrial core of the country. This inner zone appears to be protected physically—by mountains on the landward sides, by seas and a forbidding, tempestuous coast along the Atlantic facade. However, despite the seeming security of its position, inner Morocco and the inner lands of the Atlas have been conquered many times and have as often been exploited and despoiled by invaders. Because physical factors do not stand in the way of unification, it might have been expected that inner Morocco would foster the growth of national feeling, and perhaps have been the leader in the development of national unity. But it did not play these roles: it neither constituted the center, nor provided the unifying force for Moroccan integration. All the Moroccan dynasties after the Idrissides (A.D. 788 to 920) were born outside of the plateau of Morocco.

Outer Morocco is the Morocco of the steppes, those lands that lie between the Atlas and the Saharan fringes; for Algeria and Tunisia the outer zone is mostly desert. Access to this region has been easy from the Sahara; the routeways connect oasis with oasis. The unity of the outer zone derives from climate: it is a region of water shortage, and tenuous lines trace connections between those places that have water (Figure 4.3). Save for the sedentary adaptation found in oases, this is a land of caravan travel or of nomads who wander from one grazing spot to another. Although the density of population is very low, with great stretches completely empty of people except for passing bands of nomads or trader

FIGURE 4.2 *(above)* Main Boulevard, Casablanca, inner Morocco. Very modern and Middle Eastern architecture mingle in this city. *(Sochepress. Courtesy French Information Service, Rabat.)*

FIGURE 4.3 *(left)* Goulimine, outer Morocco. Goulimine is not true desert, as indicated by the stunted character of the date palms. *(Photograph by writer.)*

caravans, periodically outer Morocco, as the rest of outer Maghrib, becomes overpopulated because it is a poor land. When droughts of long or short duration occur, the outer zone becomes a land of emigration; even when there are no droughts, natural increase alone causes this to be a population-export area. Emigration is a current as well as an historic movement: in the past, it was usually nomads from the desert that swept in to conquer the better watered plains, sometimes with whole tribes partaking in the migration invasion; in the modern era, it has been part of the movement of people from the *bled* into urban

areas. The crowding in Maghrib cities and the mushrooming of *bidonvilles* is the result of this movement of people for economic reasons.

Mountain Morocco is composed of two very unequal parts. On the north are the Rif Atlas, isolated from the remainder of the country, resting along the Mediterranean edge, a sort of "hem" for Morocco. The Rif constitutes a little world to itself. Contraposed is the second sector—the mighty masses of the Moroccan Southern Atlas, stretching from the Taza Corridor to the southern edges of the Anti-Atlas, and constituting a separator of barrier proportions between Atlantic Morocco of the plains and the Morocco of oases and nomads. In Algeria the mountain zone comprises not only the Tell and Sahara Atlas but the high plateaus as well.

The inhabitants of the mountains are Berbers who are sedentary cultivators for the most part. (See Figure 4.4.) The purest Berber groups are found in the most remote and isolated places like the Rif Atlas and the pockets and valleys in the southern mountains; in Algeria they are found in the Great Kabyle and Aurès Mountains. Mountain Morocco, as mountain Tunisia and the Tell Atlas, are relatively moist, and although life in the mountains is spare, it is relatively sure. Hence, the mountain peoples have been able to live unto themselves, and to remain secluded and often dissident.

As a barrier, the Southern Atlas of Morocco vary from one part to another. The High Atlas have only rare and difficult passes while the Middle Atlas have always been scoured by shepherds in search of new pastures, and have been permeable to slow migrations and even to armies. However, swift and oppressive incursions, such as the Arab invasions, have not come this way; they have entered via the Taza gate from the Tell. Mountain Morocco, while restricting contact and lessening the shock between the two hostile Moroccos, has not been able to bind them together or to conciliate them to each other. Invasions of Tunisia have come from sea and desert; Algeria has usually been overpowered from the east or west along the shore, or by sea.

## Historic Perspective

The Atlas lands control the southern shore of the Mediterranean along half the length of the sea. Morocco and Tunisia have particularly important situations because each commands a strait. Except for the Strait of Messina, through which Greek trading cities in eastern Sicily maintained an open passage in Carthaginian days and which Italy holds today, the Sicilian Channel between Sicily and Tunisia receives all traffic between the eastern and western Mediterranean. Morocco is at once situated on one of the major crossroads of the world, and isolated. Although it stands at Gibraltar, outlet to the Mediterranean

FIGURE 4.4 Mountain Maghrib: Berber casbah in high mountain valley, rising from the soil from which is was constructed and so much a part of the natural landscape as to be almost undistinguishable. (Photograph by writer.)

and contact point of Europe and Africa, it is nonetheless isolated from neighboring lands by the physical barriers of seas, mountains, and deserts. These contrary characteristics of focalization and isolation have had their effects upon Moroccan history and conquests.

A common thread of history has linked the Atlas lands throughout the centuries. Tunisia became an independent monarchy on March 20, 1956, and was transformed into a republic on July 25, 1957. For 75 years previous to this, the country had been a protectorate of France. Algeria achieved independence on July 3, 1962. Until that date it had been regarded by the French as an integral part of metropolitan France: Algerians were French citizens, and the Algerian departments were represented in the parliament in Paris. Morocco gained its sovereignty in 1956, after being ruled by France for 50 years.

Algeria had been under French rule since 1830, although not all parts of this vast territory were completely subdued until 1847. From the outset Algeria was viewed as an outlet of opportunity for Frenchmen: the Algerian Tell was directly across the Mediterranean Sea from France, and similar in climate to southern France. After 1870 to 1871, when France lost Alsace-Lorraine to Germany in the Franco-Prussian War, Algeria was increasingly regarded as a colony that should compensate territorially for the loss of the European lands and help France to repair its damaged prestige. Official policy became one of exploitation and the dispossession of the Algerians of their lands until the 1890s, and an active course of land expropriation was pursued. A pest that had destroyed some of the vineyards of France in 1878 gave impetus to the land transfer from Algerian to French ownership. As the lowlands were taken over and settled by Frenchmen, the Tell Algerians were forced from their fertile valleys into the marginal hinterlands—the mountains and the high plateaus, and even into the edges of the Sahara. Seldom, if ever, has a movement of colonists been so deliberately planned as the migration of Frenchmen into the Algerian Tell.

Morocco is the most recently developed of the Atlas states. In 1912 when France established control over the greater part of the country, it was divided politically into three very unequal territories: the French zone, which was a protectorate under the nominal rule of a sultan, the Spanish Rif, and the small International Zone around and including the port of Tangier. These together make up the independent kingdom. As noted, the French zone became sovereign on March 2, 1956; the International Zone and all of the Spanish Rif, with the exception of the ports of Ceuta and Melilla, which remain Spanish, acceded to Morocco at later dates.

French pacification of Morocco was not swift or easy. While the conquest of the lowlands constituted no problem, Berber tribesmen in the mountains resisted subjugation; in many parts of the Atlas the Berbers have lived their own independent tribal ways for centuries, scarcely giving allegiance even to their sultans. Officially, the French considered the pacification of Morocco completed in 1932; practically, Morocco was never pacified. It was held in military subjection, and uprisings among the tribesmen of the Atlas had to be put down constantly. Morocco was the only one of the three Barbary states that had remained independent of the Ottoman Turks, who for 300 years previous to French rule held nominal suzerainty over Tunis and Algeria.

Tunisia was made a French protectorate under the treaties of Bardo (1881) and La Marsa (1883) at a time when financial conditions in the country were in disorder. France believed that the security of Algeria would be affected by the unstable conditions of the little Moslem state to the east. Theoretically the protectorate was to have been temporary, and autonomy was to be restored as soon as conditions righted themselves. However, French control was quickly imposed and, once established, was maintained until 1956.

Under the protectorate the Tunisian way of life was little disturbed, and institutions were allowed to remain unchanged, including the rule of the bey, which had been instituted in 1705 when Hussein Bey declared the country independent of Istanbul and founded the dynasty that ruled until 1957. However, the bey was only the nominal authority; the French Resident-General was the real head of state. French rule was never liked by the Tunisians, and during the twentieth century, passive resistance developed into active opposition, leading to the eventual relinquishment of the protectorate by the French. The monarchy became a republic with the deposition of the bey.

But history unfolds a succession of earlier conquerors in the Atlas lands—Spanish, Arab, Byzantine, Vandal, Roman, Carthaginian and Phoenician, in that order as we go deeper into the past. A recurring theme in the history of Barbary has been this continual turning of fortune. Few lands have been so often overrun by the horsemen of the conqueror or have so often seen the invaders' fleets assailing their coasts.

## ENCLAVES AND EXCLAVES

It is probable that relations of Iberian inhabitants with Morocco go back into prehistory, for the 8 miles of water that separate the two territories at the Strait of Gibraltar are easily crossed.

The port cities of Ceuta and Melilla have had an important role in the history of Mediterranean peoples for many centuries. Phoenicians, Carthaginians, Romans, and Byzantines have used Ceuta as a port of trade and a center of political control; the Moors embarked from here for Spain. In 1415 the city was captured by John I of Portugal, and thus it became a part of the Christian sphere of Iberia. When Spain and Portugal were united in 1580, Ceuta passed to Spain and, when these states separated in 1649, the population of Ceuta requested that the city remain with Spain, a political attachment that still holds.

Melilla also has functioned importantly since antiquity for Mediterranean peoples, but less so than Ceuta because it lacks a good harbor. Phoenicians used it as a center for trade with the Berbers, and the Carthaginians inherited it, calling the city Rusadir, a name retained by the Romans, who made it a colony. It became Spanish in 1496, when it was captured by the ducal house of Medina Sidonia, which had been empowered by Ferdinand and Isabella to take it. Ceuta and Melilla were desired by the sultans of Morocco, and their histories have been somewhat stormy, that of Ceuta more so than Melilla because the latter was farther removed from Moroccan centers of activity. Both are "presidios," a Spanish word for a garrisoned place, or fortified city.

Ceuta and its tributary territory cover only 19.36 square kilometres and have a population of only some 73,000; Melilla, 12.3 square kilometres in size, has a population numbering about 79,000 persons. Children born in the two cities, whether Spanish or Moslem, are automatically subjects of Spain. Both are ports, industry is almost nonexistent, and their only resource is fish. The cities must depend upon the outside for all of the necessities of life, even drinking water. As exclaves of Spain within Morocco, they are a problem. When Spanish Morocco was permitted to unite with Morocco, Spain retained the two specks of land on the north coast; they are garrisoned by Spanish troops. Only about 20,000 people of Moroccan origin live within the presidios; most residents are of Spanish origin. Both are considered a part of metropolitan Spain.

Ifni, lying along Morocco's Atlantic shore about 60 miles north of the southern frontier, also is small, only some 40 miles long by 15 miles in depth, with a population that is less than 40,000. Nominally held by Spain since 1860, actual occupation began only in 1934 when Spain renewed a fifteenth-century dream of imperial expansion. Boundaries were delimited by France and Spain in 1912, and changed somewhat by France in 1935.

As an exclave of Spain, lying within Moroccan territory but without political attachments to Morocco, Ifni is an abnormality. Geographically it is not a unit because it occupies the westernmost end of the Anti-Atlas; its people are related to the Berber or Arabic-speaking tribes of southern Morocco. Spaniards make up about one-tenth of the population and are usually short term residents who are military or civilian authorities. Economically Ifni is not self-sufficient. At any time, a third to a half of the working males are employed in Morocco; its chief market outlet is Goulimine to the south, not Sidi Ifni in the province; it does not raise enough food to feed itself. Historically it has been associated with Morocco.

## Physical Integrity of the Atlas Countries

In ancient times only the Grand Atlas ranges along the southern border of what was then called Mauritania were designated as the Atlas. Now the name refers to the entire complex of ranges and plateaus that extend for 1,500 miles from Cape Noun in southwest Morocco to Cape Bon in Tunisia.

Although the Atlas Mountains and the countries that share them are distinctive in their unitary character, nonetheless the separate nations have a certain physical integrity of their own. Where the Moroccan frontier crosses the Atlas complex, the high central plateau of Algeria terminates against the Middle Atlas, crushed out, as it were, by the Moroccan mountains that run transversely between the Grand and Rif Atlas to form a formidable divide; in the east, the Tunisian frontier lies just beyond the place where the Tell and Saharan ranges knot to close off the Algerian upland from Tunisia, which begins where the plateau breaks toward the lowlands. Thus, each Atlas country, although sharing geographical continuity with the other two Atlas states—climate, vegetation, adaptation—nevertheless occupies a special and unique position, and has a distinct character.

Morocco is the only country of the Northwest that is both oceanic and Mediterranean. The influence of the Atlantic is enhanced by the fact that topography turns Morocco toward the sea and outward from the continent: at the Algerian-Moroccan frontier the Tell and Southern Atlas fan outward broadening the plains and plateau portions of the country, and gaining from the Sahara a wide belt of land that without the mountains would be desert. Agadir is farther south than El Golea, and Marrakech is on about the same parallel of latitude as Colomb-Béchar and Ouargla.

Although physically analogous, for they each have an inner, outer, and mountain belt, the countries vary and are quite unlike. Morocco is almost entirely mountainous while Algeria is nearly all desert: a possible one-sixth of Algeria lies within the Atlas; in the south, however, rises the arid massif of the Ahaggar. Tunisia, although about two-thirds desert, opens an inviting coast toward the sea.

## The Atlas

### MOROCCO

The strongly marked relief that characterizes Morocco breaks into five regions—the four divisions of the Atlas system, the Rif, Middle, High, and Anti-Atlas, and the plateau that lies within the mountain arc facing and sloping toward the Atlantic Ocean; in Morocco, the high central Algerian plateaus play out. The Morocco Atlas are all blocklike horsts (see Glossary), deeply dissected, enclosing other blocks of less elevated land, so that the landscape is one of alternating mountains and tablelands and valley lowlands. The High, Middle, and Anti-Atlas are all parts of the Southern Atlas.

Among the mountains of the Maghrib the High Atlas are the grandest. They rise abruptly from the Moroccan plateau, a wall of ranges 12,000 feet high with peaks mounting to 13,000 feet, some of which are of volcanic origin. Glaciers chiseled out the long valleys, but they did their work geologic ages ago for now the Atlas have no permanent snow; in winter, however, the High Atlas stand etched in white against blue skies, a magnificent backdrop to the semibarren plateau.

In the High Atlas, Mediterranean and Saharan conditions obtain side by side: the seaward slopes, well watered, are covered with olive trees and relatively rich forest, and the valleys trail with orchards and cultivated crops; the southeast slopes, shut off from

rain-bearing winds but open to the desiccating blasts from the desert, are barren or patchily covered with scrub. Both nomadic and sedentary Berbers inhabit these mountains; agriculture tends to be confined to the high valleys.

Although the High Atlas look impregnable, they are breached at two places by paved highways that cross from the Atlantic to the Saharan side. One road goes southeast from Marrakech to Ouarzazate, the other south-southwest from Marrakech to the valley of the Sous and thence to Agadir on the Atlantic coast. The Ouarzazate highway branches again: one road leads westward to join with that that follows the Sous, the other runs east-northeast along the valley of the Dades to Ksar es Souk, a pre-Saharan center into which a number of roads converge. From Ksar es Souk roads pass north through Midelt to Meknes and Fez, and south into the oasis of Tafilalet where it connects with desert trails.

South of the High Atlas lie the Anti-Atlas, plateau-like in character, attached to the High Atlas by a node of volcanic deposits (the Jebel Sirua), separated from them by the foundered synclinal valley through which the Sous River intermittently flows. Lying in the shadow of the High Atlas, the Anti-Atlas are semi-Saharan in aspect.

The Middle Atlas trend almost north-south. A hydrographic divide, they furnish Morocco with some of its most valuable rivers. They are moister than the High Atlas and less rugged, and hence are more densely populated. Fine pastures make grazing important (Figure 4.5), forests of cedar and evergreen oak cover the slopes, and agriculture is significant, or relatively so for a mountain area. In these uplands, the Berber is both a cultivator and a pastoralist; transhumance (see Glossary) is an important feature of the animal industries.

The Rif Mountains, continuing the mountains of Andalusia, run along the Mediterranean from Gibraltar to the Moulouya valley, shutting off the rest of Morocco from the sea. It is only in their relation to the Straits of Gibraltar that the Rif Mountains have been important to the country. Under Spanish control since the secret treaty between France and Spain in 1904, the Rif politically has turned its back on the remainder of the country, and its physical character has made the isolation easier. In the fastnesses of the

FIGURE 4.5  Goats grazing on foliage of the argon tree. Morocco. The ability of the goat to subsist on meager pasturage is well illustrated in this picture. Here, as they commonly do in the Atlas lands, the agile animals have scrambled high on to the branches of the argon tree for food. (Courtesy French Information Service, Rabat.)

Rif Atlas rebellious Berbers held out against foreign domination. It was one of the strongholds from which pirates preyed upon Mediterranean shipping in the early nineteenth century, and one of the centers from which they exacted tribute and captured Christians into slavery for centuries. Tangier and Tetuan are the only cities of any size.

The High and Middle Atlas bar a great part of Morocco from the influence of the Atlantic, and place it under Saharan conditions. From the mouth of the Dra in the west to the Moulouya, Morocco is arid—desert or pre-Saharan steppe. Nevertheless, this Morocco, outer Morocco, has been historically important. Out of these barren lands groups of virile men have poured into the richer plains, and it is not by accident that most of the great events that have shaken Morocco and most of the great dynasties that have ruled the state have issued from the desert.

The Moroccan plateau, separated from the Algerian high plateaus by the Middle Atlas, extends westward from the High and Middle Atlas to the coastal lowlands along the Atlantic. North and south it reaches approximately from Rabat to Mogador. South of Mogador the High Atlas thrust a blunt and gradually lowering end almost to the seashore. A highway, winding along the coast between the mountains and the shore, dips and climbs through this rugged region. Inner Morocco rises from sea level along the Atlantic to the heights of the plateau which stands at about 3,000 feet near the base of the Atlas. Marrakech, on the plateau but some distance away from the base of the mountains, has an elevation of 1,542 feet.

Although the plateau apparently withstood the pressures of deformation that raised the Atlas—in fact, turned the direction of the mountain trend—the southern portions foundered during the disturbances of the Tertiary period. Marrakech occupies one of these depressed regions. At the northern end of the plateau, downfolding formed a syncline into which the sea intruded some eons ago. This is now the rich alluvial valley of the Sebou. Opening wide to the sea, the lowland extends eastward in the narrow corridor of Taza, a gap marking the separation (or point of contact) between the Rif Mountains and the Middle Atlas: these ranges are unconnected, although at their eastern extremities they run close together. The Taza corridor is the one gateway permitting easy passage between the Algerian Tell and the Fez-Meknes lowland which, in turn, connects with the Atlantic coast and the ecumene (see Glossary) of the state.

As previously noted, although physiography gave the Maghrib coherence, it is also responsible for the physical integrity of the three Barbary states: the Middle Atlas and Aurès Mountains nearly set the boundaries, in the west and east, between Algeria and its neighbors, Morocco and Tunisia. Morocco faces toward the Atlantic, physically turning its back on Algeria. Oujda, the eastern gateway to Morocco, is known as "the backdoor." This splendid isolation has given Morocco a certain geographical oneness. The fact that the portion of the country that occupies the fringes of the continent should be called "inner Morocco" denotes the seaward orientation of this land.

## ALGERIA

The structure of Algeria continues the Moroccan relief pattern eastward—plateaus enclosed by higher ranges, fronted by a maritime plain and backed by the great desert. But Algeria has neither the lofty, massive mountains nor the extensive plains that characterize Morocco; and whereas the Moroccan plateaus open wide onto the sea, the Algerian high plateaus are enclosed on all sides by higher elevations. Atlas Algeria is essentially a great plateau block whose northern and southern fronts, and eastern and western ends, are composed of folded ranges or dome formations.

The country divides into natural elongate zones that run east and west, and change from north to south: the "tell," the steppes, and the desert. The word "tell" could have come either from the Arabic or the Latin; most probably it is from the Latin. In Arabic the word means hill; according to the Latin (tellus), "the fruitful earth." Both are applicable: the Tell is hilly, and this is Algeria's "fruitful" land. It embraces the well-watered outer slopes and terraces of the Mediterranean Atlas, and the coastal plain that follows narrowly along the 600 or so miles of the Algerian coast.

The topography of the Tell is broken, characterized by an alternation of coastal lowlands and narrow, disconnected plateau blocks or ranges that in places reach the sea in bold slopes. Between the plateaus, and fingering back into the uplands are restricted river valleys. Most of the fertile cultivated lands of Algeria are found in the Tell, on the terraced slopes and coastal plains, and in the confined tributary river basins. Some of these valleys are covered with a deep alluvium, like that of the Cheliff River whose valley constitutes nearly one-third of the plains area of Oran, or the plain of the Mitidja, a very productive river lowland that lies enclosed behind the city of Algiers. Much of the land cultivated in Algeria is, in fact, interior in location in just such river-eroded basins, hemmed in between ranges and so shut off from the full benefit of the rain-bearing winds off the Mediterranean, and therefore requiring irrigation to be fully productive. At the mouths of these rivers are Algeria's ports—Oran, Algiers, Bougie, Philippeville, Bône, and others, the most important serving the richest and largest lowland hinterlands.

The Tell Atlas, continuing the mountains of the Rif, are expressed in a series of narrow plateaus interrupted by restricted river lowlands, or by gradually rising terracelike mountains that lead to the broad upland of the high plateau.

The high plateau is a basin of interior drainage, semiarid in character and occupied by numerous shallow depressions that at times contain brackish water; some of these shotts are large in extent, as the Shott-esh-Shergwi. Because of the semiarid conditions, grazing and the raising of alfa grass (see Glossary) are about the only occupations. Alfa grass is raised across so extensive an area, especially in the western parts of the interior plateau, that sometimes these grasslands are referred to as the mer d'alfa (sea of alfa). This is good sheep country; pastoralists who keep the animals are nomadic in their habits.

The high plateaus narrow eastward as the Tell and Sahara Atlas begin to converge, and mountainous projections, such as the Aurès and Kabyle mountains, rise from the plateau that farther west was a relatively flat surface. Precipitation, greater than in western Algeria, produces a luxuriant forest vegetation in the eastern mountains that face the coast, and permits a richer cultivation. Kabylia is noted for its figs, olives, and other fruits.

The Great Kabyle is a massive plateau block that thrusts against the sea between Algiers and Bougie. To the east lies the Little Kabyle, and along the southern edge of these plateau-blocks arcs the range of the Djurdjura Mountains. Kabylia, like the Rif, is one of the places in the Maghrib that has been left largely untouched by outside influences, becoming a place of refuge and a stronghold of Berber culture. Population density is high for a mountain area, but pressure is relieved by the emigration of males to the Tell to work.

In the Aurès Mountains, nucleus of the convergence, elevations exceed 6,000 feet. The Aurès are domal in formation, and lie more or less transverse to the general alignment of the Atlas complex, forming the closure of the high plateaus along the east. These uplands also have been refuges for intransigent Berber tribes fleeing foreign invasion and dominance. Although the Aurès receive a considerable rainfall, they lie so far south that Saharan influences penetrate the mountains, making them semiarid. A solely sedentary type of adjustment is not possible, and here the cultivation of fruits and grains is practiced in association with nomadic pastoralism. Historically the Aurès region was important: the Romans made these mountains the center of their military strength, and the ruins of ancient cities, such as Timgad situated along the edges of the mountain block attest to its greater role in the past than in the present.

A semisedentary, seminomadic way of life characterizes the mid-region of the high plateaus. These steppes are a sort of marchland between the entirely sedentary north and the nomadic and oasitic south.

The Sahara Atlas, bounding the high plateaus on the south, are not much higher than the plateaus themselves. They are arid mountains, partaking of the characteristics of the desert toward which they slope —a vast region 16° of latitude broad, and reaching east and west across more than 20° of longitude, and yet only a part of the tremendous African desert whose length is about 3,000 miles and whose width is never less than 1,000. The Algerian desert is the most complex portion of the Sahara. In the extreme south is the great Ahaggar massif, and fanning out from there, the immense system of alternating subsequent valleys and cuestas (see Glossary) with their associated differences in relief and surface. At the base of the Sahara Atlas lie the imposing *ergs*, the *Grand Ergs Oriental* and *Occidental* and several others on a less grandiose scale, all the alluvial deposits of streams that run down the slopes of the Atlas or interior massifs into the desert where they disappear.

## TUNISIA

East of the complex core of the Aurès nucleus the Atlas divide again, become lower in a series of stepped ranges and massifs, and terminate eastward as two arms in the bold promontory-peninsulas of Cape Bon and Cape Blanc in Tunisia. The southernmost of these ranges are the Great Dorsal, the Tunisian counterpart of the Sahara Atlas. Between this mountainous extension and the one on the north lies the valley of the Medjerda River, opening an inlet into the interior plateaus and the plains of Constantine; eastward, the river flows across the plain of

Tunis into the sea through an extensive delta, the only river of the Atlas lands that has a delta. Advantageous though this is, the alluvial tract along the river mouth is not fully settled because large parts are swampy; cupped along the delta front, however, are protected harbors.

The Tunisia Atlas divide the country into two broad regions that are climatically and physiographically quite different. The mountainous north, with peaks that rise above 5,000 feet and deep valleys, is relatively well watered. Cork forests grow in the northwest; the north central parts raise excellent grain and livestock, and the northeast country around Tunis and Cape Bon produces grain, livestock, grapes, citrus, and vegetables. Some parts of the mountains average over 40 inches of rain annually, but in most places in Tunisia a rainfall of about 20 inches annually is normal.

South from the crests of the Tunisian Dorsal, the mountains descend into the semiarid and then arid country that comprises the second region. Steppes near the mountains merge into absolute desert toward the south. Salt shotts, that expand and recede with the meager and uncertain moisture, cover extensive areas of the low central district where the drainage runs into the interior basins. The shotts depression of Tunisia, centered by the Shott el Djerid, is a continuation of the very extensive depression within the Grand Erg Oriental of Algeria which drains to the Shott Melghir; eastward the depression of the Shott el Djerid connects narrowly with the Gulf of Gabès.

South of the basin of the shotts, the relief rises again slightly in the central plateau of the south; however, even here elevations are below 1,000 feet. Steppelands occur on the plateau that are suitable for livestock raising and dry farming, but deserts border the upland on the east, west, and south. The western sector of this desert south of the shotts is *erg*, the easternmost portion of the Erg Oriental; the eastern portion of the desert is hammada (see Glossary).

Eastern Tunisia is a broad coastal lowland. Olives grow in a wide area of the plains littoral north of the Gulf of Gabès, and less extensively to the south; inland from the olive belt, alfa grass is produced; in the desert there are also ranges of alfa grass and several date palm oases.

## Land and People

### FORESTS AND GRASSES

In the present era, the uncultivated portions of the Tell and the Moroccan plateau carry a Mediterranean-type vegetation of brush (maquis), cacti, and evergreens, and the argon tree grows; in the Atlas there are forests of pine, cedar, cork oak, and other species; on the high plateaus alfa grass grows across extensive areas. The amount of land in forests has diminished greatly, however, and the species of brush and grass have deteriorated; grasslands and woodlands alike have contracted. This destruction was brought on by many things—the clearing of the land by settlers and random clearing by army engineers, overgrazing, cutting for firewood, failure to replant, careless exploitation such as in the stripping of cork trees, and like activities of man.

Alfa grass, cedar, and cork are commercially valuable. Alfa grass, used for paper stock, covers millions of acres of land especially on the plateaus, and cedars still grow on hundreds of thousands of acres of mountain slope (Figure 4.6). Some of the Moroccan cedars are very ancient, and are magnificent in their height. Obviously the cedar forests of the Maghrib were of far greater extent in the distant past than

**FIGURE 4.6  Cedars of the Moroccan Atlas. (Courtesy French Information Service, Rabat.)**

they are at present. This is known from the accounts of writers who described the forests and made note of conditions of river flow and land erosion that bespoke forested headwaters. Strabo stated that Morocco "was wooded" and that "trees reached very great heights"; elephants roamed the lagoons and lived along the edges of lowland forests. These writers from the past noted how accessible the rivers were, and with what ease vessels could enter them; Pliny described the Sebou as wide and navigable. In the present era these same rivers are torrential in nature, clogged at their mouths, and blocked by sandbars unless dredged.

The first terrible destruction of the grasslands of the Maghrib appears to have taken place with the invasion of the land by the Hilalian Arabs. Not only did they pillage the land, but their intrusion "intensified the practice of nomadism and the indiscriminate use of rangeland to the point of depletion." The destruction of the natural vegetation by the Beni Hilal was greater in Tunisia and Algeria than in Morocco because the latter was farther away from the Arabs' place of origin, but Morocco felt it also.

At about the same time, cities were growing up, demanding wood for fuel, construction, the tanning industry, and the like, thus contributing to the deforestation. Later, the demand for props for mining, overgrazing by goats, the stripping of cork oaks and Aleppo pines for their bark, and the extraction of stalks of green oaks for tanner's bark led to the depletion of the forests even in the High and Middle Atlas.

Soil erosion by wind and water is among the secondary effects of forest depletion: floods rise faster and higher; winds blow across unprotected soils, desiccating them more quickly, carrying the soil away. Great stretches of land, once vegetated, now lie bare.

> On the vast steppes of range land, the devastation of the herbaceous carpeting by an excessive number of livestock, and the pillaging of even the tiniest bush in order to obtain fuel, have delivered the land over to the uncontrolled fury of the winds and have made it dry up faster, sometimes opening the way for sand storms and the formation of sand dunes.[1]

[1] *Morocco*, Paris: Encyclopédie mensuelle d'outre-mer, 1954, pp. 141–147.

## CULTIVATION OF THE LAND

So long as North Africa was French, there was a duality within the economy and society, that is, modern European as against the traditional of the Maghrib, with European production oriented toward trade beyond the colonies, Berber production largely toward local consumption, or national if at all commercial in character. Most Maghrib farmers still produce for subsistence, cultivating and living on the land according to traditions that have held within the Atlas lands for centuries, selling the products of their labor in the *souks* (see Glossary); most of the French are gone.

Agrarian reforms must include more than land distribution and reclamation, therefore. Land surveys and a recasting of the entire legal basis of land tenure are called for in many parts; following this, there should be a redistribution of the population, an attempt to increase land productivity by the introduction of additional crops and new methods including the extensive use of fertilizers, the encouragement of commercial production, and market planning.

Availability of water and access to transport are important aspects of recasting and planning the economy. Under the French both water resources and transportation received emphasis, benefiting both Europeans and North Africans. Large dams were constructed, particularly in the inner Maghrib where rainfall helps to supply a part of the needed moisture. Developments in the Mitidja valley of Algeria and at Afourir in Morocco were impressive. They involved the impounding of water in reservoirs, the creation of large irrigation canal systems, installation of water pumps, and the building of railroads and several thousand miles of highways and roads. On the high plateaus of Algeria more than 4,000 water supply points were opened up to help meet the needs of pastoralists and their herds.

Irrigation works in the Maghrib are of two kinds: the systems of perennial irrigation associated with storage dams serving large areas; and the old traditional methods, modest in scale, in places somewhat modernized. Perennial irrigation is being developed as rapidly as is feasible, and wherever perennial irrigation has been introduced, not only have agricultural conditions been affected and improved, but social conditions as well. The development of hydroelectricity is a part of the large-scale water development.

Projects affecting the lands irrigated by small or medium hydraulic works, situated in zones where irrigation has been an ancient tradition, also have increased considerably in recent years. The Morocco Middle Atlas are a reservoir for water that irrigates a whole series of gardens, because out of these mountains flow all of Morocco's largest rivers—the Moulouya, Sebou, O. bou Regreg and Grou, the Mellah, and the Oum er Rebia. Along the piedmont of the Middle Atlas, and along the river valleys that lead out of the mountains, lie the lush fields and orchards of Fez and Meknes and the many other centers of cultivation less well known and smaller but nonetheless important. Springs, often of considerable size, and perennial rivers fairly regular in volume feed the cultivated lands. The valley of the Moulouya, for example, is bordered by a chain of small irrigated plots laid out on low alluvial terraces; the Sebou basin is crisscrossed with irrigation channels.

In Algeria agriculture is largely confined to lowlands along the Tell, which are Mediterranean in climate, or to oases in the desert. Even in the Mediterranean valleys, irrigation is needed to assure good production. Under the French most of this best land was in vines. Since independence these European lands have been nationalized and cooperative farming is taking over.

Agriculture is rich in northern Tunisia, and the valley of the Medjerda River is proverbial for its productiveness. Wheat raising is intensive and modern and in addition to the crops grown in other areas of the north, grapes for wine are important. But even here the picture is mixed. The valley of the Medjerda and that of its largest tributary, the Mellègue, begin in the mountains of the plateau and dip eastwards to blend into the plains that border the shore, becoming marshy lowlands along the coast. The swamps are undrained and malarial, and unused. Here, however, is land with a potential for reclamation.

Along the southern slopes of the Atlas on the edge of the Sahara, along rivers that disappear in the desert, astonishingly green *palmeraies* produce date palms and other irrigated crops that grow richly in the shade of the palm trees. The Tafilalet is such an oasis. It is fed by the waters of streams that have seeped into the sands and then been ingeniously collected by man into the underground galleries (previously described, and here called *rhettaras*) and diverted to supply moisture to the gardens. In such oases, the boundary between barren desert and productive green is a line, often an irrigation ditch or a dike. The valleys of the Dra, the Dades, the Saoura, and the Mzi are other such oases that have been wrested from the wilderness by the diversion of intermittent and often disappearing streams. The verdancy of these valleys, enclosed on all sides by aridity, is almost unbelievable. (See Figure 4.7.)

The realization of the agricultural potential of the Sahara is largely a problem of water. In the desert, rainfall cannot be relied upon at all because not only is it slight in amount but irregular as well. Wadis, which sometimes are subject to overflow in an enormous and disastrous way, for the most part carry very little water or none at all. During periods of water flow seepage adds to the ground water, and upon these reserves palm oases sometimes depend almost entirely.

Much of the water of many of the streams flowing into the Sahara seeps into their alluvial fans and becomes a part of the subsurface waters. Subsurface waters are a second great source, and the means that men dwelling in the desert have employed to secure and utilize these subsurface sources are highly ingenious, as in the case of the foggaras.

In some places, as in the Wadi Rir, the ground water shows itself near the surface in shotts; in other places, water emerges from artesian wells. In sand country, the water table generally does not lie at great depths beneath the surface, and the contour of the water table generally follows the contours of the dunes. In some of the dune deserts of the Sahara,

**FIGURE 4.7    Palm grove, Tozeur, Tunisia. (Courtesy Secetarial d'Etat à l'Information,
Republic of Tunisia.)**

such as the Suf, gardens are planted in the dunes: holes are dug into the sands to depths within reach of groundwater, and palms are planted in the depressions; the gardens are not irrigated—the roots of the date palms find their way down to groundwater and survive (Figure 4.7). The labor involved in maintaining these gardens is not that of irrigating the plots by laborious methods, but rather one of keeping sand from filling in the holes and smothering the trees, for it only takes a slight breath of wind to move the fine grains about. These are curious gardens, and they seem even more curious when observed from a distance, for the tops of the trees give the appearance of rising right up out of the sands. Only when the edge of the oasis is reached does the character of the garden appear. The houses huddle offside from the *palmeraies* so as not to take up any spots where water might grow the date palms. In these "excavated gardens," the date palm is more exclusively grown than on almost any other of the Saharan oases.

Wells of various sorts furnish many oases with subterranean water. The water thus obtained may be drawn by animal or human traction, or even by mechanical devices, including windmills. Wells can be found in all types of desert, and some are very deep, being sunk to depths of 165 feet and even more. In some places deep subterranean water pockets are very scarce. When this is true, water will be in short supply during particularly dry spells; some wells may dry up, and only a few may have water; operating wells are busy day and night, and water is sold by well owners to those without the life-giving liquid. Ghardaïa, in the Mzab, is illustrative of this type of water procurement.

Slight though the rainfall may be, the desert dwellers attempt to capture and conserve as much of it as they can. For this purpose, in the hammadas they may hollow out cisterns on the surface of the rocks. When these fill or partially fill with rainwater, they are covered to diminish evaporation. In fact, sometimes even the channels that conduct the water from wells to gardens are covered, so precious is water and so tremendous the evaporative power of the atmosphere.

Modern methods are equally ingenious and more effective. By deepening wells and increasing their number, sometimes there has been a notable addition to water supplies, and wherever it has been possible to expand the output of water, agricultural production has increased. Near Adrar, an adjustable automatic windmill now assures the oasis of a constant flow of water, tapping deep reserves that could not be used except for modern mechanics. At Sidi Mahdi near Touggourt, an even deeper well goes down to 5,575 feet, increasing the amount of water to the oasis by one-fourth. In the Algerian Sahara water wells reach greater depths than any place in the world.

In the vicinity of Colomb-Béchar a project of a different nature has been drawn up. By the construction of a dam across the Guir River at Djorf-Torba, 35 billion cubic feet of water can be stored, which besides supplying domestic needs will permit irrigation cultivation on some 99,000 acres of presently unused land. However, it is not likely that many such projects as that cited above can be effectuated in the Sahara.

The amount of artesian water that underlies the Sahara is a matter of controversy. Most geologists are hesitant about making assertions relative to Saharan groundwater, and so what is possible agriculturally in the Sahara is a matter of conjecture, and cannot be forecast until water reserves are more completely known. By deep drillings, however, the supply of water in the Algerian and Libyan deserts has been measurably increased—by over 25 percent in the Algerian since 1958 it is claimed. Much of this water development has occurred in association with mining and oil developments.

The garden agriculture of desert oases reaches a perfection of technique that can scarcely be paralleled anywhere. Cultivation carried on with less effort and persistence could not survive. In fact, it is the unfavorable and demanding conditions that evoke the effort and the excellence of the cultivation: compelling necessity drives man to employ inventiveness and skill, and to put forth great energy to overcome the difficulties and survive.

*Irrigation and Soil.* Because of the critical role that irrigation water plays in the cultivation of the soil, many problems of a technical, economic, and social nature arise. One of these is soil conservation. Badly managed irrigation systems can cause soil to deteriorate rapidly through salt accumulation. To put water on the land is not the only necessity involved: in regions where impervious clay occurs at some depth beneath the irrigated surfaces, digging drainage channels to draw off the water is as necessary as the construction of irrigation canals if the soil is to be kept from becoming salt impregnated. Often deep drainage ditches parallel irrigation conduits.

In some areas where irrigation is needed to make the soils produce, floods are a problem, as in desert wadis and in the Gharb (also spelled Rharb). The latter plain lies in western Morocco, south and southwest of the Rif Atlas, and represents a vast sedimentary basin occupying a former arm of the sea that has been filled in by the deposits of two main rivers, the Sebou and the Ouerrah flowing from the Middle and Rif Atlas. When floods inundate the land of this basin, the waters, overflowing to fill in the lower parts of the plain, have no chance to drain back naturally into the streams. Work on a drainage system was begun in 1946, and within the first decade the network of drainage channels was completed along the right bank; since then, work has proceeded along the left bank of the Sebou.

Where irrigation and drainage control are managed right, highly productive fields of vegetables, legumes, fruits, and grain are the result. Most of the cultivated lands are in grain, with barley and wheat leading; corn, and to a lesser degree, oats, and rice are also grown. Rice is a recent importation. The fruits and vegetables are almost a wonder—irrigated acres of artichokes, tomatoes, and lettuce; since the Atlas lands all have regions that are Mediterranean in climate, the species of fruit and nut trees that grow are in the main essentially Mediterranean. Olives, almonds, figs, citrus, grapes, cork oaks, pears, and apples are important, and, in the true desert oases, dates.

Algeria and Morocco possess better soil and water resources, and more favorable climates for all types of cultivation than does Tunisia. The Tunisian climate is severe, the spring and autumn droughts being particularly hard on crops and pastures. The best agricultural land is already intensively used, and any extension of cultivation requires the extension of irrigation or, in places along the coast, of drainage. Moisture diminishes southward, and as the water deficiency becomes more pronounced, agriculture becomes more difficult. Special techniques and methods of adaptation have had to be developed in Tunisia, and agricultural science and instruction, research stations, and administrative organizations for the popularization of new methods all have been employed to this end.

An outstanding example of the effort that has been and is being made is found in the famed olive growing district of the Tunisian sahel.

> It is due to a social scheme well adapted to local customs on the one hand, but more particularly to the special regard paid to climatic conditions on the other, that such splendid results have been achieved in the olive groves of the Sfax region. The olive trees in Sfax are planted at distances of 24 metres, whereas those in the north of Tunisia are set at intervals of only 10 metres. The larger ground surface in the Sfax region enables the trees to take full advantage of the meagre rainfall. If they were more closely crowded, they would only run to leaf. As it is, however, 17 trees per hectare in Sfax produce more olives than do 100 trees per hectare in the north.[2]

## PASTORALISM

Physical conditions in the Atlas lands make animal production and distribution directly dependent upon the natural habitat, attenuated only by an ensemble of factors that may be called the "agricultural environment." The climate, even within the areas with a Mediterranean regime, is steppelike or desert, with a marked tendency to dryness and irregularity. Regional differences in animal culture and type of livestock derive from climate, hydrography, and relief of the various parts of the realm and from the ecological conditions which influence animal selection and methods of raising. Nomadism and transhumance are important features of the grazing industries for all animals except cattle and pigs. It has been traditional for nomadic sheepherders to winter their flocks in the northern Sahara, and as spring comes on, to move northward into the mountains, or over the mountains into the upland steppes, or even inner Maghrib.

---

[2] R. Bigourdan, "Tunisian Agriculture," *Tunisia '54*, Paris: Encyclopédie mensuelle d'outre-mer, 1954, p. 62.

The animal picture differs in the three countries, however. In Morocco, political security, and the introduction of controls over diseases and parasites that have in the past decimated herds, have done much to develop the livestock industries. The total number of animals has grown quite steadily, although some species have numerically declined as others have risen (Figure 4.8).

This increase in the number of livestock has presented a problem, because coincident with this development, large areas of new land have been cleared for cultivation, proportionately cutting down on the extent of the pastureland. The Moroccan pastoralist does not like to decrease the number of his animals, and as a result there has been an overgrazing of the available pasture ranges, which become poorer year by year. They are being laid open to erosion, and have insufficient feed to carry the ever-increasing herds. Hunger takes an especially heavy animal toll during the summer (from July) and autumn months and if the rains are late or sparse, even during the winter.

Pastoralism has always been a Berber occupation in Morocco. Even during the French era over 98 percent of the animals were Moroccan owned. Sheep are most important, constituting the basis of the economic, social, and family life of the country's rural population, indeed, even of the religious life.

In Algeria, as the lands of the Tell were increasingly taken up by Europeans and put into cultivation, restrictions were set upon the seasonal movements of the flocks across the mountains into the better watered lands facing the Mediterranean Sea. As a result, the number of sheep kept by the Kabyles has decreased by at least one-fourth, a reflection of the inadequacy of the grazing lands. Even so, thousands of livestock perish from starvation every year on the poor pastures. Cattle have typically been raised by Europeans on the better lands.

In Tunisia, animal distribution and variety are about the same as throughout the other Atlas lands, although the pattern of distribution is somewhat more complex because of the broken character of the Tunisian relief. In general, however, cattle and horses are raised in association with farming in the better watered lands, and even in some of the Tunisian high steppes; sheep and goats are grazed in the semiarid

FIGURE 4.8 Pastoral scene of northern Tunisia—a herdsman with his flock of sheep; small donkeys, one burdened with the double basket carrier that is so common in the Maghrib; mules and a horse at rest. (Courtesy Secretariat d'Etat à l'Information, Republic of Tunisia.)

FIGURE 4.9 Camels are the burden bearers along arid and semiarid stretches. (Courtesy Secretariat d'Etat à l'Information, Republic of Tunisia.)

lands under practices of transhumance, while camels are bred in desert and near desert areas. Donkeys are raised throughout the land even in desert oases. Camels exceed the combined number of horses and mules and also exceed the number of donkeys. (See Figure 4.9.)

Many of the tribal nomads from the desert edges own land in oases, and supplement their livelihood from gardens planted to dates, and/or cereals, and fruits. Some of the nomads of the high plateaus augment their living (derived from pastoralism) by practicing dry farming part of the year. Truly sedentary cultivators are confined to the Tell and the oases. More and more, as irrigation spreads, transportation widens, and industry and mining open up labor opportunities, nomads depart from their wandering ways, and become partly or wholly sedentary.

## Riches of the Subsurface: Minerals and Fuels

The geology of the Atlas indicates a history of formation during which time a great variety of minerals were laid down in different eras at different places.

The mineral resources of the Atlas lands are remarkably alike because of the correspondence of the physical structure of the Barbary states. The size of the reserves vary, but the same minerals tend to occur in all three states. Nearly one-fourth of the phosphate rock of the world comes from here. All three Atlas states produce it but Morocco leads, mining three-fourths of all produced in Africa; Moroccan reserves are concentrated in two deposits, at Khouribga and Louis-Gentil. Phosphates are abundant in Tunisia also, and are quarried in large amounts, mostly from deposits which occur across a 330-square-mile sector in central Tunisia, the most important reserves being those of the Gafsa district. The phosphate content is lower than in the Moroccan ores, however, and specialized methods, such as washing, crushing, and processing for superphosphates, are required in order to compete on world markets. A further handicap is found in the fact that none of the phosphate beds are closer than 150 miles to a port. Nevertheless, Tunisia ranks fourth in world phosphate production, and phosphates alone make up about 15 percent of the export value, being the most important single item that Tunisia puts into international trade. Algerian reserves are much smaller than those of either Morocco or Tunisia.

Manganese occurs in Morocco and Tunisia; again, Morocco is the leading producer. In Morocco, this is largely a postwar enterprise. The most important mines are at Bou Arfa in eastern Morocco some 100 miles south of Oujda, and at Imini and Tiouine south of the Grand Atlas not far from Ouarzazate. From the largest reserves, at Imini, the manganese goes by aerial cableway across the Atlas Mountains to the railway that takes it the rest of the way to the port of Casablanca.

Oil, natural gas, iron, coal, lead, zinc, and copper also occur in the Atlas countries. Salt is likewise found, a traditional resource long an important item of trade for the population of the Sahara; for hundreds of years salt was traded for gold with the savanna lands south of the desert. Algeria is the largest producer of iron ore, although the mining of iron and lead have been intermittently carried on in Tunisia since Carthaginian days. Lead and zinc are important in all three states. In Morocco, the output value of these ores equals two-thirds that of phosphates. About fifty deposits are worked but four are outstanding, producing four-fifths of these metals—Bou Beker, Touissit, Aouli, and Mibladen. Morocco is also the world's fourth largest cobalt producer.

Minerals are Morocco's leading export, both by weight and value, with phosphates leading, followed by iron, manganese, lead, and cobalt; mineral ores and concentrates make up over one-fourth of the value of export products in Tunisia. In fact, Tunisian minerals are produced almost entirely for export, making this side of the economy very dependent upon world markets and the world political situation. Among the mineral exports are phosphate rock and fertilizer, iron ore, lead and lead alloys, zinc, and copper.

The Saharan departments of Algeria are overwhelmingly richer in mineral and fuel resources than are the Algerian Atlas lands. Aside from oil and natural gas, which occur from central Algeria eastward, the most important concentration of fuels and minerals is found in the extreme west, from the Colomb-Béchar and Kenadza coal area to Ougarta, where manganese occurs, to Gara-Jbilet (Djebilet), an iron ore center southwest of Tindouf near the Moroccan border. The latter deposit has a high iron content similar to that at Kiruna, Sweden, and reserves have been estimated at 3 billion tons. If developed and exported, the most likely route would be by rail, which would have to be built to the mouth of the Dra River on the Atlantic coast of Morocco.

It is the oil and gas discoveries of the Algerian Sahara that have been most sensational, however. Exploration, begun in 1947 and carried out across about 270,000 square miles in French territories alone, brought to light very large oil reserves at Edjelé-Tiguentourine-Zarzaïtine east of Fort Flatters, at Hassi Messaoud southeast of Ouargla, and in the Djebel Bergha south of In Salah. Oil was struck in 1956. The Hassi Messaoud and Edjelé fields are the largest. Crude oil moves from Hassi Messaoud through a 24-inch pipeline to Bougie on the Mediterranean coast; from Edjelé, a pipeline carries the oil from that field to La Skhirra, near Gabès in Tunisia. Another discovery, east-northeast of Fort Flatters and about 100 miles west of Ohanet, was made at Tin Fouye. This basin is near the route of a 30-inch pipeline that eventually will link Ohanet and Edjelé with Hassi Messaoud, a distance of 330 miles.

Algerian reserves of natural gas are also enormous. In Algeria's Hassi R'Mel field alone gas reserves are set at more than 35 trillion cubic feet, not including the deposits at Berga and Gassi-Touill, where reserves have been estimated to be one-third as large. Pipelines connecting Hassi R'Mel to Algiers, and Arzew near Oran on the Mediterranean coast have been constructed.

Of the countries of North Africa, Morocco has been most generously endowed by nature with water resources that can be harnessed for hydroelectric development and irrigation. With the completion of the high dam at Bin el Ouidane in 1955, Morocco had the largest single hydroelectric power complex and the biggest dam in Africa. Now, of course, it is surpassed in size by several others, including Kariba, Volta, and the High Dam at Aswan.

A shortage of fuel has always handicapped the Maghrib, and the development of hydroelectricity and the discovery of oil and gas were therefore important to the economy. The lack of fuel has been a hindrance to the exploitation of mineral resources. Another handicap to mining lies in the high transportation costs involved in the development of many of the deposits which, in the main, are situated in remote areas within or beyond the Atlas. But these problems are circular, because a part of the transportation problem has been the problem of fuel. This has harrassed development especially in the desert. Saharan coal resources, although not negligible, are highly localized. In some places, as in the Colomb-Béchar district, they play a vital role, the whole industrial complex here being built on local coal and nearby ores; in other places, coal is missing. Fortunately, due to the diesel engine, the oil of the Sahara makes it possible to have independent energy sources for the generation of electricity and the powering of transportation. The use of oil in the desert, therefore, is destined to increase, and must have a marked effect upon Saharan development and the economy of the whole realm.

Two other sources of energy that are seldom considered are available in the Sahara, resources that will work without depletion, endlessly and tirelessly, and that have scarcely been tried, namely, wind and solar energy. There is also atomic power. Thus, although the more traditional fuels, coal and waterpower, are highly localized or missing, it appears that this lack will no longer pose insurmountable obstacles to Saharan development.

## Manufacture, Modern and Traditional

What modern industry as has developed in the Atlas lands is largely limited to the reduction of minerals, the refining of oil, the enrichment of phosphates, the production of building materials such as cement, shipbuilding and repair, and the processing of the products of the forests, fisheries, and farms. Industry is faced with major difficulties. A shortage of fuels within the homeland still plagues Morocco and Tunisia. A shortage of capital and the reluctance of local and foreign investors to take the financial chances involved in setting up a large, modern plant also deter industrial development in all three states. Some industrial projects, new to some areas, are being developed. Illustrative are three in Tunisia—the manufacture of paper pulp from alfa grass, the development of the salts of marine marshes along the coast in the extreme south of the country around Zarzis where potash, magnesium, and other salts occur, and the construction of a steel plant at Menzel Bourguiba on Lake Bizerte, completed in the latter part of

1966. Sweden supplied a million dollar rolling mill for this steel complex, and a British firm provided ore-reducing, loading, and blast furnace equipment.

Except for Saharan projects, much of the modern industry of the Maghrib is concentrated in or near the ports. The processing of local products, other than minerals, includes the treating of alfa or esparto grass (Algeria) and cork, the processing of fish and forest products, the extraction of olive oil, and wine making.

The handicrafts are traditional, and hundreds of thousands of persons still earn their living in whole or in part by making things with their hands. They produce a great variety of objects, from metalware and leatherware to rugs and clothing. Although most of this is for the local *souk* or national market, about one-fourth of the articles produced by craftsmen are exported. There is a tendency for the crafts to die out, however, giving way to machine-made goods.

## Fishing

Every port along the long coast of the Northwest has its fishermen, but fishing is not so important as it should be in view of the richness of the waters off the Mediterranean and Atlantic coasts in fish and other marine life. Some of the finest sponging grounds in the world occur off Tunisian shores, and yet only a small part of the sponges taken are brought in by Tunisians; Greeks work these waters for many of the sponges. Daylight and night fishing with lights bring in sardines from sea and ocean; tunny are taken from the Mediterranean with nets of various sorts; lobsters are caught.

Prospects for enlarging the fishing industry are good in terms of the fish resources, but commercial fishing is a relatively recent development; organization and modernization of the industry are needed. Although traditionally Tunisians and Algerians have fished the river mouths and waters of the Mediterranean, and the Moroccans those of the Atlantic coast from Moulay-bou-Selham to Mogador, fishing has been for subsistence or local in its sale, and has but scantily supplied the needs of the coastal towns and a few of the inland centers. The Maghrib has a large fresh fish market, centered especially in and around large ports. Fish canning, and the production of fish products such as meal, oil, and the like are on the rise. Many varieties of fish are caught for the fresh fish market, including mollusks and crustaceans, but sardines are the leading variety of fish for industrial uses.

## Cities of the Atlas Lands

The Atlas lands are and always have been lands of contrasts. During the French era the population was mixed, especially in the north. There were Berbers, Arabs, Jews, and Europeans, among the latter not only French but large numbers of Spanish. Berbers and Arabs, counted as the same by the French, made up the great majority.

Extremes always seem to obtain side by side in these lands: fertile cultivated valleys among stony hillslopes; oases set in arid deserts; walled towns opposed to modern cities; minarets and Catholic bells; donkeys nudging automobiles; camel caravans and oil pipelines; black tents, mud and stone casbahs, and modern apartments looming skyward; the green north and the barren south; surface wasteland and subsurface riches. They are the expression of the strong physical differences, and the conflict of peoples, eras, and ways of life.

The twentieth century, especially the decades since the war years, brought transformations that heightened contrasts already there. Nowhere was the revolution so striking as in the cities, or where significant mineral resources had been discovered. Although the casbah remains the characteristic pattern of agglomerated living, whether in rural areas or urban centers, modernity is laying its hand upon the land. Ports were expanded and modernized during World War II; completely Western towns have sprung up where oil and gas developments are being carried out in the Sahara, and Bedouins are showing aptitude for operating modern machinery. Ancient caravan centers, like Tamanrasset, and historic inland cities are now centers of tourist attraction to which thousands of Europeans go during the cooler season. Although the traditional crafts flourish in the mountains and in the *souks* in the inner cores of urban *medinas,* modern factories have risen along the urban fringes.

FIGURE 4.10 Looking across the roof-tops of Tunis. (*Courtesy Secretariat d'Etat à l'Information, Republic of Tunisia.*)

It is an incongruous pattern that presents itself, but a pattern nonetheless: change—the ports are marchlands, the mining centers the cores of the Western World's most advanced technology and planning. In the inland centers, however, one still feels the spell of the tradition and art of the Maghrib, but change is on its way.

The great cities of the Maghrib are generally historic religious and political centers, or ports—some modern, some of renown even in ancient times. In Casablanca, Morocco has the most modern urban center of North Africa; in Tunis, Tunisia has one of the oldest. (See Figure 4.10.) Tunis, Phoenician in origin, is possibly older even than Carthage. During its early history, Tunis was eclipsed by the brilliant port of Carthage, and during the first centuries of Arab dominance, by the Islamic religious center of Kairouan. However, in the thirteenth century, when it replaced Kairouan as capital under the Aghlabite dynasty, Tunis began to rise in importance. Today it is a city of over 750,000 people.

Reference to Figure 4.11 shows that except for the artificial channel that has been dug through enclosing sandbars, Tunis is landlocked. It had re-

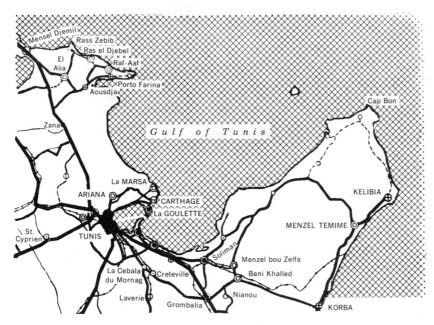

**FIGURE 4.11  Port and Gulf of Tunis.**
**The canal across the Lake of Tunis, be-**
**tween Tunis and its outport, La Goulette,**
**is shown by a thin white line. (After**
*Tunisia, 1954, Paris: Encyclopédie Men-*
*suelle D'Outre-Mer, with modifications.)*

mained that way for many centuries previous to
1893, when an opening was made through the barrier
bar that had gradually built up and robbed the
city of access to the sea; the port was locked within
the coastal lagoon known as the Lake of Tunis. The
lagoon is shallow, and only the 6-mile-long channel
through the lake, and the breach dug through the
narrow bar, opens Tunis to the shore and makes it a
port. La Goulette, its outport, is situated at the end
of the northern sandspit outside of the lagoon, directly on the Gulf of Tunis and giving onto the
Mediterranean.

The site of Tunis is a hilly isthmus, and the city
lies encased between the Lake of Tunis and the
*sebkha* (see Glossary) of Sedjoumi. Its situation,
sheltered in back of sandbars but at the head of the
Gulf of Tunis and at the outlet of the Medjerda
Valley, is excellent as an outlet for almost all parts
of the northern half of Tunisia. It connects by railroad all the way to Casablanca and Marrakech, via
a coastal route and the Taza Gateway.

Although Algiers is the largest city of Algeria, it
does not dominate Algerian sea trade as do Tunis in
Tunisia and Casablanca in Morocco. Rather, Algiers
is only one of many ports that serve the country,
none of which is outstandingly dominant. The long

narrow coastal plain, broken and made discontinuous
by penetrations of rugged relief to the sea, and the
hemmed in nature of the valley lowlands in back of
the ports account for this. Until the opening up of
the oil and gas fields in the Sahara, port hinterlands
were largely confined to the Tell, each port serving
the restricted area that lay immediately tributary to it.

The relative standings of the numerous ports are
changing as mineral and gas developments in the
desert progress. Oil pipelines terminate at Bougie
and at La Skhirra, near Gabès in Tunisia; gas pipelines reach Algiers, Arzew, and Oran. Nemours,
which serves Oujda and the Mediterranean Railroad
that drops south from that gateway city into the
Algerian desert, undoubtedly will be the outlet for
any ore or processed minerals from the Colomb-
Béchar region.

But Algiers (Figure 4.12) is Algeria's great city—
modern, with a large commodious harbor protected
by breakwalls, and a population of about 850,000
people. The buildings rise glistening white from the
edge of the water, mounting steeply up the slopes of
the coastal ranges that wall it in all around. Algiers
is Mediterranean in character, resembling European
cities on the north side of the sea. High office buildings face the waterfront, but behind and to the west

lies the maze of the casbah, teeming with its Arab-Kabyle population, romanticized in fiction, but in reality crowded with hovels and tiered dwellings that are wedged along the labyrinth of its hillside alleys. Sixty thousand people live massed within these walls, 1,600 people per acre.

During the French era, Algiers was among France's first harbors, one year leading, with Marseilles, among French ports in the amount of tonnage cleared. Aside from its export-import trade with Marseilles, bunkering and the handling of passenger ships are its most important activities. So large has been the trade between Algiers and Marseilles that they in reality rose together to their importance. However, somewhat less than half of the Algerian imports and exports pass through this harbor. As developments progress in independent Algeria and the preponderance of French-Algerian trade gives way somewhat to trade with other countries, the close ties of Algiers to Marseilles must decline. In fact, there should be a change in the trade of all of the ports—in countries of destination and origin, commodities of trade, and the like.

Oran, an Algerian city with a Spanish character, is the second port and second city in size.

Of the inland centers Constantine, 50 miles south of its port of Philippeville, is the largest. It was built by Arabs on a site that is a natural fortress, a rocky height 800 feet above a river valley and commanding the surrounding countryside. When the French captured this stronghold, it meant virtual control of all of the eastern Tell of Algeria; from this position, they were able also to subdue Kabylia.

Still farther inland are other centers, much smaller in size than the large cities of the Tell but significant far beyond what their size seems to indicate because of their importance to the areas they serve, and because they are so few in so vast a space. Most of them lie south of the Atlas, and are desert entrepôts —Ghardaïa, Touggourt, In Salah, El Golea, Laghouat, and others, all oases of irrigated gardens set in a Saharan environment, havens of green where water, fuel, and supplies can be obtained by travelers, whether caravan or other. Some of these oases towns are almost urban in character, so modernized have they become.

In general, however, the contrast between Algiers and other coastal cities and these inland desert centers is great. To go from the Tell into the world of inland casbahs and oases is almost like moving from the twentieth century into the Middle Ages. The only exception to this, among all the desert towns, are those that have grown up around, or expanded in as-

**FIGURE 4.12** Algiers, from across the port and causeway. White and gleaming, the city climbs steeply upward from the water's edge; the huddle of buildings on the upper right are part of the famed "casbah." (Courtesy French Information Service, Algiers.)

sociation with mining and oil developments: Where modern machinery extracts the subsurface riches, the twentieth century is overtaking the old, and transforming it.

Far in the deep interior, beyond the Oriental and Occidental *ergs*, oases become fewer. Tamanrasset dominates the Ahaggar, a silent, dusty town of about 300 low, reddish-brown houses of baked mud set against tall bald mountains and a rocky desert that is lunar in character. The people who live here are Tuareg, not cultivators but pastoralists who keep camels. This town is seemingly untouched by the political tensions that warred in the north and by

FIGURE 4.13 Street scene in Fez. Shrouded women and burnous- and djellaba-clad men mingle with those in western dress, while heavily burdened animals make the narrow shop-lined steets more crowded. (Photograph by writer.)

modern developments: camel caravans from the savannas still farther south continue to meet the caravans passing that way from the north. For centuries, ever since the Tuareg came to the Ahaggar, they have protected, taxed, and sometimes plundered the caravans that moved along the barely distinguishable trails which lead from the Sudan to Fezzan, from Chad to Morocco, from Niamey (1,200 miles south of Tamanrasset) to Algiers, another 1,200 miles away to the north of the casbah.

Four cities dominate Morocco—Casablanca, Marrakech, Fez, and Meknes. Oujda might be added as a fifth because it is outstanding in the east and the gateway to Algeria. All but "Casa" are inland. Marrakech, largest of the inland cities, is situated near the foot of one of the two important passes through the Atlas. Historically the city has been intimately associated with that great defile. The city itself was built by the Almoravides, who in A.D. 1062 swept from the desert through the pass to conquer inner Morocco.

Marrakech is known as the Red City because the low, sprawling casbah is constructed of red clay—red mud walls enclose the town and its *palmeraies,* and red mud comprises the material from which the houses are built. It lies on the plateau, in the valley of the Tensift, against the magnificent backdrop of the Grand Atlas which rise 20 miles away; a piping system transports water from the mountains across the semiarid plateau to the city.

Economically Marrakech[3] is a great market center both for the people of the Atlas Mountains and for nomads from the Sahara who trade hides, skins, and dates for cereals and goods from Europe. The world famous mosque, El Koutoubia, stands within its walls, which are still in fine repair and have magnificent gateways that give access to the native sector. One of Morocco's four traditional imperial cities, Marrakech is known as the southern capital.

The imperial city of Fez is the northern capital. Situated on the *Oued* Fez in the productive Sebou

[3] Pronounced ma-rä′-kesh, with the last syllable so quickly slipped over as to be almost silent. Old European writers used to call Marrakech "Morocco." In fact, as most Moroccans pronounce the name, it sounds more like *Maroc* than Marrakech.

valley, this revered metropolis of Islam is composed of two parts, the old town of Fez el Bali, a walled Berber city, and the new town, Fez Djedid, quite some distance away. The origin of Fez goes back to very remote times, but the present walled casbah was founded by Mouley Idriss II in A.D. 793. It is the "Western Mecca" of Islam, one of the most sacred cities of the Moslem world, unsurpassed in prestige by any center in Barbary, and the religious, university, and intellectual center of Morocco. Fez el Bali is an intricacy of narrow winding streets that run between houses, shops, and *souks* (Figure 4.13). A commercial and industrial center, the crafts of Fez represent the finest of Moroccan art.

Although not so large as Marrakech, Fez has a population numbering over 220,000. The city shows the marks of physical decay, but it will likely continue to have importance because of its situation just west of the Taza corridor and within one of the most fertile and productive areas of Morocco; railroads lead east to Oujda and Algeria, west to Casablanca, and north to Tangiers. Fez, therefore, commands the gateway from the West. The countryside about the city is unbelievably lush and verdant. Lying within a narrow valley, Fez and the surrounding lowlands are fed abundantly with water from the surrounding mountains. This is channeled into the city so that Fez has a better water supply than any other of the interior towns, undoubtedly one of the reasons why Fez has been able to survive for more than 1,000 years.

Meknes, third of the imperial cities and inland centers of Morocco, lies only 40 miles to the southwest, also along the southern side of the Sebou valley. The proximity of these two ancient casbahs reflects the importance of this river basin in the political and commercial life of early Morocco. Like Fez and Marrakech, Meknes is a center of the craft indus-

FIGURE 4.14 Pottery shop in Meknes. Venders and artisans of the *souks* of the Maghrib typically sell only one type of product. Thus, there are the *souks* of the rug merchants; the *souks* of those who sell articles of copper, silver, or pottery; and the *souks* of carpenters, silk dyers, and the like. (*Photograph by writer.*)

tries, and a great market center for wool, leather, agricultural products, and the like. (See Figure 4.14.)

These three cities dominate the social and commercial life of the interior. But even as this is said, the multitude of small centers where markets are carried on daily or weekly must be mentioned. Every part of Morocco is served by its market; in more populous areas and in large cities, these markets operate every day; in less populous regions, a weekly *souk,* that draws people and products from miles around, functions as the place where, and time when, business is transacted. The *souk* is an integral part of life within the Maghrib.

Casablanca (meaning, literally, White House), the economic capital of the country, is a commercial and industrial city handling most of the seaborne trade of Morocco, serving as the outlet for the phosphate ores of Khouribga, and an important fishing port. Casablanca boasts the largest artificial harbor in Africa, built because of the importance of the African theater of war in World War II. The harbor is deep and sheltered, protected by great jetties that take the buffeting of the 10- to 35-foot waves that arise in the North Atlantic and impact against the massive man-made breakwaters.

The activity of the port is closely associated with the development of Morocco. Enlarged in part to accommodate the needs of the American military base during and after the war, at present it seems larger than its hinterland demands. However, plans for further port enlargement and improvement were designed when the port was modernized. Most Moroccan industry, aside from that associated with mining, handicrafts and fishing, is centered in and around Casablanca and its annex, Fedala.

Casablanca, whose population is more than 800,000, is Morocco's most rapidly growing city. It cannot really be compared to any other Moroccan city because Casablanca is completely and intentionally modern, while Marrakech, Fez, and Meknes hold to the old traditions.

Until the turn of the century, Tangier was the outstanding port in all of Morocco. Owing to international rivalries among European powers who feared domination of Gibraltar by one power, the city and a small zone around it were made a free international zone in disregard of its function as the outlet of Spanish Morocco. The selection by the French of Casablanca as the seaport for their Moroccan protectorate contributed to the further decline of Tangier as a port. Today Tangier is a part of the Kingdom of Morocco. It remains to be seen how importantly it will function under the new political attachment. Since its change in status, the city has stagnated. The railroad leading from Fez to Tangier, connecting with the Taza Gate-Casablanca line, should contribute to the resurgence of the city and the port; the establishment of a new free zone area in the port may help to put vigor into its economy.

Rabat, the fourth and present capital of the country, is a relatively new town, planned and built by the French. With Salé, across the Bow Regreg, it is also a fishing port, but the political function is its life.

Many Moroccan towns, such as Mogador, are stirringly beautiful surrounded as they are with high embattled walls, bejewelled with gleaming white mosques, green tiles, mosaics, and the like; some, like Quarzazate, rise in the *bled* like medieval walled castles or cities where as the sun goes down, heavy gates are closed and the city is shut safely in.

# 5 DESERT STATES OF THE MAGHRIB

*In the name of Allah, the Compassionate, the Merciful. . . .*

KING IDRIS I OF LIBYA

## The Birth of Two Nations

Libya was the first of the European colonial territories in Africa to become sovereign after World War II. On December 24, 1951, it proclaimed its independence and its emergence for the first time as a coherent state, a week before the planned date, which had been set by the United Nations for January 1, 1952.

The country was constituted under clouded and uncertain conditions. Three provinces that had known no unity in the past until administratively put together by Italy in 1912 and called Libya, made up the new country—Cyrenaica, Tripolitania, and Fezzan. The term Libya itself is ambiguous. Before it was used to name the Italian North African colony, it had been applied by the ancient Greeks to North Africa west of Egypt. The Romans adopted it from the Greeks as the name of their African empire; at times, the term was used to refer to the whole of the known parts of the continent. The entities that had spatial meaning were the provinces.

Libya had practically none of the usual qualifications for independence. There were countries bordering on the new state, much better prepared to rule themselves, that remained for some years still under foreign domination. Libya was not even a geographical expression: a little over 1 million people, most of them living in backward conditions, inhabited two widely separated coastal strips and a huge desert hinterland with a few scattered oases. No common feeling of nationhood bound together the people of the three great provinces that united to form the kingdom. Tribal loyalties were paramount, and there was in fact such a feeling of rivalry among the stronger tribes, that when the country was formed, two capitals had to be proclaimed to satisfy the demands of Cyrenaica and Tripolitania. The Emir of Cyrenaica, the leader of the Senussi tribe, became king, King Sayyid Mohammed Idris el Mahdi el Senussi, popularly known as King Idris. (See Figure 5.2.)

Libya was poor and her people illiterate: 90 percent could not read or write; only 32,000 children were in attendance at school in a population where nearly half are under 20 years of age. The average annual income was estimated at between 30 and 35

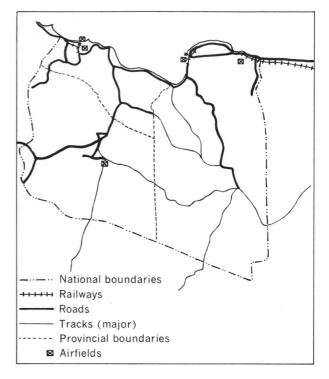

—·—·—  National boundaries
++++++  Railways
————  Roads
————  Tracks (major)
------  Provincial boundaries
⊠  Airfields

**FIGURE 5.2  Libyan boundaries and transport.**

dollars; no industrial mineral resources were known, and the economy was dependent upon agricultural and pastoral activities. There was an annual budget deficit that was being met by Great Britain, to whom the two northern provinces of the Italian colony had been entrusted after World War II until such time as the territory should be given sovereignty.

There seemed no basis or justification for an independent state except that the Tripolitanians and Cyrenaicans were pressing for it, and that the three Great Powers of the West were not disposed to have so strategically placed a piece of land become neutral or fall into hostile hands. The United States, France, and Britain consequently sponsored independence for Libya in the United Nations, and on Christmas Eve these Moslem territories became the United Kingdom of Libya.

Mauritania became sovereign about a decade later, on November 28, 1960. Whereas Libya had been an Italian possession, Mauritania was French and administered as a part of French West Africa. Like

Libya, Mauritania achieved independence under clouded conditions; and the territory referred to as Mauritania has been as ambiguous as that historically called Libya.

The name Mauritania is ancient, dating back at least to the Carthaginians and Romans. At the time of the Carthaginians the northern portions of the Maghrib were known as Mauretania in the west, Numidia in the east; when the Roman Empire was established in Africa, the western provinces of the Atlas lands were named Mauretania Tingitana and Mauretania Caesariensis, west and east respectively. These lands lay in what are today Morocco and Algeria, however, and no part of them is within the present Islamic Republic of Mauritania. The French named the present territory (a province of West Africa) Mauritania, after the people whom they found there, the Moors, or Maures as they called them. They are a people of mixed blood.

Negroes were evidently the first inhabitants of Mauritania. They were pushed south by invading Moslem Berbers, or subjugated and enslaved, during the eleventh century. Five centuries later Mauritania was invaded by Islamic Arabs who partially subjugated the Berber tribes. Intermarriage among the Arabs and Berbers led to a mixing of the people, this blend forming the Maures (Mauritanians of the north), who are Caucasian nomadic herders in the main. An unusual purity of the Arabic language is characteristic among the Maures of this country, in part due to this late invasion from the east.

It was out of Mauritania that the Almoravids, conquerors of Morocco, poured through the Atlas passes to subdue and unite that country for the first time. The Almoravids[1] were a sect of Islamic desert

---

[1] Followers of Ibn Yacin, an ascetic Moslem preacher who came from Fez to Sijilmasa to preach an austere doctrine, at first among the Jedala tribesmen. Forced to flee because of Jedala repugnance to his teaching, Ibn Yacin fled into the desert with two followers, and began a life of seclusion, absorbed in devotions. He gradually built up a following of about 1,000 disciples, whom he named El-Morabethin or Marabouts from which Almoravid derives, and instructed them to go out and "compel the world to accept" the new doctrine. The conquest of Morocco was part of this effort.

(a)

FIGURE 5.3 Two faces of Mauritania: (a) Berber man; (b) Berber woman. (Courtesy Service de l'Information, Gouvernement Général AOF.)

(b)

men of Berber blood, fired with a zeal to lead or force other Moslems back to what they considered the pure and original form of the faith. Descendants of the Almoravid sect in Mauritania are the *marabout* tribes who traditionally have provided the religious, judicial, and educational leaders of the territory (Figures 5.3 *a* and *b*). They are one of the two major groups of the Moorish majority in the country. The other are "the powerful and nomadic *hassan* or warrior tribes."[2] Among the Maures, the *marabout* are commercially more enterprising, more democratic in their tribal structure, and more adaptable to change.

French occupation of Mauritania was accomplished only through the cooperation of leading *marabout* tribes, who "adapted to French rule without ever identifying with France."[3] But many tribes refused throughout the period of French rule to submit to France, especially in the north and among the warrior groups.

As Morocco began to move toward independence in the early 1950s, the dissident tribes began to think again of the past transitory connections with Morocco, and to wonder whether some sort of union might not be worked out between the two territories that would permit Mauritania to slide out from under French rule. As the conservative (pro-French) forces repeatedly defeated the more liberal groups with nationalist aspirations, some of the leaders of the latter tribes drifted into Morocco. Partly because of this, as Mauritania began to move toward independence in the latter part of the 1950s, Morocco pressed claims to all of Mauritania with growing insistence. Most of the independent Arab states backed Morocco in its demands. Raids by Moroccan irregulars, gaining access to Mauritania across the desert boundaries of Algeria and Spanish Morocco, had to be beaten off by French forces. This was the problem that was in the forefront of all others when Mauritania gained its independence.

But Mauritania was beset with other difficulties. As in Libya, agricultural resources were meager, and

the nation was and still is characterized by tribal, racial, and economic cleavage, the latter two accentuated because they occur together, thus reinforcing each other. The liabilities were so great at the time of independence that even political survival seemed to be in question. However, since the discovery of minerals the outlook has changed somewhat, and as in Libya, is giving Mauritania a chance at the future.

The political and economic survival of Mauritania depends basically upon solutions to four immediate problems: the integrity of her borders; the extent and kind of foreign (largely French) support; the "degree of acquiescence of the Moorish majority in the new state, or even loyalty to it; [and] least spectacular but most intractable," the creation of an adequate administration and the development of a balanced economy.[4] Without French backing at times, it is likely that an independent Mauritania cannot survive. This dependence upon France creates its own problems, however, because a large part of the friction among Moorish tribes stems from this issue: to win the loyalty of the tribes, Mauritania must be truly independent. Because of this, the government has found it necessary to stand up against the French on certain issues, a circumstance not always easy for France to accept considering the manner in which it is financially sustaining Mauritania and championing its rights in international circles.

## The Lands

Over 800 miles of Libyan territory separate Tunisia from Egypt, and an even greater space intervenes between Algeria and the western borders of the Egyptian domain. Libya is large, about 2½ times the size of Texas, larger than England, France, Italy, and Turkey together, countries that recently ruled over the Libyan lands. The shoreline, while not rugged, runs an in and out course for a length of over a thousand miles along the Mediterranean, forming a deep inlet in the Gulf of Sidra, the Syrtis Major of ancient times.

From a fringe of Mediterranean lands along part of its coast, the country plunges its 679,358 square

[2] J. H. A. Watson, "Mauritania: Problems and Prospects," *Africa Report*, vol. VIII, no. 2, p. 3, February, 1963.
[3] *Ibid.*, p. 4.

[4] *Ibid.*, pp. 4 and 5.

miles of arid territory far into the interior of the Sahara. On the south it reaches to Niger and Chad, and in the extreme southeast, where it wedges farthest into the desert, it touches on Sudan.

Mauritania lies on the other side of the Sahara and with Rio de Oro forms the largely desert zone between Morocco and Senegal at the place where the Sahara meets the Atlantic. The Mauritanian coastline, 375 miles long, is barren and uninviting. It is lined by sandbanks along the entire seafront, which is nearly bypassed by rain and constantly battered by the Atlantic surf. There is only one harbor, Port-Étienne. The country extends inland from the ocean for a span of 12° of longitude, and from the Senegal River in the south, which forms the southern boundary, 11° northward to the Spanish Sahara and Algeria, just missing the Moroccan frontier. About two-thirds the size of Libya, Mauritania is nearly ½ million square miles in area, like Libya a fledgling nation of vast proportions and few people.

Water is the scarce resource in both states, and the manner of its occurrence has largely determined the way of life and the distribution of the people in different parts of these lands. In Mauritania the best watered lands are in the south along the Senegal River. This alluvial valley is regularly watered by the floods of the river and late summer rains, and here sedentary cultivation is carried on. Although rainfall normally averages about 25 inches in the southeast, the overall average of the Senegal flood plain more closely approximates 10 inches of rainfall annually, and this varies greatly as to period of onset and cessation, and pattern of fall.

North of the valley of the river lies the sahelian plain, the dry savanna, extending northward approximately to the latitude of Nouakchott along the Atlantic and Nema in the east interior. The surface of this plains region is broken by scattered dunes on which gum trees and bunch grasses grow, able to survive because the dunes conserve the precious moisture that occasionally falls, about 4 inches annually. Pastoralists, with their cattle and sheep, roam the country.

To the northeast the dunes merge into the foothills of the Adrar plateau. In this region (southern Saharan), erosion has left steep-cliffed, flat-topped mesalike formations with valleys in between. The

higher elevations wring more moisture out of the winds, and sizable date groves surround historic towns and villages. Dates have been grown here from very ancient times in such historic centers as Chinguetti, Ouadane, Atar, Tidjikdja, Tichit, and Oualata.

North of the plateau country the climate becomes truly Saharan. Shifting dunes trace their outlines over the rock surface beneath; only scattered vegetation is found because of the limited rainfall, but occasionally enough grass and brush occur to feed a few camels and sheep. This is the land of the true nomad, the camel keeper and, in the better parts, sheepherders.

The best watered lands of Libya are in the north, from where the climate merges southward from dry subtropical into tropical steppe, then desert. The lands that are Mediterranean occur as broken lines of oasislike settlements along the coast, largely in two widely separated sectors; intervening between them are the Gulf of Sidra and the steppe and desert country that borders the inlet. To the east and west, the Mediterranean sectors blend likewise into deserts. One of the dry subtropical sectors is found in coastal Tripolitania between Zuara in the west and Misurata on the northwest cape of the Gulf of Sidra; the other is represented in Cyrenaica in the region between Benghazi and Derna. The coastal district of the latter zone does not always conform to the Mediterranean regime, however, because the climate is dry even for dry subtropical, and variable, as often as not corresponding to a steppe climate.

The principal area of cultivation in the eastern province is found on the plateau south of the coastal zone. This plateau, called the Barce plain, is a limestone outcrop about 1,000 feet high that runs parallel with the coast for a distance of about 165 miles; at its greatest breadth it is possibly 30 miles wide. Along the southern edge of the plateau lie the Jebel el Akhdar (the Green Mountains), quite heavily vegetated and cultivated in places for cereals, called "green" because of a blanketing of juniper. Directly in back of these mountains the desert begins, covering the remainder of the province, which means, in fact, almost all of Cyrenaica. Several oases spot the desert. Of them Jalo (Gialo) and Kufra are the principal ones, the latter group constituting an important crossroads for caravans, especially those passing from Benghazi on the coast into the Chad country. This trail connects up farther south with Abéché, on the important arterial route running east and west into Sudan and northern Nigeria.

The Mediterranean belt in Tripolitania is likewise narrow. It holds most of the major towns of Libya, including Tripoli. Directly back of the coast the steppe begins. Topographically the steppes divide into two distinct regions, the Gefara plain and the mountain plateaus, or the *Jebels*. The plain, a continuation of the plains of Tunisia, is triangular in shape, reaching south at its deepest point about 50 miles. The southern margins extend from Nalut obliquely northeast to El Gusbat; along the inward sides lies the *Jebel,* a prolongation of the steppe plateau of southeastern Tunisia, fairly continuous and averaging between 2,000 and 3,000 feet in elevation. The eastern sector is quite well watered and produces alfa grass, but the west is arid.

South and southeast of the *Jebel,* the deserts of Tripolitania stretch into the barren wastes of Fezzan and Cyrenaica with scarcely an oasis to break the monotonous aridity. Fezzan is unmitigated desert. Of its more than 210,000 square miles only 4,000 square miles, at the most, can be cultivated, and it is estimated that at present no more than 1,250 acres, exclusive of date palm groves, are farmed. The oases lie widely scattered; among them, Ghadames and Ghat are outstanding.

Sand or rock characterize most of the Libyan desert. The hammadas, that form the outermost series of plateaus surrounding the Ahaggar Massif, extend into Libya as the Homra plateau. Patina-coated (see Glossary) limestone, the Homra is "perhaps the largest, most lifeless, barren, unbroken and monotonous of the limestone plateaus of North Africa,"[5] in the east covered with several lava flows of considerable extent, the largest being the Djebel el Soda and the Haroudj el Asoued. Along the base of the plateau two large *ergs*, the Edeyen of Oubari and the Edeyen of Murzuq, slope into the basin of Fezzan. Here a number of oases are found along the wadis

[5] A. K. Lobeck, *Physiographic Diagram of Africa*, Maplewood, N.J.: Hammond, Incorporated, 1946, reprinted 1952, p. 2.

that converge into the depression. Arid and inland though Fezzan is, and small in population, this sector of the Sahara was known from antiquity, because through this region of gardens lay the shortest and safest caravan trails that ran south from the Libyan coast into the Chad country. The Greeks knew of Fezzan long before the beginning of the Christian era.

There are no perennial rivers in Libya, but the country has a complex network of wadis that carry water after rainstorms. At times, these become rushing torrents that cause flood damage and sweep away much valuable topsoil.

## Patterns of People and Land

In both Libya and Mauritania, the composition of the population reflects to a degree the succession of foreigners who came into or swept across the land. The first inhabitants of the two coastal provinces of Libya were Berber. The ethnic character of these people was little affected by the invasions of Phoenicians, Carthaginians, Romans, Vandals, and Byzantines, but there has been a considerable admixture of Berbers with Greeks in Cyrenaica during the 14 centuries since they first came to Libyan shores to settle around Cyrene. Of the invaders, however, it was the Arabs who, moving into and across the area during the seventh, ninth, and eleventh centuries, left the deepest mark, namely, the imprint of language and religion. With few exceptions, notably the small desert centers of Aujila and Marada in the west, the Berbers of Tripolitania have intermarried with Arab stock and adopted Arab culture.

The people of Cyrenaica fall into two large groups, the most numerous being the almost purely Arabic Sa'ati who are descendants of the Benittillal and Beni Suleym invaders of the eleventh century. The second group are the Marabitin, also Arabic in culture but ethnographically descendants of original Berber or Greco-Berber admixtures. Fezzan is more varied: tribal Arabs predominate in the north; Berbers are in the majority in the northwest and west; some nomadic Tuaregs are found in the southwest; and, in the regions of the Edeyen of Murzuq and the Serir Tibesti, there are a few nomadic Tebbu (men of the Tibesti massif, the main portion of which is in Chad).

Jews and Italians form the largest minorities. Jews have lived in both Tripolitania and Cyrenaica since ancient times. They descend in part from early Jewish settlements during the days of Emperor Vespasian of Rome (about A.D. 69 to 79) and in part from Jewish fugitives from Spain in the sixteenth century. The number of Jews that remain today is small compared to those who were there in 1948, after which date a great migration to Israel took place. Jews are and have been town dwellers, engaging in trade or the crafts. Italians, the largest foreign minority, tend also to live in the cities, where they comprise the majority of professional people, skilled workers, and artisans, and "the core of the merchant class." They have retained their own culture, language, and religion, and have their own schools. Since the end of World War II many Italians also have returned to Italy, so that the 35,000 still in Libya are only about a third as many as resided there in the early 1940s.

Native Libyans are overwhelmingly rural, cultivating the land or raising livestock; fewer than 85,000 are employed in industry. The average income is low, as has been noted, but the living standard varies greatly: in the cities manufactured products and luxury items find a market; but the oasis and nomadic people have few means, and especially during and after periods of drought, keep alive with only the barest necessities.

Population in Libya numbers about 1,200,000; Mauritanians number even fewer, far fewer than 1 million.

The Mauritanians are of mixed racial composition, ranging from Arabized Berbers to black Africans, as Mauritania is a transit area and a zone of mingling for the Caucasian north and the black south. The races are grouped in two distinct societies, the Moorish, which contains large elements of Negro blood, and Negro. It is the character of these contrasting societies and the manner in which they are adapting to innovations and independence that imparts to Mauritania its distinctive nature.

The almost exclusively nomadic Maures make up about three-fourths of the population. They live in tents and move with their flocks wherever rains provide pasture, keeping cattle, sheep, goats, and camels, which among a number of the tribes provide almost all of the essentials of living: blood, milk, and meat,

especially lamb and mutton, are eaten; hides and skins are used to make tents, mats, saddles, water bags, and cushions; hair is bound into brushes; and wool and hair are woven into cloth for tent strips and robes. Animals are kept largely for subsistence, as capital, and as a sign of status rather than for commercial purposes. They symbolize wealth. In this the Mauritanians are no different from Libyans and other Saharan and near Saharan pastoralists.

The Negro minority are cultivators. They are heavily concentrated along the north bank of the Senegal River and are actually an extension of the tribal peoples of Senegal. This concentration of black Africans comprises about 20 percent of the entire Mauritanian population. The rest of the blacks are found in the date oases farther north where they likewise cultivate the land, but under conditions of serfdom and not as freeholders. Although black, these Africans are thoroughly Islamized.

Mauritania's social structure is that of the tribe, now beginning to break down because the establishment of law and order makes the protection that the tribe gives unnecessary. "The former obedience of slaves to masters and masters to the chief is [also] breaking down, and modern education and outside employment further encourage individualism."[6]

Density of population in Mauritania averages less than 2 per square mile, which has little meaning, however, since so large a proportion of the people are wanderers and since over 85 percent are concentrated south of 19°N latitude. All the cropped lands, with the exception of those in dates and other irrigated crops in the Adrar, are likewise found here. Mauritania is rural. At the most, only six towns have populations of over 3,000; among these Nouakchott, Port Étienne, and Atar are the principal centers.

Nouakchott is a new city and the new capital, centrally situated along Mauritania's only trunk road, the modern *piste de Mauritanie* which follows the old *"trik al-beidan"* (Moors' trail). Until 1957 St. Louis, just outside of the boundary of Mauritania in Senegal, served as capital, being the center from which the French had administered French West Africa, of which Mauritania was a part.

---

[6] Watson, *op. cit.*, pp. 3–4.

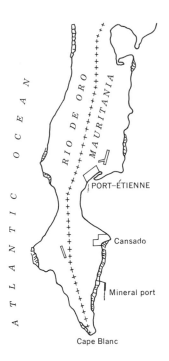

FIGURE 5.4  Port Étienne, Mauritania. (After "Mauritanie," Europe Outremer, Paris: Sociétés des Editions France Outremer S.A., no. 402, July, 1963.)

Nouakchott lies about 200 miles north of St. Louis and about 4 miles inland from the ocean, a situation sufficiently central so as not to cause tribal jealousy. Its location is remarkably refreshing for its latitude (18°N), as its name suggests; *nouak* means place and *chott* means wind. Otherwise the site has less to recommend it: the city is rising in country of loose sand and scrub brush; water is not locally available and must be piped in over a distance of 42 miles. Since there was no town formerly at this site, everything has had to be built, and with a "diversity of regional styles and a polygamous society in which a dwelling may need to house several wives" each with her children, this is not easy. Many semifabricated or entirely prefabricated houses are being used, often "arranged round interior courts."[7]

Port Étienne is not old as cities go (Figure 5.4). It was established as a fishing port and depot by the French in 1907 on the inner side of Cape Blanc, a peninsula divided between Mauritania and Spanish

[7] R. J. Harrison Church, "The Islamic Republic of Mauritania," *Focus*, vol. XII, no. 3, p. 2, November, 1961.

Sahara. The town sprawls across the desert of the peninsula in an environment so arid that between the years 1923 and 1955, water had to be brought in all the way from France to supply the little settlement. After 1955 fresh water was distilled from seawater; reserves of sweet water were discovered recently, however, some 40 miles north of the city. From this source, water is now transported not only to Port Étienne but to Fort Gouraud as well, by tank car. The port is being extended and the facilities enlarged to accommodate the export of ores.

Atar is the chief inland town, an old desert center at which caravans, passing west from Timbuktu and north from Trarza, gathered before moving on to the Dra. Since the modern *piste de Mauritanie* follows this old Moorish trail from Trarza through Atar north to Tindouf and Goulimine, Atar lies on the modern Trans-Mauritanian Highway. The ancient trade in gum arabic, salt, camels, and horses for which Atar was a major center still continues, and new trade developments have further increased its importance.

Libya has had some historic and renowned cities: Cyrene, founded in 620 B.C. by Greeks; and Sabratha and Leptis Magna, both ancient seaports of Roman Africa but established much earlier by Phoenicians from Sidon. There were others. When the Ptolemies ruled over Libya after the death of Alexander, they called the land *Pentapolis* because it had five great cities—Cyrene, Arsinoë, Berenice, Ptolemaïs, and Apollonia.

Tripoli (Figure 5.5) and Benghazi dominate the political and economic life of modern Libya. Both are ports and industrial centers, provincial capitals, and federal capitals: the National Assembly meets in Tripoli, but the King conducts his affairs of state in Benghazi. Both, however, now must share the important national government function with a third capital, namely, Beida, rising in the northern highlands of Cyrenaica. However, Beida can never match Tripoli or Benghazi in importance. Over one-fourth of Libya's people live in one or the other of the two older towns. Tripoli is approximately 185,500 in size, and Benghazi has about 70,000 people. Beida, the new federal capital, and Sebha, provincial capital of Fezzan, are the only centers outside of Tripoli and Benghazi with more than 35,000 people; most are much smaller.

FIGURE 5.5 Tripoli, looking toward the Catholic cathedral. (From The Lamp. Courtesy The Standard Oil Company of New Jersey.)

The building of Beida was controversial. Many Libyans, particularly Tripolitanians, do not favor the new capital, resenting its location and the cost of building a new city when there are already two national capitals. It is difficult to reach because of its eccentric situation on the plateau and far to the east. Further, it draws the function of government away from Tripoli, the largest and most important city and port in the most important, populous, and productive province and region of the country.

Beida is situated on the Jebel el Akhdar, 7 miles to the southwest of the ruins of the ancient Greek city of Cyrene. The new town is rising on the outskirts of old Beida, a village about halfway along the coastal road between Benghazi and the seacoast town of Derna, one of the most traveled routes in North Africa during World War II. Twenty miles westward is the spectacularly scenic pass of the Wadi El Kuf. Beida is Libya's "Simla," the summer capital to which the government can escape from the seacoast as the heat becomes difficult to endure. Ever since Idris became King, he has gone to the Green mountains to get away from the coastal lowland in summer, and ministers and diplomats have followed him. Most were hard put to find living quarters, some having found it necessary to commute the 140 miles from Benghazi. Already official foreign residences are growing up around Beida; the United States, British, and Italian embassies have summer residences at Shahhat, 7 miles away, a village that occupies the exact site of ancient Cyrene. Much is being done to beautify and embellish the new capital, to make it not only a political center but one of Moslem learning and culture as well. A number of difficulties have had to be overcome in building Beida. Among the more important is the lack of locally available water; water must be piped in from over 50 miles away.

The years since the oil era began have brought extensive changes in Benghazi and Tripoli. Modern suburbs with expensive homes and gardens have grown up around the old drab Arab towns, the relic buildings of Turkish architecture, and the Italian sectors with their commercial and residential quarters; along the outer edges, shantytowns have mushroomed as chronic conditions of hardship drive the rural folk to the cities in search of work. Possibly not so extensive as those of Morocco and Algeria because of the smaller Libyan population, these slums are nevertheless too large, spreading their fly-infested huts across the dunes, and creating problems of health, sanitation, and water supply.

The old cities also are being transformed to a degree, taking on new skylines as hotels, office buildings, and apartments rise where lower and smaller structures stood during the period of Italian rule. Even *medinas* are being remodelled in places. The momentum of growth in Tripoli and Benghazi is unmatched by any other centers.

## Livelihood

Modern development has just begun in Libya and Mauritania.

Although in antiquity parts of Libya, particularly Cyrenaica, were so fertile and fruitful that the Romans regarded it as a granary of Rome, the invasions that occurred after the decline of the empire despoiled the countryside, reducing it to desert. For more than 11 centuries Libya was a land of desolation, with little activity except for some "semiprimitive" agriculture carried on in a few oases while the hinterlands were grazed by the flocks of sheep, goats, and camels of nomadic pastoralists, which further denuded the land of its forests, grasses, and topsoil.

During the period of Italian administration (1912 to 1943), some progress was made in improving conditions: raiding and slave trading, traditional among the tribes, were halted; a good system of roads, one corresponding to the needs of the land, was constructed; ports were improved and some of the towns Europeanized; urban health and sanitation were somewhat bettered, and law and order were imposed.

The Italians left a fair legacy of public works and services to the Libyans, but not the technological means with which to exploit this inheritance, because illiteracy was widespread and trained personnel to continue the good works was lacking, a condition "which even the striking adaptability of Libyans and the rapid increase in educational facilities have been unable to completely overcome." The traditional schools taught the Koran, and had not the practical application that Western schools have. Instead the new teaching "may produce too many white-collar workers and too few mechanics, artisans, and skilled workers. Even now there is concern, for example, that agricultural schools are producing agricultural inspectors rather than better farmers. Education is inducing urban growth."[8]

It was the discovery of oil and gas that changed the economic prospects for Libya. Until then, the country's existence depended entirely upon its animals and the thin strips of productive land in the north along the shores of the Mediterranean, plus whatever bits of land could be reclaimed from the desert through irrigation. Without petroleum, therefore, Libya must have remained largely a vast, almost unpopulated wilderness of space, its people pastoral nomads and simple cultivators. Oil provides a steady revenue, and makes possible the expansion and development of all sides of the economy. The income, however, will be largely in royalty and taxes, not in wages and salaries to Libyans. "The oil industry is capital intensive rather than labor intensive, and it needs skilled workers rather than unskilled. . . . The World Bank Mission estimated that the Libyan oil industry eventually would provide direct employment for no more than about 5 percent of Libya's total labor force."[9] Therefore, despite the fact that over 90 percent of Libya is unproductive desert, agriculture and pastoralism must remain the major activities of its people.

The amount of land cultivated varies greatly with rainfall; and the amount of pasture varies in the same way, being drastically diminished during years of serious or successive droughts. Tripolitania is the most productive of the three provinces, offering both the greatest variety as well as the bulk of arable land, about 66 percent of the total acreage. Of the acres devoted to sedentary agriculture on regularly cultivated land, perhaps one-fourth are irrigated; a system of migratory agriculture irregularly produces cereals on patches that are abandoned after a short time as shown in Table 1 on following page.

But there are handicaps to farming in Mediterranean Tripolitania. In summer, violent dust storms blow out of the desert; at times swarms of locusts lay destitute the land. These calamities, compounded by the irregularity of rainfall, in total always slight in amount, often cause crop failures. Demands for cereals, vegetables, dates, and olives generally exceed production in Tripolitania, so that only in very good years is there a surplus of these products. Citrus fruits, almonds, peanuts, and alfa grass are in surplus and are exported. For more than a decade there have been extensive plantings of olives, citrus, date, and almond trees in Tripolitania. These began producing during the decade of the 1960s, and a

---

[8] John I. Clarke, "Oil in Libya: Some Implications," *Economic Geography*, XXXIX, no. 1, p. 57, January, 1963.

[9] *Ibid.*

**TABLE 1**

| Province | Area | | Population (approximate) | | | |
|---|---|---|---|---|---|---|
| | Square miles rounded | Total | Urban | Rural sedentary | Seminomadic | Nomadic |
| Tripolitania | 136,000 | 738,400 | 180,000 | 310,000 | 200,000 | 40,000 |
| Cyrenaica | 330,000 | 291,000 | 84,000 | 66,000 | — | 155,000 |
| Fezzan | 213,000 | Less than 60,000 | — | 27,000 | 7,000 | 1,000 |
| Percentage of total population of Libya | | | 24 | 39 | 18.8 | 17.8 |

Source: "Basic Data on the Economy of Libya," *Economic Reports*, Pt. 1, no. 61–10, U.S. Bureau of Foreign Commerce, 1961, p. 4.

marked increase in the yield of these tree crops is anticipated. Alfa grass, a government monopoly controlled by the Esparto Corporation, grows wild in the Jebel and the Gefara Plain.

There is no cultivation without irrigation in Fezzan, and thus agriculture is limited to oases; the leading crop is the date. However, the yield per tree is low, and production and quality could be improved. Most of the produce is consumed locally because of the isolated location of the oases and the high transportation costs which set limitations upon commercial production. It is hoped that a new paved highway, dropping down from the coastal road into the Sebha oases, will change this somewhat. Wheat and barley grow in winter and yields are good, although the total production is small; a good year may bring 1,100 tons of wheat and about 450 tons of barley. Summer cereals, particularly sorghum, occupy about half as much acreage as the winter grains.

The crops of Cyrenaica are like those of Fezzan, but with the important difference that almost all of the cereals are produced without irrigation, and due to the variability in climatic conditions, production fluctuates enormously. Social factors also handicap agriculture in Cyrenaica. There are almost 2½ times as many nomads as there are farmers. Intensive tillage of the soil requires sedentary occupation of the land, and this cannot be achieved in Cyrenaica so long as tribal institutions that sustain a nomadic way of life are dominant in the province.

Libyan agriculture is backward, and the pattern of land-ownership so complicated that where modern machinery has been introduced, full utilization has not been achieved. Both the national and provincial governments, assisted by foreign technical missions, are trying to bring changes, particular emphasis being placed upon settling the nomads into a more secure way of life by attaching them to the land and making them sedentary or, at the least, seminomadic. Resettlement projects are a part of this plan, and hundreds of farms formerly owned by Italians have been distributed to Cyrenaicans. As in Tripolitania, a program of reforestation is under way, and hundreds of thousands of sapling fruit and olive trees have been set out. It is hoped that this effort will in a few years make it unnecessary for Cyrenaica to import olive oil and oranges from Tripolitania.

Since more than one-third of Libya's population is nomadic or seminomadic, animal raising is important, but animal production and the number of animals vary greatly from year to year, for the herds are vulnerable to the vagaries of climate. Droughts cause disastrous losses of livestock from starvation and from disease as the animals' resistance weakens. Cyrenaica has about three-fifths of the livestock in the country excepting swine, which are raised only in Tripolitania. Fezzan is estimated to have only between 22,000 and 30,000 animals—goats, sheep, camels, and donkeys.

As with the Libyans, most Mauritanians are subsistence cultivators or pastoral herdsmen, only occasionally supplementing their livelihood by wage employment or the sale of produce in local markets. Despite this, and with all of the handicaps imposed by the natural environment, Mauritania produces some important products: in the Senegal valley, millet, rice, corn, sweet potatoes, tobacco, peanuts, and a variety of vegetables are grown; 800,000 date palms in the interior oases yield several thousand tons of dates annually; these irrigated gardens also grow grains, tobacco, henna, and vegetables. Gum arabic is gathered from the acacia trees in the savanna.

The most productive area of the country, in the south on the floodplain of the Senegal, is irrigated under a system of inundation as floodwaters recede from the river valley and nearby lakes. But the growing season is short, limited to the period following the floods, for there are no permanent water storage and canal systems. Water control has been somewhat improved with simple earthen dams and canals introduced by the French, but reliance tends to be placed upon the moisture supplied by the uncontrolled freshets, or upon groundwater in the wadis of intermittent streams. The farmers of the south are, as noted, exclusively black Africans.

Certain mountain valleys, irrigated with stored rainwater, are also cultivated. These are the oases which produce, besides dates, the main crop, cereals and vegetables; black Africans do the actual cultivation here also. So scarce and so valuable is the land in these oases that plots of no more than 2 or 3 yards square are often used to grow grains.

But the animal industries are the more important side of Mauritania's pastoral-agricultural -economy (Figure 5.6). This, too, is largely concentrated in the south, where animals with more demanding pasture requirements are grazed; only good users of poor forage can graze on the meager Saharan pastures. The animal herds include over 1 million cattle in the south, 5 times as many sheep and goats, and some 200,000 camels. Although in the main subsistence graziers, the Maures have always sold or traded some of their animals, and as the mining centers are opening up offering markets for meat and vegetables, Mauritanians are becoming more commercially minded. Mauritanian herdsmen normally sell about 1 million sheep and goats, and 100,000 cattle and camels to neighboring Senegal, Gambia, and Mali; camels are sold also to Morocco.

**FIGURE 5.6** These little tribal Mauritanians attend a nomad school held in a tent. (*Courtesy Service de l'Information of the AOF.*)

There are some of the same serious difficulties in carrying on farming and grazing in Mauritania that are found in Libya. Not only water shortage and uncertain pasturage but millet-eating birds and locusts plague the land. Two-thirds of the budget of the Mauritanian Agricultural Service is consumed in trying to control these pests. Crops are dusted and sprayed with insecticides, and explosives and flame throwers are used against the birds. The magnitude of the bird problem is illustrated by the fact that in one year an estimated 40 million birds were destroyed.

The government is trying in many other ways to improve conditions and methods and to protect and improve the livestock and crops. It has introduced the use of fertilizers and better seeds, and is encouraging the use of animal drawn plows instead of hand implements. Farmer training systems have been set up, and agricultural cooperatives and the cooperative use of modern farm equipment are being encouraged. A dozen vaccination centers are helping to protect herds from cattle plague, anthrax, and pneumonia. Construction of numerous simple dams to store water of rains and freshets and other water conservation projects are making possible the cultivation of more land and increasing the water holes and pastureland for livestock.[10]

## Resources of the Sea and Earth

### FISHING

Despite the restricted nature of the land environment, the long coastlines, and the relatively rich ranging grounds for fish that lie offshore both of these desert countries, fishing is not important in either Libya or Mauritania. One of the richest concentrations of fish in the world swims in the waters off the Mauritanian coast, "descendants of those fish that attracted Portuguese fishermen to African waters in the 15th century," but only one tribe of Mauritanians are fishermen, the Imragen. The rest of the tribes who live near the

coast are inhibited from fishing by the dangerous Atlantic surf. The Imragen fish just north of Cape Mirik, about 100 miles north of Nouakchott, by wading into the water with nets and encircling the fish; they do not use boats. Europeans regularly work these prolific offshore waters of the Canary Current, mostly Spanish, Portuguese, Italian, French, Greeks, and Canary Islanders. Since the establishment of Port Étienne fishing fleets have found safe anchorage, and the town has dried and shipped fish. It is sold to countries along the Guinea coast in competition with like products from as far separated centers as Angola and Norway.

Fishing is not important in Libya, either. The Libyans are not seafarers, and what fishing is done is carried out almost entirely by Greeks, Maltese, and Italians. Sponges, tuna, and sardines are the leading commercial varieties.

Sponging is a very ancient industry in Libyan-Tunisian waters, tracing back 2,000 years. Traditionally a Greek industry, less than 5 percent of the sponges taken are brought in by Libyans, who use small boats and harpoons or do skin diving in the shallow inshore waters to depths of 10 or 15 fathoms. The most successful method, yielding the largest quantity and best quality of sponges, is diving from diving boats, the latter almost exclusively Greek owned. From them the hardy Greek spongers may plunge to depths varying from 10 to 35 fathoms. This is a dangerous occupation and many divers lose their lives, a large number from caisson disease, neuralgic pains and paralysis induced by too rapid a change in pressure. The size of the fleets participating in sponging varies from season to season, but on the average they number about 80 diving ships and half again as many smaller boats.

### MINERALS AND FUELS

For hundreds of years the economies of Libya and Mauritania have been limited to subsistence agriculture and pastoral activities, but it has recently been proven that their subsurface resources are not insignificant. Most important of these resources are minerals and oil, and it is on these that both states are relying to strengthen their economies and better their fiscal standings.

[10] "Islamic Republic of Mauritania," *The Newly Independent Nations,* Bureau of Public Affairs, U.S. Department of State, May, 1963.

In Mauritania the main ore discoveries are iron deposits near Fort Gouraud in the west central region. They occur in the stark grey hills of the Kedia l'Idjil range which rises in the desert near the fort. The iron is a high grade hematite averaging between 60 and 70 percent iron content. These are phosphatic ores, but the phosphate content is low. Development is being carried out by the Société Anonyme des Mines de Fer de Mauritanie (MIFERMA), most shares of which are held by interests in France, the United Kingdom, Germany, and Italy, with the French government owning one-fourth and French private capital about 35 percent of the stock.

A 419-mile railroad from Port Étienne was completed in mid-1963. It is the country's first railway. Difficulties stood in the way of its construction because it was necessary to make a right angle turn around the southeastern corner of Spanish Sahara in order to keep the line within Mauritanian territory. Had the railroad cut across Rio de Oro not only would considerable mileage have been saved, but it would have been unnecessary to build a 1¼-mile tunnel through granite formations. The cost of securing the Spanish right-of-way was so high that the idea was dropped, but less than 8 miles of track, run across the corner of Rio de Oro, could have circumvented the tunneling. West of the tunnel the rails had to be laid across two zones of stabilized dunes, and at the head of Cape Blanc, a 20-mile belt of isolated, moving dunes that may make it necessary to readjust the alignment of the road in that area from time to time. A spur from the main line has been constructed to Akjoujt, where copper deposits have been discovered.

The copper at Akjoujt and iron ores other than those at Fort Gouraud are being mined by the Mauritanian Copper Mine Company (MICUMA), owned half by French private capital and half by the French and Mauritanian Governments. The Senegal valley is being explored for oil where indications point toward its presence, although none has so far been found. Salt is mined north of Nouakchott and close to Fort Gouraud, and sent south to Mali by camel caravan.

Libya's geologic structure precludes the occurrence of most metallic ores and coal. As a result, the coun-

try suffered from the dearth of fuels and minerals until oil was discovered, in the early 1950s. Oil is Libya's great resource. Already, exports of oil have reduced the country's dependence upon foreign financial assistance, and indications are that oil will make it possible for Libya to free itself entirely from foreign aid.

The first discovery was made in western Fezzan at Atshan, not far from the Edjelé fields in Algeria; this was small. Since 1955 exploration has been very intensive, and discoveries and developments have been rapid. In quick succession two fields opened up at Zelten and Dahra, and by early 1963 a third field, the Raguba, had come into commercial production. The first export was made in 1961 from the Zelten and Dahra through two new ports constructed for that purpose. Oil from Raguba flows through a 56-mile pipeline, connecting with that from Zelten at a point 66 miles south of Marsa el Brega, Esso's newly constructed port in Cyrenaica.

Independence in 1951 and the first export of oil in 1961 mark two extraordinary years in the history of Libya, and more than a decade of spectacular beginnings and changes. The first oil concessions were leased in 1955; by April, 1963, Libya ranked eleventh in the world in daily production of crude oil.

Although oil has been found in western Tripolitania and in Fezzan, the most important finds and the most attractive concessions are in Cyrenaica just south of the Gulf of Sidra. Here are Zelten and Raguba; the Dahra field is also close to the Gulf of Sidra, in Tripolitania. No one had explored the extreme southern part of the country up to the late months of 1962, but in August of that year concessions in the south were opened to bidders.

By the middle of 1961 the whole of the northern half of Libya was under concession, 387,780 square miles of land and 11,150 square miles of sea. Offshore drilling began in April, 1963. The offshore concession areas are divided into four blocks covering 6.7 million acres, and tests are being made in all four regions, which stretch along the Gulf of Sidra and extend seaward to 50 miles; water depths go to 1,800 feet. The Atlantic Refining Company is the operator of the drilling rig carrying out the offshore researches, and 50-50 owner with Phillips Petroleum Company of the concessions.

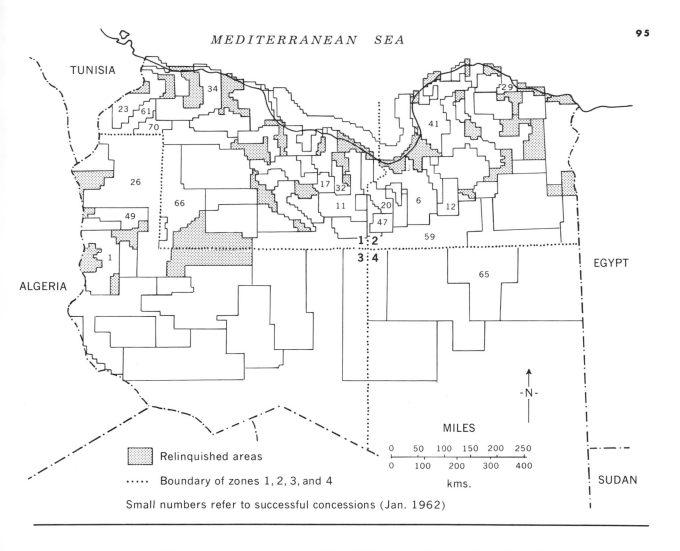

MEDITERRANEAN SEA

FIGURE 5.7 Libyan oil concessions as of late 1961. (After John I. Clarke, "Oil in Libya: Some Implications," Economic Geography, p. 43, January, 1963.)

The concession laws must be briefly discussed because they are peculiar to this country, and create unique development conditions in Libya. The 1955 Libyan Petroleum Law set the framework for intensive exploration: a 12½ percent royalty on the value of all oil produced and saved was to be paid to the Government; profits were to be shared on a half and half basis of realized, not posted, prices. In 1961 this law was amended, converting the 50-50 sharing of profits to a posted price basis; certain other conditions that laid rigid limitations upon the exploration and development of concessions were added as well.

The terms of the 1955 law had acted as a spur to two developments—rapid exploration, and a fragmentation of concessions that is "almost unknown in the more traditional oil-producing areas of the Middle East." Under the new law, concessionaires must give up one-fourth of their concessions at the end of 5 years, another one-fourth at the end of 8 years, and within 10 years concessions in the north (Blocks 1 and 2) must have been reduced by two-thirds, and in the south by three-fourths. The domain of Libya was divided into four blocks for purposes of giving out oil concessions (see Figure 5.7). The areas surrendered must be "reasonably compact" so that they can be re-leased, "but inevitably fragmentation of concessions will increase as portions are relinquished and re-awarded.[11] The revised law provides also that no operating company will be eligible for new acreage unless it voluntarily revises its original agreement to conform to the new and stiffer terms. Only four companies, Esso Libya, Esso Sirte, B B Exploration, and Gulf Oil, had done this by August, 1962; by 1963 others were contemplating the change, such as Marathon Oil. However, it is expected that most of the concessionaires who take up surrendered land will be new ones.

Oil will perhaps not stimulate any great development of heavy industry in Libya except along such specialized channels as the petrochemicals. This was begun when Esso Sirte set up a refinery at its oil terminal at Marsa el Brega. The installation of this refinery was an innovation for the oil industry because the refinery came "packaged." It was completely built in Antwerp, set upon a concrete platform that acted as the barge and later as the base on which the plant stands, and towed the 3,000 miles across the sea to Marsa el Brega. A specially constructed canal had to be dug and flooded to provide access to the permanent location of the plant.

Innovations have characterized Libyan oil exploration and development. It was for Libya that "the desert barge" was designed. As in Algeria, desert conditions make it necessary for the oil companies to modify usual procedures of operation. The desert barge is a concession to the environment, built around the idea of a compact vehicle for desert service. Besides drilling, it does workover and service jobs, pulls tubing, cements walls, and may be used in fracturing or water flooding. It gets its name from the similarity of design to a floating drilling barge.

The oil rig and the wells and the pipelines have already altered the face of the Libyan desert, but now oil may change even the shifting dunes from destructive phenomena into productive land. Esso Standard (Near East), Inc. and the forestry department of Tripolitania have experimented since 1961 with a project designed to anchor moving dunes long enough for young tree seedlings to take root. The undertaking involves spraying the dunes with a petroleum product, developed by Esso Research, that holds the sands in place. Early in 1963 a pilot project, to be eventually carried out across 123 acres of dune country in two separate areas of Tripolitania, was initiated. If this proves as successful as have earlier smaller experiments, work may be expanded. Libya has hundreds of thousands of acres of dune country, now barren wasteland, that hold possibilities of reclaiming. However, even if the dunes can be kept from moving, the moisture problem raises itself (Figure 5.8). If, as claimed, this is country that was formerly vegetated, the desert may be forced to recede, however[12] (Figure 5.9).

Little forest vegetation remains in Libya. Some minor stands of juniper, that are mostly shrubs, occur in the Jebel el Akhdar covering an area of about 425,000 acres; yet, as noted, the juniper gives the mountains their name. In some of the more isolated districts a few conifer trees occur. In Tripolitania only some 40,000 acres of scrub forest land remain, all in relatively inaccessible regions.

Reforestation is needed in those parts of Libya where trees can be induced to grow, not only for the vegetation as such but also as a means of halting the migration of sand dunes. The effort to renew the forest cover began in Cyrenaica in 1955; by 1961, over 11 million trees had been set out. The planted areas, under this plan, will eventually reforest about 225,000 acres. Since this is a long term program, it will be many years before the forests can be exploited. However, soil conservation benefits will be felt almost immediately by anchoring the dunes from encroachment on oases. For forests to grow, the trees must first take hold, however—not easy in a region of meager rain, loose soil, and wind. The Esso invention, if successful, should be a boon.

Among the few known mineral resources of Libya, other than oil, marine salt is one of the more important. It can be produced in considerable quantities in Tripolitania and Cyrenaica. The only thing that now holds down production is the limited foreign market. Natron salts occur in Fezzan, but the local demand

---

[11] Clarke, *op. cit.*, p. 42.

[12] "Esso's Oil Spray Helps Grow Trees in Libya's Desert," *Oil and Gas Journal*, p. 102, Feb. 11, 1963.

FIGURE 5.8 Stabilization of the migrating sand dunes is a feature of American oil research (Esso) in Libya: specially formulated oils are sprayed on the sand for dune stabilization along with an emulsion of petroleum resins (to serve as an agricultural mulch). *(From The Lamp. Courtesy The Standard Oil Company of New Jersey.)*

FIGURE 5.9 Encroaching sand dunes, stabilized with oil, stand still long enough for anchoring vegetation to grow. *(From The Lamp. Courtesy The Standard Oil Company of New Jersey.)*

is small and distances are so far to the coast that only between 100 and 150 tons are mined annually. Sulfur deposits in Cyrenaica are similarly handicapped. Building materials—gypsum, chalk, limestone, marble —occur in Tripolitania and are quarried to supply local demands; gypsum deposits in Libya are immense.

## Problems and Prospects

Problems of many sorts challenge Libya and Mauritania. The physical environment raises several, among them a parching lack of water, an extreme and difficult climate, and the deep erosion of the soil. All are difficult to combat. There is no water except the meager rainfall and a few streams that flow seasonally in wadis and disappear into the seemingly endless Sahara; groundwater is dependent on seepage from rains. On occasions searing winds sweep out of the desert, burning every green thing in its path, desiccating the ground. Centuries of neglect and misuse have left the soil eroded and impoverished. In Libya the greenness of parts of the coast stands out against the drought of the desert background.

Horace called Libya the "arid nurse of lions"—and lions did roam there, and were taken by the Romans for their arena circuses. The lions are now all gone, long since gone because of the carnage of the Roman era; but the aridity remains.

Remaining also, however, are superb ruins such as Leptis Magna, Sabratha, Cyrene, and Apollonia. They demonstrate what the Greeks and Romans were able to do within the limitations that the water resources imposed, and geologists believe that the country is no more arid now than then. Many cisterns of ancient Roman waterworks were built so well that they are being reconstructed for use again. There apparently is water, but it needs to be developed.

Mauritania has no ruins to indicate a former more affluent period. It has only its entrepôts of caravan travel. Its green strip faces black Africa.

### DISTANCE

Distances are still largely measured in time in these desert lands, for distances are vast in both Mauritania and Libya, people are few, and oases far between,

and hinterlands, except those producing ores or oil, are generally poor. In Mauritania, trade in ore and shipments by rail lie largely in the future. Traditionally, Mauritanian gum arabic, salt, camels, and other animals have moved slowly across the desert; the caravan trails and desert oases have been the highways and the ports, and still are to a large degree.

All population centers of Mauritania are linked by roads or trails, but only a limited sector is served by the railroad. Camel caravans still slowly wend their ways in all directions from interior Mauritania carrying all manner of things. Some, as those from the salt mines north of Nouakchott and west of Fort Gouraud, carry salt slabs by camelback; gum arabic moves by caravan to Atar, although commerce in this product has almost ceased as Sudanese production has risen. In vivid contrast to the caravan as a carrier is the airplane, already sending fresh vegetables from Atar to Nouakchott, Port Étienne, and Fort Gouraud. But modern transport across the uninhabited distances of Mauritania is expensive.

High transit costs are one of the explanations for the centralization of industry in and around the two Libyan port cities of Tripoli and Benghazi. As in Mauritania, distances between population centers and oases are long. Tripoli and Benghazi lie over 650 miles apart by road.

Most Libyan centers of any size are coastal or near coastal, and are on or near the bituminized federal coastal road, 1,140 miles long, that extends across the country and beyond its border, connecting with roads in Egypt and Tunisia. About 2,000 miles of other paved highways extend into the interior from the coastal road to the more important centers, the ones to Ghadames and the Sebha oases being the deepest. But a network of roads is not required in Libya, at least not yet. The paved road into Fezzan, completed in 1962 as far as Sebha, was built less for economic reasons than to tie that part of the country in with the two coastal provinces; the highway is not expected to pay out economically for some time, if ever. There are plans for its possible extension south into Chad.

The many secondary roads and spur lines that reach into the hinterland regions are generally unsurfaced but are suitable for four-wheeled and special desert vehicles. Outward from these the trails take over. Highways dip into the commercial oil fields. Only if oil fields should open up widely across the country would there be created the necessity for a network of roads.

There are only two short rail lines, running between Benghazi and Barce in the east and Tripoli and Suara in the west. They carry grain, alfa grass, fruit, and building stone. The construction of roads has been given precedence over that of railroads because roads are considered to be more economic and adaptable to desert transport.

But oil pipelines are important. Three connect oil fields to the coast, as noted, the Raguba line having coastal connections via the Zelten pipeline, whose terminal is at Marsa el Brega, and the line from Dahra to Es Sider on the coast. This latter pipeline now extends inland to the oil fields at Beda and Waha.

## Geopolitics

The realities of size, physical environment, and population make both the territories and frontiers of Mauritania and Libya hard to administer and protect. In Mauritania, nearly one-third of the national budget is spent on police and armed forces, and even this is far from sufficient to maintain law and order in the huge wilderness of the north, and to keep armed bands from foreign soil from crossing the Mauritanian frontiers. The Mauritanian government has had to accept, at times since independence, the assistance of French forces despite the antagonism that this arouses among some of the tribal groups.

The question of boundaries throughout the whole Sahara became acute with the breaking up of colonies into independent African states and, later, with the discovery of minerals. Although Mauritania has little that would seem worth fighting over—the iron deposits at Fort Gouraud and a bleak, unpromising stretch of desert or near desert country—nonetheless, Morocco would like to extend its control to the Senegal River, incorporating in her domain all of the Spanish territories and Mauritania. Three months before independence was granted, Morocco demanded that the question of Mauritania be brought up in the United Nations, King Mohammed asserting that

Mauritania had been an integral part of the Kingdom since Morocco became a state 13 centuries ago.

Libya also has boundary problems. Before the discovery of minerals and oil, the exact delineation of frontiers, drawn largely for administrative convenience and coinciding with regions of sparse population, was regarded as of no great consequence. In fact, the precise delimitation of boundaries has been contrary to the traditional thinking, practice, and way of life among these Arab peoples. The vastness of the deserts, the thin scattering of the population, the overriding importance of pastoral nomadism, the prevalence of communal ownership, and the concept of the unity of Islam even as regards land, all fostered an indifference to rigidly delimited and demarcated lines of division. Boundaries in the Sahara were not established until laid down by the Turks and Europeans, the British, Italians, and French; drawn as they were through seemingly resourceless desert, it is not surprising that no great stress was placed upon accurate demarcation, if they were demarcated at all, or that nearly every map of the area showed boundary lines that differed slightly. Most of the lines regarded administrative convenience above ethnic and economic factors.

When independence was conceded, national frontiers in every case followed the old, foreign-imposed administrative boundaries. Libya's outline was set down by the foreign powers mentioned above and Egypt, and there has been discontent with at least portions of these delimited frontiers. Oil was responsible for this change in attitude, if independence was not. Petroleum was discovered in Libya not far from Algeria's Edjelé field, the latter in the extreme eastern part of Algeria, and major changes have been made since Libyan independence along the Algerian-Libyan frontier; internally, the boundary between Tripolitania and Cyrenaica runs right through the Sirte field, and each province draws from the reserve, has its own pipeline, oil terminal, and new port. If an equitable balance of production can be maintained in the two provinces, this could become a nucleus for drawing the country closer together, politically and economically. If not, rancor will develop. The line that separates Fezzan from Tripolitania is also in dispute: five different interpretations are given to that boundary.

## THE FUTURE

Change in many directions has come to Libya since independence and the discovery of oil. No longer is the social structure constituted exclusively of the few very rich and the mass of the very poor; a new middle class has developed because many Libyans are now earning "vastly increased wages and salaries"; the growth in education is startling. Nevertheless, there is still a strong contrast, and a contrast that is deepening, between the vast number of tradition-bound people and those who are attempting to keep up with the modern developments that the oil boom has brought about. Important as oil has become to Libya, its importance must not be permitted to obscure the needs of the land and the people. This is Libya's greatest problem, and it is definitely an economic one.

The resolution of Mauritanian problems, on the other hand, rests heavily on factors beyond the country's control. Mauritania's greatest problems are political, and it needs the support of other African states if it is to succeed in standing up against the claims of Morocco. The attitude of bordering Algeria, huge and recently made independent, and political evolution in Morocco are factors that will weigh in future events touching on Mauritania.

Internally, . . . the essential political task is to maintain the sentiment, among both leaders and followers, that this new state is theirs, that the government is truly the agent and authority of the Mauritanian people, and that the individual can influence the decision-making process in accordance with both Moorish and Negro tribal tradition.[13]

[13] Watson, *op. cit.,* p. 6.

# 6 THE RIVER NILE

*. . . what fun to make the im-
memorial Nile begin its journey
by diving through a turbine. . . .*

WINSTON CHURCHILL

## The Ancient River

The Nile is a river of great antiquity so far as human-kind are concerned. Like the Tigris-Euphrates rivers of Mesopotamia, it nurtured advanced cultures very early, and saw them decay and decline. Egypt was one of these. By the beginning of historic times, about 3000 B.C., Egypt had developed one of the two early civilizations of the ancient world.

This is rather a remarkable river. It drains an area of over 1 million square miles and flows across nearly one-sixth of the earth's circumference, from its most remote source to the sea, a distance of more than 4,100 miles. The Nile is the longest river in Africa and the second longest in the world. Although Pharaohs sought to find its sources, where the waters of the Nile came from and the reason for the miraculous regularity of its regime remained a mystery for thousands of years. Herodotus wrote, "With regard to the sources of the Nile, I have found no one among all those with whom I have conversed, whether Egyptians, Libyans, or Greeks, who professed to have any knowledge, except a single person." Only in the latter part of the nineteenth century did these facts about the river become known.

The great length of the river and its direct north-ward course are, in themselves, impressive, because the Nile manages to maintain itself all the way across the Sahara, the only river that is not turned back or lost in those arid wastes. During Miocene times, gentle north-south folding occurred. These folds were crossed by more acute fold and fault belts that struck east-northeast. The Nile established itself in one of the north-south synclines, within which its course is held across most of Egypt. This fortuitous geologic history permitted the Nile to establish the long channel, and bounteous headstreams rising in humid plateaus give it the volume with which to cross the parched desert and reach the sea as a great and majestic river. The White Nile, moving sluggishly from lakes in Uganda and Congo, supplies the steady flow while the Blue Nile is the tumultuous "flood giver," contributing the waters that with unfailing regularity have inundated annually the valley lands along the Nile since before the beginning of historic time.

## The Nile River

The plateaus, upwarps, and mountains to the south and southeast of the Nile basin are the watersheds from which the river draws its flow. These include the monsoon drenched plateaus of Ethiopia, whose rivers rise and recede with the coming and retreating of the wet seasons, and scar the upland with gorges as they rush to make the steep descent from the mountains to the plain. They include also the Lake plateau which cradles Victoria Nyanza, and some of the associated rift valleys and mountains and volcanoes, as well as the slight upwarp of the African plateau that divides Congo and Nile drainage. From the latter, the Bahr el Ghazal draws its waters—from many tributaries that are, in their headstreams, intermittent in flow.

Along the foot of these uplands the terrain levels out, and from there to the Mediterranean Sea the gradient of the river is relatively gentle. The southern portion of the basin, comprising the clay plain of southern and central Sudan and extending from Bor to the Shabluka Gorge, about 50 miles north of Khartoum, is very flat and the gradient of the river is so gradual that there are no rapids. Within this sector lies the great swamp of the sudd. Beyond Shabluka Gorge and to the First Cataract above Aswan the river has a drop of about 800 feet in 1,200 miles. Here the terrain alternates between fairly level stretches and sharp but interrupted descents, as the Nile falls in the series of five well-known rapids over crystalline rock outcroppings. Navigation between Khartoum and Wadi Halfa is discontinuous because of the cataracts, which are rapids, not falls. Beyond Aswan, the river again flows through a country of gentle, unbroken gradient as in the south, entering the Mediterranean through the triangular delta that the Nile has built of alluviums (Figure 6.2).

The river has four segments (Figure 6.3). The White Nile, or the Bahr el Jebel, which rises in the great lakes of equatorial Africa, mingles its waters with those of the Bahr el Ghazal and the Sobat and flows on to Khartoum as the Bahr el Abyad, is the first segment. At Khartoum the White Nile is joined by the second sector, the Blue Nile or the Bahr el Azraq, which is born in Lake Tana in Ethiopia. The

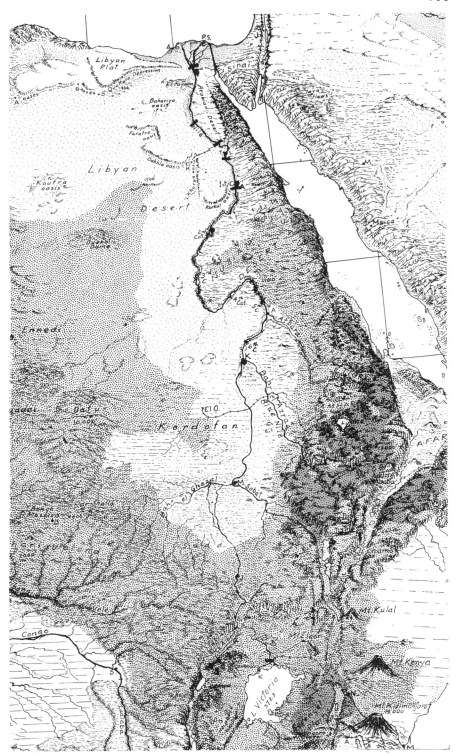

**FIGURE 6.2** Nile drainage basin.
*(Base map Physiographic Diagram of Africa, copyright A. K. Lobeck; reproduced with permission of the publisher, The Geographical Press, a division of C. S. Hammond & Company, Maplewood, N. J.)*

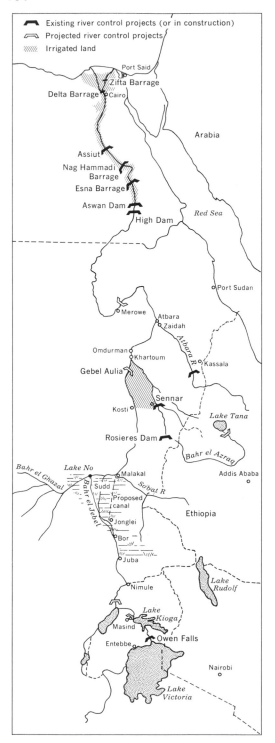

**FIGURE 6.3** **The Nile River system.** *(After Gaitskell.)*

Atbara, which also flows from Ethiopia, comprises the third; the fourth is the main Nile flowing between Khartoum and the Mediterranean Sea, in modern Egyptian known as El-Bahr or Bahr-en-Nile.

The waters that form the great and serene White Nile at the Khartoum juncture reflect the slow courses, but not the tortured struggle for survival, of the headstreams shortly after they leave the watersheds that gave them birth. The Victoria and Albert Niles are equatorial in location, but rise in environments modified climatically by elevation. In contrast to the Ethiopian affluents, these equatorial streams are relatively steady in volume, showing almost no seasonal fluctuation because they originate in a region where there is neither a prolonged period of drought nor one of unduly heavy rains.

One of man's most persistent questions, across the millenia of time since recorded history began, has been: Where does the Nile originate?

If the beginning of the Nile is taken to be the largest perennial stream that feeds into Lake Victoria, out of which the Victoria Nile emerges, then the Kagera River, rising in Rwanda and Uganda, must be the ultimate source. There is, in fact,

a just perceptible drift of water from the mouth of the Kagera across the northwestern corner of the lake to the Ripon Falls (or rather what used to be the Ripon Falls before the erection of the dam that flooded out the cascades). And if we follow the Kagera and its tributaries upstream for some hundreds of miles we find that its ultimate beginning lies in mountains over 6,000 feet high to the north of Lake Tanganyika. For ordinary purposes it would seem most sensible[1]

to regard the Ripon Falls as the source.

From the large, shallow, but almost unchanging reservoir of Lake Victoria the Victoria Nile emerges as a small stream at Jinja. Until the last decade it leapt from the lake over a series of rapids 20 feet high, known as Ripon Falls. With the damming of the river at Owen Falls, completed in 1954 and situated about a mile below the Ripon rapids, the rapids were drowned and the level of Lake Victoria raised. The surface of the lake is gradually rising. It

[1] Alan Moorehead, *The White Nile*, New York: Harper & Row, Publishers, Incorporated, 1960, p. 131.

**FIGURE 6.4** Airview of Owen Falls Dam, Jinja, and in the distance, Lake Victoria. *(Courtesy Department of Information, Uganda.)*

will take 25 years from the date of completion before the lake will crest the dam. When the basin is filled, Lake Victoria will be the world's largest reservoir. (See Figure 6.4.) Flowing through Lake Kyoga and plunging over Murchison Falls into the northeast corner of Lake Albert, the Nile pours out through the northern end of Lake Albert as the Albert Nile, changing its name to Bahr el Jebel beyond Nimule.

As one of the rift lakes, Lake Albert, deep and with a limited evaporation surface, is an excellent natural reservoir. Victoria Nyanza is less so because Victoria occupies a wide shallow depression that is no more than a sag in the plateau. Further, drainage into Lake Victoria lacks definition, partly because of dense vegetation, partly owing to the swampy character of the terrain around the lake, so that only a small proportion of the moisture that falls within the basin drains into the lake itself. Evaporation is so active from this broad, shallow water body that not more than one-fourth of the rain that falls into Lake Victoria flows out at Jinja. Although the surface of Victoria Nyanza has a greater magnitude than that of any other African lake, its contribution to the Nile is limited.

The Albert Nile has its sources south of Lake Albert. Again the ultimate beginning is questioned. Is Lake George, receiving many tributaries from the western province of Uganda and flowing through a broad channel into Lake Edward, the ultimate source? Or Lake Edward, which is fed by streams that pour in from all directions, and empties north into Lake Albert through the Semliki River? The Semliki River itself has numerous feeder streams pouring in from the edges of the rift, the most powerful tributaries being those flowing down the Ruwenzori, fed by snows that bury the summits and having such force that they have pushed the river, in a great bow, to the western side of the rift valley. The Ruwenzori are the mythical *Lunae Montes* (Mountains of the Moon) in which, according to ancient legend, were the sacred fountains in which the Nile had its source.

The Nile leaves Uganda at Nimule and enters Sudan. From Bor on and for about half of the distance to Lake No, the river waters mingle with those of the reedy, papyrus-filled sudd, filtering slowly through the morass, and losing about half of their volume through evaporation and seepage.

There is no more formidable swamp in the world than the Sudd. The Nile loses itself in a vast sea of papyrus ferns and rotting vegetation, and in this foetid heat there is a spawning tropical life that can hardly have altered very much since the beginning of the world; it is as primitive and as hostile to man as the Sargasso Sea. Crocodiles and hippopotamuses flop about in the muddy water, mosquitoes and other insects choke the air and . . . weird water-birds keep watch along the banks—except that here there are no ordinary banks, merely chance pools in the forest of apple-green reeds that stretches away in a feathery mass to the horizon. This region is neither land nor water. Year by year the current keeps bringing down more floating vegetation, and packs it into solid chunks perhaps twenty feet thick and strong enough for an elephant to walk on. But then this debris breaks away in islands and forms again in another place, and this is repeated in a thousand indistinguishable patterns and goes on forever.[2]

There are two main currents of water that flow through the sudd from the south, the Bahr el Jebel, which is the main channel, and the Bahr el Zeraf (the River of Giraffes), the latter beginning in the midst of the swamp and flowing north to join the Bahr el Jebel somewhat below Lake No. The Bahr el Ghazal (River of the Antelopes), flowing from the southwest and joining the Bahr el Jebel at Lake No, likewise seeps for part of its course through the morass of the sudd. Tributary to the Bahr el Ghazal is the Bahr el Arab, and into both of these streams, that run perennially from the southwest Congo-Nile water parting, flow "phantom" feeders that drain from the west and northwest into the larger rivers. The Bahr el Ghazal makes the smallest contribution of water to the Nile of any of the large tributaries because it loses an even greater proportion of its water through evaporation and dispersion into the sudd than does the Bahr el Jebel. "Phantom" streams contribute water along the entire Nile system.

From Lake No to the confluence with the Sobat the Nile is braided, but there are two broad, discernible channels; the larger Bahr el Jebel is the southernmost, the smaller on the north is the Lolle. A little east of Lake No, the Sobat joins the Nile and from there the White Nile, as the Bahr el Abyad, con-

tinues north to its confluence with the Bahr el Azraq at Khartoum.

Whatever periodicity of flow that the White Nile has is due almost entirely to the seasonal flooding and recession of the Sobat. The floodwaters of this river, like those of the Blue Nile, result from the rains of the summer monsoon in Ethiopia. Downstream from the junction with its two main tributaries, the Pibor and the Baro, the Sobat drains across an area of very slight gradient. Flooding is frequent during high water and much of the area becomes, like the sudd, a great vegetation-choked swamp through which the Sobat waters merely seep. It takes about three months for water flowing into the swamp to percolate through the morass and emerge at the lower end as a stream with a discernible course. The high floods of the Sobat tend to impound the waters of the Bahr el Jebel south of Lake No, and are in no small way responsible for the sudd.

The greatest of the affluents of the Nile is the Bahr el Azraq, whose headstreams lie entirely within Ethiopian territory. The regime of the Blue Nile and the Sobat are alike. They begin to rise at the end of April and by September have reached flood peak. During this period the Blue Nile carries a volume of water exceeding that of the White Nile by 15 times, forcing the White Nile to pond up above the juncture of the streams at Khartoum for a distance of nearly 300 miles. On the other hand, during the early months of the year, the Bahr el Azraq and the Sobat carry but little water, and during this period the Atbara nearly runs dry.

The Blue Nile originates "very quietly and uneventfully out of Lake Tana (6,000 feet elevation) in the northern highlands of Ethiopia. There is no waterfall or cataract, no definite current, nothing in fact to indicate that a part at least of this gently moving flow is embarked upon a momentous journey to the Mediterranean, 2,750 miles away."[3] It emerges from the southern end of the lake where the

shore line unobtrusively divides into low islands fringed with black lava boulders and overgrown with jungle. [It is quite possible for the traveler to miss it, because]

---

[2] *Ibid.*, p. 85.

[3] Alan Moorehead, *The Blue Nile*, New York: Harper & Row, Publishers, Incorporated, 1962, p. 3.

the grey-green water slips [away] in between. [There are] no villages here, and except for a few fishermen paddling about on their papyrus rafts like water-boatmen in a pond, no civilization at all. The silence is absolute. . . . It is even denied that Lake Tana is the source of the river. There is an argument—indeed it is more than an argument, it is an established and accepted belief—that the river really rises in a swamp called Ghish Abbai, some seventy miles away to the south. From this swamp the Little Abbai river courses down through the Ethiopian plateau to the south-western corner of the lake, and its waters are said to proceed through the lake itself to the opening near Bahardar. . . . All the early maps show the line of the river drawn firmly through the lake. All the latest maps give Ghish Abbai as the source.

But this is a little puzzling. Tana is a very big lake covering over a thousand square miles, with a drainage area five times as large. The Little Abbai, though ad-mittedly the largest tributary, is only one of a number of others, and except for a few months during the rainy season, there is no perceptible current from its mouth to the outlet at Bahardar; its waters become lost in the vast reservoir of the lake. . . .

This is . . . an academic controversy, and the traveller on the Blue Nile (called here the Big Abbai) will be well advised to leave it behind him. . . .[4]

Shortly thereafter the Bahr el Azraq begins the descent from the plateau to the plains through a pro-found gorge that in places is 4,000 feet deep, "boiling . . . turbulently over rocks and shallows." Although this river has its source in Lake Tana, only a small portion of its volume is contributed by the lake itself. Several large tributaries, whose waters are derived from the rains that fall in the catchment basin of the plateau, provide the greater part of the flow.

The volume of water contributed to the main Nile by the various sources varies considerably. On the average about 12 billion cubic meters of water are gathered into the Nile system within a year. Of this approximately two units leave Lakes Albert and Victoria. This, however, is reduced by half in pass-ing through the sudd. The Sobat contributes one unit so that the White Nile at Khartoum carries ap-proximately two units of water; the Blue Nile adds

four units and the Atbara approximately one so that the total volume of the river at the confluence with this last main tributary is seven units.[5] "These are round numbers in which smaller tributaries and ordinary losses incurred in travelling are ignored, but they give the general picture of the relative impor-tance of the largest tributaries."[6] The volume of the river at Khartoum, where the Blue and White Nile come together, is greater than at its mouth.

## The Basin

The river and its tributaries trace a course across a north-south belt of latitude 35° wide. Despite this large latitudinal span the number of climates, but not the contrasts, are small: it flows through equatorial, wet and dry tropical, and tropical desert lands. Con-trasts are not really in temperature but in rainfall. The amount and season of rain in any part of the basin markedly affects the volume of water that is steadily or seasonally contributed to the river. South of Bor the climate is equatorial with maxima of pre-cipitation occurring twice annually, at the time of the equinoxes. However, exposure and elevation also affect the amounts that fall (see Figure 6.5); at high elevations rainfall may reach 75 inches, while places that lie in the rain shadow may receive as little as 30 inches. From Bor north to approximately Khar-toum, rainfall decreases from about 40 or 60 inches in the south to almost none, and dry seasons increase in length from 1 or 2 months to continuous unre-lieved drought the year around; in the northern Sa-hara, where the season of most protracted and pro-nounced drought occurs during the high sun period, traces of rain occur in winter.

In Ethiopia, precipitation is not distributed evenly either geographically or seasonally. In general, annual precipitation on the plateau averages from around 50 inches to more than 75 inches in the loftier areas. Rainfall is concentrated almost entirely during the "big rains" of summertime and comes in the form

[4] Ibid., pp. 3–5. Note similarities to the White Nile head-waters controversy.

[5] After H. E. Hurst, The Nile, London: Constable & Co., Ltd., 1952.

[6] Ibid., p. 8.

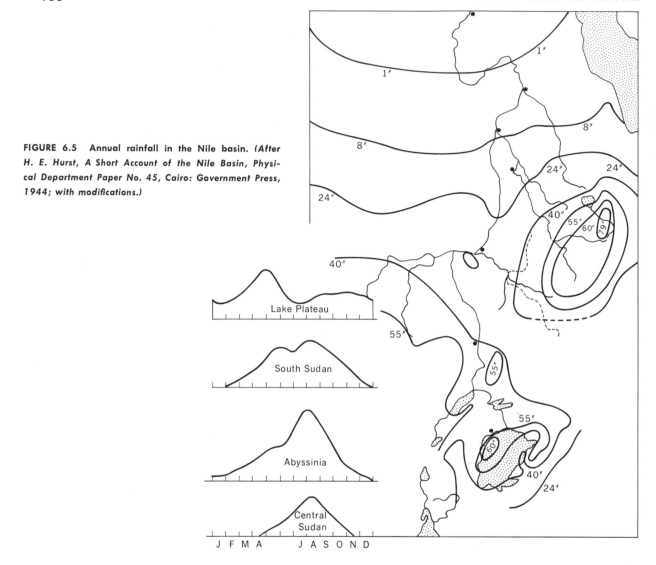

FIGURE 6.5　Annual rainfall in the Nile basin. (After
H. E. Hurst, A Short Account of the Nile Basin, Physical Department Paper No. 45, Cairo: Government Press,
1944; with modifications.)

of violent showers that cause rapid runoff; they are
heaviest in the higher parts. It is these storms that
turn the Blue Nile into raging floods. In winter the
plateau is usually dry except for the orographic rains
of February, called the "little rains," that fall at
higher elevations.

Vegetation follows climate. Where climate is rainy
tropical, forests grow; some of these are montane.
However, in most forested regions encroachment by
man has altered the character of the original cover.
North from the irregular line of the forests up to the
desert, the basin and much of Ethiopia is covered

with savanna of various sorts. In southern Sudan and
in plateau Ethiopia this savanna is in great part comprised of tall grasses spotted with clumps of trees
that are deciduous or semideciduous broadleafs; in
northern Sudan the savanna grass is shorter, and
bushes and acacias replace the larger species found
in the more humid areas; however, on the clay plain,
tall grasses, generally unrelieved by trees, form the
vegetation cover, and in the region of the sudd
papyrus sedge grows thick and high.

The desert areas through which the Nile flows are
generally bereft of vegetation. The vast stretch from

Khartoum north to the sea is almost all desert. *Ergs* alternate with *reg*, or rock platforms; inselbergs stand out sharply; along the east the desertic Etbai Ranges border the Red Sea rift. All combine with the aridity to make the region stark and barren. The only sign of life is the trail of green along the river valley. The country between Khartoum and Wadi Halfa is known as Batn el Hagar, "belly of stones," a phrase descriptive of the surface (Figure 6.6). Along this extensive sector the Nile receives only one permanent tributary, the Atbara, which at flood time is a large muddy river, but during seasons of low rainfall is represented only by a series of pools along the river bed.

The eastern Sahara is even more bleak than the western, if that is possible. And yet, in the east is the greatest of Saharan oases, namely, the valley of the Nile that splits the eastern wastes into the Libyan and Arabian-Nubian deserts. Aside from the Nile valley, the eastern Sahara is like a great desert plain almost without life.

Away from the dissected edges of the Nile valley the relief to the west is marked by little diversity.

Relatively flat plateau surfaces slope gently from the higher interior toward the north, with elevations declining from 1,800 to 600 feet to below sea level in the Quattara depression, at the base of the Libyan plateau in the north; erosion has left south-facing escarpments. The most important of these is the Marmorica escarpment, a great cliff running westward from the Nile delta, along whose base lie the famed Siwa oases and the Quattara depression. Deep-seated supplies of water feed these oases. Because of the character of the Libyan Desert in Egypt, no caravan routes cross its arid wastes except the ancient route that since prehistoric times has followed the line of habitation. Since water does not run, even briefly, across the Libyan Desert to form wadis, this portion of the Sahara is undissected: it is, over immense areas, covered with dunes and is possibly the most dangerous and least known desert in the world.

From the Red Sea edge of the Etbai ranges, the Arabian-Nubian Desert slopes to the Nile. The Etbai block, trenched along its broad back by many wadis, is narrow in the north and widens in the south. The Nile makes its great loop in Nubia around the edges

**FIGURE 6.6** Desert wasteland north of Wadi Halfa. (*Courtesy British Overseas Airways Corporation.*)

of this upland; in the south it merges with the higher Ethiopian plateau. In this portion of its valley the Nile has eroded deep gorges, quite in contrast to the open character of the alluvial valley farther north.

Few tributaries enter the Nile in its course through the Sahara, and only the Atbara runs perennially. From Aswan, on the First Cataract, to Cairo the Nile valley has a length of approximately 600 miles, and from Cairo to the delta front on the Mediterranean Sea is another 150 miles. The delta is monotonously flat. It is building on the seaward side very slowly because most of the precious silt, that formerly at floodtime was carried by the river to its mouth, now is deposited along the way, because of the controlled impounding of the waters and irrigation. The day is likely not far distant when no water will flow from the Nile into the Mediterranean because the High Dam, now in construction will permit control and storage of the excess water that now escapes.

The alluvium of the delta, varying in depth from 50 to 75 feet, is probably the most fertile soil in Africa. Not all of it is being used, however, for along the seaward front the delta is covered with great salt marshes over large areas. Lake Menzala, covering over 800 square miles and the largest, occupies the eastern side of the delta, extending up to the Suez Canal. Egypt expects in time to reclaim this marshland by pumping off the water and sweetening the soil.

The river and the valley it has eroded vary in width, depth, and sharpness of outline from place to place depending upon the character of the surface, the gradient, and the rainfall. From above Khartoum down to Cairo, the river at flood peak is about ½ mile wide; its valley is considerably wider, however. Between Wadi Halfa and Aswan, the valley is less than 2 miles wide, at one place narrowing to 220 yards; but north from Aswan it broadens to 10 to 14 miles and runs like a deep furrow through the desert for 500 miles. Abrupt scarps, up to 1,500 feet, drop from the limestone plateau to the valley. The width of the cultivated strip also varies; from no cultivation, it bulges to the maximum of 12-mile-wide swatches just below Aswan; from Nag Hammadi to the head of the delta, the average is about 10 miles; along the last 200 miles above Cairo the river hugs the east bank, and the cultivated zone lies along the west side

of the valley. Away from the river the valley lands lie untouched because of the stony or sandy character of the strath.

As Cairo is approached the slopes become lower until near the delta they merge into low hills to become scarcely confining escarpments.

## Harnessing and Apportioning of El-Bahr

The dependence of Egypt upon the Nile led to an intense and early study of the volume of water carried by the river, and of the periodicity of its flow. A Nilometer, dating from A.D. 860, is still extant on Roda Island at Cairo and records that go back 220 years earlier also exist, although they are incomplete. However, until the latter part of the last century there was almost no knowledge of the river's sources, and no explanation for the bounteousness and dependability of the Nile floods. Flowing unhampered for millenia, the river inundated the lands along its banks within the valley, making cultivation possible for the relatively small number of farmers who could take advantage of the waters. Carrying silt for hundreds of miles from its wilder courses in the mountains, and depositing the sediments in the lower and more level reaches, the great river provided not only water but fertility to the periodically flooded lands.

As population increased, however, and it became necessary to cultivate land that lay beyond those regions that flooded naturally, man had to invent means by which water could be transferred to ever larger areas of desert. Out of the ancient experiments evolved the waterwheel and other devices for lifting water from the river and channeling it to the fields. Despite their primitive character, these simple means of irrigation are still used, and all along the Nile (north of the humid lands in the south) the curious creak of the waterwheel, as it cumbersomely turns to the slow tread of the bullock or camel, is a familiar sound. The first bold engineering steps taken to control, store, and canalize Nile waters were not taken until the early part of the nineteenth century.

Large scale irrigation, that overcomes the disadvantages of fluctuation in the Nile flow, has come only as a result of planned measures. In Egypt these have been carried out by the government; 80 percent of the cultivated lands have converted from basin to perennial irrigation. In Sudan a unique feat in river control and irrigation was initiated (the Gezira scheme) through the cooperative efforts of the British colonial government, a commercial company, and Sudanese peasants who were at the time seminomadic in their habits. This program is being carried forward and extended by the government of independent Sudan.

The concept of perennial irrigation along the Nile is not new. As pointed out, the controlled application of water to the fields of the fellahin (see Glossary) has been practiced from ancient times, simple lifting devices being used to raise water from the river and wells. But it was not until Mohammed Ali, Viceroy of Egypt, introduced major methods of control that perennial irrigation became large scale. He began in 1816 by improving the river banks, and digging inundation canals to impound some of the floodwater and permit irrigation during periods of lower discharge. The first barrages, which were placed at the head of the delta across the Rosetta and Damietta distributaries, were finished in 1861. These were later enlarged and improved, and another barrage was con-

structed, in 1901, halfway up the Damietta branch. A year later the first great dam, the Aswan at the First Cataract, was completed (Figures 6.7 and 6.8). This permitted the storage of some of the waters during the flood period, and their use when the river was low. From this time on, conversion from basin to perennial irrigation went ahead steadily; additional canals were dug and other barrages constructed; drainage of the salt marshes in the delta also began.

By the early twentieth century, Egypt's canal network had been redesigned to the essential pattern it has today: three large canals feed out of the delta barrage to irrigate the western, central, and eastern sectors of the delta; and, from in back of the barrage at Asyut, the Ibrahimia Canal draws off and distributes water to the lands of Middle Egypt through a channel that parallels the Nile.

The present cultivated area of Egypt is about 6 million acres. However, where perennial irrigation is a feature of the cultivation, water control and the climate permit the raising of two or even three plantings in some places during a year, increasing the total land cropped by half, namely, to about 9 million acres. The High Dam, Sadd el-Aali, now in construc-

**FIGURE 6.7** The Nile of Aswan. The tall sails on the two boats, one lowered and the other raised, are used commonly on the Nile to drive the vessels when winds are favorable. (Photograph by C. Zachary. Courtesy Egyptian State Tourist Administration.)

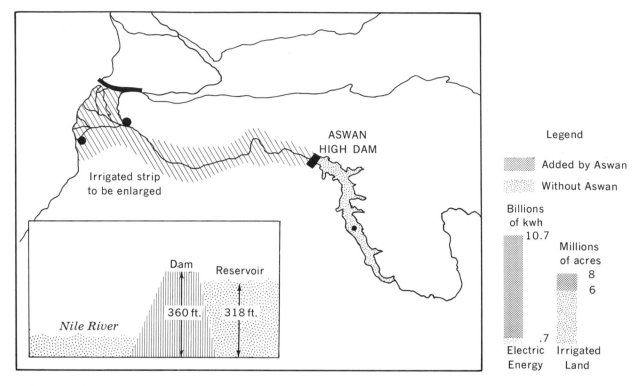

**FIGURE 6.8  The Aswan High Dam. The 300-mile lake will hold three times as much water as Hoover Dam's Lake Mead. (After The New York Times map and diagram, June 24, 1956.)**

tion, will increase this by nearly 2 million acres, thus widening the thin ribbon of green that is productive Egypt. Over 1 million acres of new land are expected to open up for agriculture and some 700,000 acres will be converted from basin to perennial irrigation, permitting more intense utilization.

The question might well be asked: Why does Egypt need a new dam 5 miles away from the one at Aswan?

Aswan Dam can control only 60 percent of the water annually discharged by the river. Through the sluices of Aswan pass all the silt rich floodwaters of summer that rush down from the Ethiopian plateau between June and October; water storage begins only in mid-November when much of the water has run through. The High Dam will make it possible for Egypt to impound and use much of what now flows away to the sea unused. The completion of the dam is not expected before 1970, and the construction of

the irrigation canals and laterals will require another decade. Completed at the same time as the dam will be power and fertilizer plants, the latter with an annual capacity of ½ million tons.

The lake that forms will flood not only cultivated land and villages in Egypt but also in Sudan, for a distance of about 100 miles south of the Egyptian border. One of the difficulties that had to be resolved by Egypt was the problem of compensation to Sudan for this drowned area; another difficulty involved the allocation of Nile waters between the two countries. However, near the close of 1959 Egypt and Sudan reached agreement on both problems. Besides settling a dispute that has kept relations strained between the two countries for a number of years, an accord on the apportionment of the Nile waters also means that additional water will be available for large scale agricultural development programs within both states.

To compensate for damages to Sudanese territory as a result of water storage behind the High Dam, Egypt paid 15 million Sudanese pounds to Sudan. The agreement provides for the creation of a joint Nile Waters Committee to consult and be responsible for all Nile water developments affecting both countries. The agreement also provides for the equal sharing of expenditures on projects to increase the total flow of the Nile as well as the equal sharing of the benefits accruing from these projects.

With the conclusion of the agreement, the government of Sudan was faced with the problem of relocating 50,000 inhabitants of Wadi Halfa, who had to abandon their homes by July, 1963. Shortly thereafter, the government announced that the refugees would be settled in the Khashm El Girba area, on the Atbara River, where a dam would be constructed. A further consequence of obtaining the agreement was the securing of concurrence of the World Bank in financing the completion of Sudan's Managil extension to the Gezira scheme, and the construction of the Roseires Dam.

Until the new accord, the amount of water available to each state was controlled by the 1929 Nile Waters Agreement contracted between Egypt and the United Kingdom; Sudan was not independent then. This agreement gave tacit recognition to Egypt's historic dependence on and rights to the Nile waters by allotting 48 billion cubic meters of the Nile's annual flow of 84 billion to Egypt; Sudan received four billion; the unallocated 32 billion cubic meters ran uninhibited to the Mediterranean. At flood time the Bahr el Azraq carries more water than both Egypt and Sudan can use; by January, however, water is already becoming critical. According to the 1929 agreement, when water ceased to be in surplus Sudan could no longer draw from the river, but had to draw on the water impounded by the Sennar Dam (see Figure 6.9).

The new contract between Egypt and Sudan is dependent upon the completion of Egypt's High Dam. When completed, it will make available 22 billion cubic meters of the 32 billion cubic meters of water formerly unused. The remaining 10 billion are accounted for by evaporation from the vast lake that the High Dam will create. The new quotas give 55.5 billion cubic meters to Egypt, 18.5 billion to Sudan.

One handicap that the new dam imposes is that it will block even more of the silt that was deposited along the valley and in the delta when the river flowed freely, silt that naturally refertilized the land annually for the farmers. Now commercial fertilizer must keep the land productive. A large fertilizer plant to be erected at the High Dam will help to

**FIGURE 6.9 The Sennar Dam on the Blue Nile. (Courtesy Ministry of Information, Sudan Government.)**

offset the loss of the silt, but it makes farming more expensive for the peasant, who even now makes only a bare living.

Sennar Dam is situated on the Blue Nile about 150 miles upstream from Khartoum. On the waters of its reservoir has depended the whole scheme of planned irrigation agriculture in the Sudanese Gezira. The dam not only stores water against the period in the year when all of the natural flow of the Nile must be permitted to run untapped into Egypt, but also raises the level of the river so that water will flow naturally out to the main conduit of the Gezira canal system.

## International Implication of Water Diversion

It is clear from the discussion that the Nile is an international river, and that the allocation of its waters is an international affair implemented through high diplomacy.

The Nile watershed, we have noted, includes parts of several political states other than Egypt and Sudan. Claims for water may one day be put forward by these riparian countries. Some already have development schemes that include both hydroelectric works and irrigation. If these are carried out, the annual flow along the entire length of the river will be affected. In general, it is the feeling of the basin states that the distribution of Nile waters must be internationally agreed upon and that the water requirements of all of the countries affected must be considered in any large plan of water diversion and development.

Until a few years ago it was generally considered that the most suitable place to provide long terms or perennial storage as security against low years was in the lakes of East Africa, because their large basins would mean that a small rise in lake level would greatly increase the reservoir capacity. A major disadvantage, however, was the dissipation of the waters of the Bahr el Jebel, through dispersion and evaporation, as the river made its slow way through the swamps. To take care of this, a diversionary canal through the sudd was suggested. Many contemporary maps show this proposed canal, named the Jonglei, although it has not yet been dug. The Owens Dam below the outlet of the Victoria Nile, for impounding the waters of Victoria Nyanza, has been completed for several years (Figure 6.4), but the great reservoir thus created has no measurable effect upon the waters or upon the regime of the river by the time the Nile reaches Egypt. The Jonglei Canal would need to be completed first, as well as a whole series of accessory projects upon which the success of the Jonglei plan depends. Egypt favored a project that would be entirely under Egyptian control. The High Dam is that project.

Control of the Nile, however, in the last analysis lies with the countries that control the headstreams—where the Egyptian and Sudanese Niles could be cut off at or near their sources. The success of the High Dam depends, therefore, upon the goodwill and co-operation of all the states upriver.

> Ultimately, . . . the creation of a system of complete regulation of the Nile will require the establishment of control works in Ethiopia and Uganda as well as in Egypt and Sudan; their operation will need to be planned and regulated by a single Nile Valley authority, and, as Egypt and Sudan become increasingly dependent on the added water supplies they produce, it will be more necessary for mutual confidence to prevail throughout.[7]

[7] K. M. Barbour, "A New Approach to the Nile Waters Problem," *International Affairs*, vol. XXXIII, no. 3, p. 321, July, 1957.

# 7 EGYPT OF THE UNITED ARAB REPUBLIC

*The higher Nilus swells,*
*The more it promises; as it ebbs,*
  *the seedsman*
*Upon the slime and ooze scatters*
  *his grain,*
*And shortly comes to harvest.*

WILLIAM SHAKESPEARE

## *The Land That Is Egypt*

Egypt—or Misr, in modern Arabic—situated in the northeast corner of the Sahara and Africa, is a country of sharp contrasts within unusual monotony. Within the valley on either side of the river bed stretch the green fields of the fellahin but just beyond, within eyesight on both sides, rise the arid walls of the valley and the dunes of the desert. Were it not for the Nile, those desert sands to the east and west certainly would close in and meet, and there would be no Egypt.

Superficially, Egypt covers a large territory, 386,198 square miles, almost as large an area as Texas and Arizona combined. But the real Egypt, the land upon which the Egyptians live and work, is only a tiny part of the whole, less than 4 percent. The Egyptian domain is a vast desert of sand and gravel, unproductive and uninhabited—but stretching across it is a long, thin ribbon of green, a garden intensively cultivated and densely populated. It is the world's largest oasis in what is part of the world's largest desert.

Here on this wonderfully fertile flood plain, in ancient days life was protected on all sides by great deserts, land was fertilized and watered by the never failing Nile, and a pattern of living was stimulated by the alternate productive and unproductive seasons as determined by the rise and fall of that river's waters. Here in this favored spot rose a great empire with an advanced civilization at a time when Europe and most of the world was a wilderness. Today, it is the home of over 28 million people, most of whom live within sight of the river. Most Egyptians are directly or indirectly dependent upon agriculture, possible because of the beneficence of the Nile; for all Egyptians, the waters of that life-giving stream are absolutely indispensable. Egypt is "the gift of the Nile" as truly today as in ancient days when Herodotus thus characterized the country. It is a land of a single resource—soil made fertile by the Nile silt, but rigidly limited in extent. Minerals are negligible, forests nonexistent.

But the best soil in the world is useless without water, and Egypt is practically rainless. Alexandria, on the coast, has an annual average of 8 inches of

**FIGURE 7.2   Looking across the Sphinx toward the desert. (Photograph by writer.)**

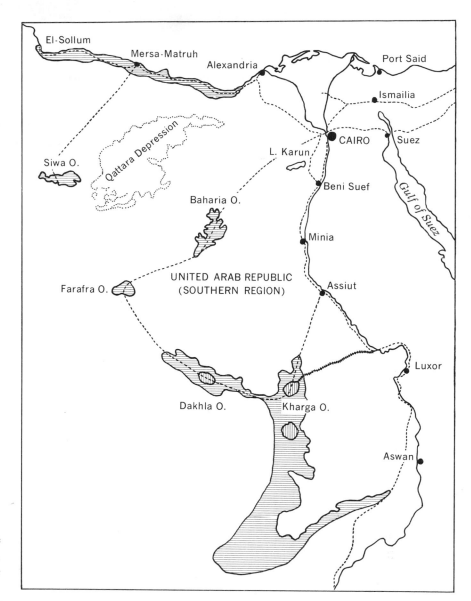

FIGURE 7.3 The five oases of Egypt outside of the Nile Valley. (From *The United Arab Republic Year Book, 1959.*)

rain, Cairo about 1.5 inches; south of the city a shower is rare, as indeed it is in Cairo. Under the high temperature and porous soil conditions prevailing throughout Egypt, this rainfall is of negligible importance. The dependence upon "watering," for the existence of every plant, animal, and person in the country, is both necessary and absolute. Water is the great limiting factor for life. No country and no people of comparable magnitude are so dependent upon a single stream. Cut off the flow of the Nile, and Egypt would perish.

The juxtaposition of so lush and fertile a region to one of such complete barrenness is almost without parallel. The desert breaks off abruptly at the edge of the cultivated strip; an almost knifelike line separates them. In places one can literally stand with one foot on yellow desert, the other in the greenery of an irrigated garden.

Half of the Egyptian frontier borders on water. On the north and east it faces the Mediterranean and Red Seas, and, because the Sinai Peninsula is a part of the Egyptian domain, it fronts along the Gulf of

Aqaba and shares a boundary with Israel. In addition, in accordance with an armistice concluded with Israel in February, 1949 Egypt holds a strip of coast along southwest Israel, namely, the Gaza coast. But the long 1,800-mile seafront runs so smoothly that it offers few harbors. The land boundary on the south blends into the northern deserts of Sudan; in the west the formidable Libyan Desert of Egypt blends imperceptibly into the equally formidable arid lands of Libya; between the Nile valley and the Red Sea lies the desert known as Arabian.

Aside from the lands watered by the Nile, there are only five oases in Egypt to be mentioned (Figure 7.3): Kharga, Dakhla, Farafra, Bahariya, and Siwa; the Faiyûm Oasis, just west of the Nile and deriving its waters from that river, is really a part of the river oasis although separated from it. The Faiyûm occupies a great depression of the Libyan Desert, connecting with the Nile through the Bahr Yusef; in the deepest part of the oasis depression is the Birket Qârûn, a lake whose surface is nearly 150 feet below the level of the Mediterranean Sea.

The Faiyûm has known periods of prosperity and periods of neglect. During the years when Egypt was under Arab and Turkish rulers, the oasis declined; it revived again under the British, and its present population is more than 670,000. The largest city, Madinet-el-Faiyûm, numbers some 100,000 inhabitants. Methods of cultivation and production per feddan compare favorably with those of the Nile Valley. A system of canals leads out from the Bahr Yusef to irrigate the gardens.

Farther away from the Nile Valley the other five oases, all east of the river, are each a tiny spot of green lost in the vastness of the desert, each one separate and distinct, and isolated from all of the others. Although beyond the Nile valley, these oases were known and settled by the Egyptians earlier than 1500 B.C. They are small: Farafra, the smallest, supports fewer than 1,000 people; Dakhla, the largest, fewer than 20,000 persons. Their importance is not to be measured by their size, however, but in their significance as watering places in otherwise barren desert for whatever caravans cross the desert must follow the line of these oases. In the days of the Pharoahs Siwa was more than a desert entrepôt; it was also an important religious center, for the oracle

of Ammon was located here. Caravans, passing east and west between the Nile valley and centers in the central Sahara, traveled generally by way of this oasis.

But Egypt's great oasis is the Nile valley and delta, the most densely settled area in the Middle East and Africa: a narrow valley, generally confined by high cliffs.

## The Egyptians

When Shakespeare wrote of Egypt's most renowned queen that "age cannot wither her, nor custom stale her infinite variety," he might fittingly have applied the words to the realm over which she reigned. Perhaps no land has seen so much history and borne it so well. An endless torrent of forces has swept across Egypt's open frontiers, and up and down its ancient river without severing the historical continuity or destroying the pattern of Egyptian life, age-old harmonies of land, river, and people.

**FIGURE 7.4   Child of the fellahin, Nile delta. (Photograph by writer.)**

From the first moment of its history, Egypt *recorded* the life of ruler and ruled along that long, thin strip of Nile greenery that constitutes nearly all there is of habitable Egypt. Fifty hundred years ago craftsmen incised in stone scenes of everyday life which differ surprisingly little from that led today in a thousand little villages along the edges of the river. After its era of early glory, however, Egypt's progress ceased, and the country stood still for about 4,000 years; in few places on earth would the "advanced" man of 3000 B.C. feel so much at home in the modern world as he would in Egypt south of the delta; a bas-relief, executed about 2500 B.C., would have been relatively up-to-date in A.D. 1900.

The history of Egypt unrolls: more than 2½ millenia of Pharaonic rule, a briefer span of Hellenic and Roman domination, 500 years of Coptic Christianity, long centuries of Islam, the whirlwind advent and departure of Napoleon, the overlordship of Turk and Britain, and finally, national independence succeeded by the overthrow of the monarchy, the political revolution, and the leadership of Nasser, an Egyptian, the first Egyptian to rule Egypt in thousands of years.

## THE FELLAHIN

But the elements of Egypt—soil, river, people—fused in an historical and cultural synthesis that links life 1,000–5,000—years ago with modern Egypt today. History whirled about the Egyptians, but life changed little; the fellahin, friendly, passive, earthy men whose vision seldom lifts beyond the level of the muddy fields they work, remain almost untouched. Blindfolded water buffaloes plod in endless circles around waterwheels on the banks of the Nile and its canals; or with long, monotonous turning of a crank, men lift Nile water into fields with Archimedean screws unchanged for thousands of years. The millions of plowmen and their animals live crowded into mud shelters, jammed into patternless villages on patches of land unsuitable for crops, villages whose mud walls are cracked and baked to the color of dust as they have been since the valley was occupied. More than any other Egyptians, these farmers are the backbone of the country. They are Egypt. They have lived by the soil, and the pulse of the river from the most distant historical past until now.

By the twentieth century, however, the number of Egyptians had so multiplied that population was outrunning food production, shattering some of the harmonious relationships between the people and the valley—as, as a matter of fact, had the irrigation schemes that began in the nineteenth century. Egypt, nonmonarchal, independent, and led by an Egyptian, must now try to restore the proportions by modifying the ancient patterns. Its main effort, and Egypt's "glory of today and hope for tomorrow"[1] is the Aswan High Dam, Sadd el Aali (or al-sudd al-'ali).

The economic base of Egypt is the crops grown by the tillers of the rich soil watered by the Nile. These plowmen, who make up three-fifths of the Egyptians, are poor. They earn, on the average, the equivalent of only 115 United States dollars a year, and survive an average life-span of but 36 years. It is difficult to raise the standard of living and increase the life-span because to do this, production must outrun population increase, and Egyptians are multiplying at a rate of 2.5 to 3 percent per annum. The pressure of population growth and what to do about it constitute Egypt's major economic problems. The cropped lands are intensively cultivated, and even if the government's high hopes for land reclamation and production are met, the population at its present rate of growth will have caught up with or exceeded agricultural gains by the early 1970s. The attempt to meet and keep ahead of the rising needs of the nation is literally a race, which becomes more acute each day, between the expanding population and economic efforts to alleviate population pressure.

. One of the most significant developments in Egypt since the revolution in government was the lifting of the ban on birth control in May, 1962, and the emphasis placed upon family planning as "a necessary means of averting a possibly disastrous population rise" in overpopulated Egypt. If the present pattern of population increase should continue, all efforts to double the national income every 10 years "will have been in vain."[2] Greater and greater dependence upon imports of cereals and livestock appears indicated, and already half of Egypt's wheat consumption is met

---

[1] Gamal Abdel Nasser.

[2] Gamal Abdel Nasser.

through imports; the annual subsidy on basic food-stuffs alone costs the government almost twice the foreign exchange earnings from the Suez Canal.

"Seven years of great plenty are coming for Egypt, but there will be seven years of famine after them and the plenty will all be forgotten in the land of Egypt; famine will consume the land." Thus Joseph interpreted the Pharaoh's dream, and over 3,500 years ago Pharaoh Ramses II, viewing the future in his prophetic dream, instructed Joseph to build a system of grain storage silos forthwith to avert periodic cereal shortages.

The same measures are being taken in Egypt in the 1960s: In 1962 the Egyptian Government initiated the construction of a network of grain storage silos, hoping to alleviate a perennial grain shortage that has remained unsolved since before Ramses' time. The present Minister of Supply, a latter-day Joseph, faces issues that would stagger the ancient Israelite. He directs a vast bureaucracy that intervenes in every household, every shipload of imported cereal, every meat shop, and most grocery shops. Nearly all the commodities that flow into Egypt are channeled through this organization.

But the premonition of hunger is never far away. A shipping strike at United States docks can halt movement of food, as did an East Coast strike early in 1963. The disastrous attack of the cotton leafworm in the 1960s ravaged not only cotton but corn and alfalfa as well. Hunger comes near when the Nile ebbs abnormally and rice fields cannot produce a crop; each time a new child is added to the Egyptian population, it looms closer.

How to eliminate this curse of uncertainty, and the impending worsening relationship between food supply and population? One way is to increase food crop yields; but the Egyptian farmer, in spite of his 5,000 years' experience, still has much to learn from modern technology in tilling the Nile valley; by world standards his yields of corn, wheat, sorghum, and beans, as well as milk and eggs, are not impressive. A second dramatic measure is one already discussed, namely, to increase the cultivable acreage through irrigation based on the Aswan High Dam. A third is the establishment of rural cooperatives, and the regrouping of the fragmented farm plots into larger fields in an attempt to obtain the advantages

of the large-scale farming that was characteristic under the old system of great feudal estates, while still retaining the concept of land ownership by many small landholders. Fellahin retain ownership of their land, but pool their plots with those of adjoining properties into large fields planted to one crop. Cooperative marketing has been introduced. When the cooperative system was initiated, there were about 1.7 million farm properties; they averaged less than 4 acres in size, and many ranged from $\frac{1}{10}$ to $\frac{1}{2}$ acre.

The developments in agriculture are not isolated from industrial planning, for all planning is within one great design; the resources of the nation are being strained to change the condition where the population increase alone consumes almost half of the 5 or 6 percent annual increase in national income as shown in Table. 2. However, the per capita availability of productive land in 1962 will be exceeded in 1972, in spite of the addition of the 2 million acres added through construction of the High Dam. Unless the people are willing to take measures to limit population growth, Egypt's enormous efforts may be merely keeping pace with a moving walk. Egypt's population increase is proportionately one of the largest in the world.

**TABLE 2**

|  | 1959 | 1960 | 1961 | 1962 |
|---|---|---|---|---|
| Population, millions | 25.3 | 26.1 | 26.8 | 27.5 |
| GNP increase, Egyptian pounds, millions | 1.25 | 1.40 | 1.56 | 1.63 |

Sources: International Monetary Fund; McGraw-Hill Department of Economics (1962: 0.35 pound Egyptian = U.S., $1.00).

## THE NOMADS

The gradual transition from total nomadism to a completely sedentary adaptation, in which cultivation replaces the grazing of animals, is a well-known social phenomenon common to many places throughout the world; it has already been noted in the Maghrib. Interesting variations occur, however, caused by local conditions. In Egypt, when nomads assimilate with cultivators, "they are said to have become *fellahin* (singular, *fellah*), a word meaning literally 'tillers of the soil,' but with a cultural social significance beyond this."[3] Because of the forbidding character of its deserts, Egypt has only a few nomads, aside from Bedouins who act as guides and lowly dragomen around the pyramids and other historical sites, and who are a peaceful caravan people of Arab origin.

Historically, however, there have been streams of nomads who have poured across Egypt. Most of the migrants passed through. Of those who remained the greatest number were assimilated to a greater or lesser degree into the sedentary manner of living of the Egyptian irrigation cultivator, but there still are some few true nomads who live on the Sinai Peninsula and in the area just west of the Suez Canal, and between Cyrenaica and the Nile delta where some Libyan Arabs live as migrants; farther south, between the Red Sea and the Nile a small tribe known as the Ma'aza are migrant. All these groups keep camels, and live in the usual black tents woven of camel or goats' hair; all are tribal in organization, each tribe having its own territory, although tribal boundaries are usually contested. To the average Egyptian even the tribal names of these groups are unknown.

The zones used by the true nomads are almost exclusively occupied by migrant groups, and any sedentary peoples found within them live in tiny oases or in monasteries. Some of the former Arabs are now partly sedentary and partly nomadic. These people, occupying land adjacent to the Mediterranean in the delta area, or along the edges of the intensively cultivated strip in the delta and valley, represent varying stages of transition from the nomadic way of life to the sedentary.

So far as the sedentary Egyptians have been concerned, problems associated with nomadic peoples have not come so much from those desert dwellers who live habitually within the bounds of Egypt as from the vast and inexhaustible flow that has poured from the reservoirs of wandering pastoralists who live in the east and west. It is the continuous struggle against the recurrent intrusions that has been problematic during all phases of Egyptian history: with but slight variations, the process of nomadic penetration of Egypt has been more or less the same; the advent of the camel gave them greater mobility. Since the time when the Moslems of Arabia conquered Egypt, most of the nomads have been Arabs. Thus, today, the terms "nomad" and "Arab" are used almost interchangeably, because as the nomad has taken up sedentary life, or even when he became seminomadic, he has come to be regarded as an Egyptian fellah.

## ETHNIC CHARACTER

Although not a part of southwest Asia, Egypt has for 13 centuries been a part of the Arab-Moslem world that started its spread from the Arabian Peninsula. At that time the Asian Arabs were paramount in Islam; today, Egypt is striving for leadership among the Arab nations.

Egypt is a Moslem state and over 91 percent of the Egyptians profess the faith. Of the remainder, a considerable number hold to creeds of various Oriental churches. The largest of these groups and the most influential among non-Moslems are the Copts, descendants of Egyptians who accepted Christianity during the first century; they make up more than 7 percent of the population. About 1 percent profess other Christian creeds; Jews number less than 0.5 percent. Linguistically, the Egyptians are Afro-Asian (Hamitic, or Hamitic-Semitic); they speak Arabic. "North Africa was at one time Hamitic, but in the past thousand years Hamitic has yielded ground before Semitic, owing to the spread of Arabic in Moslem Africa."[4]

Not until Egypt adopted the new constitution in 1956 did the country finally acknowledge itself as an Arab state. Since then it has clearly captured the imagination of other Arab and Moslem lands by its successful deposition of a dissolute monarchy and by the conception and implementation of remarkable measures for the modernization of the country.

---

[3] Mohamed Awad, "The Assimilation of Nomads in Egypt," *Geographical Review*, vol. XLIV, no. 2, pp. 242–253, April, 1954.

[4] A. L. Kroeber, *Anthropology*, New York: Harcourt, Brace & World, Inc., 1948, p. 214.

Despite the repeated incursions of wandering pastoralists on their territory, the Egyptians are a singularly homogeneous people. This is likely due to two things: the progressive assimilation of nomadic groups who inhabited the zone next to the cultivated lands (according to Awad, new nomads moved in to replace those that became assimilated, in turn to be gradually absorbed); and the proximity in which Egyptian lives to Egyptian because of the limited zone that is habitable. The imposition of a way of life by the river also contributed: the Nile is both bountiful and demanding; it suggested a way of life, in fact, made living possible in Egypt, but "the price for livelihood was a lifetime of unremitting toil." The fertile valley counterpoised against the implacable desert turned all life toward the river; "the desert was not a challenge to be conquered but an enemy to be held back."[5]

Today, about 60 percent of the Egyptians are farmers, producing approximately one-third of the national income.

[5] George B. Cressey, *Crossroads*, Philadelphia: J. B. Lippincott Company, 1960, p. 349.

## URBAN LIFE: CITIES OF EGYPT

Urban life in the valley is of great antiquity. The ruins of ancient cities, the monuments and tombs of Pharaohs and their nobility, the sphinxes and pyramids, all bear witness to urban antiquity. Thebes, Karnak, and Luxor in Upper Egypt had few rivals in the ancient world; in the delta, Memphis, capital of the Pharaohs, was built. Its site is on the left bank of the Nile about 14 miles south of Egypt's present capital, Cairo. Five miles downstream from Cairo are the ruins of Heliopolis, ancient holy city dedicated to the worship of the sun god, Ra. The contemporary great urban centers of Egypt are Cairo and Alexandria, and with the exception of Asyut in Upper Egypt, Port Said and Suez at the ends of the Canal, and the Faiyûm oasis, all urban centers of 100,000 people or over are situated on or near the delta.

Cairo (El-Qahira), with a population of over 3½ million, is the largest city not only of Egypt but of Africa and the Middle East as well (see Figure 7.5). Its site, however, is quite limited. From the Moqattam Hills on which the citadel stands dominating the

FIGURE 7.5 Modern Cairo along the Nile River. (Photograph by Sobhi Afifi. Courtesy Egyptian State Tourist Administration.)

FIGURE 7.6 The citadel, El-Kala on a spur of the Moqattam Hills, dominates Cairo. It was built by Saladin, Sultan of Egypt from A.D. 1174 to 1193. Crusaders from Western Europe, captured by Saladin's armies in the battles over Jerusalem, were employed in its construction. (Courtesy Egyptian State Tourist Administration.)

capital (Figure 7.6), Cairo extends north along the river for about 5 miles, old Cairo along the eastern side of the Nile, modern Cairo on the west bank. Situated at the apex of the delta, the city has a commanding position because it marks the converging point for delta routes of rail, river, and road traffic that move south into Upper Egypt, and for railroads, roads, and desert trails passing east and west. Delta traffic has been forced south of the apex, through Cairo, because of the barrier to transportation of the innumerable drainage channels, including the distributaries of the Nile itself. Although founded in A.D. 969, the city was not made the capital until 1863.

Cairo's population is motley—Moslem, Coptic Christian, Jewish—and includes Egyptians, Arabs, Syrians, Armenians, black Africans, and their mixtures. Because of its limited area, congestion is very bad, especially in the old city. Like other cities of North Africa and the Middle East, however, it has its modern and ultramodern structures also; contrasts within the city are extreme.

Alexandria, Egypt's second city and great port, was founded in 332 B.C. by Alexander the Great when the Macedonian conqueror entered Africa. The site is advantageous; it stands on the seafront at the northwestern tip of the delta, out of reach of silt-depositing waters; it is protected from the lashing of the Mediterranean by the Isle of Pharos, now connected to the mainland by an isthmus of sand ½ mile in width. The capital of Egypt for nearly 2,000 years, Alexandria was embellished with libraries, museums, theatres, the Pharos, a lighthouse long regarded as one of the Seven Wonders of the World, and other edifices that made it not only a beautiful city, but an intellectual center as well.

Port Said and Suez serve the Suez Canal, as does Ismailia, terminus of the freshwater canal from the Nile River.

## Livelihood

### AGRICULTURE

Agriculture is the base of the Egyptian economy. About four-fifths of this cultivation is subsistence; the rest is devoted to cotton.

Egyptian farming depends upon irrigation, and in the present day three types are practiced: inundation, or basin irrigation, under which the land is annually flooded as the river overflows; the perennial system, characterized by dams that impound and an intricate network of canals that distribute the water; and "lift" irrigation, which in various forms is widespread but contributes relatively little in actual acreage.[6]

There are three crop seasons. Between February and May the *Seifi* (summer season) crops such as cotton, sugar cane, rice, corn, peanuts, sesame, and vegetables are sown, and harvested until September. The *Nili* (Nile or flood season) crops are normally planted in July, during the period of Nile flooding, and harvested in the late fall; they include "flood rice," corn, and millet. The winter, or *Shitwi* crops are the dry cereals such as wheat, barley, flax, the pulses such as beans, clover, and peanuts, and some vegetables, grown between October and June. Seasons often overlap, however, and new crops are frequently sown before those of the previous season are harvested; in this way, the delta lands produce two harvests a year—sometimes, if crops are carefully selected, even three crops.

Cotton, long-staple and fine, is supreme in Egyptian agriculture; it is the leading commercial crop. Corn and wheat are the two most important bread grains, corn being the staple starch of the fellahin, wheat of the urban dwellers. The Egyptian Arabic word for bread is *'aish*, meaning life or living, appropriate because grain (bread) is the symbol of security for the great masses of the populace. Two other starch grains grown are barley and sorghum, but normally these are used mainly as feed; rice is also a staple of Egyptian diet and a crop that has expanded rapidly, rising by one half in less than a decade.

Dry legumes such as lentils, chickpeas, horse beans, and the like are important; vegetables grow abundantly in all seasons; onions are exported. Vegetable fat producers such as sesame, peanuts, flaxseed, and cottonseed, a by-product of cotton linters production, constitute particularly important food items, making up for the shortage of animal fats; they also are industrially used. Berseem (Egyptian clover), Egypt's leading forage crop, grows luxuriantly, producing one to four cuttings annually, and occupying one-fifth of the cultivated acreage.

[6] Douglas D. Crary, "Irrigation and Land Use in Zeniya Bahari, Upper Egypt," *Geographical Review*, vol. XXXIX, no. 4, p. 568, October, 1949.

Domestic animals are limited in numbers because it is not possible to use land exclusively for pasturage. Men and animals compete for the products of the soil, and in Egypt it is cheaper to consume crops directly than to convert them into meat and other animal products. The water buffalo cow (*gamoosa*) is undoubtedly the most important domestic animal economically; immune to most pests and diseases, it is a hardy draft animal and a good milk producer raised in lieu of cattle because of its dual function.

Agricultural techniques in Egypt are a peculiar combination of the ancient and the modern. The hand sickle, the threshing board, the wooden plow, the shaduf and the ox-drawn waterwheel exist side by side with great engineering works for irrigation, the disc plow, the tractor, and the combine. Lack of knowledge by the fellahin of the principles of plant and animal breeding, and of pest and disease control, stands in striking contrast to up-to-date government-sponsored projects. Nonetheless, Egyptian agriculture still "rests fundamentally upon the fellah with the hoe," and flourishes primarily because of manual labor which is abundant and cheap. Whether it is efficient or not depends upon the point of view; the acreage yield is high, but the per capita output is very low.

Nitrogenous fertilizer, of which Egypt is the eighth largest consumer in the world, is a most important expense that has been added to cultivation in recent decades. Until now most of this has had to be imported. Since it is needed to maintain the fertility of the soil under the system of perennial irrigation, as that system expands the need for nitrogen becomes more critical. A water electrolysis plant, for the production of calcium-ammonium-nitrate fertilizer at Aswan, started the first four of its eventual seven production lines in May, 1960.

## MINERALS AND INDUSTRY

Although the handicrafts have flourished in Egypt from very ancient times, it is only since the revolution that modern industry and mining have had their beginnings.

None of Egypt's mineral assets seem to be of major importance, but they are varied. Most occur between the Red Sea and the river. Oil, discovered on both sides of the Gulf of Suez on the Sinai

Peninsula and in the Arabian Desert of Egypt, is Egypt's major fuel. The development of the fields led to the refining of oil products at Suez and the construction of an oil pipeline to Cairo. However, Egypt is unable to supply all that it requires, and imports are in excess of what the country itself produces. Phosphates, Egypt's second mineral, are mined in the eastern hills along the Red Sea out of Hurghada, as well as west of the Nile to the southwest of Luxor. Some are used for conversion to superphosphate for fertilizing the land; about half of the phosphate produced is exported.

Iron ore occurs, and is the base for a small pig and steel industry at Helwan, Egypt's first step into iron and steel. Egypt has no coal, and coke must be imported to supply the fuel; hematite, from opencut deposits at Aswan that average about 42 percent iron, is shipped to Helwan. Other scattered iron reserves occur in the eastern desert and on the Sinai Peninsula, and a rich deposit of limonite has been discovered in the Bahariya Oasis, about 120 miles southwest of Cairo. The development of the latter reserve would require laying a railroad the entire distance, however; this is considered impractical at present because the terrain is covered with shifting sand dunes. Manganese, tungsten, gold, silver, zinc, lead, and copper are known; salt and other products of evaporation are extracted and exported. The most important producing area for salt is along the delta front.

The hydroelectric potential of the Egyptian Nile waters has been partially developed, and will be greatly increased when the High Dam is completed. Another hydroelectric project of some imagination is being considered to the north and west. This time it is not a river to be dammed, but a vast depressed waste of sand, roughly the size of Massachusetts, to be converted into a lake, namely, the Quattara depression. It lies about 40 miles from the seacoast and some 130 miles west of Cairo; at its deepest point, it reaches 440 feet below sea level, with average depths to about 180 feet. An Egyptian dream, the development would require that a ditch be excavated through the desert to the Mediterranean; through this channel, seawater would rush inland and create a source of power in the plunge into the depression. In time, Egypt would have a lake the size of Lake Ontario.

It would take about 30 years for the depression to fill, after which the inflow would be controlled, depending upon the rate of evaporation. It is estimated that the water, dropping down the cliff through turbines into the depression, could generate nearly 3 billion kilowatt-hours of electricity a year; for about a century Lake Quattara could support a fishing industry, and after that, the lake bottom could be mined for crystallized salts. German engineers are investigating this project.

Egypt must industrialize to live. All along the Nile, but especially in the Cairo area, plants are rising, producing freight cars, copper and aluminum plates, paper from bagasse and rice straw, cane and beet sugar, tires, and clothing. Along the road to the pyramids, factories turn out chemicals and pharmaceuticals; a porcelain plant has arisen at Shuba; Alexandria has new shipyards, and Suez a plant for the production of superphosphate.

Among her manufactures, textiles are important, and Egypt has one of the largest textile plants in the world located about 150 miles out of Cairo. A quarter of a century ago long-staple cotton was exported to Great Britain to be made into textiles, then reimported by Egypt as woven goods at high prices. Now Egyptian mills produce millions of yards of cotton cloth and millions of pounds of cotton yarn; about 1950 they also began to mass-produce wool yarn and textiles.

## SOCIALIZATION OF THE ECONOMY

A large part of the economy of Egypt has been socialized under sweeping changes initiated in 1961 and termed by President Nasser "Arab socialism," lately, more often called "scientific socialism."

One of the first acts was land reform involving the confiscation of properties of large landowners, and their distribution among landless peasants, 5 to 10 acres per family. Under the policy implemented, no person can own more than 100 acres of land. The move affected about 5,200 landowners who had to give up some 300,000 acres of land. In the same year, complete government control was ordered for 90 percent of what Egyptian economists call "the organized sector of the economy," namely, all businesses except retail outlets, artisans, and small-scale enterprises. The decrees affected about a third of the total economy, including agriculture, and about 70 percent of industrial production; the cotton industry was nationalized, and complete regulation over production, prices, and exports was instituted. Egypt's two largest banks, the National Bank of Egypt and the Bank Misr, were nationalized in 1960, and in 1961 all other banks, all insurance companies, utilities, and other enterprises "deemed essential" were put under state control.

Private property is still an important part of the "Arab socialism," however. Peasants own their land, but work cooperatively; properties are confiscated, but owners are compensated. Arab socialism is a unique plan, and an interesting experiment. Egypt's system might well serve as a pattern for other Middle East nations.

## *Geopolitics*

### THE SUEZ CANAL

Egypt straddles the Isthmus of Suez, that thread of land that connects two continents and separates two seas (or two oceans, in the most extended view). That is, it did until the Suez Canal placed a rift of water between the continents and connected the seas. Here, at Suez in Egypt, the Atlantic and Indian Oceans have thrust long narrow extensions far into the midst of the greatest landmass in the world, and with the building of the canal, they were connected to form the world's most important water passage.

Contacts have always been extended in all directions by Egypt, but those with the greatest international significance reach north and east. The Isthmus of Suez had formed a land bridge across which millions of people moved between Asia and Africa over millenia. It alternatively served as the military road along which Egypt penetrated Palestine and the lands beyond, and the avenue for the invasion of Egypt from the east by Persians, Israelites, Greeks, Arabs, and others. The flux of pastoral wanderers used this path. Biblical history records its importance. With the digging of the canal, that slender waterway took on equally great importance, becoming the north-

south gateway between the Orient and Europe. Control of the canal gives control of the water route. It was nationalized by Egypt in July, 1956.

The canal opened in 1869; internationally owned by a French company in which Great Britain was the majority shareholder, it was to allow unimpeded passage to ships of all nations. Running through Egyptian territory, the canal was to pass to Egyptian ownership in 100 years. Under the Suez Canal Convention of October, 1888, which became fully effective in 1904 by a Franco-British declaration, protection of the canal was entrusted to the Egyptian government in the first place and to the Ottoman government in the second; in actuality, it did not work out that way because the British army was in occupation of Egypt. Later Egypt was made a British protectorate, and when the treaty of Lausanne in 1923 officially declared Turkish suzerainty at an end, Britain was left in control of the canal.

In 1951 Egypt became a state independent of outside control, and with the withdrawal of British troops from the Canal Zone in 1955—the last British to depart from Egyptian soil—jurisdiction over Suez passed to Egypt, 14 years before the appointed time.

From the outset it was apparent how advantageous was the canal. It shortened the long route from Europe to the Orient by some 4,000 to 5,000 miles, completely reorienting ocean transport between Asia and Europe and becoming a most important link in the "British lifeline" at a time when Britain was an empire and ruler of the oceans. The Suez Canal was one of the most remarkable changes that man has imposed upon geography. Where before the isthmus had connected two continents and separated the seas, the canal severed the ancient connection and joined the waters. The reorientation of trade brought about by the Suez has never been matched. The 101-mile canal apparently traces what was formerly an extension of the Gulf of Suez that later dried up "leaving salty depressions until the canal filled them in," namely, the Bitter Lakes and Lake Timsah (Lake of the Crocodiles—so named, although there are none today). The freshwater canal, dug from the Nile to Ismailia in the 1860s to supply men working on Suez construction, now irrigates some 70,000 acres of cotton, wheat, and dates. Isma'iliya (Egyptian spelling) means the "emerald of the desert."

The Suez Canal is still being dug, because without constant dredging, it would become a filled-in dry ditch; the sides are constantly eroded by wave action; winds continually fill in sand. Ships must be conveyed through the canal because it accommodates, in general, only one way traffic: the canal appears to be wide enough to allow two ships to pass, but it is not deep enough along the edges. Ships pass along the middle of the channel, and when a convoy comes through, ships passing in the opposite direction must wait their turn in bypasses. The Ballah Bypass is the first one south of Port Said. Lake Timsah and Great Bitter Lakes also have bypasses, but beyond there to Port Taufig there are none. Maximum sailing speed is 7½ knots so as to "control bank-eroding turbulence caused by moving ships." The canal has no locks. A loan for the deepening, widening, and general improvement of the canal and Port Said was granted to Egypt in 1957, improvements that permit the canal to take ships up to 37-foot draft.

Cargo moving north has always been in excess of that moving south, because of the large shipments of raw materials to European ports. Since the opening of the canal, Great Britain has each year been the biggest shipper, although the proportion is declining. Commercially, the canal is of little significance to Egypt itself because most Egyptian traffic moves north and south, and out of the country through Alexandria and thence through Gibraltar; however, it brings in revenue.

## GAZA AND THE SINAI PENINSULA

Egypt's territories reach beyond the isthmus, across the Sinai Peninsula to the Gulf of Aqaba and to the Gaza Strip in the northeast. Although only 25 miles long and an average of 5 miles wide, the Gaza Strip cuts off a part of the coast that Israel considers its own. Here an Egyptian military government rules about 312,000 Arab people, of whom more than two-thirds are refugees driven into Gaza's sandy and desolate shelter by the war in Israel.

Gaza has seen violent days almost ever since man's earliest advent into the Middle East. From here the Philistines operated against the Israelites; here Samson brought down the temple in his epic show of strength; the Gaza Road, part of that easy,

ancient intercontinental corridor across the Isthmus, has resounded to the pounding legions of Pharaohs, Babylon, Assyria, Persia, Alexander of Macedon, Crusaders, Turks, Arabs, and British.

Most of Gaza is "a barren, unrewarding land," scorched by the sun, seldom refreshed by rain. In the north there are a few small areas of fertile soil in which grains, pulses, and orange and olive trees grow well, but the proportion of cultivable land to the total area is very small, and life for its inhabitants is correspondingly harsh. It is from the deep waters offshore that the men of Gaza have historically gained their livelihood, and sardines are still one of the main food sources of Gaza. Before the coming of the refugees, there were approximately 95,000 inhabitants. Only an armistice line, not a permanent boundary, separates Egypt from Israel along the Gaza Strip.

The triangle of Sinai stretches south from Gaza and the Mediterranean Sea, bordered in the south by two narrow gulfs that merge at the apex of the peninsula with the Red Sea, namely, the Gulf of Aqaba to the east and the Gulf of Suez on the west. The head of the Gulf of Aqaba is shared by Israel and Jordan, each holding approximately a 5-mile frontage. Control over the waterway—the only direct outlet to the sea for Jordan, and the only outlet to the Indian Ocean aside from a transit of the Suez Canal for Israel—is exercised by Egypt and Arabia-Yemen, holding the west and east shores respectively. Blockade of the gulf can be achieved through control of the small island of Tiran, which is situated just beyond the outlet narrows and held by Egypt. However, the Gulf of Aqaba is only a "backdoor" to the Levant; its use is economic only if ports on the Mediterranean are closed to Israel and Jordan.

## THE UNITED ARAB REPUBLIC

Egypt became the United Arab Republic in 1958 when it joined Syria in a federation. In 1959 Yemen became a member but shortly thereafter withdrew again. This is not the first time that Egypt had sought to unite Middle Eastern lands politically with her own along the Nile: 1,500 years before the Christian era, Egypt had entered the Middle East to conquer Syria and most of the lands immediately adjacent to the eastern end of the Mediterranean Sea, except Phoenicia and Canaan, all the way up into what constitutes Turkish territory today.

Egypt has always been more Middle Eastern than African. Religion, language, culture, and blood make it a part of the Arab-Islamic world; historically, except for penetrations along the Nile into lands immediately to the south, even most of her political and economic ties have been with southwest Asian nations. The history of conquest and counterconquest, ties and counterties extends across the centuries. Egypt has been integral in the affairs of the lands that lay beyond Suez, sometimes as a leader, sometimes as the conquered one, as during the many centuries just prior to the last quarter century.

During the era of British control the Middle Eastern ties lay dormant, but after independence, and more especially after the overthrow of the monarchy, Egypt began once more to evince its feeling of kinship with and reassert its interest in southwest Asia. Egypt was an initial signer of the pact of the Arab League, formed in 1945, and in this organization the nation has gradually advanced to a position of leadership. Its major attempt toward political integration among the Arab states has been in the formation of the United Arab Republic. This federation was short-lived because Syria broke away in 1961. Egypt retained the name although it was the only constituent unit of the Republic.

Another attempt at federation was made in April, 1963, when leaders of Egypt, Syria, and Iraq signed a charter forming the three nations into a new United Arab Republic, with a federal government designed along the lines of the United States. They adopted a single flag, with the red, white, and black horizontal stripes of the former republic but with three stars instead of two; persons from each of the countries should be permitted to visit any of the other two without visas. That was as far as positive union went —in the words of President Nasser, "threads as thin as a spider's web." The republic did not even get started; Baathists in Syria and Iraq resisted federation, and all plans for the tripartite union appear to be at least temporarily suspended. The United Arab Republic once again is made up only of Egypt.

# 8 SUDAN

*Regular as sun and moon, it
rises and falls again. The hour
comes when all the springs of
the world must pay tribute to
the king of rivers. . . .*

AMR IBN EL AS

## Sudan and the Sudanese

More than any other African country, Sudan personifies the dual character of the continent. The nation stretches from less than 4 to 22°N, from tropical forests into desert, from black Africa into the Arab-Moslem world, a part of that great intermediate belt that straddles the continent east and west roughly from the base of the Ethiopian foothills to the Atlantic, 4,000 miles away. Its population is an ethnographic mélange, a strange meeting ground of Arab and African; in Sudan, the Middle East ends and Africa begins. It is a marchland, but it is not a melting pot.

Geographically and culturally, Sudan falls into two parts. North of approximately the twelfth parallel stretches a country of savanna and desert, the latter part of the great North African Libyan-Arabian desert, inhabited in the majority by Nubians and the Beja tribes, Hamitic- and Arabic-speaking Moslems, and culturally a part of the Islamic world. There rainfall is scanty, and there is a great shortage of arable land. Many of the people are camel-owning nomads; the only cultivation is irrigated. South of the twelfth parallel is the area from which the country gets its name, Sudan, meaning "country of the Blacks." It is inhabited by a variety of primitive and non-Moslem black African tribes including some of the Nilotes, famed cattle breeders.

Sudan has been characterized as not one nation but many for it is multilingual (Figure 8.2) and multiethnic. The most marked contrasts are religious and cultural. There are, however, racial differences, as between the riverain Nubians, a mixed Caucasian-Negro people who have inhabited the Dongala-Wadi Halfa area; the Hamitic (Arab-type) camel-owning Bejas of Kassala Province; the Baggara of central Sudan, who are a mixture of Arab and Negroid stocks; and the Nilotic black Africans of the southern provinces.

More important than race, however, are the cultural and religious differences that derive from the Islamization and Arabization of the northern provinces. The tribes of the southern provinces speak African languages, are mostly pagan, and possess backward cultures and social organizations; their economy is subsistence. Any feeling of closeness or relationship that these southern Sudanese have to other African peoples are with those adjacent in Uganda, The Congo, and Kenya; the north, related to the Arab world, is alien to them.

The Sudanese number some 13 million, of whom approximately two-fifths claim membership in Arab tribes. Over 100 Sudanese languages and dialects are characterized as indigenous, but Arabic is the language at home for over half of the people. Of those who speak non-Arabic languages, about one-fifth "appear to be" Nilotic, the largest single native group.[1] Foreigners are few in number. Among them are a number who have paused in Sudan to earn money while making their pilgrimage to Mecca for Sudan lies on the ancient and much-traveled route along which African Moslems from farther west move endlessly to Mecca, many on foot and taking years for the journey.

Population density is low (Figure 8.3), and the Sudanese are distributed very unevenly across the country, with half of them living on one-seventh of the domain. Two provinces, Blue Nile and Khartoum, stand out as relatively dense. Blue Nile Province is the locale of the Gezira development, and Khartoum holds the "Three Towns" of Khartoum, Omdurman, and Khartoum North, "the major urban nucleus of the country." As between the north and south, the southern half of the country has the highest population density, in spite of the fact that all the larger towns lie north of a center dividing line. The birthrate is also higher in the south so that unless the migration of southerners to the north becomes intensified and shifts the center of population gravity northward, the density gravity line must move south. This becomes more certain as a decline in the mortality rate of the south is expected.

These facts have economic overtones because the highest densities are in the most backward sectors, the lowest in the more advanced (aside from the clustering in the tricity area and in the Gezira). Sudan is over nine-tenths rural, partly sedentary,

[1] *Population of Sudan*, Khartoum: Philosophical Society of Sudan, 1958, p. 37.

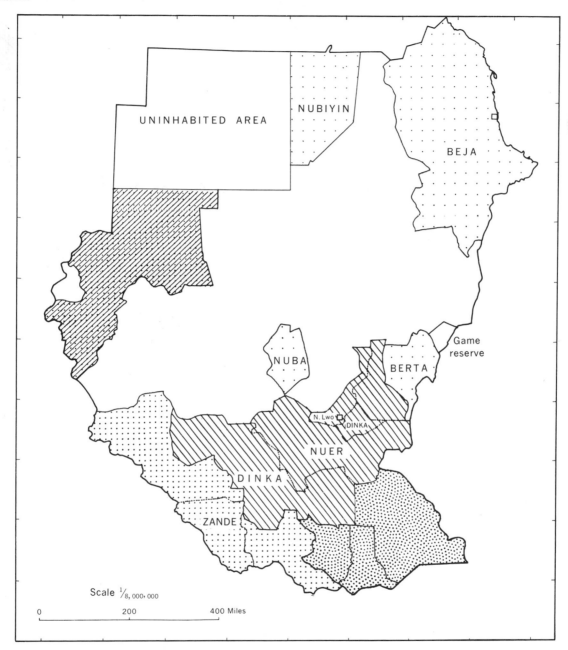

FIGURE 8.2 Language in Sudan. (Courtesy Ministry of Information, Sudan Government.)

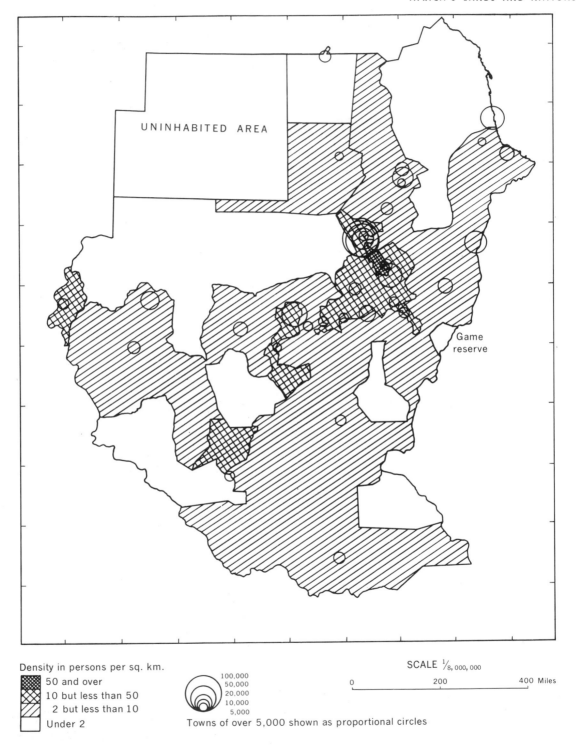

Density in persons per sq. km.

50 and over
10 but less than 50
2 but less than 10
Under 2

100,000
50,000
20,000
10,000
5,000

Towns of over 5,000 shown as proportional circles

SCALE ⅛,₀₀₀,₀₀₀

0          200          400 Miles

FIGURE 8.3 Population density in Sudan. (Courtesy Ministry of Information, Sudan Government.)

partly nomadic with perhaps 78 percent of the Sudanese classifying as sedentary, or sedentary part of the year, although anything between 15 and 40 percent could be classified as nomadic.

## The Land and the Rivers

From the southern boundary, the Sudanese landscape changes from tropical forests and woodland savannas through vast swamplands to open semitropical savannas and scrublands eventually to the sands and arid hills along the Red Sea and the Libyan and Nubian deserts.

Across all these diverse regions the White Nile, main stream of the river, flows from south to north along a course some 2,140 miles long. It is joined within Sudan by its four greatest tributaries, the Bahr el Ghazal, the Sobat, the Bahr el Azraq, and the Atbara; the sudd, swamp of the Nile, occupies much of southern Sudan. The Sudanese Nile is exotic to Sudan because it draws all its waters, except those of the Bahr el Ghazal, from foreign sources. It is, nevertheless, a phenomenon incomparable to the Niles of any of the other countries through which the river passes. In Sudan, all waters from all the divergent sources are gathered to move from Khartoum on as one majestic stream joined thereafter only by the Atbara.

Cataracts in the north and reed-choked swamps in the south have made the river difficult to travel. Nevertheless alien invasions ever since the Pharaohs have generally followed the course of the Nile southward until they reached the swamps of the Bahr el Ghazal and the Bahr el Jebel, the sudd. There they stopped. Ethnography and history in Sudan have from historic times been governed by two factors of about equal significance, namely, the White Nile's importance to communication and agriculture, and the cultural disparity and religious differences between the peoples of the north and south, an ethnic, cultural, and racial disparity that in large part can be attributed to the impassability of the sudd, which kept the south free of invasion. When, eventually, Arabs and others did make their way into southern Sudan, they came in from the east coast opposite Zanzibar.

Very different from the south is northern Sudan—desert but, as in Egypt, dividing into two parts, desert and valley. The Nubian Desert of Sudan, east of the valley, is almost completely arid, its surface *reg* or *erg*, the latter frequently in dunes or drifts. Almost no oases occur because underground supplies of water are scarce; only in some of the few wadis is water obtainable in small amounts. But these few watering points have been historically very important because they made it possible for caravans to pass that way. If anything, the Libyan Desert of Sudan, west of the Nile valley, has even less rain than the Nubian. This is reflected in the near absence of water sculpture in the landscape. Whereas a number of oases occur in the Libyan Desert of Egypt, they are rarer in Sudan; Selima and Bir en Natrun are the largest. Even these are too small to support a settlement of cultivators; they are military outposts, and watering places for caravans.

The valley of the Sudanese Nile is not wide, seldom more than 1 to 1¼ miles. It varies from place to place and the width of the cultivable strip varies accordingly. Nor is the valley by any means inhabited and cultivated continuously; there are extensive sectors that lie untouched. Vegetation along the edges of the river is uniform except that it is more luxuriant in open stretches that have not been cleared for farming; date palms are outstanding among the indigenous plants grown, but they decrease in number southward, and production is variable. Dates have been cultivated within this valley since the Second or Third Egyptian Dynasty.

Five of the cataracts of the Nile lie within Sudan, the Sixth and most southern being just above Shendi, the Second Cataract in the extreme north just south of what was Wadi Halfa. The Nile divides into reaches, largely from cataract to cataract. From the south, the Sixth Cataract falls along the lower part of the steep-walled Sabaloka Gorge, and between there and the Fifth Cataract is a broad portion of valley near the ends of which lie Shendi and Berber. This is a densely populated sector, and within this reach lies Atbara, its situation somewhat resembling that of Khartoum North because it is not within but just south of the confluence of the Atbara with the Nile. The Atbara River at this point has been bridged since 1899, and before this, Atbara city had already been selected as the headquarters for the Sudan railroad.

From the Fifth Cataract to Karima, on the west side of the big band of the Nile and just north of the Fourth Cataract, the valley is narrow and confined between precipitous slopes; only occasionally fertile terraces allow cultivation. But beyond Karima, and to Kerma just south of the Third Cataract, the valley is broad and open, and the river is bordered by alluviums along both banks; within this reach lie Merowe and Dongola. From Kerma north to the Second Cataract, the course of the Nile is winding and full of curves; many small rapids and other obstructions interfere with navigation. The last small sector of valley in Sudan, from just north of the cataract to Faras, again opens out, and the slopes become less steep. Generally speaking, this cataract infested stretch of the Nile is unnavigable, although river traffic is carried on in suitable places. Elevations along the Nile reaches between the Sixth and Second Cataracts drop 824 feet within a distance of 875 miles. Where railroads parallel the river, towns tend to be along the east bank of the Nile; elsewhere, they are on either bank. Diesel ferries cross the Nile at Merowe, Dongola, and other points to assist motor transport.

Two features of Sudanese relief are remarkable, namely, the seeming unvarying character of the terrain and the dominance of the Nile system in the drainage pattern. Between Khartoum and Juba, a distance of about 750 miles, the land rises by less than 300 feet, stretching away monotonously flat to well beyond the southern edge of the sudd. Even in the Qoz, the rolling sand country of the western provinces where dunes are characteristic, there are many wide stretches that are nearly flat or show but slight relief.

Sudan is like a basin, cradled among higher lands that lie along all edges except in the north. Most watercourses feed in toward the interior of the country, whether they originate outside Sudan or within it. The only exception to this, other than a few intermittent streams that sometimes flow down the Red Sea hills into the Red Sea or feed into the Nile across the Sudan-Egyptian boundary, is the Nile itself, which moves *through* the land. Of the streams that show on a topographic drainage map over half

are intermittent, owing to the concentration of rainfall within a few months' period. Only those rivers that rise in lakes or feed from swamps flow perennially.

All the streams, however temporary, are important to Sudan for several reasons. They provide watering places for men and animals, and temporary pastures; they supply water for cultivation in places, although perennial irrigation from the intermittent streams is not possible without the building of dams to conserve the water; and where they spread their silt laden waters into fans to form deltas of a sort, the fertile soils become sites for agricultural production. The largest of such alluvial fans are those of the Gash River north of Kassala and of the Baraka River; both cross the Sudan-Eritrea border and flow toward Tokar on the Red Sea plain. Receiving the runoff from the Ethiopian highlands and the Red Sea hills, the fans are inundated annually, the depth of floodwaters depending upon the intensity of the rains. Because the successive deposits of silt laid down by these rivers in their own beds continuously choke the channels, the floodwaters spread out over the surrounding countryside and the channels shift frequently.

## Geopolitics

Sudan, as a political entity, is not entirely an arbitrary sector of African desert and savanna as are a number of the Saharan states. It has in its hydrographic unity a physical coherence, since it lies basinlike within the arc of higher land from which the Nile draws its headwaters; and the Nile itself is a large and important fact of this unity.

The boundaries vary. Some are physical—water divides, rivers, mountains; some are geometric, driven along an astronomic line for convenience through territory that at the time of delimitation did not seem very important. Some portions have been carefully surveyed, and even demarcated; others have not been surveyed. In some places boundaries pass across almost uninhabited ground; considerable lengths run through the midst of traditional tribal lands, dividing tribal peoples from each other. Sudan, the largest state in Africa, touches on eight nations—Egypt,

Libya, Chad, the Central African Republic, The Congo, Uganda, Kenya, and Ethiopia.

It has had a turbulent political history. Prior to 1820, Sudan was scarcely more than a geographical designation, with indeterminate bounds, within which many mutually hostile petty kingdoms rose and fell. It was penetrated from time to time, but never very deeply, by the cultural and economic influence, or military might, of whatever power ruled over Egypt, until, between 1820 and 1840, Egypt conquered most of Sudan and ruled it until 1881. In that year, a Sudanese religious fanatic, who claimed descent from the Prophet and who took the title of Mahdi ("He who is guided aright"), led a revolt of his followers and drove the Egyptians and the British, who had tried to support the Egyptians, out of the country. British and Egyptian forces under Lord Kitchener later attacked and reconquered the Sudan between the years 1896 to 1898, breaking Mahdist power; they established a condominium (see Glossary) over the Sudan which lasted until the end of 1955; the following year Sudan became independent.

The condominium agreement designated the 22d parallel as the boundary between Egypt and Sudan. Shortly after the astronomical frontier had been established, a modification of the northern line was agreed upon, the new one becoming known as the "administrative boundary." It deviated from that set up by the condominium agreement in three small jogs of territory: one bulged into Egypt north of Wadi Halfa along the Nile; another larger one along the Red Sea likewise was favorable to Sudan; the third, a small bulge given to Egypt, jutted south of the 22d parallel. The reasons for the alterations were ethnic: the lands of three tribal groups were split by the parallel. The adjustments more nearly placed all Nubians in Sudan, and removed violations to the territories of the Arabic-speaking Ababda of Egypt and the Beja Bisharin of Sudan, incorporating all of the lands and peoples of these tribes within their respective countries. Thus, the "zigzag line traversing the treaty boundary and known as the 'administrative boundary'" was accepted as the border, "without treaty formality"[2] until 1964, when the boundary in

the Wadi Halfa area became astronomical again. The expected flooding of the Nile Valley to and beyond Wadi Halfa with the impounding of the river by the High Dam necessitated the purchase of this sector by Egypt from Sudan, and the evacuation and resettlement of the Nubians on the Atbara. (See the next section.)

## Land and Livelihood

All parts of Sudan lie within the tropics. Variations in climate within the country are expressed in terms of moisture rather than temperature.

There is a close association between rainfall and the type, diversity, size, and luxuriance of the vegetation, but little if any of the vegetation of Sudan is climax flora; it is secondary, due mostly to man-made fires that annually sweep across almost all of those areas that have grass or trees. Aside from this determination of type by fire, however, vegetation follows a pattern closely related to such physical factors as rainfall, soils, elevation, exposure, and the like.

FIGURE 8.4 Village in southern Sudan. A comparison with Figure 8.9 will reveal how vastly different are northern and southern Sudan. The huts in the illustration below show the relationship of south Sudan to the humid lands; in arid country the houses are of mud. (Courtesy Ministry of Information, Sudan Government.)

[2] S. Whittemore Boggs, *International Boundaries*, New York: Columbia University Press, 1940, p. 199.

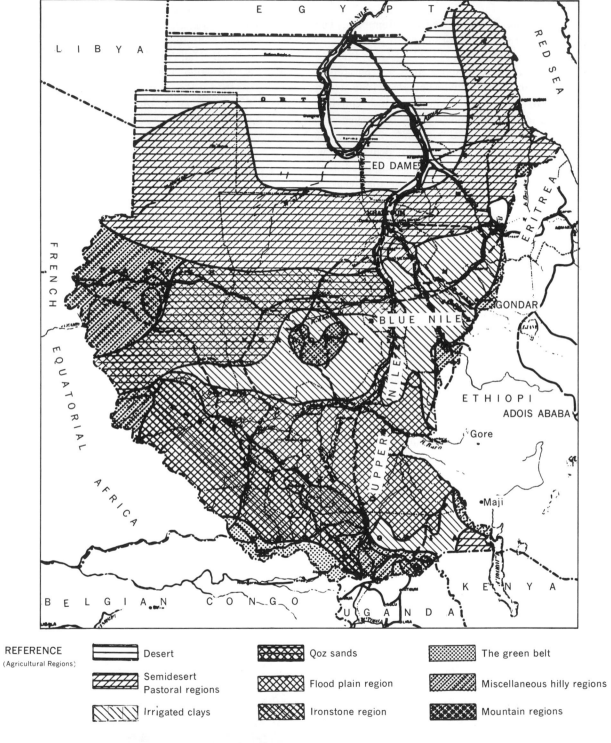

**FIGURE 8.5** Main agricultural regions. *(Adapted from map by Sudan Survey Department. Courtesy Ministry of Information, Sudan Government.)*

Since rainfall ranges from 80 inches in some southern mountains to near nothing in the north, the flora changes in form and quality from patches of three-story rain forest through broad-leaved savannas, acacia savanna-woodland, and desert scrub to barren desert; approximately one-fourth of the country falls within the latter category because at least 280,000 square miles of Sudan average no more than 3.5 inches of rain annually. There are profound changes from season to season in the vegetation in all areas except the extreme north and extreme south. In summer most of the country is lush and green, but winter finds it dry and barren with much of the grass and herbaceous cover completely gone. These seasonal changes are most important since they are at the base of the wanderings of the nomads and the migrations of the semisedentary villagers.

FIGURE 8.6    Sowing the rain-watered fields. (Courtesy Ministry of Information, Sudan Government.)

## AGRICULTURE AND PASTORALISM

Sudan is a big, unwieldy country, tribal to a large degree, poorly integrated in terms of transportation, and full of climatic problems.

In the desert of the extreme north only irrigated agriculture is possible; the extreme south, well watered and vegetated, is capable of extensive cultivation on a primitive level; the great intermediate wet and dry zone imposes and allows seasonal adaptations. It is this permissive or restrictive character that underlies the fundamental differences in population distribution and land use (Figure 8.5).

Throughout the land north of Khartoum irrigation agriculture and pastoral nomadism are the major adjustments. Across central and even into northern Sudan, irrigation farmers cultivate rainwatered fields as well for drought-resistant crops, such as millet and melons during the summer, to augment their production from the irrigated plots (Figure 8.6). Most villages have such holdings, often at considerable distances from the irrigated lands and from the villages, and to these the farmers go, camping for days at a time while planting, cultivating, or harvesting the rain crops.

The purely nomadic groups of the north keep camels. They migrate constantly with their animals, following the short rains that fall here and there for about 3 months of the year, depending upon perma-

nent water sources during the extended dry season when it is often necessary to move their herds great distances to find water and pasture. During these latter months the dromedaries graze upon thornbush or bunch grass in dry wadis or along streams. Above Khartoum sheep and goats become important, somewhat farther south, cattle; Nilotic pastoralists keep the latter. Even in the south, however, nomadism is practiced during the period of drought because people and animals must stay close to the streams to survive. Actually there is much nomadism as far south as the Bahr el Arab, and many Sudanese groups move across the border into the Central African Republic; there are also seasonal mass movements still farther south to escape the tsetse fly. These reach down to the Bahr el Ghazal and the upper Nile (latitude 5°N).

Wherever rainfall permits some cultivation, Sudanese farmers have lived and live at a subsistence level as rain cultivators. Their methods are simple and primitive, and their ways of life precarious. In the northern and central regions, some means of water conservation or irrigation are needed if land is to be tilled, and today along the White and Blue Niles, the mechanically driven pump is beginning to replace the primitive *saqia* (waterwheel) and shaduf (Figure 8.7). Here fruits, vegetables, grains, forage crops, and even cotton are raised. Along the river banks the subsistence flood- and lift-irrigation plots, which have existed north of Khartoum since ancient times, have undergone a marked conversion to mixed farming; they are now the market gardens of northern Sudan, expanding in citrus groves, vegetables, and fodder crops. Farther north yet, the ancient date industry is carried on under increasingly modernized conditions. This is along the Nile.

**FIGURE 8.7** The ancient shaduf is still used for irrigation: Dipping the bucket. (Courtesy Ministry of Information, Sudan Government.)

In central Sudan, a special method of preserving water in shallow holes (*hafirs*) is practiced among some groups who are both cultivators and pastoralists. If rain fails, however, as it often does, a whole village may migrate to search for better watered land; to live during this period, cultivators frequently must sell their livestock; if such a migrant farmer is on hand during the cotton picking season in the perennially irrigated lands, he will work as a harvest hand. Perennial irrigation can change this pattern of uncertainty.

Away from the river the sinking of deep bore wells and the building of small barrages has helped to convert nomads to agriculture, expand the gum picking industry, and develop the raising of cattle for export. In the Nuba Mountains, new wells have

encouraged diversification of agriculture, including cotton culture for commercial purposes.[3]

Land hunger, as such, does not exist in Sudan, but like Egypt, Sudan is very sensitive to the water supply. Also like Egypt, most of the commercial agriculture is in the northern half of the country where the growth of plants depends upon some form of irrigation, and the commercial crop is cotton. (Note that the Gezira is north of a center dividing line.)

Cotton, first grown in Sudan in the Gash and Tokar deltas, became an important commercial crop along the Nile only after the completion of the Sennar Dam in 1925. This permitted irrigation of the Gezira (Figure 8.8), a large tract between the White and Blue Niles south of Khartoum. By 1958 over 1.2 million acres were being irrigated there, and the amount is presently being increased by the completion of the Managil extension. The project is administered by the Gezira Board, a quasi-governmental body; profits are partly (48 percent) paid to tenants, partly (10 percent) retained by the Board for future development, and partly (42 percent) paid to the government. In addition to being the outstanding producer of the leading commercial crop, cotton, the Gezira and Managil districts are already a granary for much of the country.

Commercial agriculture in Sudan is largely confined to the valleys of the Nile and its affluents. Hence, a large portion of the Government's budget goes into the harnessing and control of the Nile waters. The Managil extension was thus supported. An ambitious 7-year plan for the carrying out of several development schemes was adopted in 1961. This includes the Roseires Dam, being constructed on the Blue Nile above the Sennar. The new Nile Waters Agreement makes the construction of this dam necessary if Sudan is to have the storage capacity required to utilize fully her share of the waters; it is dual purpose, and will bring under irriga-

[3] For an extended presentation of a specialized development undertaken in the extreme southwest by the Sudan Department of Agriculture (the Zande scheme), see Pierre de Schlippe, *Shifting Cultivation in Africa (The Zande System of Agriculture)*, London: Routledge and Kegan Paul, Ltd., 1956.

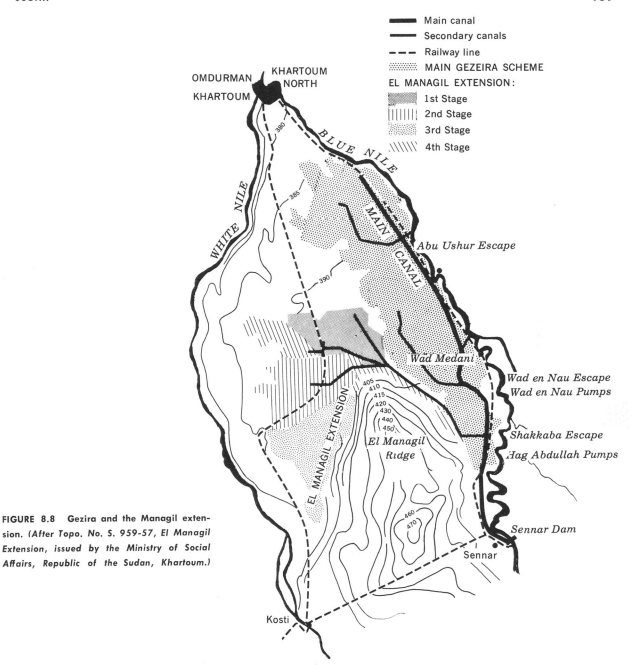

FIGURE 8.8 Gezira and the Managil extension. (After Topo. No. S. 959-57, El Managil Extension, issued by the Ministry of Social Affairs, Republic of the Sudan, Khartoum.)

tion another 1.4 million more acres of dry land, and provide additional water to some 600,000 acres already cultivated. The dam will create a lake that extends back to the Ethiopian border; at the damsite a new city is rising, Damazin, planned as the most modern city in Sudan.

The drowning of the Wadi Halfa oasis by the High Dam and the necessity of transferring the people from the area to be inundated have already been mentioned. The area of development prepared to receive these Nubians, Khashm el Girba, is in a fertile sector along the Atbara River about 250 miles east of Khartoum. A dam and a system of canals provide water for irrigation. This site was chosen because of its rich alluviums, the speed with which the selected area could be transformed into an economic unit, and because the Atbara, flowing from the Ethiopian hills close by, offered a dependable supply of water for perennial irrigation at that point.

The first settlers from Wadi Halfa arrived at Khashm el Girba early in 1964. Technologically there seem to be no difficulties. The one problem probably facing the government in this large project, which could irrigate 1 million acres of rich land, could be that not enough settlers will be available to develop even 150,000 acres.

The central clay plain of the Gezira-Managil districts is the most modernized sector of Sudan and the place where the greatest extension of agriculture has occurred. But along the edges of this area of relatively intensive irrigation cultivation live nomads, who along the west migrate in toward the center and out again, on an east-west axis, from the late spring to fall months. In the eastern portion of the clay plains, other nomads make annual cyclic migrations that may carry them 10 or even 200 miles during the course of a year. These graziers of the Gezira have no difficulty in selling their animals because of the large demand in Omdurman and Wad Medani, and even in the villages of the irrigated lands. There is no market for camels, either for work or for their meat, and so they are bought by tribesmen who take them to Egypt for trading.

The unirrigated areas just south of the irrigated lands are quite densely settled by people who cultivate crops on the natural rainfall, millet, sorghum, sesame, and the like. Ridging is a device frequently used here to conserve water for the crops because rainfall is relatively slight, about 16 to 20 inches.

Still farther south the southern clay plains region, a broad alluvial plain largely waterlogged part or all of the year by water drawn in from the Nile headstreams, is the country of the Nilotic tribesmen, primitive migratory cattle herders. The Jonglei proposals for cutting a canal through the sudd apply to this country. Quite apart from the advantages of directing the passage of water through the swamp, of permitting water to flow as required from projected storage reservoirs, and of reducing the present great water losses by evaporation from the immense water surface, the Jonglei scheme could be a first step toward the development of this vast, potentially productive sector of Sudan, now only thinly populated by subsistence cultivators and graziers. Were the Jonglei project to be carried out here, as in portions of the clay plains to the north, this part of Sudan could become a granary, but traditions and disinclination of the Nilotes to alter their way of life are against rapid change, and since Sudan experiences no shortage of land, it is likely there will be no great influx into the region.[4]

## RESOURCES OF THE LAND

From a wide belt of hot savannas that stretches across central Sudan comes 80 percent of the gum arabic that goes into international trade. This is one of the oldest commodities of the world to be carried along the routes of commerce, its documented usage going back to before 2000 B.C. Egyptian papyri record that the earliest uses were as an adhesive and medicine. By the first century of the Christian era, this product was also reaching Europe via Arabian ports, the explanation for its name, gum "arabic," and a reminder of the secrecy with which the Arabs concealed their trade routes and sources from Europeans.

Acacia trees that produce the gum, the hashab and talh, are tapped much as are rubber trees for their latex. These varieties of acacia show an unusual adaptation to their environment. Each dry season they seem to die. Beforehand, however, they manufacture the gum as a kind of life source that assures their resurrection the following spring when the light rains begin. Planted near water they produce no gum, but stimulated by drought and scorching heat, each tree will yield up to a pound of sap annually.

Today gum arabic is in short supply. Because of this and of its importance as a source of revenue, the Sudanese government proposes to further exploit and increase the cultivation of the hashab tree. El Obeid, provincial capital of Kordofan, is the largest and most famed market for gum arabic in the world; auctions

---

[4] For a detailed regional analysis see K. M. Barbour, *Republic of the Sudan,* London: University of London Press, Ltd., 1961.

held here usually set world prices. Gum arabic is Sudan's second most important export, by value normally making up 10 to 12 percent of the export revenue.

Tree varieties other than gum arabic are indigenous to Sudan, but for several decades the timber has stood neglected in favor of the development of irrigable soils and the production of cotton. Tropical woodlands cover or partially cover about two-fifths of the country. (See Figure 8.9.) A forestry inventory is in progress under which Sudan expects to locate and identify the most useful and exploitable timber and to make decisions relative to the transport of timber to population centers. Unfortunately, even in the high-rainfall woodland savanna most of the trees are too small and deformed to use for timber, or they may be of very hard woods and difficult to work.

Sudan has a number of minerals, as yet almost undeveloped. An ancient body of copper ore, believed to have been the source of the copper carried by caravan north into Egypt in the days of the Pharaohs, is being reassessed following geologic studies begun in 1957. The deposits are at Hofrat En Nahas in southwest Sudan. Present estimates set the reserve at more than 10 million tons of 3 percent copper content ore. A copper development would be a valuable addition to the Sudanese economy.

Several high content deposits of iron have been confirmed, but development of these must await the building of railroads into the areas, which lie between 15 and 45 miles inland from the coast, about 100 miles north of Port Sudan. Gold occurs and is extracted in small quantities, although in lesser amounts than in early Egyptian days; the goldfields, like the iron ore, are some distance from water and far from modern means of transportation; manganese occurs and is mined, but deposits are small and low grade. Salt is produced by evaporation of sea water; although the amounts are small, they are nevertheless enough to supply Sudan with its salt requirements.

Unfortunately no considerable reserves of minerals seem to occur in Sudan, and fuels, other than developing hydroelectricity, are lacking. As a result, Sudan appears to have neither the mineral nor the fuel base upon which any but light industries can be developed.

FIGURE 8.9  Dry savanna, Sudan. *(Courtesy Ministry of Information, Sudan Government.)*

Only a little over 3 percent of the population are classed as "secondary producers," that is, persons "concerned with the transformation of products, principally industry";[5] the number gives some indication of the relative importance of industry in Sudan. Cotton produces most of the national income. Without cotton, the country would slip back to the subsistence level of half a century ago: well over 50 percent of the export revenue comes from this fiber. Such dependence upon one product makes the economy extremely vulnerable to fluctuations on the world market, and therefore inherently weak. Because of this, the government is placing major emphasis upon diversifying agriculture and broadening the economic base. Since Sudan has neither coal nor large ore bodies, the economy must always be based first of all upon the three great natural resources of the land: the three great rivers, the two Niles and the Atbara; the soil, of which there are perhaps 120 million tillable acres of which perhaps 1 million are now utilized; and the pastures.

The economic importance of the Nile to Sudan is very great (Figure 8.10). Apart from serving as a link between the peoples of the north and south, and a major outlet into the ocean lanes, the river waters

[5] *Population of Sudan, op. cit.,* p. 45.

FIGURE 8.10  Bales of cotton ready for shipment down the Nile. (Courtesy Ministry of Information, Sudan Government.)

are indispensable to much of Sudanese agriculture and living. The old established riverine cultivation, the irrigated fields of the Gezira, and any further developments of irrigation cultivation to expand Sudan's modernizing economy alike depend on a certain and controlled availability of Nile water.

The four ancient sources of Sudanese wealth, ivory, slaves, ostrich feathers, and gold, have for all practical purposes disappeared. The development of light industries could make Sudan less dependent upon cotton prices quoted far away at Liverpool, New Orleans, and Dallas; the expansion or development of such crops as sugarcane, tea, coffee, rice, and other food plants could eliminate a possible 20 percent of now needed imports, while the scientific care of the vast grazing lands would conserve the habitat, increase the animal population, and improve the quality of livestock.

Steps have already been taken to develop along all these lines and others. In addition to the agricultural, timber, and hydroelectric developments, modern manufacture has been started. A sugar factory at Guneid in Blue Nile Province, a government-owned tannery in Khartoum South, a cardboard factory at Aroma using waste cotton stalks from the Gash cotton scheme, and a meat-packing plant at Kosti on the White Nile are among recent government steps in industry. The private sector of industry

has established, among other things, a cement factory in Atbara, a flour mill in Khartoum, several large cotton mills, and battery, paint, and refrigerator plants; and proposals, some approved, include a second cement plant at Kosti, a button factory using palm ivory, and plants for the production of shoes, cotton textiles, paper from papyrus, asbestos, bricks, and fish processing. In the deep south in Equatoria Province, where Virginia tobacco has been successfully introduced, cigarette manufacturing has begun.

*Modes of Transport.*  Transport in Sudan is inadequate for the modern developments. To get goods to and from ports to Sudanese population centers situated in the central interior involves long overland hauls for Sudan. Before railroads were built to connect with Port Sudan on the Red Sea coast, Aswan, at the head of navigation on the Nile, was practically the only outlet for Sudanese exports. It was a river port and a market center of great importance but far upstream from the Mediterranean. It acted as the entrepôt where caravans from Sudan met Nile boats from Egypt; caravans traveled regularly to connect Aswan with Berber and other places in Sudan. But in a modern era, transport by caravan is unfeasible except in a small way. Goods shipped by way of Aswan also required transshipment at Alexandria.

Railroad building was begun in 1898, after the reconquest. Today, Sudan has about 3,000 miles of railway. Regular steamer service supplements the railroads as carriers between Wadi Halfa and El Shellal just south of Aswan, linking the Sudanese and Egyptian railways; between Karima, opposite Merowe and north of the Fourth Cataract, and Kerma, just north of the Third Cataract; from Khartoum to Kosti, and from Kosti in three directions, namely, to Wau at the head of river navigation on the Bahr el Ghazal, to Juba on the Bahr el Jebel on the south side of the sudd, and to Gambela, Ethiopia, on the Sobat River.

Roads in the north, other than town roads, are only cleared tracks, mostly impassable directly after rains. In Upper Nile Province motor travel is almost entirely confined to the dry months (January through May); during the months with rain it is normally impossible to get as far south as Malakal, lying on the northern edge of the sudd.[6] In the provinces of Equatoria and Bahr el Ghazal, however, there are a number of good graveled roads with permanent bridges that are usable the year around; secondary roads are impassable after rains. There are no roads to the Red Sea coast, and attempts to cross the Nubian desert by car from the Nile eastward are hazardous in the extreme (See Figure 8.11.)

The most modern transport means, air, has taken an important place in Sudan, figuring largely both in the internal development of the country and in its foreign relations. As in a number of other relatively underdeveloped, sparsely peopled lands of great size, the airplane has met a need as a unifier and a swift means of movement. Today, most internal travel of business, government, professional men, and the like is via Sudan Airways, which serve nearly every center of more than moderate size. Internationally in many ways Khartoum is the gateway to central Africa; here many local national airlines, including Ethiopian, Chad, Ghanaian, and East African, make important connections with world carriers such as BOAC, and, particularly today, Aeroflot, the Soviet line.

## Cities

"The city" of Sudan is the sprawling urban agglomeration known popularly as the "Three Towns," situated at the confluence of the White and Blue Niles. On the apex of land between the rivers is Khartoum, the capital, striving semisuccessfully to be modern. Its name, an Arabic word meaning "Elephant Trunk," apparently derived from the shape of the site between the Nile affluents. North, across the Blue Nile, is its semimodern suburb of Khartoum North while along the west bank of the main Nile, just downstream from the confluence, is Omdurman, casbah-like, thoroughly Arabic, unchanging. The population of the Three Towns totals somewhat over ¼ million.

Khartoum has had a short but turbulent history. Founded by the Egyptians in 1823, it was kept going by the slave trade and its role as administrative

[6] When the writer wanted to go to Malakal from Khartoum in August, the only way to get in was by boat or air.

FIGURE 8.11   Camels are the beasts of burden in the dry lands and even in the irrigated areas. (Courtesy Ministry of Information, Sudan Government.)

center of the country. During the Mahdist uprising of 1884 it was attacked and largely destroyed, but was rebuilt on its present plan by Lord Kitchener, who reestablished the capital at Khartoum after his defeat of the Mahdists. It is designed on a rectangular pattern of broad streets, cut across by several diagonal boulevards.

Striking contrasts characterize the city. Today, as capital and commercial center of the Sudan, it is bustling and prosperous, with a cosmopolitan business district and many modern, multistoried structures. Some residential areas have ultramodern homes, and there is a fine modern university surrounded by a district of broad, tree-shaded streets and older, well built, comfortable homes. But many streets are still unpaved, and muddy or dusty depending upon the season; some districts are composed of flat-roofed Arab-style houses surrounded by mud walls whose dilapidated facades give no hint of the charming gardens that may lie hidden behind them. There is a good water supply, sewage system, and electric power service, but most of the milk, fruit, and vegetables come into town on the backs of thousands of donkeys, which are as commonplace on the streets as the multitudinous yellow taxicabs.

Omdurman makes no pretense at modernity. Its streets are irregular and largely devoid of pavement;

its houses are built of mud and flat roofed; its *souk* (or *Suq*) is completely of the Middle East. There are no tall modern buildings, no cosmopolitan business sector, no neat modern suburbs. Larger than Khartoum, Omdurman nevertheless reflects the past, the steppe, the Arab world; Khartoum represents the present, the proudly nationalistic new nation, the outside world.

Port Sudan, major outlet for the country, is a modern port, built from 1906 to 1908 to replace Suakin, an older port handicapped by limited space and a difficult passageway. Port Sudan is also handicapped, however, for it lies far offside from the major concentrations of people and activity, which center in and above the tricity area. However, being Sudan's only real port, and the only port along the whole Red Sea-Gulf of Suez coast, aside from Suez, where vessels can regularly take on water, it is important. Its population has reached about 50,000; its quays can accommodate five vessels simultaneously.

## Afterthoughts

Sudan was one of the first parts of central Africa to be penetrated and administered by a foreign power. Isolated, it nevertheless had contacts early with the world beyond the edges of Africa, through Egypt and Arabia. Sudan has not suddenly been opened up, or suddenly made economic contacts beyond its borders; the process has been gradual, accelerating as the current century has grown older.

While Arab slavers knew the Sudan for centuries, the first positive effects upon the country were made by the Egyptians about the middle of the last century; they introduced new crops including sugarcane, barley, certain fruits, indigo, and cotton, improved irrigation methods, and encouraged trade and the development of transportation.

During the era of the condominium, the administration of Sudan was ostensibly British-Egyptian, but it was the British who in reality held the power. They introduced many great improvements: education at all levels from elementary to university; good railways, riverboats, communications, electricity, water supply and sewage systems; health services and hospitals. They undertook the training of men for all

manner of administrative and technical responsibilities, and, most important, brought an unprecedented period of peace and security without oppression.

The prime problem of the modern state is to relax dependence upon cotton. But the difficulty is to find a crop as easy to produce and as well paying. There is the need, also, to bring a better balance between the farming-grazing side of the economy and industry, so that the overall standard of living can be raised and the repercussions of slumps on the world cotton market softened.

Another frustration to development is the disparity of economic resources among the regions and the fact that as advances take place in those areas having the greatest and most easily developed potentials, the inequality of opportunity and living standards among the people increases. Sudan is large and it has variety, but size itself is a handicap because of the marginal character of all parts of the country, the sparsity and spread of the population, and the difficulty of unifying the state politically and in terms of transportation and communication. Tribalism and the dual racial and ethnic character of the north and south harass attempts at unity; illiteracy and backward ways hamper attempts to modernize.

How do these problems compare with those of Egypt? Both countries are lands of the Nile dependent upon the river and its affluents, Egypt more so than Sudan. Literally, there is no life in Egypt without these waters; only parts of Sudan are so wholly dependent upon the Nile for life.

Egypt is overpopulated, and all the strenuous efforts being made to improve economic conditions may be able to do no more than keep pace with the increase. Egypt has 2¼ times more people on a land with tight bounds; Sudan, in a sense, has no land bounds at least in the foreseeable future, and its domain offers variety; it has land to exploit, land to spare, but development is hard, requiring irrigation or drainage or the overcoming of space.

Both countries are making tremendous efforts to improve conditions for their people. In Egypt time pressure is much more critical; but Sudan must overcome the divisive nature of its people and must learn to develop several kinds of lands in several climates as against the advantages of homogeneity of land and people in Egypt.

# 9 WEST AFRICA

*. . . winds of change are
blowing over Africa.*

HAROLD MACMILLAN

## The Realm of West Africa

West Africa is that portion of the continent that lies southward from the bounds of the countries of the Maghrib to the Guinea coast, and between the Cameroons highlands and the Atlantic Ocean. Long usage has defined the limits of the area so that it is fairly well understood. Latitudinally, it covers a span of over 21°, and a climatic range from equatorial to Saharan.

The greatest diversity is from north to south, and relief, climate, and vegetation zones stretch in east-west belts across the realm; political units generally cut across this climatic, vegetational, and topographic grain. The east-west belting of the physical features is so dominant that economic adjustments and even racial and ethnic characteristics are also rather definitely expressed in east-west alignments. Because Chad lies completely within the latitudinal bounds of this realm, and is an inland Saharan-savanna state, and because its lands carry eastward the elongate east-west climatic and vegetation belts, this country will be included in the regional discussion of West Africa. Before independence, Chad was administratively a part of French Equatorial Africa. This was an historical accident, and to call this arid and semi-arid interior-basin country "equatorial" is a misnomer. Chad is not equatorial in any part of it; it is desertic and Sudanese.

West Africa is a huge piece of territory. The distance between its east-west extremities is as great as that between San Francisco and New York, and the area is nearly the size of continental United States without Alaska. Its population, however, is not so impressive because it numbers only about 100 millions. These inhabitants are scattered disparately across the bulge, some areas being sparsely, some densely, populated. The former French lands contain less than one-third of the West Africans because great sectors are arid or semiarid; at the opposite extreme is Nigeria with more than half of the West Africans living within its borders, over 55.6 million people.

Most of the now independent states that comprise West Africa were colonies of either Great Britain or France; only Liberia was sovereign before the mid-twentieth century. French West Africa, a continuous territory that covered 75 percent of the region, was 8½ times larger than France; British West Africa, fragmented into several parts by the intervening French holdings that dipped down from the bulk of the French Sahara, was nearly 5 times greater than Britain.

The partition of West Africa into independent states has taken place since 1957. By 1961 all portions of the colonial lands had achieved self-determination except Gambia, the Cameroons, the Spanish Sahara, and Portuguese Guinea, the two latter still subject to the European powers. In the two sectors of the Cameroons held in trust by the British, a plebiscite in February, 1961, indicated the choice of the people between union with Nigeria or the Cameroon Republic. The north voted to unite with Nigeria, the larger south with the Republic. Gambia achieved internal self-government on October 4, 1963, and independence in February, 1965. Area and populations of the new states are very unequal, as are also the resources.

## The Land

A rather remarkable geomorphic uniformity characterizes West Africa. With local modifications, a south-to-north pattern of relief prevails, stretching in elongated belts east and west: low coast, uplands, inner slope. West Africa ascends from a shelving continental slope to a generally low coast that rises inland more or less abruptly to the broken edge of the plateau. A fairly continuous belt of highlands extends east and west from the plateau edge inward to about 12°N latitude. On the inner side the uplands slope again, toward the Sahara. At the base of the slope extends a wide depression from Senegal to Lake Chad, and north of this rise the Saharan massifs, the Ahaggar with its outliers, the Adrar des Iforas and the Aïr Mountains, and the Tibesti plateau. Upon the surface of the Sahara a complex relief, associated with these inner massifs, has been carved out by wind and water, while over great areas *reg* and *erg* mask the "fossil" relief of the desert plateau.

## COASTAL FACADES

The West African shores are difficult, and have markedly affected both the history and the opening up of this portion of the "Dark Continent." The natures of the shore and coast depend upon a number of elements including the nature and arrangement of the rocks, tectonic forces, relief and drainage, and climate. The approaches to the land from the sea, therefore, vary considerably along different portions. From Cape Verde to the delta of the Niger River, the West African shore alternates between low, often swampy lowlands, and rocky promontories that thrust toward or into the sea as spurs of the plateau front. Drained by many streams that carry large volumes of water and sediment during the rainy seasons, great stretches of the coast have been built up by deltaic deposits that are interlaced with sluggish distributaries, and choked with mangrove; in a number of places the coast is fringed with sandbars that enclose long lagoons. Surf and lighterage ports formerly served most of the West African shore; today, however, some fine ports have been developed.

In more detail, from the Senegal River up to the Saloum estuary midway between Dakar and Bathurst northeast winds, assisted by shore drift and great waves that billow in from the open Atlantic, are leveling an already shelving coast; river mouths are blocked by building and shifting sandspits; and behind the dune bordered shore there are often moist depressions, the remnants of former lagoons. From and including the Saloum River to eastern Sierra Leone the coast is a drowned one, and estuarial river mouths finger into the land as great V-shaped intrusions of the sea, forming a ria coast (see Glossary). Although some land has emerged along this sector of the shore, no parts are smoothed in spite of the occurrence of a broad continental shelf. In fact, the explanation lies in part in this latter fact: tides are high, and tidal scour is vigorous; seasonal winds, southwest or northeast, stir the coastal waters that lie in their paths; instead of building spits, mudflats form wherein the mangrove takes over, as along the Casamance coast of Senegal, Portuguese Guinea, and southward almost to Liberia. The Liberian shore and adjacent parts of the Sierra Leone coast are charac-

terized again by sandspits, likely owing to the lower tides.

The varied orientation of the coastline beyond Liberia has resulted in an alternation of coastal sectors that show only moderate accumulations of sand barriers, as along the western half of Ivory Coast and the central and western coast of Ghana in both directions from Cape Three Points, with those that are characterized by major accumulations with associated lagoon formation. So pronounced are sandbar and lagoon developments along parts of this coast that they rival those bordering Senegal and Mauritania. Shifting sandspits, barrier bars, and lagoons fringe the eastern half of Ivory Coast, and are typical from eastern Ghana eastward to beyond the Niger delta. In the coastal sectors of moderate accumulation, rock projections occasionally reach into the sea.

West Africa is remarkably devoid of natural harbors except where high tides or a river open a way to the sea, as at Freetown and Calabar, or at Lagos, which lies on a lagoon the opening to which is kept free of obstruction by dredging. On some of the distributaries of the Niger delta there are quasi-natural harbors.

## THE HIGHLANDS

The character of the plateau edge varies. In places it reaches down to the seashore in eroded rolling hills; in other parts it drops as an abrupt front so that a plateau escarpment overlooks a plain along the shore; sometimes rock masses reach into the sea. It takes on mountainous proportions in the Guinea highlands, and even more so in the Fouta Jallon and the Nimba Mountains, where heights of 3,500, 3,700, and even 6,000 feet are attained. The latter elevations occur in the Nimba Mountains where the frontiers of Guinea, Liberia, and Ivory Coast come together. The more impressive relief features are due to intense erosion, faulting, and in some places, to volcanism, as in the Cameroon Mountains, the highest portions of the Jos plateau, and the offshore islands that extend southwestward across and beyond the Bight of Biafra. Mount Cameroon is an active volcano.

Although there are these locally prominent highlands, West Africa is not characterized by a great diversity of relief; except in the eminences, elevation does not interrupt the east-west alignment of relief and climatic and vegetation belts. The topography is, in general, level to hilly, averaging between 600 and 1,600 feet. Slopes toward the interior are longer and more gentle than those toward the sea, and rivers draw much of their character from the difference in slope; those flowing to the Gulf of Guinea or the Atlantic are more vigorous than those that drain into the interior. Some, like the Benue and upper Volta rivers, are gaining at the expense of others by eating headward and cutting into the flow of other streams. There are great variations in volume with the seasons; some rivers, such as the central Niger, flood wide sectors of land during the rains, whereas during the period of drought excessive evaporation causes much water to be lost.

Drainage generally runs two ways from the divides —inward toward the desert, and seaward; but from the Guinea highlands, rivers flow in three directions, that is, west to the Atlantic like the Senegal and Gambia rivers, south to the Gulf of Guinea, and inward into the interior desert basin. One river, that formerly lost itself in netherlands (see Glossary), was captured by another headward-eating stream that emptied into the Gulf of Guinea. The two, now flowing as one, are the Niger, which rises in the Guinea highlands and flows northeast into the desert, where it makes an abrupt turn east, and then runs southeast into the Gulf of Guinea. The turn occurs near the point of capture in the netherlands, the alluvial fan of the north-flowing sector. Intermittent streams or even dry watercourses are characteristic of the interior. Some of these wadis feed into the great central sector of the Niger south of and around Gao. Their general lack of flow is due both to the seasonality of rains and to the filling in of the stream bed with sand, during the dry season, when the harmattan blows out of the Sahara.

## CLIMATE AND VEGETATION

The east-west alignment of climatic and vegetation belts is as pronounced as is topography. Since all of the realm is tropical, north-south temperature differences are not so pronounced as are variations in rainfall (Figure 9.2). Throughout, diurnal ranges

of temperature are greater than annual ranges, although there are seasons of cooler and warmer temperatures, particularly in the desert areas and the *sahel,* the dry savannah or steppe. But distinctions between climatic realms (Figure 9.3) are, in the main, in terms of precipitation (Figures 9.2 and 9.4), and vegetation zones (Figure 9.5) generally follow the rainfall belts.

In two places, cool offshore waters affect the climates. In the west, along the Senegal coast, the Canary Current ameliorates temperatures close to the shore, but it also brings fog and possibly accentuates the aridity. In the Gulf of Guinea cold upwells of water, of uncertain origin, occur during the late spring and summer along the coasts of eastern Ghana, Togo, and Dahomey, cooling temperatures and possibly accounting in great part for the semiaridity of these coasts, a phenomenon that has never been satisfactorily explained.

Except where elevations rise to the highland belt, isohyets run generally east-west with but slight deviation from straight lines, indicative of the great moisture contrasts north and south. Between the equatorial rain forests and the desert two vegetation zones may be distinguished (Figure 9.3): the Sudan, a savanna where rainfall varies south to north between 60 and 25 inches, depending on whether the area is on the equatorial or dry side of the belt, and where vegetation modulates from tall grass and trees to steppe and bush savanna; and the *sahel,* where rainfall is under 25 inches and vegetation is semixerophytic in character. All of the zones blend into each other indistinguishably, however, so that it is difficult to draw a line that would define where the desert ends and *sahel* begins, or where the southern *sahel* terminates and savanna commences. If lines are to be traced to separate these regions, in general northern *sahel* and Sahara will separate somewhat north of the isohyet that passes through Timbuktu, perhaps along the 9-inch rainfall line. Beyond there true Saharan conditions obtain. Southern *sahel* and Sudan separate generally along the 25-inch isohyet which runs eastward from approximately Dakar, thus putting southern Senegal, Sudan, Upper Volta, and the Fouta Jallon plateau of Guinea, and the area east from there as defined by isohyets, into the belt of wet savanna.

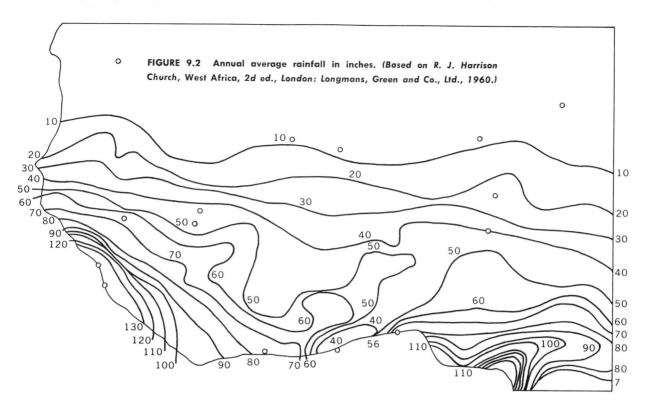

FIGURE 9.2 Annual average rainfall in inches. (Based on R. J. Harrison Church, West Africa, 2d ed., London: Longmans, Green and Co., Ltd., 1960.)

FIGURE 9.3 (Below) Climatic realms. (Based on a map from R. J. Harrison Church, West Africa, 2d ed., London: Longmans, Green & Co., Ltd., 1960.)

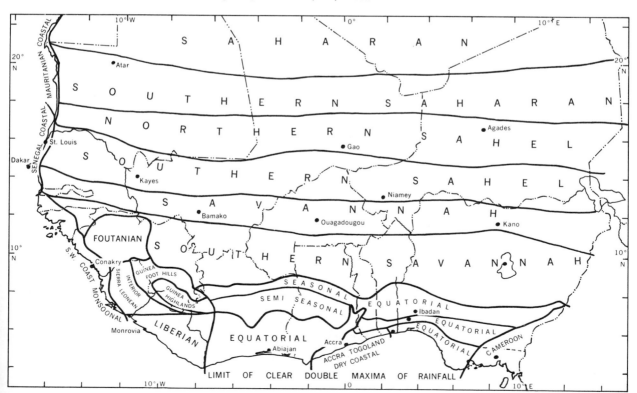

The accompanying maps show an approximation of the vegetation belts (Figure 9.5) and the division of West Africa into belts based upon seasonality of rainfall (Figures 9.3 and 9.4). The east-west orientation is striking. The maps also bring out the relatively dry character of the coastal sector in back of Accra and Takoradi. Although the rainfall regime in the latter region is near equatorial, the amount of rain that falls is low, and the number of days with rain are few.

The disparity in the total amount of rain that falls and the length of the wet season from south to north are striking; so also are the advance and recession of the seasonal rains, and the effectiveness of evapotranspiration. Where excessive amounts of rain fall (100 inches or more), especially when it is highly concentrated within one season, the moisture may have adverse effects, causing intense erosion, leaching, and rank leaf growth; it may even inhibit the

cultivation of certain plants, such as corn and rice. Montane climates characterize those regions with elevations above 3,000 feet. It can be seen that differing elevations, position relative to wind direction, and similar factors create climatic conditions that obtain only locally.

Vegetation belts coincide closely with rainfall in West Africa. Man, however, has been a powerful modifier of biologic life, destroying and changing the species, and the richness of fauna and flora; edaphic (soils and groundwater) influences also play a part, and are accentuated in regions where evapotranspiration is excessive or waterlogging of the soil occurs.

The south-north panorama of vegetation corresponds closely to that found in the eastern Sudan; there are areas of three-story rain forest in the south (Figure 9.6), and montane vegetation occurs spottily in regions toward the south where elevations are

**FIGURE 9.4** Months with at least 4 inches of precipitation. Dark line indicates northern bound of area with a double maximum of precipitation. *(Based on a map from R. J. Harrison Church, West Africa, 2d ed., London: Longmans, Green & Co., Ltd., 1960.)*

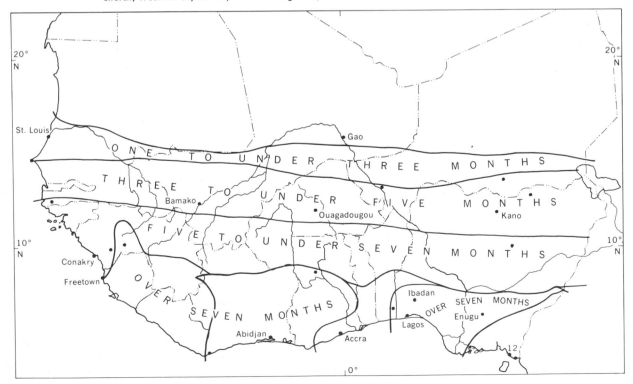

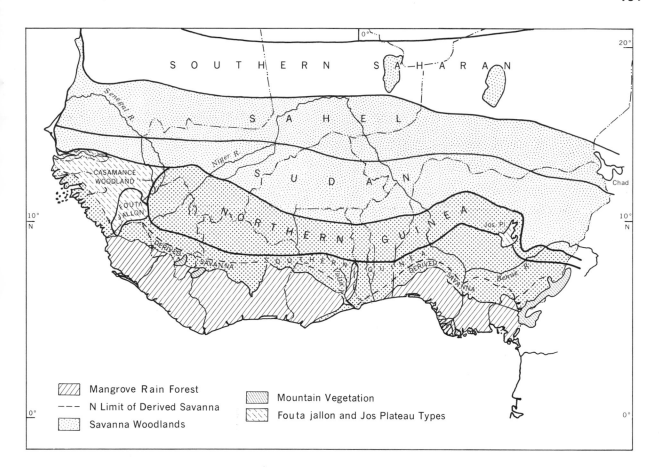

Mangrove Rain Forest
N Limit of Derived Savanna
Savanna Woodlands
Mountain Vegetation
Fouta jallon and Jos Plateau Types

FIGURE 9.5 (Above) Vegetation zones. (Based on a map from R. J. Harrison Church, West Africa, 2d ed., London: Longmans, Green & Co., Ltd., 1960.)

FIGURE 9.6 (Right) Logging the rainforests of Ivory Coast. (Service de l'Information de le Côte d'Ivoire.)

FIGURE 9.7 (Left) Thatching roof of a house with savanna grass, Kaduna, Nigeria. Grass grows 6 and 8 feet high during wet season. (Photograph by writer.)

FIGURE 9.8 (Below) Mosque of Agadès, Air Massif, Niger, is constructed af abode, typical in arid West Africa. Agadès, ancient caravan and trade center, represents the old and traditional in West Africa. (Courtesy Embassy of Niger Republic.)

greatest. Generally, to the north of the rain forests, savanna woodlands begin along quite a clear-cut boundary—not a natural one, but along a zone of derived savanna that developed as a result of recurrent cutting and burning of the rain forests. Wet savannah, here called Guinean, has taller, straighter trees and longer grass (Figure 9.7) than it has farther north; acacia seems to be generally absent. In the Sudan savanna north of the Guinean, trees are more widely spaced and on the average are shorter, but have widespread crowns and are more gnarled and deformed, and even thorny; acacias, the baobab, the kapok tree, the locust tree, and the shea butter tree are among those that are common. These trees are generally protected because of their value in one way or another. Brush and scrub prevail widely where soil conditions deteriorate.

Leaves become smaller as the *sahel* is approached, and thorns become more prevalent owing to the more active evapotranspiration and the lower rainfall and humidity. In the *sahel* savanna, acacias, thorny trees, and brush are characteristic. The prevalent vegetation reflects an adaptation to near desert conditions in the species that occur; rigid thorns, widespread or deep root systems, a wide diffusion of thorn woodland, and short clump grass in more scattered tussocks are characteristic. As the climate grows more Saharan, clump grass, green only during the brief rains, and scrubs grow in isolation or far apart, playing out on the desert edge, or occurring only in favored places where ground water supplies moisture. (See Figure 9.8.)

# Colonial Policy and Development

Since political units cut across the grain of climatic belts there is a marked coincidence, among political units with similar latitudinal span, in the type of crops that are raised, and even more coincidence in what can be raised. Disparate development has led to the dominance of certain commercial crops in certain countries, however; in others, the inherent possibilities for growing particular crops have been almost untouched. Although in all the equatorial areas cacao, oil palms, rubber, citrus, and the like could be raised, Nigeria and Ghana are the only countries where cacao production reaches important levels, Liberia and Nigeria are the only significant producers of plantation rubber, and Nigeria of palm oil. Subsistence crops, on the other hand, tend to vary with climate, their distribution having little relevance to political boundaries. Root crops predominate generally where there is not a prolonged dry season, cereals where the season of drought is relatively pronounced, and the type of starches grown show a pattern of change throughout West Africa with increasing or decreasing rainfall.

To understand the diverse development that has occurred in different parts of West Africa, it is necessary to look at the factors, other than climate, that have influenced those developments.

## FRENCH DEVELOPMENTS

Except for Gambia and Portuguese Guinea, the western savanna lands were under French administration.

French political control began in Senegal when in the middle of the seventeenth century, the site of what became St. Louis was selected as the locale for the first permanent occupation of African lands by the French. For a century no attempt was made to push inland. Some interest in tropical agriculture began to be aroused about 1820 as the French observed the success of Dutch plantation developments on Java (East Indies), and the French decided to attempt something of the same sort in Senegal, with the idea of supplying the home market with tropical products; but the venture was small, the Senegalese proved difficult to train, and altogether the attempt was not much of a success.

An expedition into th[e] the upper Niger in 18[..] cultivating cotton, e[..] culture than in Sen[..] French, thereafter, to p[..] Niger River, and to consolid[..] land in between. When explorat[..] Niger country could be reached more[..] Guinea coast, France pushed south from th[e] and succeeded in extending its largely inland [..] to the Guinea coast in several projections that lat[er] became French Guinea, Ivory Coast, and Dahomey.

The interest of the French, however, lay in the development of the upper Niger, to the neglect of the equatorial lands. Railways were planned into the Niger country from the four coasts of Senegal, Ivory Coast, Guinea, and Dahomey. As any current map shows, however, France was still far from the accomplishment of its plan to build rail outlets for the interior provinces, when independence came.

In general French West Africa (Afrique Occidentale Française, or the AOF) was sparsely populated, and inadequate labor supply and lack of sufficient capital limited development and output. The drawbacks that handicapped the AOF remain with the new states: Mauritania (included here, as is Spanish Sahara, in the realm of the Maghrib) and the Republic of the Niger are desert, and population density in the two countries is 1.5 and 5 per square mile respectively. Four of the new countries lie intermediate between the desert and the Guinea forests, namely, the savanna lands of Senegal, Mali, Upper Volta, and Chad. Mali, the largest, is about one-third desert; the overall population density of the country is only about 8 per square mile. However, within Mali are the important irrigation and agricultural developments of the French, and in the basin of the upper Niger, densities are quite high. Densities in Senegal and Upper Volta are about the same as in the upper Niger, 29 per square mile; Chad has an overall density of not quite 5 per square mile.

Lack of transportation handicaps most of the new states. In places, it is unprofitable to produce for export because the lands lie so far inland from a railhead as to be almost completely isolated. Niger has only one short interior line that connects Niamey, the capital, with Tillabéri. Mali is served by a line

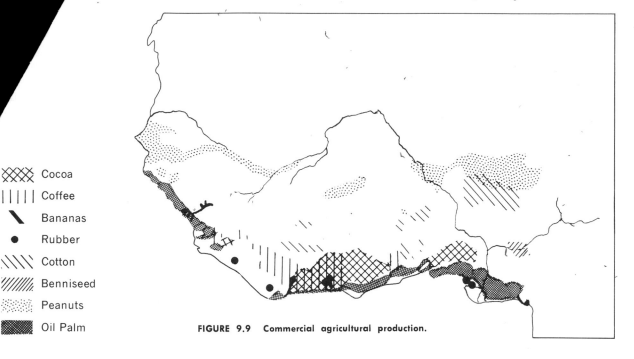

Cocoa

Coffee

Bananas

Rubber

Cotton

Benniseed

Peanuts

Oil Palm

**FIGURE 9.9   Commercial agricultural production.**

from Senegal that passes along the cultivated Niger lands through Kayes and Bamako to Koulikoro. Each of the four Guinea coast states has one line. The lines reach inland for varying distances; that passing through Ivory Coast runs on into Upper Volta to provide a rail outlet from the capital of that landlocked state. Large sections of the equatorial climates even near the coast are unable to produce for export because of the lack of transportation outlets. Senegal has the best transport network because it was the administrative center of the AOF.

### BRITISH DEVELOPMENTS

British colonization began at the coast and worked inland, and much effort naturally went into the development of equatorial crops, such as cacao and the oil palm; in the interior, especially in northern Nigeria, peanuts and cotton were promoted.

Contrary to what took place in the colonization of most equatorial and tropical lands on other continents, neither the British nor the French carried out any extensive plantation development in West Africa, with the result that most commercial production was and is done by West Africans themselves. Trading

companies have helped to spur the raising of export crops by buying up the produce, thus offering incentives. One of the most important aspects of development in British lands has been the marketing boards, which have stabilized prices and assured the sale of whatever was produced; they also have been instrumental in raising the quality of the product by rejecting inferior produce, such as cacao beans with too many bugs. Both the French and the British experimented with crops and crop varieties, and passed the information along to the African (see Figure 9.9).

In Ghana and Nigeria all the cacao produced is grown by Africans on small plots that average 1½ acres. The method introduced by the British was one not of clearing the land and then planting orchards, but of planting the trees within the natural forests, a suitable technique because cacao must be shade grown and sheltered from the wind; in Sierra Leone and Togoland, cacao growing developed along the same pattern. In Ivory Coast, Liberia, and the Cameroons, cacao is produced by Europeans on plantations, as it is also on the offshore islands of Fernando Po (Spanish), São Tomé, and Principe, the latter both Portuguese.

Cacao is exotic to Africa, having been introduced to São Tomé in 1822 by the Portuguese. During the early part of the nineteenth century attempts were made in the Gold Coast to grow it, but without success. It was not until 1879, when Tetteh Quashie of Akropong, Gold Coast, carried six beans home with him from plantations on Fernando Po, that it was successfully reintroduced. It spread from the Gold Coast to Nigeria, and 6 years later the first cacao beans were exported from mainland Africa, 121 pounds from Nigeria; Gold Coast did not begin to export until 1891. Today over two-thirds of the world's cacao comes from Africa, with Ghana and Nigeria leading as producers and exporters (see Figure 9.10).

The oil palm is another of the important export crops of the West. It is also one of the most important food plants, whether cultivated or gathered wild, because where the oil palm grows, the fruit provides most of the cooking fat for the African. Almost every cooked food prepared in areas where the oil palm grows contains some of the fresh, rich-colored gold-red oil that the Africans boil out of the fruit in small batches; every native market in equatorial Africa displays raw palm oil for sale.

The oil palm was indigenous to equatorial Africa, and grows well when cultivated; like cacao, it grows best where equatorial conditions are at their worst. As a matter of fact, cacao and oil palms are sometimes produced together, cacao being the secondary crop planted in the shade of the palm trees. Unilever at Yaligimbi, Congo, successfully experimented with this. In the wild state the trees grow very tall so that gathering the fruit is a dangerous task; cultivated palms have been bred shorter and shorter, permitting the bunches to be cut from the ground with curved knives on the end of long poles.

Oil palms are grown as a plantation crop (Figure 9.11). Sometimes, particularly on large plantations, the land is cleared of forest and the trees planted trimly in orchards. More frequently, forest areas in which oil palms grow wild are "enriched" by planting

**FIGURE 9.10** Plantation-grown cacao, Ghana. *(Photograph by writer.)*

**FIGURE 9.11** Termite hill rises jaggedly among the oil palms. *(Photograph by writer.)*

additional palm trees, or simply by some forest clearing which allows the palms to spread naturally. The
oil palm does not occur in the deep forest, but it
tends to move naturally into areas where forests are
disturbed by man's habitation and partially cleared.
Although it grows throughout equatorial Africa, there
are areas of greater and lesser production depending
largely upon whether or not the occupying Europeans
were interested in oil palm development. Nigeria and
The Congo are outstanding in the production of palm
oil in Africa, Nigeria leading the world in the export
of both palm oil and palm kernels.

Two types of oil are obtained from the one tree
and fruit, palm oil from the soft outer pulpy portion
of the fruit, and palm-kernel oil which is pressed
from the hard seed in the center of the fruit. Palm
oil is extracted and pasteurized before export; the
kernels are generally shipped in the seed state.

## PLANTATION DEVELOPMENTS IN RUBBER

Varieties of rubber plants are indigenous to Africa,
and up until the end of World War I, latex from
native trees such as *Funtumia elastica* and rubber-
bearing vines (*Landolphia heudelotii* and *L. awarien-
sis*) was shipped out. This gathering of wild rubber
came to a halt, however, as the *Hevea* rubber from
Malaya and the East Indies captured the market.
Thereafter, and until the Firestone plantations in
Liberia began to produce and export, almost no
rubber entered the world market from Africa.

Plantation rubber operations in Africa began in
1926 when Firestone leased land for this purpose
from the Liberian government, and in the same year
began clearing and planting. *Hevea brasiliensis*, native to America but grown commercially in Southeast
Asia, was introduced. The growing of rubber in
Liberia has been exceptionally successful, and up
until 1961, rubber accounted for 90 percent of Liberian exports by value. (See Figure 9.12.) Firestone has done much to encourage Liberians to plant
and grow rubber themselves; seedling trees are given
without charge to any Liberian who will clear land
and plant the seedlings. The result is that there are
now more than 2,000 Liberian farmers growing
rubber on about 60,000 acres of land that they have

(a)

(b

FIGURE 9.12 (a) Tapping the rubber tree: White liquid latex
runs into cup at Firestone Plantations, Liberia; (b) clearing the
land on the Goodrich Plantations, Liberia. (*Photographs by
writer.*)

cleared and planted with seedlings given to them by the American firm.

Agreements with the Liberian government entitle Firestone to lease up to 1 million acres of government land. Only 204,000 acres are held under concession, however, and of this 90,000 are "tree acres," that is, are being planted in rubber trees; about 68,000 acres of orchards are being tapped. Some of the Firestone orchards are already so old that trees are being taken off and replaced with new ones. Planting is, therefore, divided between old land and new, with between 1,000 and 1,500 acres of new land being planted to rubber trees annually.

In 1955 the B. F. Goodrich Company also began rubber plantations in Liberia on two concession plots of 300,000 acres each leased from the Liberian government (Figure 9.12b). A development area of 50,000 acres was selected along the Loffa River for the first orchards, and clearing of the rain forest was begun. By the end of 1960, 10,000 acres had been planted; since then, orchard planting has increased at a rate of about 1,000 acres annually, and the first trees were tapped in 1962.

Liberia was the only part of West Africa where there was a significant production of rubber for several decades. The great success of the American rubber ventures has been due in part to the careful planning and great expenditures of the American companies that have gone in; but success must also be attributed to the rubber plant selected, and to the natural environment. In the regions of rubber growing, rainfall averages 129 inches annually, and the soil is virgin and fertile. Two other countries of Africa, Nigeria and The Congo, have more than doubled their rubber production and exports in less than a decade. Most of the Nigerian plantations, both Nigerian and European owned, are in the Benin area northwest of the Niger delta. Cameroon also has made a beginning in the commercial production of rubber.

Coffee, kola nuts, coconuts for copra, and bananas are other crops produced for export in the equatorial parts of West Africa; cotton and peanuts are exported from the savannas. Among West African countries Nigeria and Senegal are the largest peanut producers, and Mali and Niger also raise large amounts; Nigeria and Chad raise the most cotton.

## Livestock

Many West Africans rear animals, and among those who do are many who practice no cultivation, and are even wholly nomadic. Climate, custom and culture, and the prevalence of the tsetse fly are all determinants of where pastoralism, or an integrated pattern of livestock rearing and agriculture is carried on. Where the tsetse fly occurs, as it does over hundreds of thousands of square miles of West Africa, the rearing of large animals is almost impossible, restricting both pastoralism and integrated farming; only small native cattle can survive the tsetse without inoculation. The definition of the livestock zones, in fact, is determined largely by the carrier of sleeping sickness. The south has almost no cattle, but is an area of cultivation where mixed farming would be very beneficial because animal manure could be used to enrich the highly leached soils. Animals are raised in numbers in the north because there the climate is drier and the tsetse less prevalent; generally speaking, sheep and camels graze in the *sahel,* and cattle in the moister parts of the savannas. Cattle rearing could be greatly extended if the tsetse were eliminated from the districts where it now prevails, and if better pasture and water supplies were available. If these conditions were improved, large numbers of people who are now nomads might be persuaded to take up sedentary ways and practice agriculture in combination with animal keeping; seasonal cattle movements, dictated by seasons of drought, would no longer be required. These migrations frequently necessitate at least the crossing of tsetse-infested country.

A considerable trade in animals is carried on between the north and south, but the political areas vary in meat consumption; per capita consumption of meat in the former British lands is far greater than in the former French territories, and Ghana is easily the largest per capita consumer of meat in West Africa. Among some of the purely pastoral people, such as some of the Fulani, cattle are kept for subsistence and prestige purposes only, and are never sold for meat unless the owner needs cash immediately or the animal for some reason is considered worthless.

Nigeria has by far the largest cattle population, and Kano is the great cattle market of West Africa.

From Kano the animals are driven on foot, or taken by railway, south into such centers as Lagos. No matter how the animals are brought to market, they arrive in poor condition. It often requires 3 months to drive the animals south; usually a number die on the way, the rest barely survive. Even the railroad journey, requiring nearly 2 days, is hard on the animals. If better means of transport were available, such as refrigerator trucks or railcars, animals could be slaughtered in the north, and the meat would arrive at its markets in better condition.

Because of its importance as a cattle center, Kano early became a market for hides and skins also, items that used to be sent by camel caravan across the Sahara. Because of this trans-Saharan trade in skins, which generally terminated in Morocco, the tanned hides of the Kano area became known as morocco leather. The fine tooling in gold also originated in Kano.

## Mineral and Power Resources

It was gold that brought the first Europeans to black Africa. In 1471 the Portuguese dropped anchor at Shama, on the delta of the Pra River in what later came to be known as the Gold Coast, and in the same year made the first direct shipment of gold to Europe of which we have a record. Previous to this, however, quite an important exchange of gold for salt had been carried on across the Sahara by caravan; it is also surmised that Carthaginians may have sailed down the Atlantic coastal waters and traded directly with the black Africans for the precious metal. West Africa has mined, panned, and traded gold for many centuries. The Falémé River and the nearby Bambouk Mountains were the sources of gold for ancient Ghana at the peak of its power about A.D. 1000.

The salt of the Sahara, more precious to many West Africans than their gold, has been dug and traded as long as gold has been; and on the Jos plateau, tin was taken and worked long before Europeans arrived, as was lead in southeast Nigeria, just east of Enugu in Ogoja Province. In fact, a number of articles of everyday use in West Africa were made from metal; brass weights, fashioned in the shapes of animals, birds, and other creatures of nature as well as allegorical figures, were used to balance the scales when measuring gold; ceremonial objects and ornaments were made of gold; bronze and brass founding, in the Benin area, may or may not have predated the Portuguese. Whichever is the case, some very distinctive pieces of bronze sculpture remain to attest to the high development of metalwork and art objects in this sector of Nigeria; where the copper and zinc with which to make the bronze came from is a mystery; the tin could have come from the Jos plateau. Throughout West Africa small blooms of iron ore were worked into domestic utensils such as hoes, hatchets, and even cooking pots.

Mining by Europeans did not begin in West Africa until 1878 when a Frenchman, Pierre Bonnat, began working the reefs of Tarkwa in the Gold Coast for gold. However, transportation difficulties and the unreliability of African labor long remained problems that restricted the scope of the operations. Gold mining was responsible for the building of the Gold Coast Railway in 1901 between Sekondi and Tarkwa, and the extensions in 1902 and 1912 to Obuasi and Prestea respectively.

Development of mineral resources in West Africa has largely awaited the opening of the mineralized area through transportation, so that in many cases, railroads have been built to permit the opening up of mines. Thus, the Bauchi Light Railway of Nigeria permitted the beginning of commercial tin mining in 1914; in 1927 the railway was extended right into the tin fields at Jos. The Nigerian Eastern Railway was constructed so that the mining of coal at Enugu could begin. An extension was added to the Gold Coast Railway in 1944 to bring bauxite from Awaso. The Liberia Mining Company would have been unable to begin iron ore operations at Bomi Hills without a railroad, and until the two new lines were constructed by companies which began developing iron ore in the Nimba Mountains and along the Mano River in 1959 and the early 1960s, Liberia's only railroad was the one built in 1951 by the Liberia Mining Company, a subsidiary of Republic Steel Corporation. It carries the ore from the mines at Bomi Hills to the docks near Monrovia. The railroad from Pepel to Marampa was opened to give outlet to the iron ores of Sierra Leone and Liberia.

Mining is important in the economy of West Africa. It accounts for a good share of the invested capital, and for large tax revenues to governments; minerals also comprise a considerable part of the value of West African exports. There are, however, differences between the former British and French territories both in incidence of mineral reserves and in their development. Although the former French territories do not appear to be minerally so rich as the former British lands, French West Africa was not so intensively prospected as were the lands of the British so that the mineral potential is not so well known; active prospecting in the French territories began only after World War II. A major deterrent to mineral development in the French lands has been the paucity of transportation, and some known deposits have not been developed because there is no economic way to get them out. Among the developed minerals of the West African realm are, in addition to gold, iron ore, tin, salt, diamonds, manganese, and bauxite.

Liberia is the major West African producer of iron ore, and, until the early 1960s, all of the ore came from the Bomi Hills reserve of the Liberia Mining Company. The Bomi Hills deposits are small but rich, assaying 35 million tons of 68 to 70 percent iron content ore that is about two-thirds magnetite and one-third hematite. Between 1 million and 1½ million tons are exported annually to the plants of Republic Steel in the United States, where the rich ore goes directly into open-hearth furnaces and used for experimental purposes. At the present small rate of production the Bomi Hills ores will last for a generation or more. Two other significant reserves were discovered in Liberia along the Mano River near the border of Sierra Leone, and in the Nimba Mountains in the east, about 170 miles inland from the coast. The Mano River deposits, which average about 53 percent iron content ore, are being developed by the National Iron Ore Company Ltd., of which the Liberian Government is the largest shareholder; production of iron ore began in 1961. The Mount Nimba deposits came into production in 1963. Development of these reserves is being carried out by the Liberian American-Swedish Minerals Company and Bethlehem Steel Corporation. The ores are high grade, and about 10 million tons are expected to be mined annually from Mount Nimba.

Sierra Leone and Guinea also have significant deposits of iron, although there has been almost no production from them as yet. The Guinea reserves are some of the largest in tropical Africa, but only those around Conakry are being tapped to any extent as yet. The iron content of the Guinea reserves ranges between 50 and 70 percent; some of the beds can be worked by open-pit methods. Mining operations did not begin in Guinea until 1949, and not until 1953 was the first iron exported. The major deposits of Sierra Leone, the Marampa-Lunsar and the Tonkolili River reserves, are mostly high grade ore with 60 to 65 percent iron content; these are the only West African reserves that were worked on a large scale before World War II.

The gold reserves of Ghana are the most important deposits of the precious metal in West Africa, and the quartz reefs of southern Ashanti and the Colony have produced 70 percent of the gold of West Africa since the turn of the century. The mine at Obuasi is possibly the "richest large goldmine in the world." Gold in Guinea is washed from the alluvial and residual deposits of the Bouré and Tinkisso Rivers; only Africans have been and are permitted to work these gold beds. Nigerian production is small and sporadic.

The development of the West African hydroelectric potential has scarcely begun. There are a number of possible sites on rivers where dams could be constructed and hydroelectricity generated—the Volta, the Niger, the Senegal, the Konkouré, and others—but the West African environment has a number of features that place difficulties in the way of such development. First, rivers are seasonal and evaporation generally high, so that very large dams are required to provide the needed storage and head of water; in areas of high humidity, insulation of cables is costly and difficult; and electric storms are a disturbance to the effective, economic, and smooth transmission of electric power. However, the need for electrical development is great, particularly for factories, mines, railways, and urban centers; and there is a high potential for development, especially in the southwest where heavy rainfall and vigorous rivers have cut gorges as the streams plunge to the coast from the Fouta Jallon and other lofty parts of the plateau.

Some small but significant hydroelectric installations have been built, but their service is local, limited to the area in which they are found. Plants along the southern edge of the Jos plateau in Nigeria provide electricity to the tin fields, and hydroelectric installations are in operation at the Grand Chutes in Guinea, where a plant began operations in 1954. The greatest projects are largely dreams that have been planned and talked about for a long time, but are still in prospect or in construction, such as the Volta River project on which Ghana places much of its hopes for industrial development; one on the Konkouré River, Guinea, will eventually harness power at the site of the Kaleta Falls near Kindia. This dam will be located sufficiently close to Conakry to supply the city with its electrical needs; but the main purpose, as in the Volta scheme, is the production of aluminum using the large bauxite deposits of the two countries.

The Volta River project (Figure 9.13) involves the construction of three dams, the largest about 70 miles north of the mouth of the river at Ajena. This dam would create a head of water sufficient to generate 617,000 kilowatts annually, of which approximately 50,000 kilowatts will be used for domestic purposes, the remainder for the conversion of bauxite into aluminum. Financing of the Volta project held up the project for several years, but it was under construction and partially completed in 1966.

A third hydroelectric project under consideration involves the Niger River in Nigeria. The plan proposes a multipurpose dam-and-storage construction, about 60 miles above Jebba, that would not only generate electricity and impound water for irrigation, but also improve conditions for navigation and fishing along the stream. Smaller schemes are also being studied. Those areas that have the highest precipitation, such as the southwest, the Cameroons Mountains, and the islands in the Bight of Biafra, hold the greatest potentials for large developments.

FIGURE 9.13 Volta River project. This map of Ghana shows the 250-mile lake that began to form in 1964 back of the dam at Akosombo. The route of the transmission lines that will serve the principal towns and industries is also shown.

## Change in West Africa

West Africa had achieved the most significant political, cultural, and economic advance of any portion of black Africa prior to its colonialization by Europeans. Great West African empires had arisen in succession before the European era, at times conquering much of the West African Sudan and even parts of the Sahara. None held together for very long, but they nevertheless achieved a political integration not attained elsewhere in Africa south of the Sahara.

The political and military achievements were matched by cultural and economic accomplishments. For nearly 2,500 years, West Africa has traded with North Africa and lands beyond by caravan across the desert. When European ships reached the shores of the Gulf of Guinea the trickle of commerce that had moved by desert train became a broad flow that was fed out through the ports, and some of the goods changed. It took the greater part of the nineteenth century to curb and eventually stop the traffic in slaves; some gold, ivory, and woods still go out, but in addition there are products of tropical agriculture, palm oil, peanuts, cacao, rubber, and the like, and industrial ores.

Like the country of Sudan that straddles the span of latitudes from equatorial to Saharan, from black to Mediterranean Africa, West Africa is a marchland. Aside from such sub-Saharan peoples as the Bushmen, Hottentots, and Pygmies, who number altogether only a few thousand, all of black Africa was populated by people who originated in what we call "West Africa." The blacks of Africa have had and still have their own area most properly in West and central Africa, though they migrated to occupy much of Africa south of the Sahara. In the past they lived also in the Sahara, which they spottily though rather completely occupied. But they have largely withdrawn from the desert, remaining only as small groups of servile peoples. Saharan peoples show admixture with the blacks, however.

Undoubtedly the most significant fact about West Africa in the past few years has been the political change from dependence to independence. In four years (1957 to 1961) the peoples of this whole great region, excepting Liberia, which has been sovereign since 1847, Portuguese Guinea, and Gambia, were accorded self-determination. In the French territories the people were given the choice of immediate independence, status as a French department, an overseas territory, or membership in the French Community. Guinea immediately chose independence.

Initially, the other countries elected to become self-determining members of the Community. Since independence, however, some of the states have withdrawn from the Community; some have attempted loose federations and/or union with blocs of other African nations; but none of these efforts at unification have stabilized sufficiently to indicate whether they are permanent or transitory alignments. Some dissolved almost as they were formed, such as the federation of Soudan (French, not Anglo-Egyptian) and Senegal to form Mali. At dissolution of the federation, the area formerly known as Soudan retained the federation name of Mali, the name of one of the illustrious West African kingdoms of the past. The lines drawn as boundaries for the new nations were lines of political expediency that had been drawn and used by the French for administrative purposes, not tribal divisions. In all instances, the provincial names were retained.

The countries that were created out of the British colonies and protectorates were already quite clearly defined when independence came. Gold Coast, incorporating British Togoland, became Ghana; the boundaries of Nigeria and Sierra Leone remained as they had been except, as noted before, that Northern Cameroon joined Nigeria.

# 10 INLAND SAHARAN-SAVANNA COUNTRIES

*You are not a country,*
*Afric, you are a concept, which we all*
*Fashion in our minds, each to each, to*
*Hide our separate years, to dream*
*our separate dreams.*

ABIOSEH NICOL

Geographic regions are intended to designate areas that have internal similarities, or show a broad, overall coherence. It is not possible for the unity to be complete; rather, a geographic region is one where men, cultures, economics, and environment interact in the same sort of relationships. Mali, Upper Volta, Niger, and Chad form such a region. They are inland Saharan-savanna lands, with common problems because of their interior position and their similar climatic and vegetational characteristics.

A different sort of region might well have been blocked out that would have grouped these four inland countries with Senegal, but then the regional association would have been based upon historic and physical characteristics while situation, an important factor in the economic development of the countries, would be disregarded. Hence, Senegal, although quite different climatically from Guinea, Sierra Leone, and Liberia, will be treated with the countries that occupy the southwest coastal sector of West Africa. They are oriented toward the sea; the inland states are land bound and hence land oriented, handicapped because they lie far from the coasts.

The inland Saharan-savanna countries lie in the heart of the northern half of the African continent, distant from the oceans and relatively inaccessible except by air. They are some of the least known of the newly independent states, although together they comprise a region more than half the size of continental United States without Alaska. Individually, the countries also are large; Chad, Niger, and Mali are each nearly twice the size of Texas while Upper Volta is two-thirds as large as California.

Semiarid in the south and arid in the north, these inland countries present a variety of landscapes despite the fact that only the southernmost margins are humid savanna, and none equatorial forest. Throughout, people are spread unevenly across the land, although the majority of the inhabitants live in the south, which is also the most productive sector; here most of the subsistence crops, and peanuts and cotton, the commercial crops, are raised. North of this southern fringe the desert nearly takes over. As sahel becomes near desert, sedentary adjustments give way to purely nomadic cultures, rain cultivation to pastoralism or oasis life. The animal keepers, depending entirely upon their herds for livelihood, migrate constantly in search of water and pasture.

This part of West Africa is racially and culturally related to the people who inhabit the African lands still farther north; racially they are in the majority Caucasian with admixtures of black, linguistically they are largely Afro-Asian, and religiously Islamic. As in Mauritania, people of Afro-Asian derivation are dominant and are in the main pastoral; the black Africans are the cultivators, inhabiting the southern zones as cultivators, or if they live in the desert and semidesert regions, they occupy subservient positions as cultivators for the overlord groups. A broad irregular zone of mixture of black and Caucasian exists between approximately 10 and 15 to 18°N.

## Mali

Mali has a storied past. Formerly the Sudanese Republic (French Soudan), it holds the lands where the most famous of the early West African empires were centered—Ghana, the Mandingan empire of Mali, and the kingdom of the Songhai; it has within its bounds Timbuktu and the historically famed salt oasis of Taoudenni.

It is mostly a dry land of livestock and irrigated cultivation; within its domain are the extensive irrigation works that were carried out by the French along the Niger River close to the netherlands, the greatest effort made by France in the development of its vast West African empire. Despite the irrigation works, its most important resources are its animals. It is a poor country of few opportunities, and many Sudanese annually migrate to more productive parts of West Africa to find work in peanut fields, on plantations, or in mines in Senegal, Gambia, Guinea, the Ivory Coast, and Ghana. In the extreme north desert takes over, and even the Adrar des Iforas, a massif of some elevation in the northeast, receives less moisture than does the Aïr massif in the Niger Republic. Southward as far as Timbuktu, and east and west from there, semidesert to desert conditions prevail. Farther south is the sahel, and beyond there dry savanna becomes merely a moister savanna.

Yet few areas of Africa have captured the imagination and endured in geographical folklore as have the lands that constitute present-day Mali. Timbuktu was a name that for centuries was "a symbol of remoteness"; it was a desert entrepôt of Saharan trade.

Timbuktu is the link between two worlds, the Saharan and that of the Niger, one of Africa's great rivers. It was founded during the twelfth century by Tuareg nomads who used to come down from the desert to the river during the dry season. The site had artesian water that was sweet and good; the name, which should be spelled Tin-Buktu, means "the well of Buktu." In the past, the city was a spiritual, educational, cultural, and trade center of the Moslem world; to a lesser degree it still is. But its day is past; the great east-west routes of the future lie far to the south, in line approximately with Dakar and Bamako; other lines will move even farther southward.

In March, 1961 Mali and the U.S.S.R. signed an accord for the construction of a railroad from Bamako to Kouroussa (Guinea), where it will connect with the line that terminates at Conakry. After the federation between Soudan and Senegal broke up, use of the rail line to the Senegalese port of Dakar stopped for some time, but it has again been reopened.

### THE PHYSICAL CHARACTER

Most of Mali is very flat and very dry, but it has some distinctive relief features that should be noted.

**FIGURE 10.2    Along the Niger River at floodtime. (Courtesy Embassy of Niger Republic.)**

The north-west is largely covered with the *erg* of the Djouf basin; in the northeast is a barren region occupied only by a few nomadic Tuareg, Adrar des Iforas, a massive outlier of the Ahaggar. To the north-west of this massif are the *reg* wastes of the Tanezrouft, like the sandy deserts of the Djouf almost empty of inhabitants. Several imposing sandstone scarps, marking erosion of the plateau, range themselves across parts of Mali, notably the Tambaoura south of Kayes, the scarp of the Manding Mountains, and the grand Bandiagara scarp extending north and south for some 200 miles from near Banfora in Upper Volta toward the Niger bend; the latter escarpment faces the twin headwaters of the Black Volta.

The Niger River curves through and drains southern and central Mali. The river sweeps down from the Guinea highlands, enters Mali a little above Bamako, and flows north-northeast into and through the inland delta called the "netherlands" of the Niger. These netherlands are the interior basin into which the waters of the Niger headstreams used to disappear before their capture by the headward-eating stream that today is the lower Niger, i.e., the sector north of the netherlands; the delta is the alluvial fan deposited by the headstreams as they issued from the mountains onto the lowlands.

Just beyond the delta, the river makes its enormous bend between Timbuktu and Gao, and then takes its southwest course across the handle of Niger and western Nigeria to its juncture with the Benue. At this point it turns directly south to the Gulf of Guinea. It is the Niger valley of Mali, and especially the inland delta just east of Timbuktu, that is the most important part of the country. The netherlands are flooded annually at the time of the summer rains as are also other riverine lands along the Niger valley (Figure 10.2).

This river and its affluents are the "life-givers" of Mali; historically, the flooded lands have been cultivated. It was, in fact, the evidenced productivity of these African-cultivated lands that led the French to abandon attempts at plantation agriculture in Senegal, and to concentrate their efforts in tropical cultivation in the interior Niger country; and control of the Niger waters was one of the earliest and boldest of the development schemes conceived in West Africa. Planning was begun in the 1920s, but the first phase of the ambitious project was not realized until the Sansanding barrage, begun in 1934, was completed in 1941 (except for temporary wooden sluices that remained in position until 1947).

The Senegal River and some of its tributaries drain western Mali.

## LIVELIHOOD

The area irrigated by the scheme is the riverine land that reaches from Segou to just short of Timbuktu, namely, the inland delta lands. Most of this region forms the "prehistoric or 'dead' delta" of the Niger, and can be irrigated by gravity flow; completion of the dam and the flood control it provides makes it possible to irrigate the lands of the " 'live' central delta" as well, thereby increasing many times over the amount of land that can be watered. In the 1930s it was anticipated that some 4,000 square miles of land would be affected as against a possible 30,000 square miles now. However, as with the project in Sudan along the Atbara, people are being drawn only slowly to this area, and one of the problems appears to be to make full use of the potential.[1]

Rice occupies about two-thirds of the irrigated delta lands, and cotton and peanuts take up most of the remainder. In the nonirrigated lands along the floodplain of the Niger, especially below Timbuktu, millet and rice are grown, and in the uplands, millet, peanuts, and cotton are raised during the rainy season. (Typical rainfall averages are, in inches: Sikasso, 55; Bamako, 44; Kayes, 30; Mapti, 20; Gao, 9; Timbuktu, 9; and it gets drier going north, and rainfall becomes less predictable.)

The irrigation developments along the Niger were made initially to further the cultivation of cotton. Today more cotton is raised without irrigation than with it. Peanuts also are a dry crop, and Mali ranks third, after Nigeria and Senegal, in West African territories in peanut production, and fourth in Africa. Rice is the great irrigation crop, and Mali produces more than her needs. However, there are few crops of Mali that will stand the expense of the long overland transport; and limited outlets are also a handicap.

[1] George H. T. Kimble, *Tropical Africa*, New York: The Twentieth Century Fund, vol. I, 1960, p. 176.

Livestock are more important in Mali than in any of the former French West African territories. The pastoralists are nomadic, migrating toward the desert during the moister season and toward the south during the period of drought. Tens of thousands of cattle and sheep are sold annually to countries to the south, and to centers toward Dakar. Bamako and Kayes are leading markets for animals as well as hides and skins.

Fishing is important to people living along the Niger, both for subsistence and trade; normally dried fish is exported to other parts of West Africa.

Although gold was a significant item of commerce during the eras of the great empires, it is of far less importance today. Nevertheless one of the chief producing areas of alluvial gold in West Africa is in the Bambouk district of Mali along the Falémé River, which is tributary to the Senegal; this was also the great producer of the past. Salt also has historically been exploited, extracted in great blocks at Terhazza and Taoudenni and transported across the desert to market centers by camel caravan. Although the salt resources are large, only about one-fourth of Mali's needs are supplied from Taoudenni today because of the competition of salt produced along the Senegal coasts by evaporation of seawater. Iron, manganese, tin, lead, and zinc also occur; iron is found near Kayes and between Kayes and Bamako.

*Cities.* Bamako, the capital of Mali, was a mere African village when occupied by the French in 1883. It grew rapidly, however, when in 1904 it became the terminus of the railroad from Kayes, where goods were transshipped to the Senegal River and thence to Dakar; when the railway was extended through to Dakar in 1924 its growth was even more rapid. Early in the century it replaced Kayes as the capital of French Soudan. By Western standards it is still not large, as the population is only somewhat over 120,000; it is, however, an important administrative and communications center. Handicrafts are important.

As the transshipment point between rail and river transportation, Kayes developed into a major market center for cattle, sheep, skins, hides, and gums. Gum arabic is collected in the savannas and exported. Its importance is far less than in the past because of the development of and competition from the industry in Sudan (of the Niles). Koulikoro is a river port, especially significant because it marks the head of navigation on the middle and upper Niger. As such it is also a market town. Many other towns might be mentioned, all small, but important to Mali. One other should be named—Gao, river port and terminus of caravan routes of the Sahara. In the past it ranked with Timbuktu as a center of commerce, affluence, and political influence. Airplanes now fly in and out of Bamako, Gao, Timbuktu, Goundam, and other cities; Bamako has international service.

## Niger

Two-thirds of Niger is desert. Like Mali, it is semiarid in the south and arid in the north; but it is more handicapped than Mali because all of its drainage is interior and erratic except in the extreme southwestern panhandle, where the Niger runs across the country. Its situation is also more disadvantageous than that of the country to the west because the sea lies still more distant. It has no rail outlets; the only means of access to the coast are via the Niger River or roads, which are poorly developed.

Niger is a big country, bigger than Texas and California together, the largest of the states carved out of French West Africa, of which it made up the Niger Territory. East-west it stretches almost 1,000 miles; its greatest north-south depth is about 650 miles. But it is a spare country with few resources, people, and opportunities. The only permanently cultivable land is in the Niger valley; away from that area cultivation becomes spotty, then peters out. (See Figure 10.3.)

The Aïr massif occupies the west central part of the Niger domain, and outward from here, east and west, extends *erg*, barren sand desert almost uninhabited and uninhabitable. The north is plateau, an extension from the Ahaggar that reaches nearly to the Tibesti Mountains. The Aïr Mountains are one of the historic power centers of the West African kingdoms. They are inhabited by Berber peoples, the most famous of whom are the Tuareg, who entered from Fezzan in the eleventh century. "They obviously had considerable contact with the Romans, because they use Roman names for the months and for many other

things. Although not Christian, they use many ornaments of cruciform pattern and, whilst professing Islam of a non-dogmatic kind, the men are veiled, not the women."[2]

A sultanate was established at Agadès at least as early as the fifteenth century. Its importance derived from trans-Saharan trade; Agadès and Aïr lay on the Ghadames road that ran from Tunisia to Katsina in what is today Nigeria.

As a center of political power Agadès was supreme until 1870, although it reached its zenith of power during the latter part of the sixteenth century, during which time Bornu (Nigeria) was made tributary to it. The French occupied the Niger territory between 1897 and 1900. The Niger-Nigeria boundary agreed upon between France and Britain was set far enough south to give the French (and now Niger) a well watered road from Lake Chad to the Niger River, but it politically severed the north-south trade routes and divided the Hausa country in two.

### LAND, PEOPLE, AND LIVELIHOOD

Over nine-tenths of the people of Niger are animal keepers or farmers. Since the only perennial stream of the country is that small portion of the Niger River that runs across the southwest corner, the people are highly dependent upon the exigencies of the climate for the success of their activities—heat, evaporation, burning sun and winds, and low precipitation. Nearly half of the country receives less than 4 inches of rainfall annually; another 28 percent averages between 4 and 14 inches. Famine and malnutrition have plagued this land through the centuries.

Millet and sorghum, or Guinea corn, are the main subsistence crops; wheat and vegetables are also grown along the Niger River. During the last few years of French tenure, attempts were made to establish cooperatives and granaries so that surplus food in good years could be stored for use in possible bad ones; the peanut was introduced as a cash crop, and between 1954 and 1958 the amount of land put to peanuts nearly doubled. Although production varies according to the weather and market prices, peanuts

[2] R. J. Harrison Church, *West Africa*, 2d ed., London: Longmans, Green & Co., Ltd., 1961, p. 263.

have provided a source of income that gives added insurance against famine. Cotton was introduced as a cash crop as recently as 1956. Although production is small, it is mounting. Permanent cultivation is limited to the Niger valley and to the land just to the east of the river and north of Nigeria in a band about 80 miles wide. In this limitation of cultivation (except for date oases) to the valley of the river that lies in the extreme southwest of the country, Niger resembles Mauritania.

After agriculture, stock raising is the next important occupation. The estimated number of livestock is large but pasture is meager and water scarce; and the continual wandering in search of water and grass, and endemic diseases have made the quality of the livestock poor. Further, among some of the pastoralists it is not the custom to sell their animals. Nevertheless, Niger is the source of some very fine leathers and hides. According to an official French source, "the label 'Maradi goat' [from Niger] is as prized as that of 'Sokoto goat' in Nigeria."

Except for the Aïr Mountains and its environs, livestock raising is confined to those parts of the country that are south of latitude 15°N, a limited area far more restricted than in Mali; cattle are highly concentrated in the south and southwest, and are generally of the zebu variety except near Lake Chad, where the peculiar long-horned Chad cattle are found. Before the number of animals can be increased, more watering places must be provided. Except in the Aïr Mountains, where water occurs at depths of 15 to 20 feet, most wells would have to reach 100 to 250 feet before yielding groundwater.

Although tin and tungsten occur in the Aïr massif mining is unimportant, one mining company producing only about 80 tons of ore annually; a lack of transport facilities also hampers their development. There is no industry in Niger except for a few peanut pressing mills and a cotton gin built by the French. Opportunities are so limited that many people emigrate to Ghana, where they usually engage in trade.

City life is almost absent. The capital, Niamey, situated in the irrigated lands in the southwest on the Niger River, has a population of less than 30,000. Only three other centers have populations over 10,000, namely, Zinder, Tahoua, and Maradi. Life is tribal, as are allegiances. To weld these independent people

FIGURE 10.3 Irrigating the land, Niger. (Courtesy Embassy of Niger Republic.)

and immense territories into a nation will not be an easy task. Zinder is the old capital, and now is the principal center for the marketing of peanuts, hides, and skins. Leather and textile handicrafts are important here. Agadès, previously mentioned, is the town of Aïr. Aside from being a political center and the place where the extensive trade in salt was organized for the whole of central Sudan, it used to be a great slave market. Today it is known for its wools, leatherwork, especially saddlery, and metal sheaths.

## PROBLEMS

Paucity of resources handicaps Niger, and outstanding is the uniform deficiency of water throughout the entire country. Aridity characterizes the land, making the climate trying and developments of any kind difficult or impossible. Remote and sparsely populated Aïr has the most healthful and pleasant climate, but it is so distant from markets that any great development of either the livestock industries or of agriculture is unlikely. The most productive regions are the southwest and south. Although both the relief of the country and the composition of its populace are varied, aridity and the water deficit circumscribe what can be done; all development waits an increase in water supply.

Another of Niger's great problems is its remote, land-locked position: to the north the Sahara continues; east and west are the countries of Chad and Mali, both poor states with transport systems but little developed. The best outlets for Niger lie to the south through Nigeria and Dahomey; both block Niger from the sea; the Dahomey route, which leads by road to Cotonou, involves ferrying rivers. In 1958 a department of the French Government allocated 6 million dollars for building a bridge at one of the particularly difficult crossings. The shortest routes to the outside are along the roads from Maradi to Katsina, and from Zinder to Kano. From Kano goods can move by rail to the port of Lagos, 700 miles distant in the south. Peanuts, which make up 75 percent of the total value of Niger's exports, go out via Nigeria; so also do the hides and skins, and what little gum as is exported. Imports face the same distances and transport costs.

## The Republic of Chad

### THE CHAD BASIN

Lake Chad, shared by four countries, lies in the midst of a large depression that is more or less enclosed on all sides by higher relief features—the Tibesti of Chad, the Aïr of Niger, the plateau of northeast Nigeria and the Mandara Mountains of Cameroon Republic, the Ubangi-Chari uplands of the Central African Republic, and the mountains of Darfur in Sudan. Rivers, perennial and ephemeral, drain to the interior from all these eminences, and the region around the lake is essentially a sand desert that is an alluvial plain built up by the deltaic deposits of rivers, especially those that flow from the south, the Chari-Logone system and the Komadougou.

The plain becomes a quagmire during the rainy season. Lake Chad, in fact, lies in the midst of an enormous area of swamps and is extremely variable in size. From season to season and between good and bad years, it expands and contracts: Since the terrain about the lake is very flat, an additional depth of even 1 foot can enlarge the water covered area by several

hundreds of square miles; on the other hand, a strong, desiccating wind can, almost equally as fast, shrink the lake and return large areas to dry land. Lake Chad has at times been far larger than it is at present. When the climate was more humid, the lake overflowed into the Bodélé (the lower Chad basin or the Chad netherlands, about 250 miles to the northeast) through the Bahr el Ghazal, now a dry wadi. The portrayal of Lake Chad on maps is rarely correct.

Although the Chad basin has no outlet to the sea, some of the waters that normally drain into the basin are beginning to find their way to the Gulf of Guinea, for the headwaters of the Benue River are slowly cutting back the divide that separates the upper Benue from the Chari. In time this subsequent stream (see Glossary) will undoubtedly capture the waters of the Chari; already, during the rainy season, the two systems connect. This will hasten the drying up of the swamps and the recession of the lake.

### THE LAND OF CHAD

The Republic of Chad occupies a large part of the Chad depression. Topographically the country itself is basinlike with a plain, in the west central area centered by the lake, that fans upward to greater heights on all sides except where the sandy plains of Chad and Niger merge. On the south the Ubangi-Chari upland marks the water divide between the Chad and Congo basins. The Chari and the Logone are the largest rivers that drain toward the north. They flow into Lake Chad as a single river, forming a single delta because at Fort Lamy the Logone joins the Chari; they are perennial streams, for they rise in moist equatorial uplands. Streams from the Darfur at times are tributary to the Chari, such as the Aouk and the Selamat, but more frequently they lose their waters in the sands before they reach the river; the majority are ephemeral, their beds dry wadis most of the time. In the northeast, the basin rises to the Ennedi Mountains of Chad, where peaks rise to 4,756 feet and then slope toward Sudan.

On the north the desert mounts to the heights of the Tibesti massif, which covers nearly a sixth of the country; from here wadis, only occasionally carrying water, lead into the basin. The Tibesti is a gigantic dome of volcanic origin about 250 miles in diameter.

Thrusting upward from the relatively flat plateau that surrounds it on all sides to elevations of over 11,000 feet, it is an impressive and arresting feature; its greatest eminence, Emi Koussi, is a superb extinct volcano. The sides of the dome are deeply scarred by dry riverbeds, indicative of times when the channels carried more water. Tibesti is like the other massifs of the Sahara; both the stream pattern and faunal remains indicate a past that was more humid.

Chad is the largest of the inland Saharan-savanna states, its domain nearly as great as the combined areas of Washington, Oregon, California, Nevada, and Idaho. It stretches across 15° of latitude, from 8 to 23°N, in the heart of northern Africa—almost a thousand miles from the Red Sea, nearly 2,000 miles from the Atlantic to the west; north and south the nearest coasts are almost 600 miles away. It is, therefore, landlocked; inaccessibility is one of its foremost characteristics. This and its tropical location make Chad what it is.

*Habitat, People, and Adaptation.*  Water supply is the major problem in the Chad; perennial rivers are few in number, and rain is concentrated or small in amount. Vegetationally, it ranges from wooded savanna in the south through bush steppe into the Sahara. In the south the wet and dry seasons are of about equal length, and rainfall averages between 35 and 47 inches, concentrated during the high sun period; in central Chad the dry season is longer, the wet season shorter, and rainfall averages between 20 and 35 inches; in the north the dry season lengthens, rainfall is slight and unpredictable, and vegetation is almost absent; in other words, the desert prevails. The Tibesti Mountains are moister than most of the northern half of the country, however, especially in the higher parts, and there are places along the base of the dome where enough water emerges for cultivation; at its base in the south lies the Bodélé depression, a region of oases.

As in the other inland Saharan states, water forces people to concentrate, leaving wide areas unpopulated or inhabited only transiently by nomads. On the alluvial plains of the Chari-Logone rivers in the southwest, sedentary cultivators grow cotton and peanuts as commercial crops, and millet, sorghums, and cassava as subsistence starches. Cassava was unknown in

Chad until the 1930s when the French introduced it here. Since then it has spread rather rapidly from people to people, northward as far as it will grow. Paddy rice, introduced during World War II, is successfully raised in the alluvial lands that lie between the Chari and Logone rivers.

Cotton is grown by dry farming methods. Although cotton has been raised by Moslems for local use for a long time, it was not until the introduction of dry farming into southern Chad that it became commercial. A good deal of research has been put into cotton culture, and both quality and production have risen. Under the French, bonuses were paid for land put into cotton; this also encouraged the Africans to plant the industrial crop. Twenty-five factories gin and bale cotton, and an oil mill for pressing the seeds recently has been built. This produces not only the oil but seedcake, which is used as fertilizer and as fuel for the mills.

In the southern half of the country, both cultivation and animal keeping are practiced. Few of the people are purely nomadic. The savannas carry large numbers of cattle, sheep, goats, camels, and horses, and the animal industries are more important than farming. Beyond the 15th parallel the people are oasis cultivators or nomadic pastoralists. About 50,000 herdsmen roam across the moister parts of the more than 230,000 square miles of arid lands; population averages one inhabitant to every 4 or 5 square miles. There is little that is contributed to the economy from the north.

The country is overwhelmingly rural. There are only three towns of any size in Chad, Fort Lamy, Moundou, and Fort Archambault. Fort Lamy numbers fewer than 75,000, Fort Archambault fewer than 20,000 inhabitants.

Although the Chad has large numbers of livestock, the income from them is small, for the quality is poor because of inadequate pasture and water supplies. Meat and milk are locally consumed, and animal products are exported both on the hoof and as meat; leather is an item of trade. Modern meat-packing is done at Fort Lamy, and the town takes care of about four-fifths of the animals processed; Fort Archambault and Abéché have smaller facilities. Nigeria takes most of Chad's animal exports; the rest go to the Central African Republic and Cameroon.

*Problems.* Chad is contrasted in climate and opportunity between the north and south, and the diversity between the two parts is further emphasized because the north tends to be racially Caucasian and Islamic in religion, and the south to be Negro and predominantly non-Moslem. In this it is like neighboring Sudan. Since there are a number of ethnic groups and a great deal of linguistic variety, French is the official language of government and the one spoken commonly among the educated, but unity is difficult.

The economy is based largely on subsistence agriculture and pastoralism, partly because Chad is a poor country and arid, partly because of handicaps imposed by its isolated landlocked position. Even within the country transportation is difficult because distances are vast, and there are no payloads. Most of the crops and animals raised are consumed locally, although, as noted, animals, cotton, and peanuts are exported.

Some rare minerals have been discovered, such as tungsten in the Tibesti Mountains, but only natron (native sodium carbonate) is mined. Most of this likewise is consumed within the country, leaving only about 3,000 tons annually available for export to Nigeria and the Central African Republic. Again it is in part transportation that has delayed development of the mineral resources, although the backward character of the culture also plays a part.

A considerable amount of the traffic (passenger and goods) within, and in and out of the country goes by air. A look at the map of Africa will explain why. Chad has no railroads. There are innumerable trails within the country, and three arterial land routes out of the Republic that give access to and from the Gulf of Guinea, the Atlantic, and the Nile; all focus on Fort Lamy. One leads south to Pointe-Noire and Douala, the second west-southwest to Port Harcourt, and the third heads directly across Sudan to El Obeid and north to Khartoum.

Some of the waterways are navigable only during part of the year. The Chari River between Fort Lamy and Fort Archambault can be navigated only from July to February; but from Fort Lamy to Lake Chad it is navigable the year around. Natron and dried fish are shipped south along this stretch of the river. The Logone, although navigable above Fort Lamy, has so tortuous a course that barges must be short, which limits the value of the waterway. Logs float down some of the streams into Chad from the Central African Republic.

## Upper Volta

Although Upper Volta is the smallest of the inland Saharan-savanna states, its latitudinal position is better than that of the other countries for it lies farther south and has no desert; all of its lands are savannas that range from the Guinea type or wet woodland into *sahel*. Most of the country is cultivable, therefore, although there are many places where the land is unproductive.

Because of its southerly location, Upper Volta receives more rainfall than do the other inland states of West Africa. The southwest lobe of the country has an average of about 46 inches a year, concentrated between May and October; the central region receives an average of 33 inches, concentrated within a slightly shorter season, usually from May to September; toward the north this declines to about 29 inches; the extreme north is *sahel*. Relative humidity is very low during the height of the dry season, especially in the central and northern parts, and evapotranspiration is excessive.

The surface of the country is almost monotonously level. There is a slight slope toward the south, and an occasional steplike drop in the terrain; some granite domes occur, and escarpments are found in the sandstone region in the west. Some of the latter are impressive, especially that of the Sikasso plateau facing southeast toward Banfora; its steep edges rise up over 500 feet.

The nature of the rocks makes water a problem in almost all parts of the country. In the southwest sandstone area, percolation of water is very rapid, and the water table lies far below the surface, making the digging of wells expensive and difficult. Throughout most of the rest of the country, on the other hand, the rocks are generally impermeable, and waters run off so rapidly that stream beds are either flashflooding or dry. A study of any good map of Upper Volta will show that nearly all the rivers of the country are ephemeral, tending to become perennial only near or beyond the borders; the Black Volta and Oti rivers are exceptions to this. The country drains to the Volta River, and to a lesser extent, to the Niger.

## THE LAND AND THE PEOPLE

The population is about 4 million. Small as this is for a large territory (Upper Volta is nearly the size of Italy), it is larger than that of any of the other states within this region; but the uneven distribution of the people makes some areas unduly dense, others un-inhabited. The emptiest lands are the swamps and floodlands, where disease-carrying insects abound: the lands bordering the major streams, that is, the three Voltas and the Bougouriba, are generally un-settled up to 12 miles outward from the riverbanks because they flood, and they are infested with the tsetse fly, vector of sleeping sickness; north of Pama is an enormous swamp area in the Fada N'Gourma district where the *Simulium* fly prevails; the bite of this insect may introduce larvae into the eye, causing blindness. In the extreme southwest is another empty area. Population clusters in the center of the country, making this sector overdense. Despite the extent of the almost empty regions, the overall density is 5 or 6 times that of any of the other dry inland states.

Interior location makes it difficult for Upper Volta to develop any large export trade. It does have an advantage, however, that the other states inland from the coast do not have, namely, it is connected by rail-road from Ouagadougou, which is centrally situated, to the fine port of Abidjan, Ivory Coast. The major population centers, therefore, are served by a 733-mile-long rail line. Although freight charges are high, by opening up an efficient outlet to the sea the rail-way encourages the expansion of commercial agri-culture and the development of new industries.

Nine-tenths of the people are cultivators or animal keepers. Aside from subsistence starches, cotton and peanuts are the principal crops raised, and they are the cash crops. Peanuts are most important in the south and southwest where rainfall is most sure. Crushing mills for obtaining peanut oil have been erected in Bobo Dioulasso, and most of the peanut crop that is exported goes out in this form; the less bulky, more valuable product stands the shipping costs better. Rice cultivation has been introduced, and appears to have a promising future. The oily fruit of the shea tree (karite) is gathered in the south, and provides the main source of fat for local use; some is also exported. Sisal is cultivated on plantations by Europeans in the southwest around Bobo Dioulasso, but the amount grown is small because the cost of production is high in Upper Volta as compared with similar costs in the East African plateau.

In 1962 the Volta government contracted with the United Nations' Special Fund for the development of a program of agricultural experiment, demonstra-tion, and training. The experiment involves nearly 3,000 acres of land southwest of Ouagadougou where mixed farming methods will be tried out; a breeding station for sheep, cattle, and poultry, a nursery of trial plots for seed selection, and a vocational school for agricultural training are also part of the project. Water is provided from a tributary of the Black Volta and from wells sunk at the site of the experiment.

Livestock are Upper Volta's leading produce, how-ever, and animals and animal products represent more than half the export revenue taken in. Because of the prevalence of the tsetse fly in the more humid south, only the small African-type cattle are kept here; in the north, zebu cattle prevail. Sheep, goats, donkeys, horses, and hogs also are raised, and sheep numeri-cally represent about 2½ times the number of cattle. Improvement in animal breeding and the varieties bred is desirable but difficult. However, it is estimated that there is good pastureland for grazing many more head of cattle if adequate water can be obtained. Ouagadougou has a well-equipped, modern meat-processing plant.

Dried fish are an important export, second in value to animals on the hoof. They are caught in rivers and raised in fishponds, and dried before being shipped. Exported fish bring in over 1 million dollars in reve-nue a year.

*Prospects.* Many of the people of Upper Volta are skilled cultivators. But for the majority, the frustra-tions of unproductive soil, extensive erosion, primitive methods of agriculture, and a deficiency of water have made the country one of the major sources of labor migration in Africa; there is a large seasonal move-ment of labor to cacao and coffee plantations, and to cities in both the Ivory Coast and Ghana.

Volta has little mineral wealth. Gold occurs, and has long been mined in the territory, but the annual yield is less than 500 pounds of fine metal. Manganese and bauxite are known to occur at Kiéré in the west, and there are two well-known "native workings" of iron. The ore from these mines is primitively smelted, and used only in the making of domestic tools and implements.

The difficulties that stand in the way of Upper Volta in its attempts to modernize and develop its economy, and lift the level of living of its people, such as remoteness from market-outlets and transportation costs, water shortage, poor soils, endemic diseases, and a relatively dense population that is often insufficiently nourished, seem almost insurmountable.

France began trying to overcome some of these handicaps a number of years ago. Between 1947 and 1960 grants totaling over 50 million dollars were made by France to Upper Volta for development; about one-third of this was used to extend the railway from the south to Ouagadougou. Some progress in disease control and eradication, notably in sleeping sickness, was also made.

These are achievements not to be discounted. However, the country is resource-poor, lacks capital, and has a difficult climate as well as a people who are little educated and technically untrained, for the most part, to overcome the difficulties. The country will not have an easy time.

# 11 SOUTHWEST COASTAL STATES OF WEST AFRICA

*You cannot find a peril so great
that the hope of reward will not
be greater. . . . Go forth, then, and
. . . make your voyage straightway.*

PRINCE HENRY THE NAVIGATOR

Historically and until about the turn of the century, these lands were known as Senegambia and the Grain Coast, so called from the old trade in "grains of paradise" (*Amomum melegueta*), a kind of pepper. Since then, they have been designated as they are today— Senegal, Gambia, Portuguese Guinea, Guinea, Sierra Leone, and Liberia. All but Liberia were parts of the African empires of France, Britain, and Portugal; today little of this coast is still held by these powers. Neither Britain nor France retains dependencies; Portugal, however, has given up none of her African holdings, and Portuguese Guinea and the islands of Principe and São Tomé in the Bight of Biafra remain to her, a reminder that the Portuguese were the first to explore and establish posts and an empire along the West African coast. As with other early held Portuguese lands in Africa, slaves, obtained from African intermediaries, were shipped out as well as gold, ivory, and "grain" (melegueta pepper).

These African riches were in part the reason for the rise of Lisbon to great eminence. Although Portugal has been in Portuguese Guinea since its discovery in 1446, the interior was not pacified until 1912.

Politically, the Southwest coastal region is a mosaic of states. Liberia has been independent for over 115 years and Portuguese Guinea is still colonial, while in between are the now independent, formerly colonial territories of France and Britain. Gambia and Sierra Leone are sovereign states but remain in the Commonwealth; Guinea cast off all ties with France upon independence, while Senegal is a member of the Community of Nations.

Environmentally there is considerable unity. South from Senegal's southern boundary and all the way across Liberia, perhumid to humid conditions prevail and rainfall averages from 59.1 to 118.1 inches annually; in places, it goes considerably higher. This sector is climatically equatorial monsoon or tropical highland, and vegetationally ranges from equatorial forest, to a forest-savanna complex, to woodland savanna of the moist type. Only Senegal and the little riverine enclave of Gambia lie beyond these limits; they might, on the basis of climate and vegetation, have been treated with the inland Saharan-savanna countries, for here in the north the baobab grows, and in terms of moisture the lands are generally subhumid to semiarid with a rainfall that varies from approxi-

mately 59 inches on the moister Casamance edges, where the climate is monsoonal, down to about 15 inches in the north and interior, which are the dry sides; vegetationally they range from moist woodland-savanna to dry woodland-savanna, to grass-brush savanna and tropical steppe (southern *sahel*). In terms of their physical environment, therefore, they are more like the interior lands than the equatorial monsoon coastal countries, and have served as outlets to some of the territories that are inland and land bound. Because of their coastal situation, however, Senegal and Gambia are not faced with the same problems that a land-bound position imposes. They are maritime lands, oriented toward the sea to which they are historically and commercially tied; and their interests, opportunities, and, generally, their development have differed from those of the inland Saharan-savanna lands.

Coastal Guinea, Sierra Leone, and Liberia are some of the wettest lands in Africa; the farther south one goes along these southwest-facing lands, the greater the moisture. More rain falls on Sierra Leone than on Guinea; more in Liberia than in Sierra Leone.

Although Sierra Leone has 3 months during which less than 1 inch of rain falls, the climate is equatorial. It does, however, show the influence of the southwest coastal monsoon in the very heavy precipitation that characterizes the high sun period. A range of mountains that penetrates to the sea in a northwest-southeast trending peninsula causes excessive rain (230 inches) at the highest elevations, and even at Freetown rainfall averages nearly 140 inches; interior Sierra Leone has an average equal to that of the higher parts of the Fouta Jallon in Guinea; in the lowlands, it generally exceeds 90 inches.

The torrential nature of the rain and the excessive amounts have detrimental effects on the soil, which is leached and eroded. Such a moist climate should produce a rainforest. In the past it did, but the practice of shifting cultivation wiped out the primeval forests long ago. Today, in their stead, a deteriorated type of vegetation, that ranges from high bush to grass flats, has taken over. Only from 3 to 5 percent of Sierra Leone can be classified as forest, and this includes mangrove trees.

Liberia is also equatorial: the country extends from 4°13′ to 8°35′N, and humidity and rainfall are both high. In the coastal areas rain averages about 140 inches annually, and in the southwest, inland, and the southeast about 100 inches; where elevations rise to some height, as on Cape Mount, rainfall averages may mount to 200 to 240 inches. Despite the equatorial location and rainfall, however, Liberia has seasons based on rainfall, with rainier and less rainy seasons. The dry, or less rainy, seasons are not so pronounced as farther north, but there are two, the long one from about November to April, and a "secondary middle-dry" season in late summer. Even during these seasons, however, relative humidity remains high, averaging 82 percent.

## Senegambia

The Portuguese discovered the Senegal and Gambia rivers and were the first to make settlements on these coasts; and it was with the Portuguese that both British and French interests had to compete when they sought out the area for trade or colonization. The British were already established on the Gambia River when the French began colonizing Senegalese territory; an agent of an English trading company ascended the Gambia River from 1618 to 1619, and Fort James, built on a small island about 20 miles in from the river mouth, was established in 1644. St. Louis was not settled until 1658.

Until French West Africa broke up into independent countries between 1958 and 1960, Senegal had been the headquarters of administration, research, and development for all of French West Africa. This was the first part of West Africa to be settled by the French, the first two colonies being established on the islands of St. Louis at the mouth of the Senegal River and Gorée just off Cape Verde. It was from the St. Louis-Cape Verde area in Senegal that the opening up of the rest of French West Africa took place, although consolidation of the vast territories was carried out by a three-pronged pincers movement coming from the Maghrib in the north, the Senegal River in the west, and Brazzaville in the south. It was from the Senegal River that the Niger River was attained; the territories of the French Soudan and Niger were conquered from here also. When France

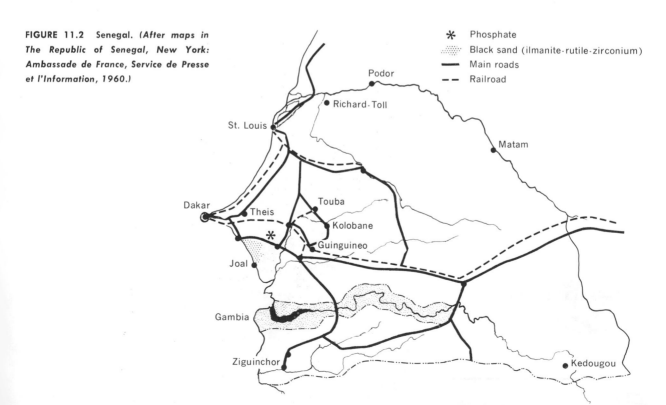

FIGURE 11.2 Senegal. (After maps in The Republic of Senegal, New York: Ambassade de France, Service de Presse et l'Information, 1960.)

✳ Phosphate
Black sand (ilmanite-rutile-zirconium)
— Main roads
– – Railroad

decided to obtain frontage on the Gulf of Guinea, it was from the desert and savanna lands that they made their penetrations to the Guinea Coast, not, as was the case with the British, from the coast and inland. Thus, the headquarters in Senegal played a critical role in the extension of French control and development in West Africa.

Gambia, a sliver of a country lying along both sides of the river of the same name, reaches from the coast inland for about 210 miles. It is a riverine enclave, set completely within Senegalese territory except along its tiny seafront. The enclave follows the twisting course of the river, averaging about 20 miles in width near the coast and 12 miles farther inland, the smallest country in Africa both in size and in population.

Previous to independence, which came in February, 1965, Gambia had been a dependency of Great Britain, and comprised two parts: the Colony, made up of the towns of Bathurst on the island of St. Mary at the mouth of the river and Georgetown on the mainland plus some adjacent land, altogether only 30 square miles in size; and the Protectorate comprising the remainder of the territory.

The Gambia River is one of the finest waterways in Africa. It is navigable to ocean vessels up to 13 feet in draught from Bathurst 150 miles upstream to Kuntaur, and to smaller seagoing ships as far as Georgetown, 176 miles up from the coast; riverboats pass to Fatoto, the last river port with regular service; above here to Koina at the tip of Gambian territory

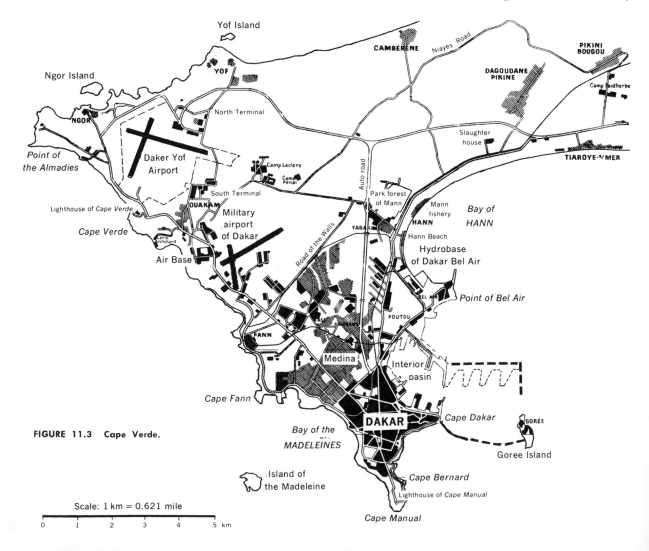

**FIGURE 11.3  Cape Verde.**

Scale: 1 km = 0.621 mile

0    1    2    3    4    5 km

(also the tidal limit of the river), the river is navigable to launches. There are more than 30 Gambian river ports at which government boats call regularly, and during the rainy season the river is navigable to launches beyond the Gambian borders.

The usefulness of this fine river is limited by political bounds that cut off most of its natural hinterland, however. Had this river been in Senegal, the port at its mouth might well have obviated the construction of the port of Dakar, about half way between St. Louis and Bathurst, for the Gambia River is a much better and more natural outlet than is the Senegal.

## THE LAND

Senegambia is largely a region of plains, less than 650 feet in elevation except in the southwest, where plateaus form the foothills of the Fouta Jallon Mountains; here altitudes reach 1,650 feet. Much of the land is dune country, and between the dunes, in many places, are clayey depressions that hold freshwater lakes edged profusely with vegetation. Cape Verde (Figure 11.3) lies quite centrally along the coast; to the north the shoreline is relatively smooth, to the south greatly indented.

Four rivers drain this land—the Senegal, Saloum, Gambia, and Casamance. Of unequal length, they run somewhat parallel to one another to the sea. All are navigable, the Senegal for 155 miles inland at all seasons, and during high water for twice that distance, the Gambia River throughout its course in Gambia and on into Senegal.

Climatically Senegambia is tropical wet and dry, but with sharp contrasts between coastal and interior regions and along the coast from south to north. Along the Casamance coast in the south rainfall averages 64 inches, with over 75 percent falling in 3 months (July to September) and less than ½ inch during the 6 months from November through April; the Casamance coast resembles the coastal monsoon lands just south. Dakar, also coastal but farther north, has a mean rainfall of less than 23 inches, more than 85 percent of which falls from July through September while 6 months have no measurable moisture (December to May) and November averages only 0.1 inch.

The climate of the shore regions is quite equable, however, especially north of the Casamance coast owing to the effect of sea and land breezes, both of which have cooling effects; also important are the effects of the cool Canary Current that flows offshore and of "the north-northeasterly marine trade winds that bring a refreshing coolness and greater humidity during the dry season."[1] Humidity tends to be high, and temperatures lower and less variable than inland, although there are temperature differences between the southern and more northerly coasts.

Rainfall decreases inland, as well as from south to north in the interior. The interior is also handicapped because it is affected more severely than the coasts by the desiccating harmattan that blows out of the desert from the northeast during the dry season; during the brief wet season, winds are from the southwest. Central interior Senegal is a semiarid plateau region, called the Ferlo, whose surface is scarred with wadis that are relics of a more humid era. Only along these old watercourses is groundwater to be reached relatively near the surface; elsewhere it lies so deep that vegetation is *sahel*, and the region is almost uninhabited. Along the northern interior boundary of Senegal is the Fouta, a floodplain along the south bank of the Senegal River matching the Chemama (north bank of the river) in Mauritania; in the mouth of the Senegal River, on what is known as the Ouala, lies St. Louis, a port since the middle of the seventeenth century but unimportant today.

## HISTORIC AND MODERN PORTS

The situation of St. Louis caused the decline of this historic port. It lies on an island within the estuary of the Senegal River, protected and close to the trade routes along the African coast, but handicapped because of the nature of the river mouth. At the head of the delta the Senegal divides into several channels. Some of these are now abandoned, no longer acting as distributaries for the river, or are intermittent, carrying water only occasionally; saline swamps, with interspersed dunes, are characteristic along the western delta front. A detail of the delta shows that the

[1] R. J. Harrison Church, *West Africa*, 2d ed., London: Longmans, Green & Co., Ltd., 1961, p. 185.

**FIGURE 11.4**   Port of Dakar. (*Photograph Aerienne Verbelke.*)

mouth of the river has been turned south so that it now runs parallel with the shore, behind the long sandspit known as the Langue de Barbarie. The spit, with the consequent closure of the river outlet, has built rapidly though irregularly, putting St. Louis farther and farther up the channel. In 1850 the head of the spit was less than 3 miles beyond the port; today the Langue de Barbarie is 15 miles long and averages nearly 100 yards in width. It constantly changes as the sand shifts and settles; the estuary is and always has been hazardous to shipping. In the past, this site and situation made St. Louis defensible; today its position is a handicap. St. Louis, however, was the largest fishing and fish processing center in all of French West Africa. The town has spread from its original site on the southeast bank where the river turns south, onto the sandbar across the river.

Dakar (Figure 11.4) superseded St. Louis as a port, but St. Louis remained the capital of Senegal and Mauritania until 1958, when the territory became independent. Then the capitals were moved to Dakar and Nouakchott respectively.

Dakar was the most modern and important city in French West Africa, although the first permanent settlement was not made here until 1857. Gorée, on an island just off Cape Verde taken from the Dutch by the French on behalf of Senegal Company in 1677, had been the first capital of French West Africa; St. Louis had been the leading port. The difficulties of St. Louis's situation, and the building of the railroad between St. Louis and Dakar in the 1880s led to the replacement of St. Louis by Dakar as the outlet for French West African lands; it was made an important French naval base in 1898, and in 1902 the capital was moved from Gorée to Dakar. Gorée and St. Louis decayed as Dakar rose. The railroad diverted most ocean commerce to Dakar from the Senegal River, and stimulated the production of peanuts along the rail line.

Today Dakar, about 400,000 in population, is one of Africa's great cities. It has three major functions to make it great, administration, harbor activities, and industry. The city occupies the southern spur of double-pointed Cape Verde and curls around the bay. The harbor lies on the eastern side of the Cape, naturally protected along the west, northwest, and southwest, and by breakwaters to the north-northeast and the southeast.

Bathurst was not founded until the early part of the nineteenth century; Gorée Island had been held by the British during the Napoleonic Wars, and used as a base for the control of the slave trade. When Gorée was returned to the French (1816–1817), it became necessary for the British to establish another base of operations, and the site of Bathurst was chosen for a fort. The port and city have a strategic situation because they lie on an island (St. Mary's Island) that commands the narrows at the river mouth. The site is not good, however, because Bathurst was built on two low sand dunes separated by a depression. Until a dike was built in 1949, the ground on which the city stands was like "a waterlogged sponge" during the period of annual floods; it was also a pesthole of malaria, dysentery, and yellow fever. Redevelopment of the city is not easy. There is an acute shortage of space despite the fact that there is land to be reclaimed as a result of the building of the bund.

Bathurst is small, the latest estimate of the population of the "Colony" (Bathurst and vicinity) being a little over 31,500. All Gambian exports go out through this port, which is also the capital. The wharves lie along the end of St. Mary's Island, facing upstream.

## LIVELIHOOD

Church states that "Senegal is largely summed up in two words—Dakar and groundnuts"; so too with Gambia—Bathurst and groundnuts (see Glossary). Both countries are overwhelmingly agricultural. Except for the benefits derived by Dakar as the French

administrative center for West Africa and by Bathurst and Dakar as ports then and now, their wealth is the land. Mineral resources are meager and only recently developed. They include ilmenite-zircon sands in Senegal near the mouth of the Saloum River, and a concentration of the sands at Djifère that yield titanium. These ores were the first minerals developed, and Senegal is the second largest producer of zirconium ores and concentrates in the world. It ranks among the first ten producers of ilmenite, although its production is only slightly over 1 percent of the world production. Phosphate rock occurs, and is mined and processed; limestone is used in cement manufacture; basalt and laterite are extracted and used for surfacing roads. The only mineral that is known to occur in Gambia is ilmenite, found about 30 miles south and west of Bathurst. It was exploited between 1956 and 1958, but was abandoned because it was uneconomic at the going prices.

Senegal raises few livestock, most of its requirements for meat being cared for by cattle driven in from Mauritania. The greatest concentrations of cattle, sheep, and goats are found east of Dakar in the Diourbel-Kaolack region where the Serer people practice mixed farming. In the north, nomadic and seminomadic Fulani keep many herds of animals. In terms of population density, the number of animals reared is high.

However, these facets of the economy are insignificant as compared with agriculture. Peanuts are the mainstay of the Gambian-Senegalese economy: Senegal is the world's fourth largest producer, the largest commercial grower, and the exporter that is closest to European markets. Over four-fifths of the value of exported goods from Senegal is represented in peanut oil and cake and shelled peanuts; over nine-tenths in Gambia. All of the crop in Gambia is raised by African farmers who are assisted with the planting and harvesting by some 10,000 to 20,000 "strange farmers," seasonal laborers who come across the borders from Mali, Guinea, and the Portuguese lands. These migrant workers sometimes cultivate their own plots of peanuts as well. The migration of these laborers is an impressive one—one of the outstanding movements of seasonal labor in West Africa.

Millet, the outstanding food crop, is usually grown in rotation with peanuts because the latter are a "robber" crop. The association of cultivation with animal rearing is also a good practice because manure can be used on the fields. A very important region where both farming and animal industries are carried on is on the floodlands of the Fouta: as the floods subside, sedentary cultivators plant millet; and as the crops are harvested, nomadic Fulani and Mauritanians migrate into the Fouta to pasture their animals until the floods return. The floodplains of the Senegal River are thus used by both sedentary and migrant peoples alternately, in sharp contrast to what is found all around the area.

Rice, cassava, yams, pulses (intercropped with cereals), and maize are raised as subsistence crops, but there is a tendency for peanuts, as a cash crop, to be planted instead of food crops, a dangerous trend. Rice is especially important in Casamance, the region that lies south of Gambia. Here raffia, oil palms, teak trees, bamboos, the kapok tree, and mangroves all grow.

Gambia faces her independent future with no railroads, less than 100 miles of surfaced roads, and one airport. Although several British efforts were made to develop the economy, they failed rather badly; and Gambia has not developed its greatest resources, namely, the river and its situation. It would appear that Gambia might benefit economically by federation with Senegal or Mali. Then the river could come into its place within its true hinterland, much larger than at present.

## The Guineas

### PORTUGUESE GUINEA

As early as 1650 Portugal was forced out of all parts of West Africa north of the Equator except Portuguese Guinea and the islands of Principe and São Tomé. Portuguese Guinea is more correctly called the Portuguese Province of Guinea, an Overseas Province of metropolitan Portugal. It is a small piece of land, about a third the size of Portugal. Some ½ million people live here, mostly African.

The province extends from a low, swampy, and deeply indented coast through plains into low plateaus and the foothills of the Fouta Jallon. The country divides into two broad and contrasting regions along a zone that marks the limits of the tidal and mangrove swamps. To seaward is a swampy coast, deeply indented by estuaries; many islands dot the offshore water at high tide, but at very low tide they connect with the mainland. Mangrove grows luxuriantly along the shore and up along the river estuaries, backed in turn by thick forests of Casamance and swamp woodlands. The climate is coastal monsoon, producing about 80 inches of rain annually, and having 5 very wet months during the time when the southwest monsoon winds blow, and 7 months that are nearly rainless. During the latter period, the harmattan does not normally affect the area until near the end of the season. The interior is higher and drier, and vegetation is a moist woodland savanna.

The two regions contrast also along human and economic lines. The interior is Islamic and basically nomadic pastoral; whatever agriculture is practiced is simple, although crops of cotton, peanuts, vegetables, fruits, and starches are raised by those who farm. Traditionally, the people of the interior have a contempt toward those who work the land. Those who live on the coast are sedentary cultivators. They practice mixed farming, reclaiming swampland for the cultivation of wild rice and keeping animals (cattle and hogs) largely for the manure that can be obtained for their rice fields; they dike their rice fields to control the application of water. Rice is the major subsistence starch. Fishing and boating are usual, and they also gather the products of the various palm trees, i.e., coconuts, oil from the oil palm, and raffia.

Oil seeds make up nine-tenths of the exports. Peanuts rank first, palm kernels second; copra, palm oil, and peanut oil cake go out in far lesser amounts. Despite the importance of peanuts as an export, rice seems to have a better chance for development than do peanuts because the extensive swamplands offer almost unlimited areas for the expansion of this crop.

No railroads serve Portuguese Guinea, but all of the major rivers are navigable for about 100 miles inland, and the coastal lagoons are also used. These, with about 2,000 miles of dirt roads, meet the needs of the province. International airlines call at Bissau, the capital and port.

## GUINEA

Arcuate Guinea, which became a Republic in October, 1958, borders on six other nations. From its western flange, which faces on the ocean and lies between Portuguese Guinea and Sierra Leone, it curls around Sierra Leone to terminate on its eastern flange against Liberia; along the inner border Senegal, Mali, and Ivory Coast are its neighbors.

## The Land

The French sometimes called Guinea *le chateau de l'eau* because within the highlands of this country rise the headwaters of the greatest West African rivers—the Bafing and Bakoy, which are headstreams of the Senegal, the Gambia, the Niger, and two large tributaries of the Niger, the Milo and Sankarani. A number of shorter rivers flow southwest to the coast, including the Konkouré and the Great Scarcies.

Guinea shares all the physiographic divisions that characterize West Africa as a whole: coastal lowlands, uplands, that in Guinea are largely the complex of the Fouta Jallon and Guinea highlands, and the dry interior slopes and plains.

The coast, like that of Portuguese Guinea, is a drowned one so that river mouths and valleys finger inland as estuaries. A high tidal range and lack of any constant longshore drift have inhibited the formation of sandbars and coastal lagoons; instead, a combination of factors has led to the accumulation of mud near the river mouths, which are fringed or choked with mangrove; mangrove swamps border almost the entire coast. In two places narrow thrusts of upland reach across the plains and muddy mangrove flats to the coast: Conakry lies on an island tip of one of these spurs of rock, the Kaloum Peninsula; the other terminates as Cape Verga. They provide well drained corridors across muddy swamps. A causeway connects the capital on Tombo Island with the mainland.

The coastal plains are narrowest in the vicinity of Conakry, and widen both eastward and westward— westward to surround the Fouta Jallon even in the north where the Guinea lowlands blend with those of Portuguese Guinea and Senegal, eastward along the valley of the Great Scarcies River which forms part of the western border of Sierra Leone.

Guinea mounts in elevation from the submerged swamp and mangrove-bordered coast to the heights of the Fouta Jallon and the Guinea highlands. The Fouta Jallon occupy most of the interior northwest. They are a massive plateau of relatively flat-lying strata, but mountainous in character because of their profound dissection; deeply trenched valleys, gorge-like in character, scar the surface while in between the chasms the massif is made up of relatively flat divides called *bowé*. Although maximum elevations are rarely above 3,500 feet, these mountains are impressive and majestic. They rise as a series of step faults along the west and north, more steeply from the coast than from the interior; in the east, the slope is gradual and the river channels shallower. Soil is thin in this area, for the heavy rains wash the soils into the streams and eventually carry them to the sea. Cultivation and overgrazing add to the hazard of erosion.

The pastoral Fulani, who make up 40 percent of the Guinean population, have been attracted by the healthful climate to these barren heights, and the flat divides are densely populated despite the fact that many parts are almost bare of vegetation; with their small African (Ndama) cattle, they carry on transhumance between the high and low pastures as the seasons change; the high pastures are grazed during the wet season, the lowlands during the dry. In the valleys agriculture is practiced by black Africans who were brought into these isolated locations as captives of war by the Fulani to raise crops for them; today they live as free cultivators. Both the *bowé* and the gorgelike valleys hold populations that are dense for mountain regions.

The Fouta Jallon and the Guinea highlands are the greatest watershed in West Africa. They divide along a zone of lower ground, about 2,000 feet in elevation, between Mamou and Sierra Leone; here also the rivers part, the Niger flowing northeast, the Senegal flowing north and west, and the Scarcies and Konkouré south.

The Guinea highlands are rounder and more gentle than the Fouta Jallon although they rise higher, reaching their maximum height in Mt. Nimba (6,070 feet).

Although the crests of the higher peaks tend to be bare of vegetation, the mountains are tree covered, and in the more inaccessible places rain forest still remains. The trend of the Guinea highlands is southeast-northwest; but transverse rivers have cut the mountain mass into blocks, and upthrusts of crystalline rocks, that form the basement of these uplands, in places have caused the formation of ridges that rise above 5,000 feet. The whole structure is complex and varied in form, in contrast to that of the Fouta Jallon.

The soil in these mountains is relatively rich, and it has been a region productive of both subsistence and plantation crops of rice, the oil palm, corn, cassava, kola nuts, and coffee. Of the minerals iron, graphite, and others occur, but development awaits a rail outlet, and among the things standing in the way of a short route to the sea are the international boundaries to the south. The easiest way out from eastern interior Guinea lies across Liberia.

The slopes and plains of the interior are drained by the Niger River and its tributaries. The plains, about 1,000 feet high, are interrupted here and there by projections of higher relief that represent either granite domes or sandstone detachments of the Fouta Jallon. Such an occurrence of hard rocks at Kouroussa brings a cessation of navigation on the Niger; they are also responsible for gold-bearing river gravels and quartz veins.

Guinea is equatorial-monsoonal, so that climatic differentials are largely due to differences in elevation or exposure. The coastal plains and the western slopes have heavy rainfall (Conakry averages 169 inches, Boké, 111 inches), over 90 percent of which falls between June and October; humidities and temperatures are high, reaching their most oppressive stage in April; the months from December to April each receive less than ½ inch of rain. The coast is unhealthful. Today some of the mangrove marshes have been reclaimed for rice cultivation, and efforts are being made to recover even greater areas of these otherwise useless swamps. Rice, bananas, maize, the oil palm, and kola nuts are raised, and to a lesser extent, pineapples. This is a good climate for bananas, and bananas are the major commercial crop of Guinea; oranges and orange oil, pineapples, palm oil, and kola nuts are also raised for export.

The plateau highlands are drier than the coastal plains, but the seaward slopes of the Fouta Jallon receive a highly concentrated heavy rainfall, and moisture conditions are those of alternative flood and drought. The plateau divides, originally forested, now rarely have stands of climax vegetation because of repeated firings by graziers. The powerful streams, excessively erosive, have made the region relatively inaccessible by their sculpturing of the high relief. Perhaps the greatest problem facing Guinea is the need for conservation of its soils and pastures. It has been estimated that as little as 10 percent of the country can be cultivated or grazed without taking some kind of precautions if further grave damage is not to be done. The problem is accentuated by the excessive rains within a concentrated period, making soil conservation difficult to carry out.

Bananas are cultivated in the damp valleys of the mountains; above these lowlands citrus, pineapples, coffee, kola, maize, and millet become important.

Inland, rainfall diminishes: Mamou averages 79 inches, Kouroussa 66 inches, the interior foothills receive still less; in the northeast there is a small region that receives less than 50 inches. These areas of lesser rain lie generally in the rain shadow.

*Industrial Potentials.* Guinea has a rich potential for economic development. It is the largest producer of bauxite in Africa, and fourth largest in the world. Gold has been recovered in Guinea for centuries both from veins and river gravels. Diamonds and iron ore occur. The bauxite and iron are well situated for development for important bauxite reserves occur on the Los Islands opposite Conakry, along the railroad at Kindia and Dabola, and near the coast at Boké; large, rich iron deposits, among the largest in the world, lie on Kaloum Peninsula just beyond Conakry.

At present only the first step in the conversion of bauxite is being carried out, namely, the production of alumina. This is done at both Kindia and Dabola. Eventually electric power, developed on the Konkouré River at Kaleta Falls, will convert alumina (shipped to the power) to aluminum.

Iron ore is extracted from the Kaloum deposits, only 5 miles from the Conakry wharves and connected with them by the new rail spur. Two other huge deposits await development in the Smandou

Mountains in eastern Guinea and in the Nimba Mountains, the latter shared between Liberia and Guinea. Prospects for the development of these reserves were given impetus when Liberia gave Guinea assurances that the ores could be sent across Liberian territory to the coast. (See Figure 11.5.)

Diamond deposits were reported in 1963, and while it is too early to estimate their importance, they are large and for the first time in Guinea in kimberlite pipes. Until now, Guinea has taken diamonds from stream gravels and sands, never before having found any of the diamond-bearing veins that are the sources.

FIGURE 11.5 Mount Nimba workings of the Lamco joint venture enterprise in Liberia, 160 miles from Monrovia, near the Guinea border. (Courtesy of The Grängesburg Company, Liberia Division, Stockholm, Sweden.)

Illicit diamond mining and smuggling are major problems in Guinea and deprive the state of millions of dollars' revenue yearly.

Guinea appears to have a large waterpower potential in the river gorges that are fed by the tremendous rains. However, the pronounced dry season counterposes problems; vegetation on the plateaus is so thin that it does little to hold back runoff and curb soil erosion; and there are few lakes to act as reservoirs.

A lack of adequate transport facilities deters development in Guinea, and the building of roads and railroads is made more difficult because of the interposition of Sierra Leone and Liberian territory between a large part of Guinea and the coast, as we have noted. National lines are circuitous rather than direct, therefore longer and the transport of goods more costly. There is only one Guinean rail line. It curves inland around Sierra Leone from Conakry to Kankan, with no branches except the 5-mile spur from Conakry to the producing iron beds. The railway was constructed under great difficulties, not so much for the purpose of giving the best service to Guinea as to help the French pacify the country and give France access to the upper Niger where, as the nineteenth century drew toward a close, France and Britain were actively competing with each other. The moderate payloads do not meet the high costs of running the rail line.

Several roads serve the country, and in late 1964 Guinea embarked on a 7-year plan to build a modern roadnet that would meet the needs of development. However, for much of the country the easiest routes to the sea or to markets are across the territories of other nations. Those parts of the Guinea highlands near the Liberian frontier find an outlet through the port of Monrovia, and as a result, commercial cultivation is expanding here; rice, grown in the Niger valleys, is sent down the affluents of the Niger and the main stream for sale in Mali.

Conakry is the major port for Guinea. As noted, it is situated on one of the two spurs of hard rock that reach to the shore across this otherwise swampy coast. It has a fine natural harbor, although on the north side protection is not all that might be desired. The export of alumina and iron ore has led to an enlargement of port facilities. Conakry itself is an interesting city and a favorite of the French among West African cities; population is about 115,000.

## Lands of the Freedmen

Three small states in Africa were set up by foreign powers as homelands for liberated African slaves—Gabon, Sierra Leone, and Liberia. In this they are unique. The settlement of the "Colony" of Sierra Leone "was devised" for that purpose in 1787; the protectorate over the rest of the territory was not declared until a century later.

Slavers were active along this coast between the sixteenth and eighteenth centuries, and when Britain decided to patrol the West African shores in an attempt to prevent illicit bondage of Africans, Freetown was set up as the center of the antislave naval operations. For nearly 50 years, from 1808 to 1854, Africans captured by the British on slaving vessels were settled in the Colony whenever it was not possible to determine the land of their origin. Descendants of these freedmen, who are generally of mixed blood, are called Creoles in Sierra Leone. They have attained a higher level of development than have the black Africans indigenous to the interior parts of the country.

The Colony was under British philanthropists from 1788 until 1807, when it was transferred to the British Crown. Sierra Leone became an independent state on April 27, 1961. Under the British system of dividing the territory into two parts, the Colony occupied 256 square miles and, just before independence, had about 125,000 persons in residence; the Protectorate was more than 10 times as large in area and population.

Unlike its neighbor to the west which remained dependent to the British for nearly 175 years, Liberia has never been subject to an outside power. In this it is unique among African nations. It was established as an independent state, and for many decades was the only sovereign black African nation, a status that gave the little country some uncomfortable moments in its history because it found itself without a protector when its rights and territories were trespassed upon.

The idea of an African state to which freed American slaves could be repatriated was conceived by the American Colonization Society, and planning began in 1817; from 1822 on, "free people of color" emigrated from the United States to what later became Liberia. These liberated Africans from America, plus a few who were set free from slaving ships seized upon the high seas, formed the core of a group whose descendants became an elite that even today holds most of the economic and political power, namely, the Americo-Liberians. Providence Island, near the mouth of the St. Paul River just below Monrovia, is the place where "the first settlers landed." About 20,000 repatriated Africans were thus settled, and most of these had arrived in the colony by 1825. The first 3 years were the years of "the great migrations," following which almost no more African expatriates arrived.

They found the country occupied by tribal peoples native to the area, and during its early years the little colony in and around Monrovia had a constant struggle with native Liberians who were hostile to the intruders. In 1833 another small territory, called the Independent African State of Maryland, was established on Cape Palmas. It maintained itself as a separate entity until 1857 when, as Maryland County, it united with Liberia.

## THE LANDS

*Sierra Leone.* Like so much of the southwest coastal district, the shoreline of Sierra Leone is a broken one and deeply indented with estuaries. Except where higher land breaks across the plain to the coast to terminate in the mountains of the Colony, the plain is low, and swampy from the seafront for about 20 miles inland. Mangrove grows in the tidal marshes, while farther inland sedge swamps are inundated by wet season floods; the soils of these sedge marshes are deep, rich alluviums that dry out during the dry season. Beyond the marshes the land, gently undulating, slopes gradually up to the interior plateaus, the continuance of the Guinea highland, to the mountains situated toward the northeast frontier facing Guinea.

Sierra Leone divides into three provinces and the Sierra Leone Peninsula, which was formerly known as the Colony, or Colony Peninsula on which the capital, Freetown, is situated. The peninsula is mountainous, rising steeply from the coast to two famous peaks, Picket Hill (2,912 feet) in the south and Sugar Loaf Mountain (2,494 feet) behind Freetown. Around the base of these peaks mangrove forests cover much of the swampy flatland; generally, the slopes are

forested because a reserve was set aside some years ago to cut down soil erosion. Freetown harbor is one of the finest natural harbors in the world. It is situated on the large, deep Rokel estuary and in the shelter of hills. The town, about 125,000 in population, spreads up into the hills; through its port pass palm kernels, cacao, ginger, coffee, bananas, and the like.

South Western Province of what was the Protectorate is a region of tidal swamps and marshland. Mangroves grow endlessly along the estuaries of the five large rivers that dominate this province; the climate is hot and humid, and population is sparse. The fiber extracted from the raffia palm (pissava), and used in making brushes and brooms, has been the main crop from this region, but recently rice growing has greatly expanded in the swamps and marshlands.

Northern Province has more climatic variety than the remainder of the country. Here the rain forests (with palms) give way to sparser and shorter trees which in turn blend into the profusion of grasses of the wet savannas. In the extreme northeast, out from Kabala, nomadic pastoralists keep herds of dwarf African cattle (Adama) which, during the dry season, are driven to Freetown for sale and slaughter. Tribal swamps prevail in the west across great areas and here, as in South Western Province, wet rice cultivation is beginning to make the land productive. Great iron ore deposits occur east of the tidal marshlands, at Marampa.

South Eastern Province, central eastern in location, is the richest part of the country. Here alluvial diamonds are scattered in the gravel of the Sewa River, and here is the only area where any extensive areas of high forest remain. Equatorial in climate, but topographically upland so that drainage is good, the province is well suited to the cultivation of coffee, cacao, and oil palms. Soils are leached, however, and soil erosion is a critical problem.

*Liberia.* Liberia resembles Sierra Leone in its equatorial character and its relief. Four regional belts may be distinguished, differentiated in terms of topography, climate, and vegetation. The coastal plain, extending the length of the shore and inland to between 20 and 40 miles, is low; mangrove swamps, shallow lagoons, and sandy beaches characterize this area; few hills interrupt the flat, low terrain. It was in this region that the Americo-Liberians settled, establishing the colony that eventuated into Monrovia on the upper part of the ridge of Cape Mesurado.

The swampy coast merges into rolling hills that are a continuation of the coastal hilly belt of Sierra Leone. Rain forest covers most of this sector, and here most of the plantations have been developed, the Firestone and Goodrich plantations as well as most of those owned by Liberians; the Bomi Hills iron ore development also lies within this area.

The hills rise higher inland, at times mounting in steep scarps to the 1,500- to 2,000-foot heights of the interior plateau; both plateau and hilly forefront are also covered with rain forest. This region is sparsely populated and little known; tribal people spread thinly across it, living in primitive villages and practicing migratory agriculture; communication is generally by footpath. One road runs inland northeastward from Monrovia nearly to the border at Ganta. It becomes a secondary road shortly after the Firestone plantations are left behind, bumpy and unsurfaced. In the dry season, the dust from the red laterite colors henna red everything that moves along it; in the wet season, it is bogged with mud; beyond Suakoka the road becomes even more difficult. Only little planes that can land on a tiny spot of ground or helicopters have been able to negotiate much of interior Liberia up to the decade of the 1960s. Inland ore developments now in progress, with the contingent railway and road construction, should be a boon to the country. Along the northern frontier the Guinea highlands rise in domelike crests to elevations of over 4,000 feet. Topographically, Liberia is quite complex. Even in the hill regions, single masses of rocks may rise above 3,000 feet, especially in the west.

As in other tropical countries, Liberian soils are leached; but the climate is a permissive one, and things grow easily. Because of the leached soils, tree crops do best, and rubber is the outstanding cash crop of the country.

*Development.* Sierra Leone and Liberia, two of the smallest countries in Africa, are also among the most undeveloped. A strong rivalry between the Colony and Protectorate held back development in Sierra Leone; the country is quite backward. Liberia, held and governed by Negroes from its inception as a nation, had not the benefit of the foreign financial and technical assistance that most European colonial powers gave their dependencies; nor did the Negroes have the capital or the know-how to develop the resources.

With the beginning of American investment, however, things began to change: American business interests have carried out most developments, and have given the country most of the economic strength that it has. Firestone and Republic Steel are the American firms that first went in; it was they who began to disclose the potentials of the African state.

Economic difficulties plagued Liberia until just before World War II. Then its strategic situation led to the construction of Roberts Field, an airport, and to improvements in road and port facilities. The deepwater harbor of Monrovia on Bushrod Island, north of Cape Mesurado, was constructed with American Lend-Lease in the late 1940s. Monrovia is the only free port in West Africa.

Although the Firestone rubber operations began in 1926, real benefits from these enterprises were not felt for some years. The Bomi Hills development of the Liberia Mining Company (Republic Steel) commenced in 1951, and Liberia's first and only railroad until 1961 was constructed to carry the ore from the mines to the ore port just outside Monrovia; this line is about 50 miles long. The only improved roads in Liberia, until 1960, were constructed by these American companies, and after completion turned over to the Liberian government, whose responsibility it is to keep them up.

Recently, other large deposits of iron ore were discovered: in the Bong Mountains northeast of Monrovia, along the Mano River in northwest Liberia, and in the Nimba Mountains near the border where Liberia, Ivory Coast, and Guinea come together. The Nimba deposits are being developed by Lamco, a company jointly owned by Swedish and American (Bethlehem Steel) interests, and the Liberian government. The latter puts up the resource, the foreign interests the money: Bethlehem Steel has one-fourth interest in the project; management is supplied by Sweden. This is the first time that the Liberian government has participated as a shareholder in such a development; previously it has acted as a "legislative referee, royalty claimant or tax assessor and collector."

Development of the Nimba ores required the construction of a 160-mile railroad from Buchanan, which serves as the outlet port, into the Nimba range, and 22 miles of all-weather highway and 160 miles of temporary roads. These transport constructions will not only open up the minerals area but should stimulate forestry and agriculture all along the way, bringing the now remote interior in contact with the more developed parts of Liberia.

The Bong Mountain mines are being developed by Delimco, a German-Liberian venture. The government of Liberia and Ruhrwerke, a consortium of four German steel firms, each own 50 percent of the company. Production from these mines began in 1964. A railway connects the mining region with Monrovia. The National Iron Ore Company has the concession to develop the Mano River ores. This company uses the Bomi Hills railway for a 40-mile distance to a point where its own line branches off from that of the Liberia Mining Company's road. Both companies are constructing new ore docks to expand the capacity of the port of Monrovia.

How important American developments are to Liberia can be read from Liberian exports, which rose from $2,813,100 (American dollars) in 1939 to $82,609,000 in 1960. Rubber was the first product to be exported in quantity and until 1957 made up two-thirds or more of the value of Liberian exports; until 1961 it continued to exceed all others. In that year, however, shipments of iron exceeded in value

those of rubber, chiefly because of the drop in world price of rubber; but the figures reflect the growing importance of minerals to Liberia. Table 3 indicates the overwhelming importance of these two commodities to the Liberian economy. The United States is Liberia's biggest customer and supplier; normally American imports from and exports to Liberia represent over half the total for the African state.

The extent to which American investing companies have contributed to the stability and development of the Liberian economy is illustrated in the following, only two instances of several. During the depression of the 1930s, when Liberia was on the verge of bankruptcy and the League of Nations proposed that Liberia be put into the equivalent of an international receivership,[2] Firestone took over the international loan, and thus averted calamity to the small country. Second, the two American rubber companies, Firestone and Goodrich, have established a policy of issuing, free of charge to any Liberian who will clear land for his own gardens, seedling rubber trees to establish a plantation.

On the other side, Liberia is very proud of its historic link to the United States. In Liberia the United States and the Western nations have a strong African ally.

Major in the economy of Sierra Leone are rice, oil palm products, and minerals. Gold, diamonds, and platinum occur in alluvial sands. Although gold production is small, alluvial gold occurs widely in the stream gravels that drain from the interior eastern half of the country. The mother lode has never been discovered. Nuggets of platinum are taken from stream alluviums on the Sierra Leone Peninsula, and ilmenite deposits occur in the northern part of the peninsula. Chromite occurs, and iron ore is found in several places, as are also silver, lead, corundum, antimony, ceramic clays, lignite, and asbestos. Diamonds are Sierra Leone's largest single export; one-fourth of the world's gem diamonds come from here. As in Guinea, illicit diamond mining is one of Sierra Leone's most troublesome problems. As in the case of gold, the primary diamond sources have not been discovered.

## TABLE 3

| Exports, value in U.S. $ | 1953 | 1960 | 1962 |
|---|---|---|---|
| Total exports | 30,998,300 | 82,609,000 | 67,635,000 |
| Rubber | 21,110,300 | 39,060,000 | 25,662,000 |
| Iron ore | 5,815,400 | 34,642,000 | 32,397,000 |
| Palm kernel | 1,874,300 | 1,952,000 | 776,000 |
| Diamonds and uncut stones | 3,800 | 2,299,000 | 4,557,000 |

Sources: 1953 data, *Invest-Trade-Prosper with Liberia*, Monrovia: Bureau of Information, Department of State, p. 38; 1960 data, *Yearbook of International Trade Statistics, 1960*, New York: United Nations, p. 345; 1962 data, *ibid.*, 1964, p. 442.

[2] A countersuggestion, made by the British Foreign Office, was that the United States administer the country as a protectorate.

# 12 FROM THE IVORY COAST
# TO THE NIGER

*. . . beating and laying open
the way where and how this
Golden Trade should rise.*

RICHARD JOBSON

Aside from Greek trading activities along East Africa, coastal West Africa was the first part of the continent, beyond the North, that became known to Europeans. The Portuguese opened up this sector and were the trailblazers for the other Europeans, who followed once the way had been pointed—Dutch, English, French, Germans, and Danes.

The southern lands along the Gulf of Guinea were named for the most prevalent commodity of trade that flowed out from these African shores. Sierra Leone and Liberia were known to early European explorers and traders as "the grain coast"; beyond there, from west to east, were the Ivory Coast, the Gold Coast, and the Slave Coast that extended from Togo across Dahomey and Nigeria.

West African empires of European states appeared and dissolved, enlarged or shrank as sections were snatched from one nation by another in the European scramble for shares of the land and trade and riches of this portion of the old-new continent. But despite the early beginning of trade in West Africa, it was merely the edges of the continent that were held and contested. As the eighteenth century drew to a close, so little was known of the interior that not even the courses of the Gambia, Senegal, and Niger rivers had yet been traced.

But by the beginning of World War I, the struggle for and partition of West Africa had come to an end. Portugal and the Netherlands had long since been eliminated from the lands of the Guinea Coast; Germany held Togoland and Cameroon; the remainder were French or British, arranged in an alternating pattern. With Germany defeated in the war and the mandate system set up, both Togoland and the Cameroons were divided and mandated to France and Britain. The British mandates were administered as parts of larger colonies, Togo with Gold Coast, the two sectors of Cameroons with Nigeria; but the integrity of the French mandates was maintained, and each was administered as a separate province within the larger frame of French administration; French Togo became a part of French West Africa, the French Cameroons of French Equatorial Africa. After World War II, the League of Nations mandates became trusteeships under the United Nations, but were still entrusted to France and Great Britain.

It is in this setting that the boundary lines of the independent states were traced. When French Togo pressed for reunification with the old tribal lands that for about 3 decades had been integrated with the Gold Coast Colony, British Togo voted to join Ghana, rejecting the old tribal tie. The southern sector of the British Cameroons, however, elected to join the Republic of Cameroon (formerly French), and only the smaller, northern sector united with Nigeria.

All the countries of this region have been independent since 1957.

## Ivory Coast

Ivory Coast became a republic on August 7, 1960. Its domain is essentially the same as that comprehended in the French West African province of the same name, although from 1933 to 1947 a large part of Upper Volta was attached to the coastal state. For this reason, many preindependence maps show Ivory Coast considerably larger than the present domain. The state is, however, the largest of the former French West African lands that share the equatorial forests of the Guinea coast.

Blocky and rectangular in shape, it borders on five other countries, and has a 340-mile coastline along the Gulf of Guinea. A zone of lagoons impounded by a long, narrow sandbar closes off the eastern half of the coast from the sea; only by the breaching of this bar was it possible to make a port of Abidjan, formerly barred from access to the ocean. Although constituting a major barrier, the sandbar is at no place wider than 4 miles. The western half of the coast is high and rocky; low cliffs border the shore, often extending as craggy points that alternate with sandy indentations.

### THE LAND

The "ivory coast" was so called because in early years it was much frequented by traders in ivory. It stretches across 6° of latitude, from the coast with its equatorial climate and rain forests inland into savannas (Figure 12.2). Equatoriality is exceptionally

FIGURE 12.2 Typical village of the savannas, Ivory Coast. (Courtesy Service de l'Information, Côte d'Ivoire.)

FIGURE 12.3 Aerial view of a village in the rain forest, Ivory Coast. (Courtesy Service de l'Information, Côte d'Ivoire.)

pronounced in the south. There is, however, a coastal phenomenon, found also in Ghana, of a central drier belt with wetter sectors to the east and west; although not so pronounced as in Ghana, this drier coast averages about 60 inches of rain as against 92 inches in the west (Tabou record) and 77 inches in the east (Abidjan); the number of days on which rain occurs varies in much the same pattern, the central area having an average of 75 days with rain as against 130 in the west and 150 in the east. Two seasons of maximum rainfall are characteristic throughout the country except in the highland area west of Man. Here rainfall is higher than in most Guinea coast regions of the same latitude, and there is but a single maximum of precipitation.

In spite of the variations in rainfall in the equatorial south, the southern third of the country has a climax vegetation of true rain forest throughout (Figure 12.3). Because of the difficulty of clearing this forest for agriculture, the railroad, when it was built by the French, was pushed *through* the forests and into the savannas beyond, and the first developments took place in the interior despite poorer soils and less moisture. Now, however, most of the commercial cultivation is in the forest zone; from here also come tropical hardwoods, less significant as exports than the products of cultivation, but nevertheless important.

Precipitation decreases inland in central Ivory Coast, but still remains high. Bouaké, almost central in the country, receives an average of 46.7 inches. Although this area was originally forested, burning and clearing by man have reduced it to grasslands, with wooded vegetation along the streams. Rainfall is higher in the north than in the central sector.

Ivory Coast rises gradually and evenly from the coast to elevations of somewhat over 1,300 feet in the interior. In the west, where the Guinea highlands play out in the Man Mountains, heights of nearly 4,000 feet are reached. In general the relief is monotonous, however, gently rolling and lacking in marked physiographic features.

## PEOPLE AND LIVELIHOOD

The dense forests in the south and the difficult character of the coast—the sandbar, lagoon-blocked eastern coast and the cliffs in the west—delayed development

of Ivory Coast for a long time. A small population of less than 3½ million people has also been a handicap, and to overcome a deficiency of labor, people from Upper Volta, a country overpopulated for its resources, have been encouraged to move into Ivory Coast.

Resources are largely those of land and forests; there are few mineral workings despite favorable geologic indications for such occurrences. Nevertheless, this country is one of the most flourishing in West Africa. Its prosperity is based upon crops cultivated for export. Subsistence crops vary from rice in the southwest, cassava and plantains (see Glossary) in the southeast, and maize throughout the equatorial belt, to yams in the central portions around Bouaké, and Guinea corn, millet, maize, and peanuts in the drier, more infertile lands of the savannas farther north, the usual subsistence crops for these varied climatic zones in West Africa.

The commercial crops are also typical of those grown in other parts of West Africa with similar climates except that in Ivory Coast the variety is greater. Coffee, cacao, bananas, the oil palm, pineapples, and cotton are the major cash crops, and are important in that order.

Ivory Coast is the largest exporter of coffee in Africa. The coffee grows in the forest belt, raised by Africans: *Robusta* and other lowland varieties grow on the plains; in the Man Mountains, *arabica* and other upland varieties are becoming significant. Parasites and root diseases are a problem at various times and places, but certain varieties have shown a greater adaptability than others, and the tendency is to take out the susceptible varieties and plant those that show resistance.

Cacao also grows in the forests. The cacao belt of Ivory Coast is an extension of the cacao-growing sector of Ghana; half of the crop is concentrated in two small centers just west of southern Ghana, namely, around Abengourou and Dimbokro. Even more than coffee, cacao is grown by Africans.

Bananas grow well along Ivory Coast's equatorial coast and the commercial production is found here, largely a French enterprise. Pineapples, also exported, are raised in the lagoons around Bingerville. A preferred market in France assisted and fostered the development of these commercial crops, and France still takes over half of all that are exported.

The people of Ivory Coast live almost entirely off the land, nine-tenths of them being tillers of the soil, animal keepers, fishermen, or gatherers of the products of the forests. Cattle are numerous in the savanna lands especially, but Ivory Coast is not self-sufficient in meat; hence, farmers are being encouraged to keep livestock and poultry.

Ivory Coast is judged to have the greatest stands of useful timber in all of West Africa, and wood, especially mahogany and African teak, is an important export. The only significant mineral development is the taking of alluvial diamonds from the rivers, especially from the Bou tributary of the Bandama River. About half of the diamonds are of gem variety. Copper and gold are also exploited.

### THE OLD GIVES WAY TO THE NEW

Abidjan, the capital and chief port, did not acquire either of these functions until 1934. Before then it was blocked from the sea by the sand barriers. Grand Bassam, directly on the water, a French port and fort since about 1700, was the outlet for Ivory Coast and for a time (1908 to 1931) the capital as well. Grand Bassam is an ancient trading center, and was the greatest commercial port of the territory for over 2 centuries; only when the Vridi Canal opened a passage into the lagoon from the coast did Abidjan supplant it. The canal, begun in 1936, was not completed until 1950 because of the war. The ports of Tabou, Sassandra, and Grand Bassam have only local importance because only Abidjan has railroad connections with the interior. The railway runs via Dimbokro, Bouaké and Ferkessadougou across the borders of Upper Volta to Ouagadougou.

## *Ghana of the Gold Coast*

Ghana became a sovereign state within the Commonwealth of Nations in March, 1957, with a constitution worked out by the British and Ghanians previous to independence. On July 1, 1960, the constitution was changed and another adopted that made Ghana a republic which still maintained ties with the Commonwealth. From that time on, Ghana moved toward socialism patterned along the lines of the Communist states, with a dictatorial head and ever increasing governmental control over industry, resources, people, and land, including the setting up of state farms—until February 24, 1966, when a military coup overthrew Nkrumah, who was out of the country on a visit to China.

Without a doubt, Ghana as a nation is one of the most advanced in Africa. There are several reasons for this, some directly related to Ghana only, others related to Africa as a whole. First, Ghana is a small but richly endowed and populous country, where accessibility poses no great problem to the establish-

FIGURE 12.4 (a) Relief map of Ghana; (b) rainfall; (c) population density. *(With modifications, from E. A. Boateng, A Geography of Ghana, London: Cambridge University Press. Courtesy Cambridge University Press.)*

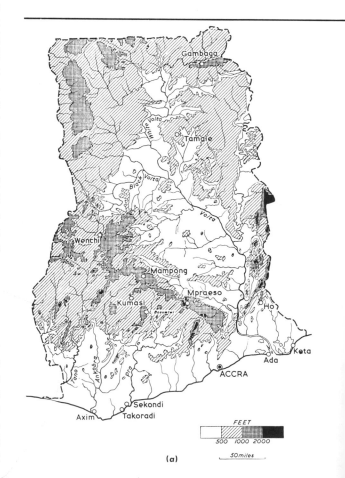

(a)

ment of a good school system, as it does in a large, unevenly populated country like The Congo, or in rugged and poor Ethiopia; the world's largest producer and exporter of cacao, rich in mineral resources of gold, diamonds, and manganese, Ghana has the resources to support its people at high living and literacy standards. A second factor has been the relative unattractiveness of West Africa as a permanent home for mid-latitude people and the relative attractiveness of plateau East and South Africa. The result has been that schools in West African territories, including Ghana, were integrated while the opposite has tended to be true in the east and south; there has been less of a double standard of education for blacks and whites in West Africa than elsewhere. A third factor relates to the political intentions of the ruling countries. Where it was anticipated that the Africans would eventually govern themselves, as in the British territories of West Africa, Africans were trained for self-government and at the same time prepared for "civilized living."

## THE LAND

Ghana is about the same size as Great Britain and so relatively a small country in area. It comprehends not only the three provinces of the former Gold Coast, that is, Northern Territories, Ashanti, and Gold Coast Colony, but the British trust territory of Togo as well. It is situated almost centrally along the Guinea coast, bounded on the east and west by countries that were formerly French, and like them extends from the savanna lands to the coast across changing bands of climate, vegetation, and relief. It is more completely equatorial than Nigeria, less so than Sierra Leone and Liberia.

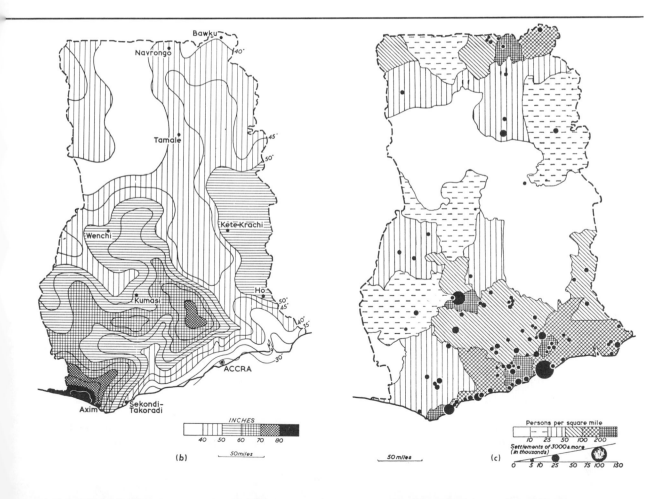

(b)

INCHES
40  50  60  70  80
50 miles

(c)
Persons per square mile
10  25  50  100  200
Settlements of 3000 & more
(in thousands)
0  5  10  25  50  75  100  130
50 miles

As is true along much of the rest of the Guinea coast, a strong surf beats incessantly along Ghana's shore leaving the coast devoid of natural harbors. The continental shelf slopes gently up from the sea, which is shallow; until the deepwater harbors of Takoradi and Tema were constructed, ships had to anchor offshore in the open roadstead and goods had to be lightered in. This is still done at Accra; ocean vessels anchor about ½ mile offshore in the deeper, calmer waters while surf-boats traverse the distance across the dangerous surf-ridden tides to the land.

The shore varies considerably, the character of any particular stretch depending upon several things including the power of the waves and the manner in which they beat upon the shore, the nature of the rocks, and relief. Where hard rocks have been able to withstand the erosive wave action, strong promontories project as headlands; where the rock structure is weaker, bays and inlets may have eroded in which soft sands accumulate; in places, barrier bars and lagoons border the seafront. Thus the coast of Ghana divides, in broad terms, into three sectors: the lagoon coast west from Cape Three Points; the "promontory coast" between Cape Three Points and Accra where the shore consists of a "succession of bays and headlands, and lagoons are comparatively rare"; and "the delta coast" east of Accra, essentially the alluvial, lagoon-dotted delta of the Volta River.[1]

Immediately back of the coast, from east of the Volta River to Axim in the west, is a zone of low coastal plains that vary in depth up to 60 miles; occasionally, small ranges of hills or isolated peaks break the monotony of the plains character, but this zone is generally a featureless, sedimentary coastal lowland made up of shale, limestone, sand, and clay. This coastal zone is unusually dry for its latitude. Although the soil is not poor, vegetation consists of a derived grass scrub, with only an occasional isolated tree.

Inland lies the plateau, back of Accra dropping abruptly to the lowland as a high ridge. The plateau is dissected into rolling hill and mountain country,

generally below 1,500 feet in elevation; in central Ashanti and eastern Togo, however, there are steep heights which in many places reach to more than 2,000 feet; the latter, the Togoland Mountains as they are sometimes called, continue into Togo and Dahomey. Between the Togoland Mountains and the uplands of central Ghana lies the portion of the plateau drained by the Volta River. The Volta plateau narrows where the river breaks through the edge of the upland in a gorge before reaching the coastal plain. Here, across the lower Volta, a dam is being constructed.

Ancient folding and volcanic activity raised mountains in Ghana that are now largely worn down to almost unrecognizably low elevations. However, and very important, intrusions of lava left laccoliths, sills, and dykes (see Glossary) that have given rise to valuable mineral resources, as in the Tarkwa region where gold reefs akin to those of South Africa occur.

## LAND AND PEOPLE

Population density is greatest in the southeast and southern parts of the country and in the extreme northeast. Density tapers off from the northeast and southeast, and from the north and south into the interior of the country, where a diagonal band of low density, averaging fewer than 10 people per square mile, extends from southeast to northwest centrally through Ghana. The low density found in northern Ashanti and in the central and eastern parts of the Northern Region is due largely to the occurrence of infertile soils and other adverse natural conditions, such as a scarcity of water during the dry season and floods during the wet, prevalence of the tsetse fly, paucity of minerals, isolation, and unsuitability of the area to cacao culture except in the south.[2] However, that isolation does not necessarily entail low population density is shown by the fact that in the more fertile, well watered northeast, which is much more inaccessible, density is high.

---

[1] E. A. Boateng, *A Geography of Ghana*, London: Cambridge University Press, 1960, p. 21.

[2] R. J. Harrison Church, *West Africa*, 2d ed., London: Longman's, Green & Co., Ltd., 1961, p. 365.

Ghana lives largely on its agriculture, for more than three-fourths of the people make their living by tilling the land. In the north, which is almost entirely agricultural, this proportion may run above 90 percent; southward, dependence upon cultivation decreases while industry, mining, and the like increase; in the northern savannas farming is largely subsistence; southward, it becomes more commercial. As in Ivory Coast, most of the commercial crops are grown in the forest zone in the Eastern and Western regions, and southern Ashanti; in the coastal savannas of the southeast, some commercial cropping is done, but this serves a local rather than a national or an international market. Much of this coastal tillage and that in the northern savannas are migratory, although coconuts are raised for copra and oil palms for oil.

Subsistence crops change as climate varies. In the southern half of the country root crops such as cassava, yams, plantains, and maize are important. Because of decreasing moisture these give way gradually to grains and animals. Cattle, raised for meat rather than milk, are more important in the northern savanna than in the savannas of the coastal zone; but the north is handicapped by inadequate transportation facilities, and frequently cattle must be driven long distances to the markets in the south. Although the coastal savannas are both agricultural and pastoral, integrated farming is not a feature of the area because the cattle keepers are pastoralists from the Northern Region who have moved down with their animals; they practice no cultivation.

The forest region is agriculturally highly productive. Subsistence crops are raised under the practice of shifting cultivation, and cacao, the major commercial crop, under a system of forest enrichment whereby the cacao trees are planted within the natural forests without clearing. Yet the total amount of cacao thus produced is greater than in any other country in the world. Ghana is the world's largest producer and exporter; 90 percent and more of Ghana's farm revenue comes from cacao. It is grown on small plots, usually 1 or 2 acres in size, by Ghanaians, and not as a plantation crop.

The development of the cacao industry in Ghana has been spectacular. Several isolated attempts to introduce the plant were made in the latter part of the nineteenth century, and from these beginnings, the cultivation has spread to the forest areas of the Eastern and Western regions, and of Ashanti. From an export of 40 tons in 1896, the industry expanded until, in 1924, over 220,000 tons of cacao beans were shipped out. From that year, exports of cacao have varied. The cacao is shipped out mostly in the form of beans, as illustrated in 1960 when, of 310,900 metric tons of cacao products exported, 307,700 metric tons were beans; since 1960, when over 300,000 tons of cacao beans went into international trade channels, the annual export has been close to or above 400,000 metric tons.

Cultivation of cacao was most heavily concentrated in the Eastern Region in the beginning, but it has moved steadily westward, and western Ashanti is now the leading producer. Several factors account for the decline in the Eastern Region: many of the oldest trees are here, and the age of the plants is a factor; and some of the plantings failed because of adverse soil and climatic conditions; but the greatest cause of the decline has been the attack of swollen shoot, most damaging in eastern Ghana. Although endemic to Ghana, for some considerable time the cacao of Gold Coast appeared to be relatively immune to the disease. Eventually the trees were affected, however, most greatly in the areas where cacao had been longest cultivated. With the discovery that swollen shoot is caused by a virus, the government has been able to take some measures to control the disease.

It is estimated that about 1.2 million acres of land are planted to cacao, not, it must be remembered, in orchards but under a system that might be called forest enrichment. Marketing is handled through the Cacao Marketing Board. The entire crop is sold—at least all the beans that are accepted by the Marketing Board on the basis of quality standards, and quite a rigid system of inspection has been put into effect. Cacao makes up, by value, two-thirds of the exports of Ghana, and the country produces one-third of the world's supply. The preponderant importance of this crop is likely to decline, however, at least proportionately because it makes Ghana very vulnerable to changes on the world market. One of the major aims in Ghanaian industrialization is to diversify the economy and remove this threat.

Palm oil is also a crop of the forest zone, and an important item of internal trade; palm kernels are exported in small amounts. Coconuts grow along the coast, and kola nuts are produced northwest of Accra, both with cacao and as a replacement crop for cacao.

However, although agricultural in economy, it is for its minerals, and especially gold, that Ghana has been historically most famous. Gold Coast got its name from the trade in gold that was important from the ninth century on, moving by caravan overland to North Africa and so to Europe, or by sea. Although diamonds, manganese, and bauxite also are found, it is gold that is Ghana's mineral.

The precious ore occurs both in veins and in alluvial sands and gravels; thus Ghana has gold workings that are underground, opencut, and dredged. All the major deposits are in Ashanti or the Western Region, are in fact concentrated within 60 miles of Dunkwa, lying about midway between Takoradi on the coast and Kumasi. Ghanian gold is remarkably rich; the Obuasi reserves are the highest grade gold ores in the world. Ghana ranks as second gold producer in Africa and sixth on the globe, but gold is not exported.

The earliest railroads in Ghana were built to the Tarkwa goldfields from the coast in 1901, when the Sekondi-Tarkwa railway was opened; this was extended into the Ashanti goldfields at Obuasi in 1902 and the following year to Kumasi. In 1912, gold mining interests promoted the opening of the line from Tarkwa to Prestea, and in 1943 to 1944 a branch was run from Dunkwa into the bauxite reserves at Awaso.

As gold was the stimulus that led to railroad construction in the west, so cacao furnished the incentive for the beginning of rail connections in the east. Beginning in 1909, railroads began to push inland from Accra, reaching Kumasi, after a delay in construction during the war years, in 1923. In 1928, another line was opened from Huni Valley to Kade; it was uneconomic for a long time because a good net of roads serves the area. This branch was extended to Accra in 1956, giving fairly direct rail access from that city to the port of Takoradi; a line also reaches from Accra to Tema, Ghana's new and developing port.

Tema, east of Accra, has been developed as an artificial harbor and is expected to replace the port of Accra. The first berth at Tema was opened to shipping in 1958; Tema and Tema Township are also the center of Ghana's industrial developments. When the total, enormous Volta power becomes available (the first sector was opened in 1966), the township will have unlimited power resources.

Twenty-seven coastal towns, including Accra, have served as ports for Ghana at one time or another. All are on open roadsteads; Sekondi, like Accra, was one. The port of Takoradi, main exporter of cacao, superseded Sekondi after its completion in 1928.

Kumasi, inland trade center and capital of Ashanti, is a great cultural, commercial, and political center. Since independence, the political role of both Kumasi and Ashanti has declined as this, the greatest tribal kingdom in the Gold Coast, merged with the other tribal kingdoms to form the new nation.

## PLANNING FOR THE FUTURE

Ghana, whose economy is based upon the production of a limited number of primary agricultural and mineral products, is only on the threshold of industrialization; but it is making strenuous efforts to diversify and industrialize, and much of this hinges upon the completion of the Volta River project. This involves a dam at Akosombo behind which a 250-mile lake, which began to fill in 1964, will form; by 1966, enough power was being produced to supply electricity to all the main towns of southern Ghana and adjacent rural areas. Valco, the United States consortium composed of Kaiser Aluminum and Reynolds Metals, will be the largest industrial consumer; 500 miles of transmission lines are expected eventually to distribute power.

To accelerate the change of Ghana from an essentially agricultural, tribally oriented society into a modern semi-industrialized state, great emphasis is being placed also upon political and economic organization, endeavoring through labor, youth, farm cooperatives, and other associations to increase both stability and productivity.

# The Slave Coast

## POLITICAL HISTORY

Slave raiding had been a curse in West Africa before Europeans began their traffic in human beings. The African tribes kept slaves, getting them through forays that were engaged in specifically for that purpose, or using prisoners of war. The momentum of enslavement had increased when trans-Saharan traffic opened new outlets, and slaves became a real commodity of trade. But when Europeans began to demand slaves to supply a world market, holding out to the chiefs the persuasion of European products in exchange, slave warfare and the preying of one tribe upon another, one African upon another, developed into a nightmare of horror: the interior was unsafe for anyone, and Europeans seldom ventured away from the fortified coasts. Most of the slaves for 3 centuries, between 1500 and 1800, were taken from the lands that faced on the Bight of Benin, and that shore became known as the "slave" coast. Togo, Dahomey, and Nigeria are the states that occupy this frontage today.

Togoland became an independent sovereign republic on April 27, 1960. In the three-quarters of a century since its frontiers were first drawn at the Berlin Conference of 1884, Togo experienced three colonial regimes. German occupation dated from July, 1885, when Nachtigal of Germany signed a treaty with King Mlapa III of Togo "placing Mlapa's few thousand lagoonside dwellers near the coast under German 'protection.'" Although the German occupation was severe, it was good both administratively and in advancing development of the territory.

During World War I Togo was occupied by French and British forces, and the colony provisionally divided between the invading forces approximately along the boundary where the two foreign units met; the British occupied and held Lomé, the capital. After the war, the League of Nations mandated Togoland to Britain and France. The boundary between the mandates was drawn somewhat to the west of the earlier provisional line, and France received the greater share of the territory, including Lomé. After World War II the mandates became trusteeships of the United Nations under Britain and France, and a slow process of preparing the people for independence began. In 1956 the Autonomous Republic of Togo was established in the French zone, and in the same year a referendum was held in British Togoland to determine whether the inhabitants desired unification with the people in French Togo or union with Gold Coast.

The southern part of Togoland is occupied by the Ewe people. When the first provisional lines were drawn by France and Britain dividing the German colony, and when they were redrawn for the mandates, the boundary between the two zones ran directly through Ewe territory, dividing the tribal people and placing them under the two different foreign administrations. When the 1956 referendum was held, the Ewes in British Togoland voted strongly against union with Gold Coast, and expressed themselves in favor of continued trusteeship-status under the British until independence should unite the two parts again. However, the population of northern Togo is non-Ewe, and these people voted for union with Gold Coast; representing a majority, the British zone thus was absorbed into Ghana. The Republic of Togo is comprised of that part of the former German colony that became the French mandate.

The name Dahomey commemorates one of the most powerful West African chieftaincies of the twelfth century and onwards, as do the towns of Cotonou and Popo. The first official contact with the French was through a trade agreement signed between France and Dahomey in 1851. When violations of the treaty occurred, France intervened with troops (1889 to 1894) and annexed the territory. It became a republic within the French Community on July 11, 1960, but on August 1 of the same year Dahomey withdrew from the Community and proclaimed itself an independent republic.

At the time of Dahomey's independence proclamation, Portugal held a small enclave within the bounds of the new country, Ajudá, a bit of land containing a fort but no residents, namely, Fort of São João Baptista de Ajudá, founded in 1788 within the port of Ouidah. One year later, on August 1, 1961, Dahomey seized the enclave, which had been administered as a dependency of São Tomé and Principe. Until slavery was stopped along the West African coast, Ouidah had been one of the most important slaving centers along the Gulf of Guinea.

Nigeria emerged as an independent nation, with membership within the Commonwealth of Nations, on October 1, 1960. Independence was not a new idea to Nigeria. It had been planned for and worked toward since 1922, when the first step was taken toward the development of constitutional government. In that year a Legislative Council was created, concerned mainly with legislation in the southern protectorate but dealing also with certain financial matters in the north. Although original plans of the form of government were altered and modified over the succeeding decades, the Nigerians had been trained and educated for self-rule so that when independence came, there was a core of educated Africans who could lead the state.

Nigeria is a large nation, 356,699 square miles in size—one-third larger than Texas, greater in area than England, France, and Italy combined. The Niger, her great river, is longer than the Missouri, and the Niger delta larger than that of Egypt's famous delta of the Nile. Three regions, the Eastern, Western, and Northern, federated to form the country, each region representing a former entity of political administration under the British. Within the new federated nation each region has had its own government, with an elected parliament and a regional premier. The Colony of Lagos became the Federated Territory of Lagos, comparable to the District of Columbia, where the national parliament convenes.

A fourth region, the Midwest, was established in the fall of 1963; like the Northern, Eastern, and Western Regions, it has its own premier, legislature, civil service, and courts. It was carved out of the Western Region, made up of Benin and Delta provinces, which border the western banks of the lower Niger River, 15,000 square miles in area and 1,500,000 in population. A referendum overwhelmingly approved the creation of the fourth region, and an interim administration was agreed upon until general elections should be held, after which it should follow the political pattern set by the other three regions. Questions raised relative to the Midwest Region concern not so much the problem of government as the future of the region and, even more especially,

how its creation will affect minority groups in other parts of Nigeria who have agitated for the creation of a region for themselves.

The northern sector of the British Cameroons became a part of Nigeria on June 1, 1961, in accordance with the results of a plebiscite held in February of that year. It was integrated into the Northern Region, but will continue to be administered as a separate province, called Sardauna Province.

Although an independent country within the Commonwealth of Nations since October, 1960, and operating as a republic, Nigeria did not officially become a "Republic" until October, 1963. In the interim it was "a monarchy, with Queen Elizabeth II as its monarch." The nation has retained its Commonwealth ties, recognizing the British sovereign as Head of the Commonwealth.

Although the history of Nigeria as a sovereign nation is short, many of the tribal peoples have backgrounds of ancient traditions and culture. Kano, the renowned walled casbah of the Hausa people, has written records tracing back 1,000 years; its craftsmen invented the art of making morocco leather;[3] the indigo dyes of the Sahara's famed "blue people" originated here, and blue materials are even today very prominently worn among the people of this area. At Ife were discovered the noteworthy bronze sculptured heads, dating back to the Middle Ages but still posing a mystery as to their creators; hundreds of years ago Oyo and Benin had craftsmen skilled in the working of gold and brass. Ife, Oyo, Benin, and Kano are still famous centers of African arts and crafts.

## THE LAND

Togo and Dahomey are long and narrow, slivers of countries, fronted by coasts that are characterized by barrier bars and lagoons. Bordering the sea in an almost straight line, the coastal strip, about 3 miles wide and built offshore from the river mouths, is low, sandy, flat, and monotonous. No natural harbors are found along this shore, and the waves break full and

---

[3] A fine kind of leather, prepared commonly from goatskin tanned in sumac, or subjected to chrome tanning, and dyed on the grain side. Many pieces of morocco leather are stamped in gold leaf designs.

FIGURE 12.5 Pirogue on the lagoon of Porto Novo, Dahomey. (Courtesy Service de l'Information, AOF)

continuously, making shipping difficult. The lagoon belt consists of a chain of shallow lakes with interconnecting passages: Lake Nokoué is the lagoon of Cotonou; it connects with the lagoon of Porto-Novo, which is 12 miles long, the latter, in turn, connecting eastward with the Lagos Lagoon in an excellent inland passageway (Figure 12.5). The Ouidah Lagoon and that of Grand Popo are to the west of Cotonou. Only at Grand Popo and Cotonou does this lagoon belt have outlets to the sea. About 100 yards outward from the present barrier bar, another sandbar is forming that will in some future time be the coastline. Many of the lagoons have silted so that they now are used to cultivate cassava, vegetables, corn, and cocoyams on small patches; rice could very suitably be raised here also; fishing in the lagoons and coastal lakes is extensive.

Just east of the lagoons is the massive delta of the Niger River. Mangrove prevails widely along the shore, especially around and up the mouths of the distributaries. The Niger delta is a tangled waste of mangrove swamps, uninhabited except for some fisherfolk who huddle along the stream channels, setting up their weirs to intercept the fish as they ascend the river. Inland from the mangrove swamps, freshwater marshes occur, especially east from Port Harcourt to the Cameroons border and up along the lower Niger. Beyond these marshes, the rain forest begins.

The coastal plains beyond the lagoons rise to the tablelands and mountains that make up the plateaus of the north—broad, monotonous plateaus that in Nigeria are known as "high" Nigeria or, sometimes, as the "High Plains of Hausaland." In Dahomey domes and lateritic cappings are common, and soil is thin and infertile; these features extend on into Togoland.

Northwest and northeast Nigeria are not so high as the north-central sectors, where the Jos plateau averages 4,000 feet and reaches heights of over 6,000 feet. The lower plateaus of the northwest are cut through by the valley of the Kebbi River, which flows south through a broad plain into the Niger; the plateaus of the northeast slope toward and drain into Lake Chad through such streams as the Komadugu, the Yedseram, and other smaller ones. This part of Nigeria is really a portion of the Chad basin. South of the Niger the plateaus, a continuation of those of Dahomey, are lower, falling away to coastal lowlands.

East of the Niger and south of the Benue the rock strata, tilted and emerging at the surface and of varying resistance, incline gently upward toward the east in a long synclinal slope; where resistant rock strata occur, escarpments (cuestas) have formed, separated by valleys that coincide with strata of less resistant rock. From the western sector of the Niger delta the Anassama alluvial plains rise gently from southwest to northeast to the Akwa uplands. The east-facing cuesta of the uplands drops to the Mamu-Imo low-lands, which slope upward to the Ude plateau. The plateau in turn drops on the east to the Cross River plains. Northeast of the plains stretch the Adamawa plateaus, largely in Cameroon Republic, averaging 1,200 to 1,500 feet in elevation but rising to eminences of 6,000 and even 8,000 feet. The latter are largely of volcanic origin. The most prominent escarpment is the one facing the Cross River plains, and there, on the eastern slopes of the Ude plateau, just west of Enugu, important coal beds occur.

The Niger River and its major affluent, the Benue, divide Nigeria into three great blocks that have considerable correspondence to the political regions, although the boundaries of the Northern Region lie somewhat below the broad spread of the Niger and Benue as they flow together. The Western Region occupies the southwest, being essentially in the sector south of the Niger; the Eastern Region lies in the southeast, and is essentially the area south of the Benue.

## The Republic of Togo

Togo is one of the small countries of Africa—about the size of West Virginia, with a population of only a little over 1 million. The south, being Ewe, is linguistically, tribally, and culturally homogeneous; the north is tribally and ethnically more varied.

The country is agricultural; and since climate is varied, crops are diversified. Close to the coast oil palms, coconuts, corn, cassava, and bananas are produced, and near the border of Ghana around Palime, cacao and coffee, Togo's leading exports. Where forest blends into savanna, cotton, peanuts, and kapok are typical, as well as animals; for its size, Togo has a large number of sheep, goats, hogs, and cattle.

Trade channels through the port of Lomé despite its being rather unsatisfactory because of shallow offshore waters and shores lined by lagoon-backed sandbars. It has been proposed that Togo be served by ports other than its own, but there are reasons to support the improvement of port facilities at Lomé: first, to make ready for the export of the phosphates that are to be developed; second, Tema and Cotonou, the closest developed ports, are quite a distance away.

Lomé is fairly well served by railroads, and thus makes a good outlet for agricultural exports. One factor that complicates the handling of goods at both Lomé and Cotonou, however, is the high concentration of exports in a 4- or 5-month period. The country has several hundred miles of improved roads suitable for trucking, and a network of secondary roads.

Although Togo's future seems tied to agriculture, minerals should contribute to the economy. High quality phosphates near Lomé give promise of a million-ton annual output when developed; chromite occurs at Atakpamé near the railroad that extends inland from Lomé; it has been known since 1907. Important deposits of iron ore have been discovered at Kompa and Kandi.

## Dahomey

Dahomey, although twice as large as Togo, is another of Africa's small countries; but though its people number only slightly over 2 million, it is the most densely populated state in West Africa. Its economy is tied to the land, the oil yielding palm being Dahomey's basic resource; oil palm products make up about three-fourths of the country's exports. Locally and nationally coconuts, peanuts, and shea nuts are traded, while castor beans, cotton, kapok, coffee, and tobacco are being developed as export crops. Trade in these five crops is small, however. Cattle are kept in the north, but are not very numerous; hogs, poultry, sheep, and goats are raised throughout the country. Dahomey must import lumber, which it gets from Ivory Coast.

Some minerals occur, but mining has not yet begun. There are large deposits of iron ore at Banjeli, good reserves of chromite around Tanguieta and, it is thought, in other areas. Tanguieta is nearly 200 miles from the nearest railhead, however, and since the railhead is another 275 miles from Cotonou, the port and economic center for Dahomey, it is unlikely that the ores will be developed very soon. Ilmenite occurs in the south and rutile deposits, with a titanium-dioxide content of up to 95 percent, are found in the north; placer gold occurs. Whatever industry has developed is still associated with the processing of the products of cultivation; the mining and processing of ores remain to be developed sometime in the future.

Dahomey reflects its centuries-long role as a part of the Slave Coast. Ouidah, 23 miles west of Cotonou, was for a long time possibly the greatest slaving port along the Guinea coast; the ancient capital, "royal city," and slave center of Abomey also retains the flavor of the past in some of the outstanding examples of traditional architecture that still remain. Around Abomey are large oil palm plantations, established by prisoners (who were to have been shipped as slaves) when the slave traffic was stopped. Traders suggested palm oil production as an alternative item of trade. Porto-Novo on the lagoon is the present capital, but economically it does not compare with Cotonou in importance and plans are in the making for a shift of the capital to Cotonou.

FIGURE 12.6 Distributional features of the Nigerian economy: 1. Regional boundaries; 2. northern limit of the tsetse; 3. northern limit of the southern root economy; 4. southern limit of the northern grain economy; 5. groundnuts (peanuts); 6. cotton; 7. tin; 8. benniseed; 9. cacao; 10. rubber; 11. principal palm oil; 12. subsidiary palm oil areas. *(After J. R. V. Prescott, "The Geographical Basis of Nigerian Federation," The Nigerian Geographical Journal, June, 1958.)*

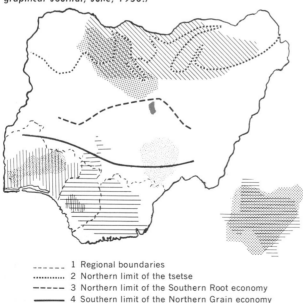

------  1 Regional boundaries
...........  2 Northern limit of the tsetse
-----  3 Northern limit of the Southern Root economy
———  4 Southern limit of the Northern Grain economy

5 Groundnuts (peanuts)      9 Cocao
6 Cotton                    10 Rubber
7 Tin                       11 Principal palm oil areas
8 Benniseed                 12 Subsidiary palm oil areas

## Nigeria

If one country in West Africa were selected to typify the vast realm of the hump, Nigeria would most nearly fulfill the scope of physical characteristics. Extending across approximately 10° of latitude, climates and vegetation range from equatorial rain forest to *sahel* with its scrub and scattered clump grass. Nigeria has a greater variety of climates than any other West African state; only true desert is lacking—and northeast Nigeria might be characterized as near desert. In general, rainfall is greatest in the southeast and south, and declines toward the north and northeast.

However, the rainfall pattern is not entirely smooth: certain areas appear to lie in a rain shadow, such as portions of the lower Benue and lower Niger, and in southern Nigeria the climate is semiequatorial, so there are strong contrasts between the eastern and western sectors. Rainfall in the southeast is excessively high and there is no dry season, whereas in the southwest the moisture received averages between 40 and 60 inches and there is a short dry season; between these two areas (central-south), rainfall averages about the same as in the east, but is more variable from year to year. Throughout the equatorial belt there are double maximums of precipitation. Due to the heavier rains of the southeast, soils are more eroded and leached than in other parts of the south.

Vegetation reflects the variations in climate. Rain forest is best represented in Eastern Province and into the Cameroons; areas of Western Province that were formerly in equatorial forest are now largely in secondary forest types, especially in Yoruba country, although the 3-story climax vegetation is still to be found in portions of Benin and Ondo provinces. Beyond the rain and secondary forests is a belt of derived savanna that grows ever wider as the climax vegetation gives way before the destruction of man. The northern margins of this zone, which reach approximately to a line that runs from "Iseyin, Ilorin, Kabba, and Oturkpo and then north-eastward,"[4] represents the former limits of equatorial forest.

Varied savanna covers the remainder of Nigeria.

[4] Church, *op. cit.*, p. 450.

All the savannas are of deteriorated types, because man has recklessly cleared the land by burning and cutting, so that long grass (during the wet season) and brush prevail; widely scattered baobab trees and other drought-resistant varieties also occur; on the Jos plateau, a derived vegetation of clump grass and giant cacti is characteristic. The plateau is starkly arid during the dry season, and the aridity is visibly apparent in the sharp outlines of the topography and the canyonlike gorges in which streams intermittently flow. From the southern sector northward the species of savanna changes to a drier type until, in the northeast and toward Lake Chad, *sahel* takes over.

## PEOPLE AND POPULATION

Nigeria has over 55 million people, making it the most populous country in Africa and one of the largest nations in the world. Thirty million of these Nigerians live in the Northern Region, which contrasts with the rest of Nigeria in climate and in being Moslem in religion and tradition.

Tribal groups tend to concentrate in one or another of the great regional divisions of the country (Figure 12.7). Numerically, the Hausa, Ibo, Yoruba, and Fulani are the strongest groups, in that order. Hausa

FIGURE 12.7 Distribution of principal tribal nuclei in Nigeria. (After J. R. V. Prescott, "The Geographical Basis of Nigerian Federation," The Nigerian Geographical Journal, June, 1958.)

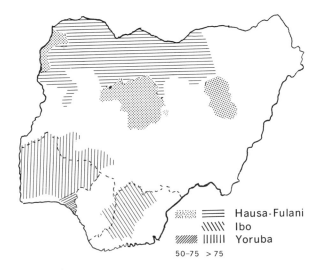

Hausa-Fulani
Ibo
Yoruba
50-75  > 75

and Fulani dominate the Northern Region, although other notable tribes, such as the Kanuri, Tiv, and Nupe, live there also; Yoruba are dominant in the Western Region where the Ijaw also are strong; Ibo are politically outstanding in the East although Ibibio and Edo also comprise large ethnic groups. Nigeria has over 250 tribal groups, and as many separate languages or dialects. There is no African language common to all of Nigeria; the official language is English, an interesting commentary upon the impress of Britain upon the country.

Another significant way of looking at the tribal distribution is in terms of climate: the peoples of the Eastern, Midwest, and Western regions live in the humid forest and coastal lands; those of the Northern Region in the savannas that grow progressively drier toward the northern reaches of Nigeria. As noted, the north is proudly Moslem; although skins are black, manners and tradition are more Arab than African; in contrast, the three southern regions are largely Christianized, or hold to tribal religions or superstitions.

The independent country inherited a tribal problem which has not lessened with the years; if anything, it has grown stronger. With each tribe living more or less within its ethnic boundaries and with its own leaders and legislatures, Nigerian nationalists had reasoned that tribalism could be restrained if not eliminated on the national level. This has not proven to be the case; rather, this tribal regionalism has accentuated the struggle for power at the national level. Elections in December, 1964, almost split the country into two parts; in January, 1966, a military coup overthrew the constitutional government. The greatest danger of disruption lies between the Moslem north and the relatively non-Moslem south; religion and cultural traditions 1,000 years ago make the Northern Region especially distinctive, and climate helps to accentuate the differences between these two broad areas.

In the main Nigeria is rural, and yet there are large urban centers whose African populations number above 100,000. Generally speaking, the north and east have few large cities; the west has more; in fact, the Western Region has in Ibadan the largest all-black African city to be found on the continent; its population numbers between 600,000 and 1 million. The few large towns of the North are far apart; generally, people live in small villages. In the Eastern Region there are even fewer cities than in the north, but villages are larger and closer together because of the denser population. Onitsha, the great native market center of the Eastern Region, is about 80,000 in size; Port Harcourt, perhaps 75,000 on an eastern distributary of the Niger delta, is the port for the oil lands. In contrast, the Western Region has, in addition to Ibadan, four native cities of over 100,000.

Density varies greatly among the three regions (considering the Western and Midwest as one) and the Federal District. Although the following densities are not to be taken as absolute, since population statistics are considered inaccurate, they are indicative: Northern, 67; Western, 148; Eastern, 269; Lagos, 12,963 per square mile.

FIGURE 12.9  Mosque of Kano. (Courtesy Federal Information Service, Lagos.)

FIGURE 12.8  Child of Northern Nigeria from a village between Kano and Tofa. (Photograph by writer.)

## REGIONS

*The North.*  Northern Nigeria is the largest of the regions, embracing over three-fourths of the area and over half of the population of the country. (See Figure 12.8.) It is wet and dry tropical in climate and vegetation, hot and semiarid to arid; its roads are dusty and unpleasant to travel during the dry season; its crowded, bustling markets and walled towns remind one not of the rest of black Africa but of the Moslem north in the Atlas and Saharan lands. Northern Nigeria is another marchland where an adopted religion has impressed a strict code of living and way of life upon a people that before the coming of Islam and the conquest by the nomadic Fulani, had traditions and cultures not dissimilar to those farther south. There are also subtle differences that distinguish the Nigerian north from the rest of the Islamic world, however (Figure 12.9).

The Hausa, the majority people, are traders, farmers, and craftsmen; the Fulani, conquerors and still politically ascendant in the north, are a powerful minority group; they remain the overlords of the Hausa, whom they invaded and subdued. Tall, slim "blacks" who have straight black hair, the Fulani are a pastoral people, and magnificent horsemen.

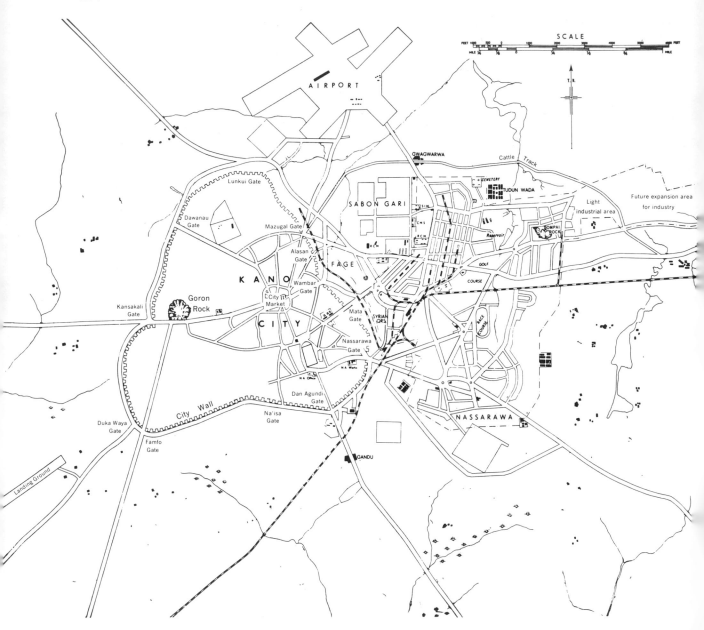

**FIGURE 12.10  Kano and environs. The old city lies within the walls on the left. (Courtesy Survey Department, Government of Nigeria.)**

Kaduna, centrally located, is the Northern capital. Although only about 35 years old, it is a city of over 50,000 people; but it does not have either the splendor or the reverence accorded Kano and Sokoto, the older cities of Moslem Nigeria.

Kano is at least 1,000 years old (Figure 12.10). Its markets are crowded with masses of traders buying and selling things; dingy stalls face uneven, crooked pathways that wind among the booths. Through the several gates that give access to the walled city—

walls that are more like heaps of earth thrown up into dikes than ramparts of a town—pass herds of sheep, goats, cattle, camels, and people; camels, cattle, and donkeys rest under the occasional shade of trees outside the gateways. Along the highway that leads away from the modern city, the European city that has grown up beside the ancient walled town, are Kano's famous pyramids, great geometric mounds of groundnuts, 9,000 bags to the pyramid, for Nigeria is the world's largest peanut exporter, shipping out ½ million tons annually, and supplying about a third of the peanuts that go into international trade.

Kano, although the largest city and chief trade and industrial center in Northern Region, is only third in size in Nigeria. It is, however, Nigeria's greatest cattle market. Among the modern industries that have developed here are peanut crushing mills, meat canneries, and sugar and textile factories. As we have said, the ancient crafts are also important.

Sokoto, spiritual center of the north, was formerly the capital of the Fulani sultanate. It is held in great reverence by all Moslem Nigerians. Sokoto is not, however, important as a trade center; the town of Gusau, situated southeast of the religious center on the railroad from Zaria, serves the northwest as the market town.

Most of the animals produced in Nigeria are raised on the dry savanna lands of the north because over large parts of the country the tsetse fly keeps people from raising cattle. Most of the herds are owned by Fulani and are raised for their meat; dairying is of lesser importance although on the increase; cattle hides are exported. Sheep and goats likewise are found heavily in the north, and goatskins are an important item of trade, especially the red goatskins of Sokoto, the world-famous morocco leather. In the humid forestland of the south only the Muturu dwarf cattle are found. These animals do not breed well and are not good dairy cattle, so they are kept only in small numbers, mostly for prestige, dowry, or ceremonial purposes. On the plateau, not yet infected with the tsetse, both the dwarf Muturu and the large, humped zebu are found.

Nigeria is not rich in mineral resources, but on the Jos plateau in the Northern Region (Figure 12.11a and b) are found the nation's tin deposits, whose production equals about 5 percent of the world's annual

(a)

FIGURE 12.11 (a) Stark topography indicates the arid character of the Jos Plateau; (b) village on the Jos Plateau. Building beside the rocks for concealment is effective once the clay walls and grass roofs fade. (Photographs by writer.)

(b)

total. Tin has been mined on the plateau for several decades. It occurs in places in combination with columbite. Before columbite was recognized as an important metal, this ore, which occurs in the younger granites, was thrown away as waste. Now Nigeria supplies over 80 percent of the world's needs of this strategic mineral. The demand for columbium fluctuates widely, however, and so is not dependable as an item of trade. The city of Jos is the main center of the tin mining industry, but other deposits occur in the provinces of Bauchi, Zaria, Kano, and Benue. Oyo, in the Western Region, has a small deposit that is worked, and there is one in Calabar Province that has not yet been developed.

The Northern Region possibly looks as much north as it does south, although this is not so true today as it was in the past. Trumpets formerly heralded the arrivals of caravans out of the desert at Kano; in this modern day, the same long trumpets announce the arrival of planes, a colorful pageantry that unites past with present. It serves as a reminder that Northern Region is landlocked, and that at least from the belt stretching from Kano northward, it is more akin to the desert than to the moist south. For years Kano took a leading role in the organization of trans-Saharan trade.

*The East.*   The Eastern Region stretches between the lower reaches of the Niger River and the Cameroons Mountains. Facing outward on the Gulf of Guinea, its coastline is a barrier bar behind which mangrove swamps, interlaced with tidal waterways, reach inward until they blend with rain forest.

Eastern Region is equatorial in climate and vegetation. Oil palms and oranges are commercial crops, and agriculture is its principal occupation. There are no peanut pyramids here as in the north; but yams, arm length in size sometimes, float down the Niger in junklike, covered dugouts to big, native market centers, like Onitsha, where heaps of yams indicate the importance of this starchy food in the diets of the people of the East. In the north, millet, guinea corn, maize, and rice are the subsistence crops. Rice, although it has been started in the Eastern Region, is grown almost exclusively in the north, and is heaviest around Sokoto. In the two southern regions the root crops, yams and cassava, are eaten.

The capital of the Eastern Region, Enugu, owes its importance to the discovery of coal in 1909. These are the only coal deposits in Nigeria and are very important. The production is consumed almost entirely by the railways and by plants generating electricity. Exploration for oil has been carried out in Nigeria since 1937, mostly by Shell-BP Petroleum Development Company of Nigeria Limited, and almost entirely in the Eastern Region. With the discovery in 1956 of oil in commercial quantities in two fields (Afam and Oloibiri), explorations accelerated, and since then several other fields have been proven capable of commercial production. Natural gas also occurs, and gas from the Afam field now generates electricity for portions of the country. The old slave port of Bonny, on an island at the front of the Niger delta in the east, serves as an oil terminal; its wells came into operation at the end of 1960. On the tidal swamps of the small island, oil derricks mingle with equatorial forest giants and stilt-rooted mangrove; and black oil, escaping from the pumps, makes the white sands slimy and murky.

Once adequate reserves of petroleum have been proven in Nigeria and production sustained, a refinery may be built by Shell-BP. This would be economically beneficial to the nation because Nigeria could then supply its own needs in kerosene, gasoline, diesel, and fuel oil, and Nigeria is very short of chemical fuels. The discovery of petroleum in Nigeria changed the whole outlook in industrial development for that nation.

Port Harcourt is the headquarters for Shell-BP. It is the port for the Eastern Region, the second Nigerian seaport, and the nation's most important river port. It lies 41 miles up the Bonny distributary of the Niger River. Its site handicaps shipping, however, because of the restricted space that the river allows on the bend; the wharf angles, "reducing the usable length of berths and limiting the space for port facilities, thus impeding movement of goods to and from transit sheds."[5] As ships pass up the stream to the port, they move through a channel that is lined along both banks by dense mangrove thickets.

[5] William A. Hance, *African Economic Development*, New York: Council on Foreign Relations, Inc., 1958, p. 95.

FIGURE 12.12 (a) Oil palm bunch at stage of florescence; (b) bunches of oil palm fruits grow in clusters at the head of the palm trunk where the fronds splay out. (Courtesy INEAC.)

*The West.* The Western Region, including the Midwest Region, extends westward from the lower Niger to the borders of Dahomey. It also fronts on the Gulf of Guinea, and as in the Eastern Region, the continental coastline is hidden in part behind barrier sandbars that enclose the long lagoon, known as the Lagos Lagoon, on which Lagos is situated.

Western Region is commercially productive of equatorial crops. Nigeria is the world's second largest producer of cacao and most of this comes from the southwest. Nigeria is the world's largest producer of palm oil and palm kernels, and part of this comes from Western Region. Oil palm products rank second to cacao in the Western Region, but are of first importance in the East. In fact, commercial agriculture in the Eastern Region is almost entirely dependent on the oil palm (Figure 12.12*a* and *b*). The most important Nigerian rubber production is in Western Region.

Lagos-Apapa in Western Region is the main port for Nigeria. It is a lagoon harbor, as the discussion has already indicated; nearly three-fourths of the import and half of the export tonnage passes through its wharves. It was made a seaport in 1913 when an opening was cut through the barrier bar giving access to the ocean. The Customs Wharf, along the Lagos waterfront, served for many years as the main port, even after wharves were built at Apapa (1926), and despite the congestion in the old Customs Port; five additional berths were added at Apapa in 1956, all equipped with the most modern loading and storage equipment. Congestion, however, continues to be a problem at the Customs Wharf, and Lagos has, besides, a "problem of maintaining its protecting sandbar which will apparently require more or less continuous transferral of sand."[6]

Lagos, the tropical island that is Nigeria's capital, is an articulate and sophisticated city and yet one of the most African cities in West Africa. A feeling of vitality pervades the capital, not only along the har-

[6] *Ibid.*

bor front where skyscrapers are beginning to rise, but also in the crowds of Nigerian hawkers, market women, and children who fill the alleyways that are a part of the tangle of streets of the old city that is still largely slum, where the smell from the lagoon is almost overpowering. The city has spread to the mainland, but the Nigerians who live in the old town are reluctant to leave Lagos Island even though the native quarters of the island are overcrowded and the streets jammed with people and with cars trying to honk their way through the human mass. The bridge that connects Lagos Island with the mainland sector of the city carries an uninterrupted flow of bicycles, pedestrians, and automobiles, though the last are least prominent in the flow. Lagos is the second city in size in Nigeria.

The Western Region has other large and important cities. Ibadan, capital of the region, is (as has been noted) the largest all-African city in tropical Africa, and the largest city of Nigeria; Europeans and Asians together number only slightly over 1,000. Despite the fact that a major university, University College, is located here, and that it is an important center for trade, crafts, and industry, Ibadan does not have the structure of a city; it is, in reality, an immense village —the leading town of the Yoruba people. It derives much importance from its position in the midst of Nigeria's leading cacao belt.

Other Western towns of significance include Ife, the spiritual capital of the Yoruba; Oyo, an art center where the leather crafts using sheep and goatskins, cloth dying and weaving, calabash and wood carving, and the like are of importance; and Benin, in the Midwest Region, most famed for the historic carved bronze heads. This city also carries on such crafts as carving wood and ivory.

## ECONOMIC PLANNING

The bulk of Nigeria's agricultural exports are handled by marketing boards, regionally set up. Shortly after World War II, produce-marketing boards were established by statute to handle the sale of the main commercial crops. The Cacao Marketing Board, established in 1947, was the first to be created; in 1949, marketing boards for oil palm products, peanuts, and cotton were begun.

In the mid-1950s the system was reorganized on a regional basis, and the produce-marketing board disappeared. Regional boards were established by legislation, which also designated the commodities to be handled. At first, a Central Marketing Board acted as "a common shipping and selling organization" for the regional boards. This was later replaced by the Nigerian Produce Marketing Company, Limited, whose functions are much the same as were those of the Central Board. Each board is advised by a statutory representative committee.

The marketing board has proven to be a good way of handling the agricultural export produce of Nigeria, most of which is raised by small farmers on small pieces of land. They serve to stabilize prices for the producer during good years and bad, to set up standards of quality and so to improve the quality of the product; they assure the small producer of a reasonable return, and through their program of loans to producers, of investments, of grants, and of endowments for purposes of research and economic development, they bring benefits not only to the farmers but to the economy of the country as a whole.

Nigeria is able to grow a great variety of agricultural products, in fact any of the crops cultivated in West Africa, ranging from the equatorial tree crops in the south (the oil palm, cacao, kola nuts, and rubber) to peanuts and cotton in the north; from cassava, yams, maize, sugar cane, and bananas to the dry grains, such as millet and Guinea corn. Of these palm oil and kernels, cacao, rubber, peanuts, and cotton are exported, while yams and kola nuts are very important items of internal trade. This wide range of cultivated produce is made possible by the latitudinal span of the country, by the varied nature of the relief, climate, soil, and vegetation, and by the varied cultures of the people with their differing methods of cultivation and crops.

There is little plantation agriculture because the policy of the British and of Nigeria has been to discourage alienation of land to non-Africans. Only about 16,000 acres of land are under European plantations, but there is an increasing amount that is being thus developed by Nigerians, both privately and by development corporations.

Important as are the commercial crops to the economy of the country, they make up only about 20 percent of the total agricultural production. Food crops for home consumption make up the other 80 percent; commercial agriculture is still in its beginning stages. Methods of cultivation are generally not good, although they have improved; the African farmer is slow to change his ways. Subsistence farming is generally practiced, but the quantity of subsistence crops that is locally or nationally sold or traded is enormous.

The importance of the cattle industry, especially in the north under the Fulani, and of the trade in leather and hides has been noted. Despite their commercial importance, however, cattle are often kept only for prestige purposes or killed in ritual services.

As a producer of lumber Nigeria is outstanding; the country is the largest exporter of unsawn timber in Africa, and the value of wood products (lumber, fuel, and pitprops using mangrove trees) traded within the country is greater than the value of the timber exported. About 20 percent of Nigeria is covered with high forest; of this, approximately one-third is in forest reserves. The Western Region, which has the highest proportion of such reserves, leads in the amount of timber cut; nearly three-fourths of the sawn timber and four-fifths of the value of the timber, and almost all of the exported woods come from the southwest.

Hydroelectric installations are taking an important place in the planned developments of Nigeria. In February, 1963, a plan for a "Nigerian TVA" was submitted to the Government. This proposal involves the construction of a dam on the Niger River at Kainji and the creation of a reservoir 100 miles long and 465 feet deep. The planned hydroelectric installations will be capable of generating more electricity than any single hydroelectric installation in Western Europe, and more than the entire continent of Africa was producing in the mid-1950s. By bypassing the Awuru rapids by a canal and lock, wide stretches of the Niger now usable only by canoes will be open to commercial navigation. The dam will also: increase the fish population and thereby become a notable source of protein for the Nigerians; supply electricity for industrial developments and domestic use; and carry a road which, it is claimed, will allow the detouring of cattle around the tsetse-infested country which must now be crossed to reach Jebba. The size of the Kainji Dam, as planned, would regularize the flow of the Niger and provide a constant flow of power, "with a probability of interruption only once in 100 years."

It will mean the resettlement of about 60,000 persons to a new town to be erected on the shores of the lake, because the historic town of Busa and the Foge Island basin would be drowned; and it will create a new river port at the end of the lake opposite Kainji, at Yelva.

Transport facilities in Nigeria are both diverse and fairly extensive, and transportation has frequently been the deciding factor in restricting or encouraging development of minerals or commercial agriculture. Navigable waterways are important: boats move 450 to 500 miles upstream from the mouth of the Niger, depending on the season, whether dry or wet; up the Benue to Yola near the border during the rains, a distance of over 450 miles above the confluence of the Benue with the Niger; seasonally, some other streams can also be navigated, such as the Cross River.

Although there is nothing that corresponds to a railroad net, Nigeria is served by nearly 2,000 miles of rail line. The system is one of trunk lines that extend from Lagos to Kano, and from Port Harcourt to Enugu and Kaduna, with branch lines to a few important centers. Commercial developments generally have dictated the plan of rail service that has emerged.

There are thousands of miles of roads, of which about 22,000 miles are classed as all-season. They may, however, be seasonally disagreeable to travel, especially during the dusty dry season because only about 4,000 miles of hard-top exist. The roads, nevertheless, carry a tremendous traffic that moves on foot, bicycle, auto, and truck. However, more and better roads are needed, and road construction is being carried out rapidly—so rapidly, in fact, that road maps become outdated before they can be distributed.

# 13 CENTRAL EQUATORIAL AFRICA

*Never to have seen anything but*
*the temperate zone is to have*
*lived on the fringe of the World.*

DAVID FAIRCHILD

## Political Definition of the Realm

The equatorial lands of Central Africa were the last portions of the continent to be discovered and explored. They remained "dark," unknown, and their great river untraced long after most of the rest of Africa had been probed. It was a Portuguese, Diôgo Cão, who was the daring discoverer of the mighty Congo. He called it Zaire, a name the river retained for several centuries. Latitudinally, the realm extends from about 13°S to beyond 14°N, and includes the former colonial lands of France and Belgium, namely French Equatorial Africa (except Chad) and the Belgian Congo, and the two tiny holdings still belonging to Portugal and Spain, Cabinda and Rio Muni, also known as Spanish Guinea.

The realm is not wholly equatorial nor does it include all African lands that are equatorial; hence, the use of the term "central." However, since all the countries included are either crossed by or have some portion of their boundaries no farther than 3° from the Equator, this definitive term is used to designate the realm. The northern portions of Cameroon Republic, most of the Central African Republic, and much of the Katanga Provinces in The Congo are, however, wet and dry tropical.

While under France, French Equatorial Africa was divided administratively into the four provinces of Tchad, Oubangi-Chari, Moyen-Congo (Middle Congo), and Gabon. The new states that emerged into independence in 1959 and the boundaries between them correspond to the provincial delineation used by the French: Tchad became Chad Republic, Oubangi-Chari the Central African Republic, Moyen-Congo the Republic of the Congo, and Gabon the Gabon Republic. The French Cameroons was accorded independence as the Cameroon Republic in 1960, and in February, 1961, Southern Cameroon of the British mandate voted by plebiscite to unite with that Republic.

The Belgian Congo became the sovereign state of The Congo in 1960, a single, large African country. The Belgians had no intention that the Congo colony should be split into several countries along the lines of Belgian administrative districts (Léopoldville, Kasai, Katanga, Kivu, Orientale, and Equateur provinces) as had happened in most of French Africa.

Strong separatist movements, however, found expression in terms of administrative divisions. Katanga, richest of the provinces in known natural resources and the most developed, did in fact declare itself independent and remained so for many months, issuing stamps and in other ways proclaiming its sovereignty. The defection was not recognized by the Congolese government in Léopoldville, however, and Katanga eventually was forced back into the union. Spanish Guinea and Cabinda, the latter a Portuguese exclave of Angola, are still dependents of European powers.

## The Land

The term "equatorial" suggests the monotonously warm humid climate and the rain forests that prevail over a large part of central Africa. Within this realm, however, humid climates merge into wet and dry as periods of drought lengthen; vegetation passes from rainforest to a forest-savanna mosaic with tall grass, to moist (and then dry) woodlands and savannas, and to grass savannas and steppes as distance from the Equator increases. The equatoriality of The Congo is modified by elevation because The Congo is essentially the plateau basin of the Congo River, generally higher on the edges and sloping inward; mountains occur along the east. The former French equatorial lands straddle the Chad and Congo basins and the intervening divide.

### RELIEF

The Chad and Congo basins are shallow depressions on the continental plateau. Relatively low, they nevertheless have elevations that range from about 1,000 to 3,000 feet in the center, rising higher toward the edges. The divide separating the basins is a broad tableland, in places rising to over 4,500 feet, that runs centrally through the Cameroons and generally eastward across the Central African Republic. The Chari and Logone Rivers are the main streams that flow down its north slope into the interior of the Chad depression, an enormous area of swamps which lies separated from the coast by the Cameroons Mountains. Southward flow the streams that are tributary

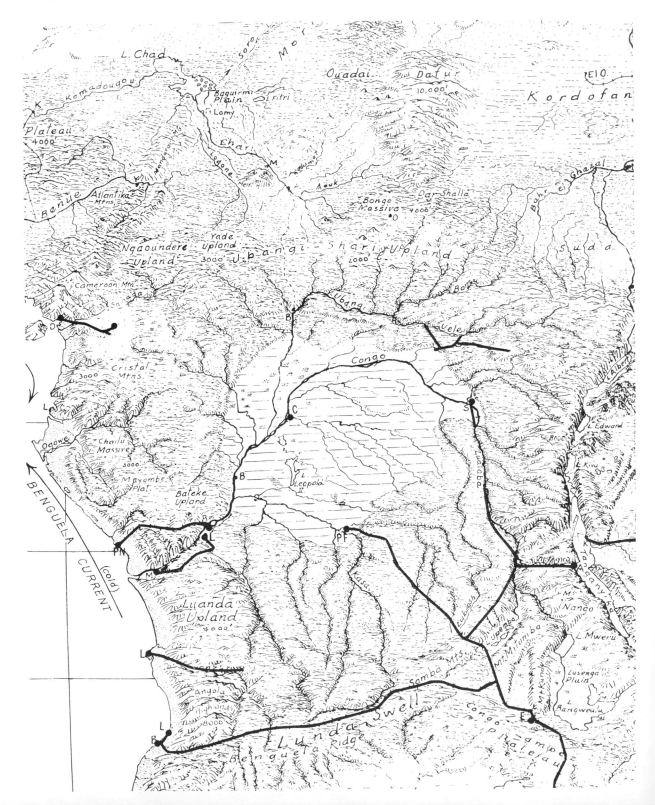

to the Congo River; of these, the Ubangi is the largest, itself a mighty river with many feeder streams.

The Congo basin, occupying a central position on the African plateau, is separated from the basinlike surface of the South African plateau by the Benguela-Lunda swell and, in the east, by the western rift (western part of the East African rift) and its associated mountains from the East African plateau. The Congo River drains to the Atlantic through a narrow-necked outlet. The basin character was formed, subsequent to the uplift of the African plateau above sea level, by the erosive action of streams working upon the surface, and by later uplift and warping around the edges. Despite the swells around the edges, the basin today has a remarkably flat character, partly owing to filling in from the peripheral rims. Nowhere is the basin less than 1,000 feet in height. The lowest portions lie along the main channel of the Congo River between 16 and 24°E longitude and 2°N and 3°S latitude; the highest relief is found along the eastern edges where elevations reach to above 9,800 feet, one mountain, Ruwenzori, towering to 16,795 feet.

Relief along the southern edge of the basin, above the lowest portion along the river, is due only slightly to erosive forces; here the Benguela-Lunda swell that forms the divide between Congo and Zambezi drainage is, in the main, simply an undissected portion of the African plateau. "It is so flat for 500 miles that in times of heavy rains water ponds on the divide and flows in part to the Atlantic and in part to the Indian Ocean."[1] In the east, the drainage pattern was greatly disturbed by the rifting of the East African plateau.

[1] A. C. Veatch, *Evolution of the Congo Basin,* Washington, D.C.: Geological Society of America, 1935, p. 161.

FIGURE 13.2 (Left) Relief and rail transport of Central Africa. *(Base map Physiographic Diagram of Africa, copyright A. K. Lobeck; reproduced with permission of the publisher, The Geographical Press, a division of C. S. Hammond & Company, Maplewood, N.J.)*

## CLIMATE AND VEGETATION

From the west coast, equatorial and semiequatorial heat and humidity extend inland, in about a 5 to 9° band on either side of the Equator, across the southern part of Cameroon Republic, Gabon, and the two Congos all the way over to the rift valley mountains. Because of altitude behind the coasts, however, the equatorial character is not so pronounced as in the Amazon basin of South America, where the whole interior drainage tract lies essentially at sea level. Nevertheless, the drainage basin of the Congo River system and the land tributary to the Sanaga and Ogowe rivers in Cameroon and Gabon comprise what is generally regarded as central equatorial Africa, geographically speaking.

As noted, the Equator cuts across the middle of this region. However, a truly equatorial climate with rain forest is characteristic in less than a third of the area, occurring across a band of territory that lies astride the Equator, bending northward along the west and southward in the east, broader on the south side of the Equator than on the north. Along the east, the equatorial belt terminates abruptly against the buttress of the East African plateau; in the south it disappears as the central basin rises to the plateaus of Angola and the Rhodesias; in the north, it gradually and intermittently passes into savannas of varying types. Some of the characteristics of savanna are markedly apparent in the north even before the Uele River is reached; beyond the Ubangi affluent in Central African Republic the climate is definitely wet and dry; here the elevations of a 2,000-foot plateau assist in making the climate tropical rather than equatorial. In southern Congo the rainy tropics become wet and dry somewhat south of the latitude of Albertville.

All parts of central Africa, however equatorial, have rainier and less rainy periods, those areas closest to the Equator having two rainier and two less rainy seasons; one of the drier periods is usually very short.

Temperatures in the equatorial belt vary little, and annual ranges are smaller than diurnal ranges, the former being only about 5 degrees; diurnal ranges may reach 20 degrees or more. This constancy of temperature produces a monotonous climate that, along with the persistently high humidity, produces in human beings a feeling of enervation. As elevation rises, temperatures become more moderate, ranges increase, and monotony decreases.

Vegetation changes with latitude, altitude, and local conditions. Rain forest occurs only spottily; savanna of various kinds takes over as forests play out; rivers are usually bordered by swamp forests (Figure 13.3) or by gallery forests that are thick and dense, but change a short distance back from the river; interriverine areas across much of Congo are parklike, or only grasslands over broad areas. In places, as along the base of the Ruwenzori Mountains, long tropical grass, 10 and 12 feet in height (Figure 13.4) merges into the forests of the lower slopes; but from the heights of the northern rift mountains, one looks out over dense rain forest, the thick tree growth extending right up to the base of the mountains and even mounting the lower flanks; south of approximately 6°S grassland and brush, or acacia-grass savanna prevail, as around Lubumbashi.

FIGURE 13.3 Swinging bridge carries people safely above sectors of swamp forest in the Lake Tumba area of The Congo. (Photograph by writer.)

Soil and drainage conditions are important determinants, after latitude and altitude, in influencing the character of the vegetation, and vegetation microzones occur within the broader zones that are climatically and altitudinally determined, so that within a small area savanna may change from short grass and thorn scrub, to brush and/or dry forest, to parklike, to long tropical grasses (elephant grass); forests stand juxtaposed to grasslands, as in the Mayumbe, or grasses or forests may be advancing at the expense of the other, under natural conditions, all within a very small area, as in the Lake Tumba region south of Mbandaka. The vegetation pattern would have to be presented in minute detail to record the variety and quick change that typifies much of central Africa. Where elevations rise high enough, as in the Cameroons Mountains and rift valley highlands, equatorial and tropical varieties give way to temperate species; the slopes of the Ruwenzori have one of the most remarkable mosaics of floral change with altitude to be found in the world. Across wide areas deteriorated types of secondary vegetation have replaced the climax forests and savannas, as a result of burning by man for purposes of cultivation or hunting, or of lightning-set fires.

## Land Utilization and Policy in Equatorial Africa

### FRENCH

The active penetration of Gabon and Middle Congo by the French took place in the last 2 decades of the nineteenth century. Oubangi-Chari was gradually included, but the Chad was not entirely taken under control until World War I.

The early opening up of the colonies was carried out under the concessionaire plan, already effectively used in the exploitation and development of equatorial lands by the Dutch and British in the Far East. This was a method of land development through European entrepreneurs who held monopolistic rights of exploitation over specific resources or regions.

The era of big concessions came to an end in the French lands in 1929; for a number of reasons it had not worked out successfully. There followed a period

FIGURE 13.4 Elephant grass along the west base of Mt. Ruwenzori in The Congo. (Photograph by writer.)

of small concessions, granted to promote the plantation development of tropical crops such as rubber, cacao, bananas, and oil palms. This was all European. Only later did the French begin an active policy of stimulating the cultivation of commercial crops by Africans, particularly of coffee, cotton, and, in Gabon, of oil palms.

The early economic policies of the French were exploitive, and resource and agricultural development actually did not begin until the 1930s; French Equatorial Africa was known as "the stepchild" of France. The earliest plantation developments were handicapped also by insufficient capital, a lack of experience in the raising of tropical crops, units that were too small to be remunerative, and a lack of official encouragement. The most successful were those that were situated near the coast in Gabon, growing cacao, vanilla, coffee, citrus (for lime citrate production), and to a lesser degree, palm oil and rubber. Only cacao became commercially significant. Until the end of World War II, the economy of French Equatorial Africa was based largely on the export of wild products gathered in the forests by the Africans, woods, rubber, palm kernels, sesame seed, copal gum, salt, native soda, wax, and ivory. Only in Gabon had Afri-

cans settled on the land to raise crops for export; the rest of the African cultivators practiced a migratory agriculture for subsistence purposes only.

The most successful innovation of the French for the improvement of farming among the Africans was the *paysannat*, a system that was designed to convert migratory cultivators to sedentary occupation of the land, by "altering the environment in which they live." This method of group planning was used successfully not only here but also in the Belgian Congo, and by the British in southern Anglo-Egyptian Sudan under the Zande scheme. The system involves land planning and crop rotation, designed to conserve and restore soil fertility, better the food supply, and encourage the raising of cash crops; each individual farmer becomes a landowner.

## BELGIAN

The Congo did not become a colony of the Belgian state until 1908. From 1878 it was a territory developed by an association known at first as Comité d'Études, but controlled by the King of the Belgians, Leopold II. The Congo project began when Leopold convened a geographical congress, formed the Comité d'Études, and hired Henry M. Stanley to explore, and on subsequent trips, to establish trading stations along the Congo River. Stanley negotiated over 400 treaties with Congolese tribes, obtaining for the Committee powers of protection over the river lands.

Official international recognition was accorded by the Berlin Conference, called in 1884. It acknowledged the sovereign rights of Leopold's International Association over most of the Congo basin, and over the outlet to the sea, "under international guarantees of neutrality and free trade." The Niger also was opened to trade by all nations on an equal basis by nations attending the Berlin Conference. In July of the following year, the African lands of the Association Internationale du Congo (as the Comité d'Études was now called) were transformed into the Congo Free State, with Leopold as its sovereign. It was an "independent sovereignty," a sort of personal estate because the Belgian parliament refused to enter into the imperialistic venture.

Over the next several years the bounds of Leopold's African domain were so adroitly negotiated by a series of treaties with colonial powers holding contiguous colonies, that eventually the Free State comprised a vast empire of 900,000 square miles, rich in rubber-yielding plants and ivory.

To finance the development and protection of this personal kingdom, Leopold used not only his own private resources but went heavily in debt to the Belgian government; he incurred further expense in his determination to buy up all foreign holdings. A remarkable advance in the output of ivory and rubber, regarded as the major resources of the area, made the Free State a more paying proposition after the first few hard years, and Leopold held his vast empire until 1908.

He was assisted out of his financial difficulties by concessionnaire companies to which he gave proprietary rights. Some of these operated monopolistically within their designated territories until the independence of Congo in 1960. As late as 1959, le Comité Special du Katanga still collected the taxes, and had rights of development and sale over lands, forests, and minerals in the Katanga; la Compagnie du Kivu and other corporations held like though lesser powers throughout the Belgian colony; Unilever, an English corporation, held all rights to the plantation develop-

ment of the oil palm; all transportation developments were monopolistic. Although a later development, it is interesting to note that Sabena was the only international airline that crossed the boundaries into the Belgian Congo. Congo was like a Belgian preserve.

Some of the exploitive practices of forced labor forced the conversion of Leopold's Free State into a colony of the Belgian government (1908). Although the companies granted concessions by King Leopold lost almost none of their powers or privileges as a result of this transfer, the policies adopted by Belgium for the development of this mineral-rich equatorial landholding were sound and farsighted.

Subsistence migratory agriculture is still the main type of native cultivation, but the Belgians made a notable beginning in training the Africans to grow money crops. The *paysannat* system in several forms was one of the two basic practices introduced for the conversion from the subsistence to money economies; government agricultural advisors, working closely with the African farmers, also promoted the development of commercial cultivation. Wherever the environment permitted cattle to be raised, animal culture was being introduced and supervised. A great deal of scientific experimentation, on both subsistence and commercial crops and on animals, was carried out by the Belgians. Their development program, spearheaded by the two scientific institutes of INEAC and IRSAC,[2] was the most outstanding in Africa. INEAC was concerned largely with crops and soil, forestry, and animal research, and plant and animal diseases; IRSAC was the broader of the two institutes, and less directly interested in plant research as such. INEAC's activities were on a far larger scale than those of IRSAC, however, and closer to the people; the INEAC scientists and advisors worked directly with the individual Congolese farmer. IRSAC was purely experimental. The *paysannat* was the special medium through which the scientific findings of both organizations were carried to the Africans.

[2] L'Institut national pour l'étude agronomique du Congo Belge (INEAC) and l'Institut de recherches scientifiques en Afrique Centrale (IRSAC): in translation the Institute for the Study of Scientific Agriculture in the Belgian Congo, and the Institute of Scientific Researches in Central Africa.

# 14 EQUATORIAL LANDS NORTH OF THE CONGO RIVER

*Who, from seeing choice plants in a
hothouse, can magnify some into the
dimensions of forest trees, and
crowd others into an entangled jungle?*

CHARLES DARWIN

The Congo-Ubangi rivers marked the boundaries between French and Belgian territories in equatorial Africa except for a stretch about 150 miles up from and including the Congo mouth. The lands north of the rivers were all French. These territories were neither first discovered nor first explored by Frenchmen, however. The Portuguese had traced the coast of equatorial Africa (1470), and Britishers had been the first to explore Lake Chad and vicinity (in 1823). However, the French were the first colonizers here, settling on the Gabon River in 1841 and founding Libreville 8 years later.

The remainder of the French equatorial country was explored and settled from Brazzaville after its establishment in 1880: These French penetrations first extended northward into the Ubangi hinterland, but by 1897 had pierced through to Lake Chad. A series of agreements with other powers, from 1885 on, established the extent of the French equatorial colonies. Chad, although desert and steppe (and hence climatically like the French Sahara) was nonetheless administered from Brazzaville as one of four provinces of French Equatorial Africa; only when the greater portion of the German Kamerun was mandated to France in 1919 was it incorporated under the French Equatorial administration.

## Cameroon Republic

Germany had declared Kamerun a protectorate in 1884, and boundaries with Nigeria and French Congo, as French Equatorial Africa was first called, were agreed upon in 1893 and 1894 respectively. French and British forces captured the territory during World War I, however, and following the cessation of hostilities, Kamerun was mandated by the League of Nations to these two European states, the larger portion going to the French; the mandates became trusteeships of the United Nations under Britain and France, after World War II, with but little change in policy and internal administration.

On January 1, 1960, the French Cameroon became independent as the Cameroon Republic; as noted, plebiscites were held in the two sectors of the British Cameroons, the Southern Cameroon electing to become a part of the Republic of Cameroon, increasing

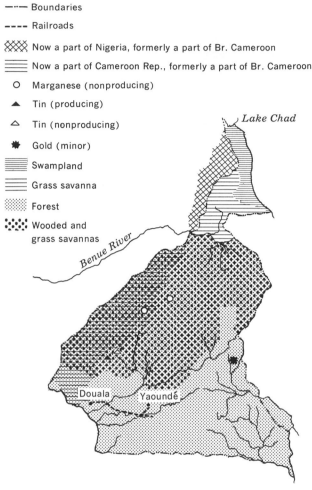

—··— Boundaries

---- Railroads

XXXX Now a part of Nigeria, formerly a part of Br. Cameroon

≡≡≡ Now a part of Cameroon Rep., formerly a part of Br. Cameroon

O    Marganese (nonproducing)

▲    Tin (producing)

△    Tin (nonproducing)

✳    Gold (minor)

≣    Swampland

≡    Grass savanna

∷    Forest

∷∷   Wooded and
     grass savannas

**FIGURE 14.2   Republic of Cameroon.** *(After The Republic of Cameroon, New York: Ambassade de France, Service de Presse et d'Information.)*

the area of the Republic by about a tenth, and the population by nearly a fourth.

The Republic of Cameroon, roughly triangular in shape and twice as long as it is wide at its broadest part in the south, extends from a humid climate that produces rain forests in the south into dry savanna at its northern point where it borders on Lake Chad.

The addition of Southern Cameroon to the Republic brought some remarkably beautiful country into the state: the spectacular Cameroon Mountains cover much of this section of the former trust territory of the British; even the areas with lower altitudes are broken and hilly, and waterfalls and rushing streams abound, coursing down precipitous slopes. Dominating the mountains near the coast is Mount Cameroon, 13,350 feet high, an active volcano that has erupted five times in the last 100 years, the last eruptions occurring in 1954 and 1959. The slopes of this mountain have fertile soils and are the basis of rich agriculture, both plantation and native subsistence.

The southern half of this former British territory was originally a dense rain forest. However, the logging of hardwoods and clearing of land for plantations and native cultivation, particularly near the coast, have made deep inroads on the primary forest. Adjacent to the coast, therefore, the face of the landscape is changing rapidly: where tall trees once stood, plantations of bananas, cacao, rubber, coffee, and oil palms now flourish; the most conspicuous reminder of the rain forests that in the past grew so luxuriantly here are the logs that move in lorries from farther inland to the ports.

North and northeast of the Cameroon Mountains the country is not so developed; large tracts are still under high forest, much of it preserved because it was placed under reserve by the British as the territory's "forest estate." Here plantation development is less marked; where there are plantations, the abundant bananas of the coastal areas tend to give way to coffee and cacao.

Inland some distance from the coast the lowland-mountain topography gives way to plateau, with higher peaks rising above the general level of the tablelands; the rain forests of the lowlands and lower slopes merge into forest-savanna complexes, and finally into grasslands interspersed with eucalyptus and cypress. This is the Bamenda plateau, an area largely of native subsistence agriculture, although coffee *Arabica* has recently been planted by some African farmers, and a few plantations have been established.

Because of the mountainous topography, the Southern Cameroon has a delightful, healthful climate; tropical, it nevertheless does not have the oppressive heat and humidity of the surrounding lower lands; where lowlands occur, the Cameroon climate is of course no different from that in other equatorial low-lying regions. Because of the generally favorable climate, many Europeans have been attracted to the area; Douala, however, is considered one of the worst spots along the African coast, climatically.

To the east, the former French territory, the nucleus of the new Republic, has several regions topographically expressed. Along the coast are equatorial lowlands; in the west are high mountains which are a continuation of the Cameroons Mountains of Southern Cameroon. These slope generally eastward. In the central part of the country is the Adamawa plateau, over 4,000 feet high and the drainage divide of Cameroon; north of there the land becomes lower, and tends to be grass covered. The north drains generally to the Chad basin, but at times, when the flow of the Logone River is captured by the Benue, also to the Gulf of Guinea through the Benue-Niger system. The southern part drains west through the Sanaga and other lesser rivers to the Gulf of Guinea.

The Cameroon economy is basically agricultural. The broad latitudinal span of the Republic makes possible the wide range of tropical crops that are grown and exported. Peanuts and cotton come from the northern savanna lands; equatorial products, including tropical woods, cacao, bananas, palm oil, rubber, and coffee from the south. Subsistence crops vary in the same way, changing from root crops and rice in the south to millet in the north; cattle rearing is very important in the north.

Some industry has been started, particularly in the region of Douala. At Edéa, just south of Douala, a plant for the electrolytic processing of imported alumina was completed in 1956, and aluminum is exported; power is supplied by electricity generated at dam installations on the Sanaga River. Although some minerals occur, most of the deposits are minor or undeveloped, and minerals make up only 0.5 percent of the exports by value.

The British trust territory was more developed than the French sector, and the question naturally rises: Why did these people elect to separate from Nigeria and unite with the Cameroon Republic? The reason seems to lie in the resentment that was felt by the people of Southern Cameroon toward the dominant role played by the Ibos of eastern Nigeria, to which they were politically attached. In Northern Cameroon (British) the ethnic makeup and general development was about the same as in the Northern Region of

Nigeria under which the Northern trust territory was administered, and fear of being a dominated minority was not present. Southern Cameroon had received regional autonomy several years before its unification with Cameroon Republic. It is a valuable addition to the Republic, which had experienced but slight development during its years of French rule.

Yaoundé is the capital, but Douala, situated on the estuary of the Wouri River, is the main commercial city and principal air and seaport for Cameroon Republic. Since World War II the port's capacity has been tripled by the addition of deepwater berths, mechanized equipment, and quay extensions. Previously, ships had to anchor 25 miles off the coast, and goods and passengers were lightered to the shore; now the dredged channel permits seagoing vessels to come into the port and dock beside deepwater quays. A bridge across the Wouri permits the connection of railroads coming into the city from opposite directions.

Kribi, a lighterage port, and second seaport of the Republic, serves only its immediate hinterland; its traffic is small compared to that of Douala. Garoua, a river port on the Benue, opens up river transport in "the handle" of Cameroon; Bota and Tika are small ports in Southern Cameroon that take care of the export-import trade for much of that sector of the Republic. As at Douala, trade through these ports has greatly increased in the last decade, but is small compared to that of the larger city.

Transportation is a problem in Cameroon. There are only two short railroads, the longer one toward the east branching near its terminus to connect with both Yaoundé and Mbalmayo. It extends inland from Douala via Edéa only about 125 miles; the other line is shorter, running north from Douala about 75 miles. They will not begin to meet transport needs if the country is to develop. Produce from the north goes out via the Benue through the river port of Garoua. Roads are being constructed, and a "trunk line" highway now connects Douala with Bangui on the Ubangi River. There are proposals for the construction of a railway in the eastern interior that will run north and south to connect Batouri and N'Gaoundéré, and from Batouri will turn east to Bangui in the Central African Republic, and from N'Gaoundéré northeastward to Moundou in Chad.

## The Central African Republic

The Central African Republic is appropriately named for it lies in the geographical center of the African continent. As a province of French Equatorial Africa, it was called Oubangi-Chari after its two greatest rivers.

Latitudinally, the country reaches from about 4 to 10°N. It is wet and dry in climate, the dry period occurring between December and February. The remainder of the year has rains but is characterized by a double maximum of precipitation, June being somewhat less rainy than May and the months from July on; very heavy rains occur from July through October. Vegetation is principally a high savanna of tall grass with scattered trees; in the south, however, some rain forest grows, while in the north, drier savannas take over.

The Central African Republic, which became independent on August 14, 1960, is a large country about the size of the state of Texas. It is handicapped, however, by its situation 300 miles from the coast; its outlet to the sea is across the Cameroon Republic and through Douala.

Topographically it is a vast rolling plateau about 2,000 feet in elevation, that drains in two directions, north into Lake Chad through the Chari River, south into the Congo River through the Ubangi. This is the divide between the Chad and Congo basins. Most of the country drains south to the Ubangi, however, so that its waters eventually reach the Atlantic through the Congo River. The Chari River never reaches the sea; it flows from the plateaus of the Central African Republic about 1,000 miles to empty into Lake Chad.

### THE PEOPLE AND THE LAND

The population, a little over 1 million, is small for the size of the country and spread unevenly over the land. Settlement tends to be heaviest in the river valleys and along the Chad frontier; the east and northeast, by contrast, are nearly empty, with some 71,000 inhabitants scattered across an area of over 90,700 square miles.

The population is rural, with over nine-tenths of the Africans making their living by cultivating the land. Urban living is almost nonexistent. Bangui, the capital, with a population of about 77,000, is the only city of any size; the next largest are Bouar (20,700) and Bambari (19,700); several towns have up to 5,000 inhabitants.

African languages and dialects are everywhere prevalent. French, however, is widely spoken among Africans in and around towns, and elsewhere in the places where French influence was directly felt. Most of the people still hold to African religions, although there are small minorities of Christians and Moslems. In recent years a rather large number of Moslems have immigrated into the country; they tend to be better educated and economically more advanced than the nationals; many are traders; some have even become administrators in government. Preference, however, is given to trained Central Africans. Since independence, many Nigerians and Africans originating from the Cameroons have been expelled.

FIGURE 14.3 Major subsistence crops of the former French equatorial lands. (Reprinted from *The Staple Food Economies of Western Tropical Africa* by Bruce F. Johnston with the permission of the publishers, Stanford University Press. © 1958 by the Board of Trustees of the Leland Stanford Junior University.)

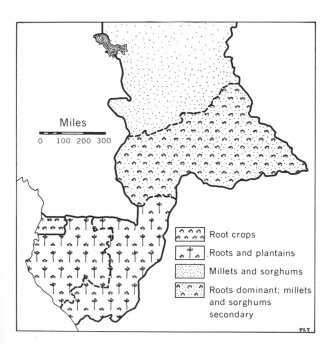

The nation's economy is largely subsistence. Three crops bring in most of the export revenue, and for all practical purposes form the base of the money economy, namely, coffee, cotton, and peanuts; however, some rubber, tobacco, palm kernels, and sesame enter international trade. Cotton, not introduced until about 1930, now is grown throughout the country except in the forests and along the northeastern frontier. Acreage and production have steadily, though slowly, increased; both cotton fibre and seed are exported.

Coffee cultivation started earlier, but not until after the mid-1950s did it begin to be accepted widely by African farmers as a money crop. Peanut production began to increase at about the same time. Some stock raising is carried on, but the country does not supply its meat requirements; prevalence of the tsetse fly accounts in part for this. Lumber is cut and exported, part going to Congo, floated to its destination in log form.

Little is known of the mineral potential. Small quantities of gold and alluvial diamonds are produced, and although diamond production has fallen, rough stones still account for between 10 and 15 percent of the Republic's exports; prospecting for primary diamond deposits is in progress.

Industry is minor but developing, especially in the Bangui area where both electricity and transport are available. The first hydroelectric installations were constructed at Bangui during World War II, and the electrical output augmented in 1955, when a plant at Boali began to operate; further developments, planned in the M'Bali and Vangaria valleys, will send additional power to Bangui. As yet, manufacture is entirely concerned with the processing of local products and the supplying of African consumer needs, such as the pressing of peanuts and palm fruit for oil, cotton ginning, leather tanning, textile and shoe manufacture, brewing, slaughtering of animals, the sawing of lumber, and the like.

Transportation facilities, although sufficient to meet the needs of the country at its present stage of development, are limited. The Central African Republic has no railroads; a trunk line road (see page 212) extends inland from the port of Douala in the Cameroon Republic to Bangui, river port on the Ubangi River. This highway and other roads, and the rivers are the communication links and outlets of the country. There are over 370 miles of navigable waterways, but the volume of the rivers varies with the seasons, and sometimes the water is so low that it makes the streams difficult and even impossible to navigate; even the flow of the Ubangi is irregular. Although work has been begun to improve this waterway, it will take years to complete; the main tributaries of the Ubangi in the Central African Republic, the Ouaka and Kotto, are choked with vegetation and unnavigable. The Ubangi-Congo river system is navigable between Bangui and Brazzaville; beyond there, rail transportation to Pointe-Noire opens up a good outlet to the sea. Bangui, leading port on the Ubangi, is being improved and expanded.

The road system meets present needs because the country has undergone little economic development and does not require a transport network. There are now about 12,500 miles of roads, one-third of which are usable year-round for trucking. According to plans, sometime in the future a railroad will be built from Bangui to Yaoundé (Cameroon Republic) where it will link with the line to Douala. This would benefit not only the Central African Republic but Chad and the two Congo republics as well because it would open a direct line for portions of these countries to the Atlantic; another projected railway would connect Bangui with Fort Lamy in Chad Republic.

Three major airfields and a number of secondary landing strips allow the country to be fairly well served by air. The field at Bangui is being enlarged. But the country and its somnolent capital are without railway or good road links with the outside world. Air service and river traffic are the main lifelines.

Efforts are being made to advance the economy, both by the government and by France. Most of this effort is centered on agricultural improvement and the expansion of commercial crops, and on the extension of transport facilities. The Central African Republic remains, however, an underdeveloped country, handicapped by the backwardness of its people, the lack of knowledge of its resource-potential, and its inland position. Bangui, the capital, lies along the mist-shrouded banks of the Ubangi River, sprawled and smothered amid tropical vegetation. There are few distractions for foreign residents of the town, most of whom are Frenchmen.

The country has about 1,000 miles of unguarded frontiers with the politically turbulent Congo; along its other borders lie Sudan, Chad, Cameroon, and the Republic of Congo (Brazzaville), all countries within which Communist influence has been increasing. In March, 1965, the Central African Republic accepted a loan from Communist China—which opens the country to Chinese penetration.

## Gabon, the Forest Republic

Although the coast of Gabon was explored as early as 1470, it was not until the Congress of Vienna outlawed the slave trade that the French made official contacts with the area: they were appointed to prevent illicit slave trade along the Gabon coast. In 1839 and 1841 Bouet-Willaumez, a French naval captain, negotiated friendship treaties with the African kings whose territories lay along the northern and southern sides of the Gabon estuary; in 1849, when a slave ship was captured, the captain freed the Africans, and put them ashore on the Gabon coast, settling them in a village that he named Libreville. Gabon thus resembles Liberia and Sierra Leone in its founding.

At first administered as a part of the French Congo, in 1903 Gabon was made a separate administrative region, and 7 years later was organized as one of four provinces of French Equatorial Africa. Independence came, with Gabon becoming a republic within the Community of Nations, on August 17, 1960; Libreville became its capital. A little over 100,000 square miles in area and less than ½ million in population, Gabon is the smallest among the former provinces of French Equatorial Africa, but the richest. Its wealth to the present has lain in the dense rain forests that cover almost the entire country; only a few areas of savanna are found, east of Franceville, south of Mouila, and along the lower Ogowé River.

The country is almost rectangular in shape, and has a long coast for its size. It is bisected by the Equator and equatorial in climate. (See Figure 14.4.) Topographically it is not so simple; the terrain rises from a shore to a coastal plain to plateaus to mountains. The plain varies in width from 18 to 125 miles, extending farther inland along the valleys of the

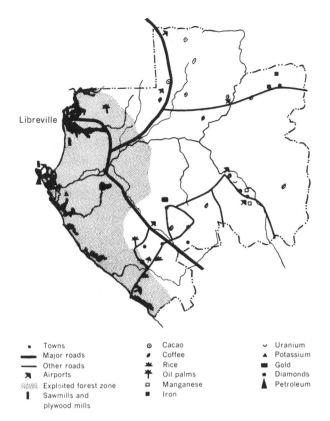

Towns •
Major roads ▬
Other roads ▬
Airports ⤫
Exploited forest zone ▨
Sawmills and ▮
plywood mills

Cacao ⊕
Coffee ✦
Rice ✵
Oil palms ✚
Manganese ▢
Iron ■

Uranium ⌄
Potassium ▲
Gold ▬
Diamonds ✳
Petroleum ▲

**FIGURE 14.4   Gabon Republic. (After the Gabon Republic, New York: Ambassade de France, Service de Presse et d'Information.)**

Ogowé and N'Gounie Rivers like a great V; altitudes on this lowland never exceed 1,000 feet elevation. The shoreline is deeply indented by river estuaries from the northern frontier to beyond Cape Lopez; the latter is actually not a cape because it is separated from the mainland by distributaries of the Ogowé River. South of the cape lagoons, barrier bars, and mangrove swamps line the shore.

The coastal plain is encompassed on all sides by plateaus, except toward the sea and in the extreme southwest and northwest. These uplands vary in height, and are cut through by the deep channels of rivers whose courses, dropping to the plains, are interrupted by rapids. Mountains rise above the plateaus in several sectors of the country. The Crystal Mountains in the north have elevations of over 2,950 feet; in the southeast the Birogen Mountains rise and in central Gabon the Chaillu Mountains. The latter contain the highest peak in the country, and are the main watershed of Gabon.

The country is intricately drained by streams, most of which are tributary to the Ogowé, the largest. This river and its feeders drain nearly the whole of the country; although the headwaters of the main stream rise in the Republic of Congo, most of its course lies in Gabon. Entering Gabon south of Franceville, the river describes a great loop, and flowing west and then southwest, essentially bisects the country before emptying into the Atlantic centrally along the Gabon coast. Its channel is navigable along a stretch of only about 150 miles, however, because of the many rapids in its course; this is true also of the affluents of the Ogowé, even the largest, namely, the Ivindo, Okano, N'Gounie, and Sébé, being navigable for only short distances in certain places. These rivers, like the numerous shorter streams that tumble out of the plateau to the sea, are used mainly for floating the millions of board feet of logs that make their way from the rain forests of Gabon to the coasts for processing and export.

Libreville was established on one of the shorter rivers, namely, the Gabon (which is, in reality, the drowned mouth of the Como River), the port-capital situated near the ocean end of the deep, broad protected estuary. Port Gentil, somewhat south on Cape Lopez, lies on one of the distributary mouths of the Ogowé. Because the affluents of this river drain across all portions of the Gabon uplands, pouring their waters through all parts of the forest lands into the mainstream, Port Gentil has become the great focal center for logs that are floated downstream: most of the cut timber feeds to the Ogowé and thence to the coast. Until manganese was discovered not long ago, the processing and export of timber were almost the sole functions of the port.

## LAND AND PEOPLE

A relatively large, resource rich country with few inhabitants, unevenly scattered—that is the man-land picture in Gabon. The urban centers and mining and lumbering regions have the highest population densities; areas along rivers and roads also run high; but the great stretches of mountains, forests, and swamplands are almost uninhabited. The people are rural, generally living in small village agglomerations of less than 100 inhabitants; only Libreville and Port Gentil have grown to any size.

The economy is thriving, and contrary to what is true in most of tropical Africa, Gabon has a favorable balance of trade owing largely to the exploitation of the country's lush forest resources. Gabon is a forest state. Millions of board feet of timber are cut annually, and floated down the rivers to mills and ports on the seacoast; undressed and semifinished okoumé wood, and other woods in finished plywoods and veneers are exported. One of the largest plywood factories in the world is located at Port Gentil on the coast of equatorial Africa. Industry has been based largely upon the processing of timber in sawmills, and of the production of plywood and veneers in woodworking plants. Most of this is found in and around Port Gentil.

The plywood and veneer industries use a softer species of timber than that employed for making cabinets and for general construction, and among the woods most in demand is okoumé (*Aucoumea klaineana*). It is found only in Gabon and Spanish Guinea and to a lesser extent in Congo, but so great is the demand that it leads all other woods exported from the Atlantic side of Africa. However, supplies of okoumé accessible to ports are declining, and so new woods are being sought that can substitute for this valuable timber. Ebony and mahogany are also cut and exported. Some gathered forest products still are sold, such as palm nuts, fibres, and the ongokea nut, used in paints and varnishes; during World War II, latex was collected from certain lianas.

Studies are under way to introduce new industries based on the forests, for example, the manufacture of cellulose and packing materials. Aside from the industry based on the forests, manufacture in Gabon is concerned with processing food products, such as refining whale and palm oils, and packaging rice. These are expected to increase; petroleum refining, and the production of petrochemicals and cement are planned to begin in the not distant future.

Development in Gabon has centered on the forests, and not on agriculture or, until recently, minerals. Cultivation is mainly subsistence with bananas, cassava, and taro as the basic African starches. Gradually commercial agriculture is being taken up, and some crops are raised for sale especially cacao, rice, coffee, peanuts, and the oil palm, but this has scarcely begun. Cacao leads among farm exports.

## MODERN DEVELOPMENTS

Gold and diamonds were the mineral exports from Gabon in the past, but in recent years production of the precious metal and gems has been small. More important today are the minerals needed for modern industry, and Gabon has reserves of several of these, some described as "impressive."

In 1951, a large reserve of rich manganese ore was confirmed and explored at Moanda in the upper Ogowé River valley. It had been discovered in 1938 by French geologists, but the start of World War II had prevented detailed work in the field. Extraction posed no difficulties. The greatest obstacle to development was transportation: a railroad was needed to carry the ore to the coast, and enormous natural obstacles stood in the way of construction. The line, 170 miles of track driven across the coastal plains and the forest girt plateau from Port Gentil to near Franceville, was completed in 1963. Its realization involved the construction of three major and a dozen minor bridges, some 40 culverts, and a 45-mile-long cable railway, one of the longest in the world, across the densest portions of the rain forests; it links also with the Congo-Ocean Railway of the Republic of Congo. By late summer 1963, the first ½ million tons of manganese were shipped to the coast for export; facilities for treating the ore, and port enlargements have been installed at Port Gentil.

A rich deposit of iron ore, assaying 60 to 63 percent iron content and with reserves up to 250 million tons, has been confirmed in northeast Gabon at Mékambo; development of this field likewise awaits railroad construction. Petroleum occurs in the sedimentary basin around Port Gentil. Production began only in 1957, but already crude petroleum ranks second in value among the exports of Gabon; woods rank first. Manganese is considered the potentially most valuable mineral. Although the rivers hold a large possibility for hydroelectric development, electric power as yet is produced by thermal stations using oil for fuel.

Prosperous as is the country, Gabon nevertheless has had to contend with most of the difficulties that are found in other equatorial lands of Africa. Dense forests make transportation costly and difficult, the climate is harsh, and there is a shortage of labor because of the concentrated character of the industry and the dispersed pattern of population settlement. Aside from the railway completed in 1963, roads and waterways are the only means of surface transport for goods and people; however, since water transport is dangerous and discontinuous, movement is largely overland. Road development is recent; the difficulties of road building and upkeep are many, and the expense great. Despite this, roads have almost replaced waterways except for moving timber. Airplanes help surmount some of the difficulties imposed by terrain, rapids, and climate; Gabon has over 100 landing strips, with Libreville and Port Gentil the major airports.

These ocean ports are also the leading seaports within the country. Libreville is relatively less important today than in the past, and Port Gentil is highly specialized, used only as the outlet for forest products and now manganese, from Gabon. Pointe-Noire, in the Republic of Congo, is far more important as a port for equatorial Africa than either Libreville or Port Gentil, as it handles about half of the traffic that passes out from the former French lands. However, the Gabon ports have protected harbors, and plans are underway to improve both. The harbor at Port Gentil is being deepened, and its berths extended so that when the present improvements are completed, it will have a harbor and harbor facilities comparable with those of the Congolese port; a large protective mole is under construction at Libreville. Further port developments include quays to be built at Mayombé, now an open roadstead, and at Ovendo on the Gabon estuary.

## Republic of Congo

### PRELUDES TO INDEPENDENCE

Two states of Central Africa claim Congo as a name. They are the countries that formerly were the Belgian Congo and the French (or Middle) Congo of French Equatorial Africa.

This is not the first time that people in the two territories have competed for certain rights. The rivalry began in the last quarter of the nineteenth century when de Brazza and Stanley raced to establish claims for their respective sponsors (France and Belgium's King Leopold II) along the banks of Stanley Pool, across which Brazzaville and Kinshasa now face each other.

In 1875 Savorgnan de Brazza, the Frenchman, had penetrated to within a few days' march of the river that Stanley had traced from its headwaters to its mouth a year before, namely, the Congo; in February 1880, on a second expedition, he arrived at the lakelike pool, later named Stanley Pool, before Henry M. Stanley, who was now making his way along the river length for the second time, this time going upstream from the mouth. In September of that year, de Brazza signed a treaty with Makoko, the chief of the Batéké, who gave France the right of "protecting" his tribal state. The treaty also included rights to the land along the pool on the north bank of the river, the site chosen for the city later to be built by and named for de Brazza, namely, Brazzaville, thus frustrating some of the plans of Stanley, who had anticipated claiming the whole of the Congo River basin for King Leopold. De Brazza also explored the Niari-Kouilou area through which the easiest access from the pool to the sea passes. Pointe-Noire is the port that grew up on the ocean side of this route. Most of the territory north of the Congo-Ubangi was claimed by France, and these claims were later confirmed at Berlin in 1884. Thus the colorful beginning of the European era of Middle Congo, now the Republic of Congo.

As the administration of equatorial Africa began to take shape, the territory was divided into four provincial units, of which Middle Congo was one; Brazzaville was chosen as the administrative center; here the Governor General resided. From the first, therefore, Brazzaville grew as an important city in equatorial Africa. Today it is a quaint, quiet-moving town in great contrast to the bustling modern city of Kinshasa on the other side of the pool.

### CHARACTER OF THE LAND

The Republic of Congo emerged as an independent nation within the Community of Nations on August 15, 1960, a country slightly smaller than Montana, inhabited by fewer than 800,000 people.

Straddling the Equator in a general northeast-southwest direction from 5°S to 4°N, the Republic is equatorial in climate. It faces on the Atlantic Ocean along about a 100-mile seafront, where waves and currents have built sandspits that enclose lagoons and lakes. The coastal zone extends inland for about 40 miles as a low treeless plain beyond which the Mayombé escarpment rises like a backdrop 1,600 to 2,600 feet in elevation, mountainous in character and paralleling the shore. The plateau edge is deeply cut by the gorges of the Kouilou River, and the area is entirely rain forest.

Inland is the Niari Valley, a vast depression that runs generally east and west, and is covered with savanna; on the north, it slopes up toward the wooded plateau of central Gabon, southward toward the tree-less Plateau-of-the-Cataracts. The area bordering Stanley Pool is generally hilly and mostly treeless, blending into the grasslands of the Batéké plateaus on the north. These uplands, dry and monotonous in character, are separated from each other by the deep valleys of the Congo affluents that flow into the main stream from the north; in the more northerly portions of this plateau belt, wooded ravines along the streams cut through savanna-covered tablelands. In the low-lands along the Congo River a dense forest grows; in many places, these river flats are almost continuously inundated.

From the characterization of the vegetation, it can be seen that although the location is equatorial, the lowlands and plateaus differ considerably in climate. The Congo lowlands in the northeast are humid, with rain falling the year around and averaging about 98 inches; the southwest plateau region has a wet and dry type of climate, characterized by a long dry season, and a shorter wet season during which an average of 60 inches of rain falls. Temperatures in the lowlands and uplands differ also.

The rivers are generally navigable because the heavy rains swell the waters of the streams. The Congo and the Ubangi, main tributary of the Congo from the north, are fully navigable above Stanley Pool in all parts that touch on the Republic's territories. But they are boundary rivers here, and are shared with The Congo to the south. Below Stanley Pool cataracts hinder the passage to the sea so that the Congo River cannot be navigated from its mouth

into the African interior. It should be noted that about one-fourth of the way to the sea southwest from Brazzaville, the Congo River ceases to touch the territory of the Republic, and for some distance flows only through The Congo territory; near the mouth, from Matadi to the coast, it forms a boundary between Angola and The Congo. Even the smaller rivers of the Republic, the Niari, Kouilou, and the Sangha, which lie entirely within the bounds of the country, are navigable along extended reaches because of improvements that have been made.

## PEOPLE AND LIVELIHOOD

The small population spreads very unevenly over the country; only the Brazzaville area and the coastal plain have even moderate densities; the forest zones and the Batéké plateau hold few people, averaging under 1 inhabitant per square mile.

The Republic of Congo is underdeveloped, and underexplored for resources. It has a deficit economy based primarily on agriculture, but cultivation of the land produces few commodities that go into international trade. The Congolese are subsistence farmers who own their land; but their farming brings them little cash income, and three-fourths of the produce is locally consumed.

The deficit is somewhat balanced, however, by foreign aid and capital investment, and experiments with new crops are being carried out in the Niari valley; it is expected that commercial agriculture will develop on the best lands. Subsistence crops are the usual ones grown in rain forest regions, that is, cassava, plantains, and yams, as well as rice and sugar cane. Fruits, long grown for local consumption, are now beginning to enter the export trade, especially pineapples and citrus; vegetables raised by Africans supply urban markets. Oil plants, i.e., the oil palm and peanuts, provide the largest exports among cultivated products; copal, which is solidified resin used in varnish manufacture, and rubber are next in importance; cacao, tobacco, and coffee also are commercially grown in very small amounts. Animals, raised mostly in the Niari valley, are not numerous because the climate is harsh and the tsetse fly prevails. However, small herds of tsetse-resistant strains of cattle have been developed; sheep and hogs are kept.

Lumbering is the Republic's single most important industry and forest products supply the major exports; almost all the Congolese wood goes into international trade. More than half of the surface of the country is forest covered, the greatest reserves being in the north. Because of inaccessibility, only a small part of the vast timber reserves is exploited; in the north, swamps make the timber stands difficult to reach and work; throughout the country, except in the extreme south and southwest, a lack of transport facilities handicaps the industry. Construction of a rail branch (the COMILOG) north to the Gabon border from the Congo-Ocean Railway, in 1962, tapped important reserves of virgin timber, however.

Of the more than 200 known species of wood that grow in Congo, only a few are cut for commercial purposes, and only two are important, namely, limba, of which the Republic is the largest producer in the world, and okoumé. Most of the limba goes to West Germany for furniture manufacture; okoumé is used for veneering and, in Congo, cut exclusively for a new veneer plant at Pointe-Noire. Manufacturing, while increasing, produces only about 11 percent of the national income; although the Republic is probably more industrialized than any of the other former French equatorial lands, the development level of this sector of the economy is low. Consumer products make up most of the items manufactured. Industry centers around and in Brazzaville and Pointe-Noire and, to a lesser degree, in the Niari valley at Jacob.

Mining is unimportant. Lead at M'Fouati is the only mineral that has been developed on any scale; tin and gold are taken by primitive methods. New placer gold and alluvial diamond deposits have been discovered, and prospecting is being carried out for the discovery of other ores, particularly zinc, copper, and radioactive minerals; the production of petroleum was begun at Pointe-Indienne, not far from Pointe-Noire, in the summer of 1960. An annual output of about 630,000 barrels is expected. Natural gas occurs, and large potash deposits are known in the Holle region near the rail line, and in several other districts; potash and petroleum appear to have the greatest commercial potential.

A dam is being planned on the Kouilou River that will produce electricity on a large scale, and serve as a basis for new industry. One hydroelectric plant on the Djoue River, outside of Brazzaville, supplies that area with electric power.

*Transportation.* The country is served by a good transport system, adequate for the needs of the Republic and well kept up. The Congo-Ocean Railway, completed in 1934, links the main river port of Brazzaville with the country's major seaport, Pointe-Noire. It runs a difficult course through equatorial forests and down the Mayombé escarpment; 92 bridges and 12 tunnels are necessary to negotiate this passage, and annual upkeep is high. Pointe-Noire has an artificial harbor, construction of which was begun directly upon the completion of the railway. It is planned to expand the port facilities to permit the shipment of the manganese from Franceville (Gabon Republic) through the harbor; as noted previously, a rail spur connects the mine field with the port.

The tonnage that moves through the river port of Brazzaville is nearly half as great as that which passes through Pointe-Noire. This river port is the junction between the Congo-Ocean Railway and the river traffic of the Congo-Ubangi system, just as is Kinshasa, and both river ports are important bulk break points; as such, they serve the other territories within the Congo River system. The Ubangi is navigable from the Congo juncture to Bangui despite the fact that the course of the river just below Bangui is hindered by the Zinga Falls. Improvements, such as the removal of rocks and the installation of luminous buoys set up along the course, permit shipping to move up and down the river despite the rapids, for tugs pull the barges across the dangerous portion of the course.

Over 4,000 miles of all-season and over 650 miles of seasonal roads serve the domain. Upkeep is costly, however, because heavy rains constantly wash out the roads. Any extension of road building will require the use of heavy machinery, as in Gabon, because rain forest will have to be cleared away before road construction can begin.

## International Ties and Cooperation

The Community of Nations, which had been set up by the constitution of the Fifth Republic of France, underwent important changes during the course of 1960. Following the May 18, 1960, amendment to the constitution of the Fifth Republic, adopted by referendum on September 28, 1958, a member state could by agreement become independent without thereby ceasing to belong to the Community.

The 12 African states and the Malagasy Republic chose to become independent. Six states decided to remain in the "remodeled" Community, while others preferred to retain ties with France through bilateral agreements. Of the six that remained within Community, four—the Central African Republic, Republic of Congo, the Gabon Republic, and the Republic of Chad—were former provinces of French Equatorial Africa. The Malagasy Republic and the Republic of Senegal are the other two members. Of the central equatorial lands, only Cameroon severed the ties. The Cameroon Republic signed agreements of co-operation with the French Republic outside of the Community, however, on November 3, 1960.

# 15 THE CONGO:
# BASIN NATION OF THE RIVER

THEN I SAW THE CONGO, CREEPING THROUGH
   THE BLACK,
CUTTING THROUGH THE JUNGLE WITH A
   GOLDEN TRACK.
*A negro fairyland swung into view,*
*A minstrel river*
*Where dreams come true.*

VACHEL LINDSAY

**FIGURE 15.2    Estuary of the Congo at Matadi.** *(Photograph by H. Goldstein, Congopresse.)*

## The Basin, the River, and the Nation

The Congo takes in the greater part of the Congo River basin. It is a large country, about as long as it is wide, extending across nearly 19° of latitude and longitude. One-third the size of the United States, it was 80 times larger than little Belgium on which it was colonially dependent. It lies in the heart of Africa, with the Equator cutting across its northern sector. Geology has acted to modify its equatoriality, however, because all of The Congo, except for a small area around the mouth of the river, is a basinlike plateau having elevations of 1,000 to 1,200 feet near the center of the basin and rising higher along the margins. The most accentuated edge is found along the rift valley in the east; on the north the edge of the basin rises to the Congo-Chari rivers divide, and in the south to the Benguela-Lunda swell, the water parting between the Congo and Zambezi rivers.

Only a narrow neck of land gives the Congo access to the Atlantic. Here, as the plateau breaks to the coastal plain, the great river issues forth from its highland-rimmed basin and drops toward the sea in a series of tremendous rapids that bar all navigation. In the past, rivers have usually been the means of access to new continents, but these insurmountable rapids effectively kept Europeans out of the Congo basin and kept central Africa unpenetrated for nearly 400 years. After most of the other African streams had become more or less known, there was not yet enough knowledge about this great river to trace the nature of its course within its basin. The map of central Africa was a blank until Stanley traced in the outlines of the Congo, first downstream from the east to the Congo mouth in 1876 and 1877, and, beginning in 1879, headward from the Atlantic. It is probably because the rapids were so effective a barrier that the great rich heart of Africa remained to be taken, at long last, by one of the smallest countries in the world. Had the rapids not been there, the Congo basin would most likely have been explored, if not occupied, long before by Portuguese, Dutch, French, or English.

Measured by its annual flow the Congo is the second largest river in the world, second only to the Amazon (Figure 15.2). Despite this, it is not a turbulent stream, and it seldom carries more water than its channel can manage. It has a great circuitous course embracing all of its basin. Beginning as the Lualaba, the Congo main stream curves in circular fashion westward and, from its northern arch, bends southwest again and so flows into the sea. Its large northern tributary, the Ubangi, rings the territory between the Congo River and the northern frontier.

The Kasai, flowing along the south side of the basin through Kasai and Bandundu provinces, is a mighty river in its own right, and was mistaken for the Congo itself by some early explorers; its headwaters and those of the main stream rise not far apart in Katanga. Only along the east is The Congo not tributary to its great river, and, even here, one of the rift lakes, Tanganyika, empties to the Congo through the Lukuga River. Here, in the Congo basin, is the greatest hydroelectric potential in the world. The drainage basin of the Congo is vaster than that of the Mississippi River.

## Problems of Independence

The Congo became independent on June 30, 1960. Belgium had been hopeful of a peaceful transition, and of the formation of a single great country comprising all the provinces of the colony. But lack of preparation for political self-determination, the sudden decision of Belgium to grant independence, and personal ambitions and tribal rivalries among Congolese frustrated attempts at unification for more than 2 years. Eleven days after the King of the Belgians recognized the "independence and international sovereignty" of The Congo, Katanga declared itself a republic independent of the rest of The Congo. It remained so until 1963, when it was forced back into the "union," a nebulous term when speaking of The Congo. Since Katanga's capitulation, the country has been torn by rebellions in other provinces.

Six provinces made up the Belgian Congo; and political rivalries after independence more or less expressed themselves in provincial terms, especially at first. This was soon translated, however, into tribal and regional rivalries seeking expression, with the result that in 1962, The Congo was subdivided into 21 provincettes, and the demand for further fragmentation still went on. Bitter and ancient tribal feuds have broken out: Tribal rivalries and regional loyalties, in this more than 900,000-square-mile country where some 14 million scattered inhabitants speak an estimated 250 African languages and dialects, continue to handicap the nation-building phase that was planned to follow the end of Katanga's secession. (See Figure 15.3.)

The fragmentation added to the problems of central control. Based as it is upon tribal areas, the division into provincettes led to fierce jealousy over provincial rights, and bitter resentment of too much central government interference. New provinces were formed to satisfy tribal discontent, which in some sectors led to recurrent tribal clashes, particularly in the Kasai, Kivu, Oriental, and, to a lesser extent, Equator sectors. The first tribes to demand provinces of their own—and this was soon after independence— were the Bakongo in Bandundu Province, the Baluba of Kasai, and the Baluba of Katanga. Their claims seemed strong; yet, by acceding to their demands, the government lifted the lid on a Pandora's box.

FIGURE 15.3 (a) Provinces of the Belgian Congo, 1959; (b) provincial division as of July 1, 1966. As a comparison of the two maps shows, several reminders of past African history—Léopoldville, Stanleyville, Elizabethville, and Coquihatville—have gone the way of such other historical places as Constantinople, St. Petersburg, and Batavia, "relegated by changing times to geography's scrapheap."

Many of the new provinces, particularly those farthest from Léopoldville, became like semiautonomous fiefs. In the north and east, several carried on profitable but illegal barter trade with Sudan and Uganda, refusing to pay revenue to the government in Léopoldville. It was in these sectors that rebels were the strongest. The many little provinces were straining the country's resources because each had a complete set of Government officials. The fragmentation had, in time, to be checked, and this occurred on July 1, 1966, when the provincettes were combined to form 12 provinces. The old provincial lines of the colonial era were generally followed except for the division of some into several provinces (see Figure 15.3a and b). On the same date, some provincial and most non-African city names were changed.

In many regions in the interior of the country the breakdown of the economy, resulting from the long period of civil war and the hurried departure of most of the Belgians, forced many people to return to subsistence living. This in turn revived tribalism, in which allegiances extend little further than the tribal hinterlands. Under these circumstances, the reentry of Katanga into The Congo following the end of its secession had less immediate impact than was expected. There are more than 20 parliamentary parties and splinter groups, 16 of them represented in the government since mid-1963.

## PROSPECTS FOR THE CONGO

Can this large and diverse land be united?

The Congo is the third largest country in Africa, as large as all of Western Europe if Iberia is left out. As many miles lie between Kinshasa (Léopoldville) and Lubumbashi (Elisabethville) as between Moscow and Berlin; it spans out 5°N and over 13°S of the Equator, from dripping rain forests to broad yellow savannas, from sweeping plains to the almost inaccessible heights of the misty Ruwenzori.

Its people also are varied. Here are the Pygmies of Africa and the so-called "Pygmoids," a group of Congolese in the Lake Tumba region having some of the characteristics of Pygmies but who are larger in size; even a few of the 7-foot-tall Watusi, whose traditional home is on the plateau above the rift valley, in Rwanda and Burundi (to mention only the most unusual types), live in the vicinity of Lake Kivu.

Although the integrity of The Congo territory was achieved by the ending of Katanga's secession, a national consciousness has not developed. People are thinly spread across this great land, group separated from group by forests, rivers, swamps—nature's great dividers; but tribalism, which is fostered by such isolated living, is perhaps a greater obstruction to unity than nature's barriers.

Only the airplane reduces distances and overcomes the obstacles of environment: no road connects Kinshasa and Mbandaka (Coquilhatville); only short spurs reach into the forest-swamp-savanna country between the two river ports. It takes 8 days to go from Kinshasa to Kisangani by boat: as night falls over the Congo, utter darkness seems to settle across the land; riverboats slowly and painfully pick their way among the shoals of the river, powerful head lamps swinging their light shafts from shore to shore to pick up the occasional directive signs; radar screens relay the shallows. Straining through the blackness, between what seem to be immense spaces, flickering fires may gleam momentarily and then the vast darkness takes over again; a port with electric lights is like a haven that rests afloat in the blackness. Isolation, not community, is perhaps the outstanding characteristic of this country.

In addition to the barriers to unification imposed by the habitat and by tribalism is the fact that even the concept of nationalism is foreign to the Congolese; the tribe, not the nation, is within their experience and understood. The colonial regime imposed a rule that united the vast territory in a political administration, but in no sense created a nation of Congolese. The Congo is still a country of tribes, many of them. Several types of "barriers," therefore, will have to be eliminated if The Congo is to become a "nation."[1]

[1] For definition of "nation," as used here in two senses, see Lucile Carlson, *Geography and World Politics*, Englewood Cliffs, N.J.: Prentice-Hall, Inc., 1958, p. 192.

## THE MEASURE OF THE DISRUPTION
## WROUGHT BY CIVIL WAR

Throughout The Congo as a whole, large business enterprises have remained relatively intact during the period of disturbances; it is mostly small business that has left. Union Minière du Haut-Katanga and other affiliates of Société Général—commercial, financial, transport, agricultural, other mining interests—stayed on. They dominated the economy of the Belgian Congo, and they dominate the economy of The Congo, holding, therefore, considerable political influence. The Catholic Church also came through with its vigor and power undiminished; it has, in fact, expanded so that the Catholic Church, with its more than 600 mission stations and 6,000 missionaries, still maintains the dominance that it formerly held over education; three-fourths of all primary and secondary schools in Congo are Catholic, as is Lovanium University at Kinshasa.

Native tribal chiefs have regained some power. Although the Belgian administration frequently worked through the traditional heads of tribes, the Belgians did not hesitate to move without the chiefs if circumstances indicated that was the best course. With the provincettes based on the tribe, chiefs often had to make the final decisions, and both the provincial and central governments had to deal with them. This new balance of power was, however, only temporary; during the long months of strife, there was really no authority in The Congo except that which the United Nations provided for a time; thus, the traditional tribal leaders stepped in. Whether these forces can assure order for a sufficiently long period to allow political leaders to work out a more enduring and popularly based government, or will themselves override national for tribal or provincial interests, still remains a question. The new provincial division is an attempt to upgrade nationalism and decrease tribal power and regionalism.

The economy as a whole has deteriorated little: the products of manufacture have increased, since independence, by 40 percent; agricultural production has risen above the 1959 level. The country's roads, riverways, bridges, airports and railways are basically intact, although they have become impaired by several years of inadequate maintenance. The benefits of this essentially strong and productive economy are not reaching down to the people, however, partly because the fiscal and monetary system are inflated and unsound; government spending exceeds its income by 3 times; paper money is issued to fill in the gap.

As in other parts of Africa, unrest, or fear and privation, in the rural areas has impelled large numbers of people to go to urban centers to seek work; Kinshasa has grown from 300,000 (1959) to well over ½ million. Most of these people live in shantytowns at the edges of the cities, or overcrowd the already jammed native quarters. It is the old story repeated; there are not enough jobs to meet the demand. By way of example, it is estimated that three-fifths of the available labor force of Kinshasa are unemployed.

As yet the shock of war and tribal trouble has kept these Congolese quiet, but unless reforms are introduced and effective government implemented, The Congo could erupt into not merely tribal or factional warfare but into full-scale revolution; the 1964 to early 1965 rebel action in Kisangani and its hinterland almost reached this scale. Communist assistance and censure of the Kinshasa Government by most other African nations heightened the strength and morale of the rebel factions.

## RESTORATIVE MEASURES
## TAKEN BY PRIVATE INDUSTRY

Union Minière du Haut-Katanga and other affiliates of Société Général have continued investing in their vast properties throughout the crisis years, by this means registering their confidence in The Congo's future. In 1962, 20 million dollars was put in by Union Minière for restoring and expanding facilities and benefits to its employees; of this, 5 million dollars was spent for schools, medical centers, and other comparable facilities. Exact data are not available for the other companies. New copper mines at Kambove and Kamoto came into operation in late 1963. In September, 1963, the old "national route" for Union Minière's copper and cobalt exports was reopened; this 1,200-mile rail and river transport complex had not been used since shortly after the riots that followed closely on the 1960 independence proclamation. Previous to this, the all-Congo route had carried some 40 percent of the shipments from the Katanga mines to Kinshasa and Matadi. The alternate routes by rail through Angola to the port at Lobito and to Beira in

Mozambique, along which all outward shipments moved during the dispute over Katanga's secession, will continue to carry much of the freight as before.

In addition to the mining interests, railway and other commercial companies have borne a major share of the reconstruction costs, although a part has come from the United Nations' Fund for Civilian Operations in the Congo. Through these combined agencies, repairs have been made on roads and communications that were damaged in January, 1963, during fighting between United Nations and Katanga forces; a temporary span was put across the Lualaba River at Bukama, where the bridge had been destroyed and a second bridge, also destroyed, was rebuilt at Lubilash. Electric power lines to Rhodesia, badly damaged, were once again exporting electricity to The Congo by May, 1963.[2]

## The Urban Legacy of the Belgians to the Congo

Several large urban centers grew up under Belgian administration, particularly where such cities were the capitals of provinces, or ports, or centers of mining development. Matadi is one of these, the only ocean port of importance in The Congo, situated 80 miles up the estuary of the Congo River and connected by railroad with Kinshasa. The immediate hinterland of Matadi is restricted, but its trade hinterland is not immediate to the city but rather the great territory that reaches inland beyond the rapids below Stanley Pool. Matadi is the national outlet for the Congo basin, handling over 65 percent of the imports and about 50 percent of the exports of the country. It stands

at the head of ocean shipping, as beyond Matadi no navigation is possible because of the rapids. Railroads, airplanes, and roads carry the traffic between Matadi and Kinshasa. Boma and Banana, lying closer to the mouth of the Congo than Matadi, are unimportant by comparison. Boma is the outlet for the Mayumbe,[3] and only about 6 percent of Congolese trade passes through its harbor. Banana, earlier of some note, has lost much of its commercial status.

The capitals of the old provinces were all important cities. Four are river or lake ports, Kinshasa, Mbandaka, and Kisangani on the Congo, and Albertville on Lake Tanganyika. All these cities, with the exception of Mbandaka, are also transshipment points, which increases their importance. Luluabourg and Lubumbashi, also provincial capitals, are important trade and industrial centers, situated on the rail line that connects the mining fields of the Katanga with the Kasai River at Port Francqui, and thence with the Congo River ports of Kinshasa and Matadi; at Jadotville, 60 miles from Lubumbashi, are the head offices of Union Minière. Bukavu, capital of South Kivu province, is one of the four largest cities in The Congo but except for air transport, it is relatively isolated. It is connected only by road and air with other parts of The Congo, and Africa. It is, however, the most important urban center in eastern Congo.

All of these are modern Europeanized cities, unusual in Africa south of the Sahara. Except for Dakar, West Africa has no comparably modernized cities; only those in southern Africa, and Nairobi in the East are worthy of comparison with those of The Congo—and the cities of South Africa greatly surpass those of The Congo in their size and urban character; those of East Africa do not quite measure up.

With the new provincial division of the country into twelve constituent units, some new capitals had to be designated (see Figure 15.3b and Tables 5 and 6); Léopoldville, formerly both provincial and national capital, became an autonomous city, remaining the national capital of The Congo with its name Africanized to Kinshasa, but losing its status as provincial capital to the town of Bandundu.

[2] In December, 1966, the government of Congo essentially seized the Katanga assets of Union Minière du Haut-Katanga and, in addition, demanded that "the domicile and central management of the company be transferred from Brussels to Kinshasa"—a move rejected by the board of directors of Union Minière. Pressure against the company had begun early in 1965. In retaliation for seizure of its Congolese assets, the company "declared commercial war against The Congo" by trying to secure a worldwide boycott of copper produced from the Katanga properties. (For further details see "Statement of Union Minière du Haut-Katanga," Dec. 23, 1966, and Jan. 4, 1967, New York: Belgo-American Development Corporation.)

[3] Note the difference in spelling of this word by the French and Belgians. (An even more accurate French spelling is "Mayoumbe.")

## Resource Development

About half of The Congo is covered with forests of one sort or another. Rain forests occur locally, as in Central Congo (the Bas-Congo), along rivers, and in the east; interriverine areas are frequently grassland or grassland with scattered trees; swamp forests and tangled growths line many streams. Although there are a number of useful tree species, they are so scattered that only about 2 percent of the usable timber is being cut for commercial purposes, and most of this is in the Mayumbe. Here, as in Gabon, plywood and veneering are important among the products being turned out; copal is gathered by Africans; the best industrial copal is found in the mud at the base of trees or in muddy areas where trees used to grow. In the north and south, savannas of varying sorts completely take over.

Cultivation is both subsistence and commercial. Plantations producing palm oil, cacao, coffee, tea, cotton, rubber, pyrethrum used for insect powder, and sugar have been developed, and most of the same crops, particularly cotton, coffee, oil palms, and tea, form the basis for the commercial cultivation of the Congolese. Subsistence cultivation is still the main type of native cultivation, however, although the Belgians had made a fine start in training Africans to grow money crops. Root crops like cassava and yams, plantains, and the like are the basic food crops of the Congolese, who also typically keep chickens for their eggs, and goats.

But important as is agricultural production in The Congo, it is the mineral wealth that has accounted for its prosperity. The Belgian Congo was one of the richest colonial holdings in the world, and The Congo has one of the finest resource bases on which to build a viable economy and prosperous people.

Two-thirds of the value of the exports from The Congo come from its mines. Katanga is the richest province,[4] and in Katanga, under a concession granted by Leopold II of Belgium in 1906, Union Minière du Haut-Katanga has held all rights of mineral exploitation: Union Minière alone mines 7½ percent of the

[4] The economic analysis will be made in terms of the old provincial regions since regional reorganization is still in a state of flux.

world's copper. Compared to this giant of industry, the other mining companies of The Congo are small. Copper, cobalt, tin, diamonds, uranium, and manganese are the most important ores and stones found in The Congo, but zinc, iron, coal, tungsten, cadmium, tantalum, and lead also occur.

The developed copper mines, worked solely by Union Minière, are in the extreme southeast centering in and around the Jadotville-Lubumbashi area adjacent to those of Zambia. Although production of Zambian copper exceeds that of Katanga, the grade of the ores is somewhat higher in The Congo, and higher also than American and Chilean ores. A further advantage of the Katanga deposits lies in the fact that they can be worked by open-pit methods. One-third of The Congo's exports are made up of copper products. Although Katanga is the only province now producing copper, this may not always remain so because promising deposits have been discovered in the Bas-Congo in the Madimba region. Katanga (The Congo) ranks sixth in world production of this ore; in spite of the political and social upheaval, copper production markedly increased in 1960; since then, there has been a slight decrease but it remains high, as shown in Table 4.

**TABLE 4** The Congo Copper Production
thousands of metric tons

| 1955 | 1959 | 1960 | 1961 | 1962 | 1963 | 1964 |
|------|------|------|------|------|------|------|
| 235.1 | 282.1 | 302.3 | 295.2 | 297.0 | 271.3 | 277.3 |

Source: *Statistical Yearbook*, New York: United Nations, 1965.

The Congo ranks third among African countries as a producer of gold; the principal deposits are in Kivu and Orientale provinces, but the Kasai also has some. More important are diamonds; The Congo has, over the years, been one of the biggest producers of diamonds in the world, of both the industrial and gem varieties. The first deposits discovered, and the most important, are in the Kasai where they occur in the gravels of the lower Kasai River and its tributaries. From here about 600,000 carats of diamonds, quite equally divided between industrial and gem quality, are taken annually; most of the production of industrial diamonds comes from the Bakwanga gravels, east-southeast of Luluabourg. In the extreme northern part of the Congo in the Uele area, some diamonds are recovered from the gold mines. This area is a small producer, however.

The Congo is Africa's largest producer of tin ore and smelter tin. The tin region lies mostly east and southeast of the Lualaba River extending from northern Katanga across the Maniema district of South Kivu into North Kivu, and east and west from there for about 200 miles. For many years most of the tin was produced by placer mining; more and more, however, the tin is taken from lodes. Methods of mining vary from pick and shovel to the most modern machinery.

The Congo is also by far the world's largest producer of cobalt, the chief producing region being around Kolwezi in Katanga, where it occurs in association with copper. The structure of the ore beds and the ore content are very uneven, however. The presence of uranium in The Congo was first disclosed in 1913, and 2 years later the famed Shinkolobwe deposit was discovered. For years this reserve was one of the major sources of uranium for the Western world. However, in 1960 Union Minière in Brussels announced closure of this mine because of exhaustion of the ore; stockpiles of uranium ore kept the concentration plant operating during the first quarter of 1961. Radium occurs in some of the uranium deposits in the copper area.

An unlimited potential for the development of hydroelectricity is found in the Congo. Belgian plans for the construction of a huge project that should be constructed in stages were far along when independence came, but whether it will be carried through very soon remains to be seen. It was known as the Inga project, and was to have been built at a place where the lower Congo narrows, southwest of Stanley Pool and the rapids; one of the major purposes was to provide power for the establishment of industries that would lessen the dependence of the rest of The Congo on Katanga. Katanga opposed the project, partly because the financing would come in large part from Katanga industry, but also because it would establish an industrial center competitive with Katanga.

## Provinces of the Belgian Congo

### BANDUNDU PROVINCE AND KINSHASA

Geographically, Bandundu Province is varied. To the west, Central (or Bas-) Congo controls most of the lower reaches of the Congo River except those

**TABLE 5** Area and Population of the Provinces of the Belgian Congo

| Province | Area, square mile | Population |
|---|---|---|
| Léopoldville | 363,000 | 3,300,000 approx. |
| Equateur | 403,293 | 1,725,000 |
| Orientale | 504,037 | 2,360,000 |
| Kivu | 256,570 | 2,120,000 |
| Katanga | 496,965 | 1,595,000 |
| Kasai | 321,535 | 2,080,000 |

Source: See old and new provinces in Figure 15.3.

**TABLE 6** Old and New Names of the Capital Cities of the Provinces of The Congo

| Province | Old capital | New capital |
|---|---|---|
| Kongo Central (Central Congo) | Songololo | Songololo |
| Bandundu | Baningville | Bandundu |
| Equateur (Equator) | Coquilhatville | Mbandaka (Bandaka) |
| Uele | Paulis | Isiro |
| Kibali-Ituri | Bunia | Bunia |
| Haut-Congo (Upper Congo) | Stanleyville | Kisangani |
| Nord-Kivu (North Kivu) | Goma | Goma |
| Sud-Kivu (South Kivu) | Bukavu | Bukavu |
| Nord Katanga (North Katanga) | Albertville | Albertville |
| Sud-Katanga (South Katanga) | Elisabethville | Lubumbashi |
| Kasai-Oriental (Eastern Kasai) | Mbuji-Mai | Mbuji-Mai |
| Kasai-Occidental (Western Kasai) | Luluabourg | Luluabourg |

Source: Based on information received from the Embassy of The Congo, Washington, D.C.

that lie seaward from Matadi; from here, the river forms a boundary shared with Angola. At its mouth the river channel is drowned, becoming a broad deep estuary that extends inland beyond Boma, and continues offshore for a considerable distance as a deep gorge; mangrove grows thickly along the lower river reaches.

The Congo flows to the Atlantic through a low swampy plain; at irregular distances from the shore, the coastal lowland plays out and the relief becomes hilly as the eroded edge of the plateau is attained close to the sea south of the river, farther inland along the river itself and on the north. (Matadi, river port about 80 miles from the coast, is built not only along the river front but sweeps on up across the slopes of great hills.)

North from the river is a region of Bas-Congo known as the Mayumbe, a hilly area varying between 160 and 800 feet in altitude and covered with rich rain forests that are an extension of those of Gabon. These forests contain a variety of valuable trees suitable for cabinet and furniture woods, veneers, plywood, and wood for general construction; oil palms abound. This is the only region in The Congo where timber is cut for export, and here also the most active program of forest enrichment was carried on. Under the Belgians the limba tree, fast growing and suitable for furniture and woodwork, was the principal species planted. Tropical fruits such as bananas and pineapples grow well, and these are exported through nearby ports.

The drop from the plateau surface to the coastal plain takes place across many miles. Between Matadi and Kinshasa this hilly country is known as the Crystal Mountains: Elevations average about 2,500 feet, but the highest point, Mount Uia, ascends 3,465 feet. The hills of this sector are covered with savanna and low bush that becomes thicker along the slopes to the river, where it often merges with forest. Falls and cascades tumble down from the plateau, interrupting the smooth flow of the Congo River, and making the landscape one of great beauty. Along the railroad that runs between Matadi and Kinshasa much of the savanna has been converted into pasture where cattle graze; and on Mateba, the big island in the center of the river, large cattle stations have been established.

The new, abbreviated Bandundu Province lies east of the Congo River. Across it, and nearly bisecting it, flows the Kasai, a large tributary of the Congo, from the time of David Livingstone long mistaken for the Congo itself, to unite its waters with those of the greater river. The direction of flow of the Kasai main stream is toward the west-northwest, but most of its affluents run as innumerable, almost parallel rivers and runnels practically due north, rising, as do the tributaries that join the Congo from the south, on the Benguela-Lunda swell, somewhere inside the borders of Angola. This stream pattern is especially pronounced in Kwango, southeastern Bandundu Province. Port Francqui, situated at the approximate head of navigation of the Kasai, river entrepôt of the Kasai country and major junction of rail-river transport for the great mining regions of the Katanga and Kasai provinces, lies just beyond the provincial bounds of Bandundu in the province of Western Kasai.

During their courses down the slopes of the divide in the south and northward to about the latitude of Kikwit, the gradients of these tributary streams are steep, and falls and rapids make them unnavigable. Beyond here and to their confluences with the Kasai or Congo, however, they are open to navigation almost all the way. The central basin of the Congo is supposed to have been covered with an inland sea in a distant past; but of this sea, only the marshy Lake Leopold II remains.

The southern plateaus and mountains of Kwango are savannas, but in the central basin of Bandundu Province the vegetation becomes forest in which huge groves of oil palms grow indigenously. This would be secondary, not primary forest because the oil palm moves only into secondary forests, never into rain forests. The oil palm is the chief source of wealth in this area. While this is not a mineral-rich part of The Congo, copper deposits have been discovered; and as previously noted, here on the lower Congo is the site of the proposed Inga project.

Out of this province was taken the autonomous capital city of Congo, Kinshasa, also the administrative center for the colony under the Belgians, then called Léopoldville. Situated along the left bank of Stanley Pool (Figure 15.4), Kinshasa is the terminus of river transport on the great central portion of the Congo River, navigable without interruption from

FIGURE 15.4    The port of Kinshasa faces Stanley Pool; across the Pool is the twin port of Brazzaville, established by the French. The modern commercial district of Kinshasa can also be seen. (Photograph by H. Goldstein.)

here to Kisangani, above which rapids again impede boats from moving; beyond, any goods shipped into Congo by rail from the seaport of Matadi break bulk at Kisangano. Kinshasa is, therefore, an important commercial and business, as well as administrative, center. Launches shuttle across Stanley Pool many times daily between this city on the south side of the pool and Brazzaville on the north. Kinshasa is a beautiful modern city, with impressive residential suburbs; and its main thoroughfare is a brightly lighted, well landscaped boulevard.

## THE NORTH: EQUATOR, UELE, UPPER CONGO, AND KIBALI-ITURI

Beyond Bandundu Province along the Congo River are the provinces of Equator and, further east, Uele, Upper

Congo, and Kibali-Ituri (the latter three formerly Oriental). Equator Province occupies a large part of the basin of the former sea. This sector is now covered with a rich equatorial rain forest except in the north, where forests merge into and become savannas. The rim of the basin is higher than the central portions and land is well drained; however, in the vicinity of the rivers and at the confluence of the Ubangi with the Congo, the terrain is always marshy. Surface conditions (due to marshes and forests) are so bad in all of Equator Province, except in the extreme north, that movement is forced onto the rivers; under Belgian administration all but the northern sector was closed to travelers except as they journeyed by riverboat. Equator Province has more miles of navigable waterways than any other province of The Congo. Mbandaka, situated on the Congo some distance northeast of the Congo-

Ubangi confluence, is the major city of Equator—river port, provincial capital, business center. It lies quite isolated, however, from other important centers, its only connections via the river; as one approaches the port by boat at night, it looks small, pregnable, and lonely in the black vastness of forest that engulfs its lights on all sides.

The three eastern provinces of the north are topographically quite simple except in the northeast. They slope very gently from the north, which is the rim of the Congo basin, toward the center. In the east the rim is higher, being formed by the edges of the western rift, of the great rift valley that terminates in Lake Albert; the mountains here rise to peaks of almost 10,000 feet, and average elevations are about 6,000 feet. Rain forest in the southern portion, the vegetation of the northeast provinces gradually becomes savanna along the Uele River and the Sudan border. Here is Parc de la Garamba, an animal reserve that under the Belgians was open only to those pursuing scientific study. A number of rare species of African animals are found, such as giraffes and the white rhinoceros, as well as large herds of elephants and members of the cat family.

About two-thirds of the northeast provinces are covered with rain and secondary forests, and yet development in this province is quite notable. Cleared land produces cotton; forests, naturally rich in oil palms, have been further enriched by the interplanting of more oil palms; these form groves worked by the Africans, while oil palm plantations occupy cleared land. Gold occurs, the biggest mines located at Kilo-Moto.

Kisangani, situated just west of the Stanley Falls, is the upper terminus of navigation in the middle Congo, and the starting point for the rail-river transport moving south. Railroad yards, an important dock area, and a major airport bespeak its significance as a bulk break and communications center, as well as a trade town.

Ethnographically, these provinces are very interesting, both historically and today. Remains of Paleolithic and Neolithic tribes have been uncovered in the north and northeast; pure strains of Pygmies, and Bantu, Sudanese, and Nilotic types inhabit the area. The Ituri Forest, often thought of as Pygmy-land, is in Kibali-Ituri Province.

## THE KIVU PROVINCES

Kivu has perhaps the greatest natural beauty of any of the provinces. It straddles the western limb of the great rift valley, shares the Ruwenzori Mountains and lakes Edward and Kivu with Uganda, and has within its borders the remarkably beautiful Semliki valley as well as the whole of Parc Albert (Albert National Park). The ranges bordering the western rift are more impressive here than in Kibali-Ituri Province, averaging 6,000 to 10,000 feet, while the mighty Ruwenzori pushes its snow-covered summits to nearly 17,000 feet. The slopes of the mountain are covered with an unusual variety of vegetation altitudinally zonated while at their base stretches a great expanse of tropical forests.

It is obvious that the slope of the Kivu provinces is from the east toward the interior. The eastern edge breaks off suddenly, so that the uplands seem to look down upon the lake-studded valley of the great rift where Nile and Congo drainage divide, between lakes Edward and Kivu, in the Mufumbiro volcanic chain. The divide, closer to Lake Kivu than to Edward, extends east-west across the depression. Nine volcanoes make up the Mufumbiro group, and activity in the area has been very recent.

The eastern Kivu has a healthful and moderate climate compared to that of the interior lowlands, and so the Kivu area has become a health and tourist resort center as well as an important area of commercial cultivation. Tea, coffee, pyrethrum, and stock raising are important here; both Europeans and Africans like the area.

There is a tendency to think of the rift area of eastern Kivu as synonymous with the Kivu provinces. But to do that is to omit the large portion of the provinces that occupies the western Kivu, namely the Maniema region. The history of this sector is tragic, for it was one of the places that first felt the effects of Arab slave raiding; its past is told in stories of kidnapping, massacre, and looting. In the current era, the Maniema region is economically important, particularly as the locale of important tin and gold mines. South to north across Maniema runs the Lualaba River; the mighty stream changes its name to "Congo" about where the Stanley Falls occur, or somewhat south of these rapids.

## KATANGA PROVINCE

The Lualaba rises far to the south, close to the southern border of South Katanga Province. Like the Nile it passes through a sudd, in this case Lake Upemba, another swamp region of floating vegetation that moves hither and yon at the will of the winds, and causes navigation to be difficult or impossible.

There are a number of opinions where the Congo begins: In the Lualaba? Or the Luvua flowing out of Lake Mweru? Or in the Luapula, that rises in the swamps of Lake Bangweulu and flows into Lake Mweru? A strong affluent of the Congo emerges out of Lake Tanganyika also, namely, the Lukuga. Were it not for the Mufumbiro divide between lakes Kivu and Edward and the interruptions that the cascades impose, there would be a continuous water passageway from the Congo estuary on the Atlantic to the Nile delta and the Mediterranean; a small stream, the Ruzizi flows out of Lake Kivu into Tanganyika.

Katanga spreads across the southeastern portion of The Congo, over the northern slopes of the plateau swell that forms the eastern portion of the Congo-Zambezi divide. On the divide, altitudes average between 5,000 and 5,300 feet, and in the east reach up to 6,500 feet. The upper slopes are badly eroded; higher peaks are bare, and lower slopes are covered only with a dry bush and savanna, but rivers flowing down the side of the divide give Katanga a high potential of hydroelectricity. Along the east the rift lake, Tanganyika, forms the provincial and national boundary. It fills the clefted valley from side to side and here along the edge of the rift are found the highest elevations of the province. The divide between Congo and Zambezi drainage just about marks the boundary between Katanga and Zambia.

Although the Katangas have some natural features that are of interest in themselves, such as Lake Upemba in the national park of the same name, it is not for their natural beauty but for their minerals that the provinces are famed—copper, cobalt, manganese, zinc, uranium, coal, tin, and radium. They are also highly industrialized, particularly in the copper district around Jadotville and Lubumbashi.

Apart from industry and mining, Katanga also offers great possibilities for the breeding of stock, for the plains of Katanga, which make up a great part of the provinces, are immense tropical grasslands; the provinces are essentially a savanna country with gallery forests along the river courses. Stock raising is already important, and much research has gone into attempts to breed cross strains of native, Indian, and European stocks, breeds that will improve the quality of the meat and the production of milk, but that will at the same time, show stamina for resisting the effects of climate and tropical diseases. Dairying is advanced in Katanga for a tropical African country, and the dairy business, supplying the mining and industrial centers, is modern and mechanized. Agriculture produces an excellent variety of tobacco, raised as a cash crop; cotton and corn are also grown.

Four-fifths of the taxes of the Belgian Congo normally came from Katanga. Hence, Katanga has played a dominantly important role in the economic and social life of the country. The political control of Léopoldville has chafed the people of Katanga for a long time, and they have not liked the heavy burden of almost carrying The Congo financially.

## THE KASAI

The Kasai, centrally situated in southern Congo, topographically is like the other provinces: It is highest in the area where its borders are coincident with those of the national state, and slopes toward the interior, sharing part of the central basin. As in Kwango (Bandundu Province), rivers flow from south to north —first, down a rather steep gradient with rapids and falls; in the lower reaches, less turbulently so that they are navigable. The streams all rise on the Lunda-Benguela divide where elevations average about 3,300 feet.

Kasai is a savanna, etched with gallery forests along the streams except as the central basin is reached; there equatorial forests interspersed with wide glades of grassland take over. Generally, marshes are absent because the land is higher than that to the northwest.

The Kasai is a richly productive land; grasslands offer good pasturage for cattle; agriculture produces such commercial crops as coffee, cotton, rice, maize, and oil palms; its alluvial sands and gravels yield diamonds. Kasai Province is the greatest producer of industrial diamonds in the world; at times, in the past, it has taken first place in the output of gem diamonds also. In 1963, out of a total world production of 28,000,000 carats of gem and industrial diamonds combined, Congo produced 14,784,000 carats; out of a world production of 21,200,000 carats of industrial diamonds, 14,468,000 carats were taken in Congo.[5]

[5] *Statistical Yearbook*, New York: United Nations, 1964.

Across the Kasai, from the mining areas of Katanga, runs the ore railroad of Congo, one of three branches that diverge at Tenke, this line being the only wholly Congolese transport route. Of the other two, one runs west to the Atlantic through Angola, and the other east to the Indian Ocean through Mozambique. The Congolese line terminates at Port Francqui.

# 16 SOUTHERN AFRICAN REALM

*Mile upon mile of ridge and*
*    kopje, bush and candid waste*
*Sun dried and empty, tacit as*
*    the sea. . . .*

RUDYARD KIPLING

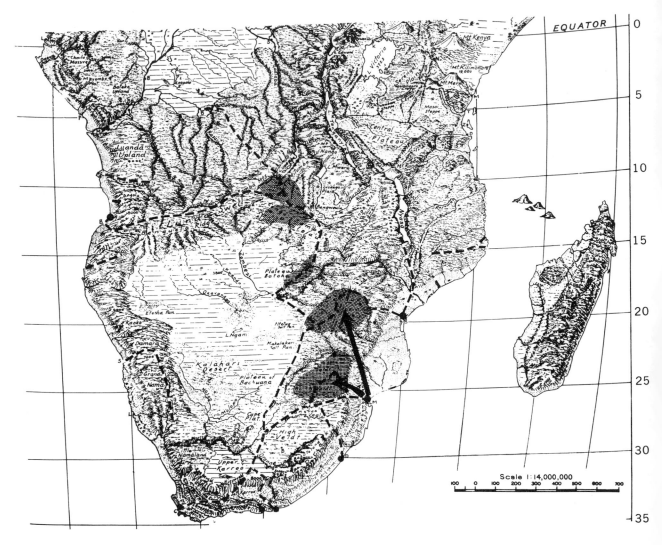

**FIGURE 16.2**  Relief map and main lines of access to industrial centers in interior southern Africa. (Base map Physiographic Diagram of Africa, copyright A. K. Lobeck; reproduced with permission of the publisher, The Geographical Press, a division of C. S. Hammond & Company, Maplewood, N.J.)

## The Realm

Like several other portions of the continent, southern Africa is saucerlike in its physiographic character. The interior represents a sag in the African plateau that rises on all sides to higher ground (Figure 16.2).

This sector of the plateau, raised by tectonic forces, has stood above sea level at least from the beginning of the Mesozoic era and onward because the surface is covered with sediments that are not of marine origin, but were laid down by wind and fresh water. It ranges in elevation from less than 3,000 feet to the heights of Thabana-Ntlenyana in Lesotho, 11,425 feet high. The lowest sectors, if the erosional troughs of the middle Zambezi and Limpopo and the lower Orange rivers are excepted, lie in the Makarikari and lower Molopo basins in Botswana. In between the two extremes are some prominent heights in scattered areas. In the east, there are volcanic Mount Rungwe (10,412 feet), the Mlanje mass in southern Malawi

(9,840 feet), the granite peak of Namuli in Mozambique (7,980 feet) and the border mountains in the eastern portions of Rhodesia where elevations rise above 8,000 feet in Inyangani (8,250 feet). On the plateau in Angola, Morro do Moço and Serra do Chela rise 8,613 and 7,510 feet respectively, and in the Auas highlands south of Windhoek, Mount Moltkeblick reaches 8,150 feet.

It is likely that the edge of the plateau at one time formed the coastal margin of the subcontinent, but as rivers eroded the escarpment and as the sea floor emerged during uplifts, the edge of the plateau no longer dropped directly to the sea forming the coastline, but became a more or less mountainous zone that separated the plateau from the coastal zones. In time, as the plateau edge retreated and the sea floor continued to be exposed along the shore, the belt between the plateau and the shoreline became so broad that it no longer constituted merely a coast; great plains were built up that in some places were hundreds of miles deep, as in Mozambique.

Southern Africa is separated from the central African basin along the divide between Congo and Zambezi drainage, a water parting that is composed of several parts. The Benguela plateau (or swell) in the west represents the highest portion of the plateau of Angola, and extends about equally north and south of the continental divide. The Lunda upland lies mainly to the east of the main headwaters of the Zambezi River in Zambia, and continues eastward in the elongated narrow Muchinga highland that forms the watershed between the Luangwa and Luapula rivers.

Some problem is raised in the east whether the northern boundary of southern Africa should lie to the north or the south of Lake Nyasa. Nyasa is one of the rift lakes and there are valid reasons for including it in East Africa. However, hydrographically it belongs with the south because Lake Nyasa is a part of the Zambezi system, draining into that river through its outlet, the Shiré River, and thence to the Indian Ocean; structurally, it is also closely associated with the formation of the plain of Mozambique, another reason for including it in southern Africa.

East from the head of the Luangwa valley, the divide continues along the Poroto Mountains, volcanoes whose highest point is reached in Mount

Rungwe; and east from there, it follows the northern edge of the Ruvuma basin of southern Tanganyika.

Southern and East Africa comprise "High Africa"; "Low Africa"[1] begins at the Lunda-Benguela and the rift valley divides. Thus southern Africa has characteristics that relate it to the remainder of the continent, but it also constitutes a geographical region with characteristics peculiar to itself. If the water parting is traced across the continent it will be seen to coincide quite remarkably with the political boundaries. Major deviations are found only in the extreme east and west.

The Benguela railroad, taking its course essentially along the crest of the water partings, points out the importance of the divide; it follows the crest from Nova Lisboa east to Capeio, where it enters the basin of the Cuanza River, whose headstreams have cut headward for a distance of 120 miles south of the general line of the divide. East of Munhango, where the railway leaves the Cuanza Basin, the water partings of the Zambezi headwaters on the one hand (Lungue-Bungo, Luena, and Chefumage rivers) and the Kasai headwaters on the other, mark the divide. The lowest portion lies in the Kalahari sands area between the two plateaus, a region about 400 miles in width, covered with sand to varying depths.

Climatically there is no abrupt change between southern and central Africa; in fact, climates tend to show sharp changes rather more east and west than latitudinally, varying only gradually from north to south. Rainfall shows the most marked variance with latitude between the central and south, but changes are so transitional that a line of difference does not occur.

Included in this realm are Zambia, Rhodesia, Malawi, the Portuguese territories of Angola and Mozambique, the Republic of South Africa, South-West Africa, and Botswana, Swaziland, and Lesotho.

Southern Africa divides into three physiographic regions: the plateau with its central basin and peripheral highlands, the Great Escarpment, and the margins and coast of the continent.

---

[1] S. Passarge, *Südafrika*, Leipzig: Quelle Meyer, 1908.

## Physiographic Regions

### THE GREAT ESCARPMENT

The Great Escarpment separates the plateau from the continental margins.

Since the rock structure of the plateau varies from place to place, the Great Escarpment also changes in character because weathering and erosional processes work with unlike effect upon differing surfaces. Where rock formations that are very hard and resistant cap softer rocks, the escarpments are abrupt, clifflike, and linear; where the rocks are softer and more homogeneous, the plateau edge is irregular and the slopes relatively gentle.

Along the east, the Drakensberg Mountains mark the edge of the plateau, in the Natal-Lesotho area forming the most abrupt and prominent part of the Great Escarpment (Figure 16.3). This is due to a capping of basaltic lava horizontally laid down, in places to a depth of nearly 4,500 feet. The result is the rugged and steep escarpment, running continuously for about 300 miles, that is the backdrop of Natal. These highlands are barriers to transportation:

a glance at a transport map will reveal that no national highway and no railroad cross the escarpment in the 250 miles between Queenstown, northwest of East London, and van Reenan's Pass, that lies northwest of Durban; and along the entire eastern border of Lesotho, no road of any kind crosses the escarpment. The Drakensberg are also a barrier to the southeast trade winds, Natal benefiting from the abrupt plateau front, which forces the winds to rise, cool, and drop moisture; the interior regions, shut off from these benefits, are semiarid to arid.

The water divide of southern Africa, south of the Limpopo, lies along the escarpment edge, so that the rivers of Natal tumble the short distance down abrupt slopes to the sea while the west flowing rivers, the Vaal and Orange, flow from the eastern edge of the plateau all the way across southern Africa to the Atlantic coast. (See Figure 16.4.)

South of the lava formations the plateau edge, although well-defined, is not so abrupt as in Natal and Lesotho, where the rock is protected by lava. Here rivers have eroded headward into the weaker strata to form deep embayments along the plateau front. North of the Natal-Lesotho border (Figure

FIGURE 16.3 A road winds its way across the Natal grasslands toward the foothills of the Drakensberg Escarpment. (Courtesy South African Information Service.)

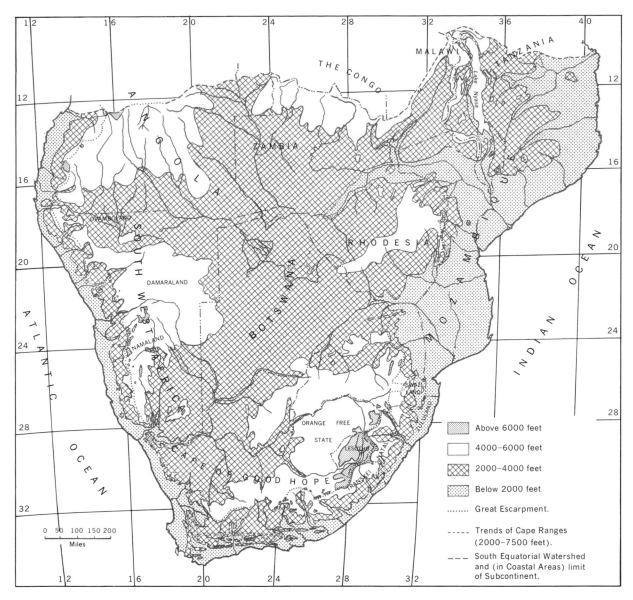

**FIGURE 16.4   Altitudinal zonation in southern Africa. (Base map from John H. Wellington,** *Southern Africa,* **London: Cambridge University Press, 1955, vol. I, map II, with permission and courtesy of the author and the publisher.)**

16.5), the Drakensberg (between Natal and Transvaal, and here known as the Transvaal Drakensberg) are inconspicuous compared to their mighty proportions in Lesotho. The escarpment nevertheless still acts as the watershed between Atlantic and Indian Ocean drainage. To the north of Utrecht, the water divide follows the highest peaks, outliers of the beds farther south, all over 7,000 feet high. However, headward erosion by streams has worked inward into the plateau so vigorously here that the hard rock cover is discontinuous, and there is no line that defines the margin of the plateau. Farther north, however, the

FIGURE 16.5 Zulu kraals dot the mighty hills of Zululand, Northern Natal. Note the gully erosion. These mighty hills are simply the stream-dissected edge of the African plateau. (Photograph by writer.)

Great Escarpment again becomes well defined, although horizontal beds of dolerite (see Glossary) at varying heights cause the scarp face to be terraced. Between Piet Retief and the Amsterdam-Ermelo road the edge of the plateau is a continuous scarp except where the headwaters of one river have captured those of another to make a deep incision in the wall. However, at Bankop on the Amsterdam-Ermelo road the terrain changes; there is no escarpment, but granite spurs occurring here and there make it possible to trace the edge of the plateau. The plateau here, known as the highveld, is about 5,300 feet in height; it descends gradually between the spurs left by eroding rivers; in some places, the rivers have cut veritable gorges, such as the Komati, which occupies a trench 3,000 feet deep. Into such trenches the plateau drops steeply.

Still farther north the character of the Great Escarpment again changes; it no longer serves as the water parting between Indian and Atlantic drainage because the divide has an east-west trend. Thus, the Olifants River flows north before it turns east to join the Limpopo, and all of the other tributaries of the Limpopo, such as the Crocodile and Marico rivers,

descend down north-facing slopes into the main stream. The present line of the escarpment front in this region is apparently due to the headward cutting of streams eroding back into the flexed and probably faulted edge of the plateau.

## CENTRAL PLATEAU AND PERIPHERAL HIGHLANDS

The plateau itself divides into two great physiographic regions, the arid central (or Kalahari) basin, and the circumferential uplands.[2] The central basin extends north and south some 1,200 miles from the Orange River to the Benguela-Lunda swell, and at its widest, about 800 miles east and west, encompasses an area of about 630,000 square miles. It is entirely covered with sand—a feature that continues into The Congo, probably making this basin one of the most extensive continuously sand-covered surfaces to be found in the world. Rock projections occur only here and there

[2] Reference was made particularly to John H. Wellington, *Southern Africa, a Geographical Study*, London: Cambridge University Press, 1955, pp. 52–97, for the discussion of the Kalahari basin and the rimming uplands.

as outcrops of the floor. "Fine to coarse," smoothed and "frosted" by the wind, red in places where iron oxide forms a surface on the grains, "whitish" where more moisture obtains, the sand covers the basin to varying depths, in places being 300 to 400 feet deep. Almost everywhere it is covered with a vegetation of grass, shrubs, and even trees. In the dry dune country of the southern sector, vegetation anchors the dunes so that they do not migrate.

The basin subdivides into three sectors on the basis of hydrography: the southern and northern Kalahari, and the Etosha basin in the northwest. The boundary between the northern and southern regions is the rise in the sand, between Kanye in the east and the Nossob River in the west, which acts as a watershed, i.e., the Bakalahari rise. South of the swell two quite distinct types of sand surfaces occur; most of the north and east are level to gently undulating, and covered sparsely with grass or shrubs, while in the south and southeastern sectors the surface is covered with dunes—not isolated sandhills, but "long, continuous ridges roughly parallel, though often merging and divagating in a confused pattern,"[3] and running roughly with the prevailing winds, which are northerly to northwesterly. When forming, the dunes must have been bare and moving; now they are generally stationary because of the grass and scrub cover; in places where overgrazing has almost obliterated the vegetation, however, the dunes have begun once more to migrate.

Two systems of "twin" rivers, that flow in from opposite directions, provide the most important drainage for the region south of the Bakalahari divide. The Molopo and Kuruman rivers, the "twins" flowing from the east, emerge from "limestone eyes" (springs). Since all of the water that runs from the headstreams of these rivers is used within a few miles of their sources for irrigation, only the portion that is derived from rainstorms flows away; the river courses across the Kalahari sands, therefore, are shallow and narrow. In the past, however, the two streams were more powerful, in places cutting gorges 100 feet deep and eroding channels over 175 feet in width. Both the Molopo and Kuruman lose themselves in the interior

shortly after joining their wadis, near the middle of the basin, with the "twins" from the west, the Nossob and the Auob.

The Nossob and Auob rise in the high Auas plateau near Windhoek. Each has two headstreams that during the rainy season send great floods of water down the slopes into the basin. At the base of the highlands, however, where the slope breaks to the limestone plain, the two rivers become only a series of pools; not even during floodtime does water normally reach the lower courses of the wadis.

Just west of the confluence of the Molopo and Nossob, all along the edge of the dunes, lies a region of great pans (see Glossary) or dry "lakes" known as the Mier country. Some of these pans are very large, such as Hackschein which is 15 by 7 miles in size, and Koppies Kraal pan 6 miles across; the floors, level and hard, now serve as roads offering temporary surcease from the difficulties of traversing the dunes.

North of the Bakalahari rise, the northern Kalahari stretches uninterruptedly to the Congo-Zambezi watershed. This basin differs from that to the south but slightly; sand covers the area completely, although there is no regular system of dunes as there is in the south. Instead, the north is rather remarkably level, only gentle but broad swells, that are scarcely distinguishable to any one but a surveyor, breaking the monotony here and there. In some places, however, as along the delta of the Okovango, these are large enough to dam up drainage; they are particularly pronounced where rock outcrops also occur, the latter being more common in the north than in the south.

The greatest contrasts between the drainage systems of the north and south Kalahari are due to climate, and particularly moisture: rainfall grows greater from south to north, averaging between 6 or 7 inches in the southern basin but at times reaching 10 inches, increasing gradually northward to about 10 inches just beyond the rise to over 25 inches in the interior swamps, and near the northern edge exceeding 50 inches. It is here that such great rivers as the Zambezi, Okovango, and Cuando rise; the volume of water carried by these northern streams is far in excess of that that flows in the southern basin.

Except for the extreme western region of the northern Kalahari, which drains into the Etosha Pan as a separate system, drainage north of the Bakalahari di-

[3] *Ibid.*, p. 55.

vide "constitutes a single system,"[4] flowing from the Bakalahari and continental divides toward the interior, some of it lost in the central swamplands of the arid Okovango basin and Makarikari salt pans, much in the north being tributary to the Zambezi River and flowing out to the Indian Ocean. The courses of the rivers originating on the continental divide are well known, and the regimen of each is well understood; but of the drainage that flows into the Makarikari depression there is much uncertainty. It is even possible that parts of this barren desert region have never been visited by human beings.

The Etosha Pan and drainage area occupies about one-tenth of the Kalahari. This sector is a roughly rectangular basin largely effected by the erosive action of streams, although the pan itself (about 60 by 25 miles in size) lies in a structural depression. The basin stands at an elevation of 3,549 feet, and is covered with a sandy clay that is slightly saline in most parts. It is a difficult region.

The area north of the pan is inhabited by the Ovambo people, who spread across the frontier of South-West Africa into Angola. The basin floor has an extremely low gradient on the aggraded plain, and during the wet season about 60 percent of this land floods as the waters from the tangled, shallow channels overflow their banks; on the other hand, during the dry season, droughts frequently occur. Salinity of the soil in the regions surrounding the pan and a high water table make agriculture impossible for a long distance north of the pan; Ovamboland has a definite southern limit to agriculture determined by salinity, a condition rare in the world.

The Cunene River, rising on the continental divide and flowing strongly south in its upper and upper middle course before turning westward, has a special relationship to the Etosha basin. It appears that although a fossil channel suggests that in the past there may have been some flow into the basin from the Cunene, none of its waters can drain toward Etosha Pan in the present era. However, because of a great water diversion scheme sponsored by the government of South-West Africa, Cunene waters are being used to irrigate lands cultivated by the Ovambo: two 60-mile-long canals have been built from the Cunene

to carry floodwaters to Ovamboland; and a pumping station to pump water into the canals and a dam that will produce hydroelectricity are to be built at the site of the Ruacana Falls on the Cunene.

The higher lands of the plateau swing in a semicircle all around the edge of the basin from the *planalto* of Angola southward and around to the Indian Ocean side across the velds of South Africa and the savannas of the Rhodesias, narrowest along the western rim of the basin, broadest along the east. Since these uplands are structurally complex, they must be regarded as more than simply the basin rim despite the fact that where sedimentaries comprise the peripheral rocks the slope is generally toward the center.

The *planalto* of Angola is the highest part of the Benguela plateau, straddling the continental divide so that the northern side of the swell slopes to the Congo. Near the divide much of the surface is level, and rainfall is usually over 60 inches. The streams rising here are vigorous rivers even during the period of drought, with broad channels and gradients of 10 to 20 feet per mile. This part of Angola is the most healthful portion of the country, also, and here the European population is largely concentrated; it is, besides, free of the tsetse fly and suitable to stock raising.

The southwestern sector of the Benguela upland is known as the Chela-Otavi highlands. Sá da Bandeira, the most important commercial center, is located in the northern part of the Serra do Chela (Chela Mountains), and just to the west is the highest portion of the region, namely, the Humpata upland, 7,510 feet high. The Cunene River in its lower course forms a part of the boundary between Angola and South-West Africa and flows through the plateau. South of the river, the area becomes increasingly arid; even the lower Caculuvar River, which rises near Sá da Bandeira and flows into the Cunene from the north, is almost completely dry during most of the year in its middle and lower channel; on the other hand, during the greatest summer rains, it becomes a raging torrent. The belt that has been cut through the plateau by the Cunene is 30 to 40 miles in width and is similar to a mountainous region in its broken relief.

South of the Cunene, karst topography has developed throughout much of the area. However, in the valleys around and west of Grootfontein there are many springs, and some of the finest cultivable lands of South-West Africa are found here. In the limestones at Tsumeb are valuable copper ores, and at Grootfontein and Abenab copper, zinc, and lead occur in the limestone rocks. The only regions of the Chela-Otavi highlands that are suitable for profitable habitation are those around Grootfontein and in the Humpata plateau and the upper Caculuvar basin.

Great Namaland (or the Namaqua highlands) is the driest sector of the plateau of South-West Africa. Rising 4,000 to 6,000 feet above sea level, its western margin is generally sharply defined; in the east it slopes off into the Kalahari sands. The southern part of the plateau is a vast sterile region, but in the central and northern parts, conditions are better. Although the central sector of the plateau is also barren, valleys, such as those of the Great Fish and Konkip rivers, allow some little cultivation, but they are more important for their fine grasses, which support many sheep. Sheep farming is the major occupation. In the north, although rainfall reaches about 12 inches, soils are generally too shallow for cultivation. The grasslands and bush country of this highveld make excellent grazing land, however, and so the area is mainly pastoral. Beef and dairy cattle, and, more important, karakul sheep are the main support of those who live here.

Eastern Namaland, east of the Namaqua highlands, is generally about 1,000 to 2,000 feet lower than the plateau to the west. Several features stand up prominently about the plain, such as the crater of Mount Brukkaros rising steeply upward for 1,800 feet and terminating in a vast crater 2 miles in diameter, and the Little and Great Karroos Mountains. Rainfall averages between 4 and 10 inches, and hence vegetation is scanty, mainly scattered brush and tufted grass. The only type of land utilization possible is sheep raising; but when given enough grazing space, merino, karakul, and native fattailed sheep thrive.

South of the Orange River, in Cape Province, is a region that somewhat matches eastern Namaland, namely, Bushmanland. In the west, where it is known as Little Namaland, the rather low sandy plateau rises to the Great Escarpment, which is pronounced along here. It is between eastern Namaland and Bushmanland that the Orange River cuts its gorge through the rock. Rainfall averages only 5 inches in Bushmanland, but rises somewhat higher along the loftier western margin.

The Orange is South Africa's largest river, rising in the high mountains of Lesotho and along the borders of Natal. A topographic map of South Africa will show that except for the country that drains to the Limpopo, practically all of the interior plateau lies within the drainage basin of the Orange-Vaal system; a rainfall map will show that after its juncture with the Vaal, the Orange traverses or abuts on lands subject to extreme drought.

> The whole of the catchment lies in the summer rainfall area—September to April. In the high mountains of the eastern watershed the annual rainfall may be as much as 80 inches, but this decreases rapidly at the lower altitudes. East of Longitude 26°E the mean annual rainfall is generally in excess of 20 inches and is fairly consistent, although, even in this area, there are considerable differences in the total amount of rain from year to year. West of the 26th meridian, the mean annual rainfall gradually diminishes until, near the coast, it is 2 inches or less. It is also very erratic. In certain years, sufficient rain may fall to cause extensive flooding, which may be followed by three or four years of practically no rain.[5]

South Africa, richly endowed in many other ways, is relatively poor in water resources. Consequently, a vast multipurpose project of water conservation and distribution and hydroelectric development is under way on the Orange River. Involved in the scheme are three primary projects, namely, two large dams on the Orange River and a tunnel under the watershed between the Orange and Fish rivers, and many secondary ones. When completed "the whole of the Karroo and North Western Cape districts" will come under the plan.[6] It will also assure the new development of lands, now in jeopardy, in the Fish and Sundays river valleys. These rivers rarely flow today, because their sources are in areas of low and uncertain rainfall and because intense water and soil conserva-

[5] C. P. Robinson, "How the Orange River Project Will Work," *Optima*, p. 30, March, 1963.
[6] T. B. Bowker, "Claiming the Bounty of the Orange River," *Optima*, p. 28, March, 1963.

FIGURE 16.6 Transvaal lowveld farm. Subtropical conditions permit the cultivation of a variety of orchard and garden crops. Frangipani tree in foreground with a citrus orchard beyond. *(Courtesy South African Information Service.)*

tion has been carried out by Karroo farmers on the watersheds serving these rivers.[7]

The gorge of the Orange River begins at Aughrabies Falls and ends at the downstream end of the great bend. Where the river has worked its way through hard rock the gorge is narrow, but where softer rocks and granites are found the channel becomes wider because the steep affluents have been very erosive. The deepest canyons are found in the lower portions of the gorge, especially along the lower Fish and Konkip rivers where canyons several hundred feet deep have been carved. Except for a few level places along the river where it is possible to irrigate the land, the area through which the Orange River runs is rock or sand wasteland, or, in patches, bush country. This mountainous and rugged country, bordering the stream, is known as the "river range."

Above Aughrabies Falls, south of the river, is the region known as the Cape middle veld. The surface is generally flat except where broken by occasional outcrops of lava deposits or granite. The river gradients are gentle, the climate arid, and these two features have combined to produce "a peculiar type of pan called in Afrikaans a *vloer* (floor)": rivers wander over the surface, flooding wide areas when they meet obstructions of any size (as dolerite outcrops), and numerous mud basins are the result. The soils tend to be of clay, and often brackish, so that irrigation can be practiced but rarely. However, sometimes the waters of the inundation floods are used: the water that floods the land is given time to sink in, at which time the fields are planted. This system is known as *saaidam* (sowing dam). The middle veld extends northeastward into the upper valley of the north-flowing Hartz River. Here lime is so heavily concentrated on the surface that no cultivation is possible.[8]

The boundary between the middle and high velds shows no clear line of demarcation. They blend into

[7] *Ibid.*

[8] Wellington, *op. cit.*, pp. 74–75.

each other, and a rather arbitrary figure of elevation is taken to distinguish them: the plateau surfaces that are 4,000 feet or higher are regarded as highveld. In terms of climate and vegetation, however, the highveld is quite distinct from the middle veld. In the east, the edge of the highveld stands out because it coincides with the escarpment; on the west, its bounds may be taken as the 4,000-foot contour; in the north it is somewhat more intricate but, westward, the 4,000-foot contour can again be taken, while eastward along the north, it blends into the bushveld.

From the western 4,000-foot contour, the highveld rises to 6,000 feet in the Witwatersrand and to over 11,000 feet in Lesotho. Although the Basuto highlands are distinct in themselves, they are also an integral part of the highveld because of their hydrographic association with the veld; the Orange and Vaal rivers both rise here; and, in the southwest, the highlands and highveld actually merge. Most of the surface of the highveld is rather extraordinarily level because of the horizontal formations of which it is composed; so tabular is the appearance that it appears in many places to have been peneplained. However, much of the flat character is due to structure, as the river valleys demonstrate: all of the strong rivers are cutting deep valleys. The vegetation is grass except in the southwest, where bushes predominate. North of the Vaal River the generally level surfaces disappear in the Witwatersrand area. However, west and east of these ridge formations the surface is again level, in fact, remarkably flat to the west in the Transvaal.

The Kaap plateau, which extrudes like a peninsular limb of upland west of the Vaal River, is also a part of the highveld. A roughly rectangular region, it extends approximately from Vyburg to south of Griquatown just west of the confluence of the Vaal and Orange rivers. The eastern edge is a limestone scarp, the Campbell rand, that overlooks the dry valley of the Hartz River. Within a limestone cave in this escarpment area an important anthropological find, the Taungs skull (*Australopithecus africanus*), was discovered. Since the rainfall averages not more than 10 to 15 inches, the surface has not developed to the maturity of karst topography. However, small dolines (see Glossary) spot the region, and there are large springs that emerge from the limestone, as from the

"eyes" at Kuruman and Griquatown. On the Kaap plateau, population distribution is determined by the availability of water, obtained from springs or boreholes.

North of the highveld lies the lopolith (see Glossary) of the bushveld of Transvaal. Predominantly flat near the center, it rises on all sides along the periphery; the basin floor lies 2,000 to 3,500 feet above sea level and rises to 6,000 feet along the edges. In the area of the Springbok flats horizontal deposits of shale, sandstone, and lava have decomposed into very rich soil. However, rainfall is so low that cultivation is not possible without irrigation.

North of the basin the land rises again to the Waterburg plateau, which ranges from 3,500 to 6,900 feet in altitude and is highest in the southwest. In the main the plateau surface is undulating, but it varies; soils are thin, and vegetation is grass or bush; few regions are suited to agriculture. Most of the population is concentrated in the valleys where the land along the rivers can be irrigated.

The basin of the middle Limpopo lies in a broad depression along the northern margin of the bushveld, and extends to the Mozambique plain. The extreme northeastern portion is occupied by the middle Sabi River and its tributary, the Lundi. A few miles west of Messina, at the Tolo Azime Falls, the Limpopo begins its descent from the plateau, and river erosion has greatly dissected the land. Plateau elevations are about 2,000 feet. It is here in the valley of the Limpopo that the plains fringing the plateau become widest. The Limpopo, which is sometimes called the Crocodile River (after the headstream originating in the veld near Johannesburg), draws its waters from both the South African veld and the plateaus of southern Rhodesia, but it is one of Africa's less important rivers. However, since it drains through well-watered country, there are lands of considerable economic importance within its basin. Bushveld covers most of the sandy soils of the river valley on both the Transvaal and southern Rhodesia sides. The entire bushveld lying north of the highveld, including the Limpopo basin and extending on into Rhodesia, is, as the name suggests, covered with scattered bushes. Altitude decreases toward the north and tropicality increases with the result that frosts, so typical on the highveld, are almost absent along the Limpopo.

The plateau of Rhodesia and Zambia is relatively simple, most parts of the upland being comprised of a great flat-to-rolling surface that has an elevation of about 4,000 feet above sea level on the southern side, and slopes to the Zambezi valley on the north. The highveld is the most healthful region. It extends from approximately the 3,000-foot contour (which marks the beginning of the lowveld, a distinction that is less important physiographically than in terms of human usability); malaria and other diseases are much more prevalent at the lower elevations. The eastern portion of the plateau in the south is higher and more dissected than the rest and in this part the upland has a mountainous character. Grass savanna with scattered trees, that become denser with distance northward, is the typical vegetation; in the Zambezi lowlands, tropical forests producing mahogany and teak occur. Although wet and dry in climate, the plateau in general is well watered (20 to 35 inches of rainfall) and most of the region can be cultivated. Rivers have not yet cut up the highveld to any degree.

The surface of the Lunda swell on the opposite side of the Zambezi valley in Zambia resembles the plateau of Rhodesia, although the headward erosion of rivers has caused dissection to be more advanced on the surface of the upland. This is perhaps due to the greater rainfall. The Lunda upland continues eastward in the long and narrow Muchinga highlands which connect with the highlands around Lake Nyasa.

*The Zambezi River.* In general, the surface of the Rhodesian-Zambia plateau is regular and below 4,000 feet elevation. Through the middle of it run the great trenches of the Zambezi River and those of its affluents. Two great gorges extend northward from the main valley in the Luangwa and Nyasa-Shiré troughs; the trough of the Zambezi, a structural fault known as the Gwembe Trough, begins to the southwest of Wankie and extends to just west of the confluence of the Luangwa with the Zambezi. Within this, the river channel lies. Formed during the period of folding and faulting in East Africa, it is a spectacular trench, the northern wall rising in one place 2,400 feet above the river; all along this escarpment, transverse gorges, eroded by tributaries of the main stream, notch the rock wall. The fault of which the Gwembe Trough is a part may continue southwestward toward the depression in which the Okovango delta and Lake Makarikari lie.

The Zambezi drains a vast basin of 400,000 square miles. The river reaches across parts of Botswana, Zambia, Angola, and Mozambique, and forms all of the boundary between Zambia and Rhodesia. In its upper basin it drains a great shallow depression, in the drier parts of which many of the headwaters are not perennial; the main stream, however, always carries water and is navigable. A few miles to the west of where the trough begins, the Victoria Falls drop from the broad body of the river down the walls of a deep cleft, rushing away as a narrow but deep and erosive torrent. This is known as the Zambezi or Batoka gorge.

The Zambezi is one of Africa's great rivers, and the construction of the Kariba Dam (Figure 16.7), begun in 1956 and completed to its full potential for hydroelectric development in 1963, is permitting the utilization of some of its great resources. The site of the dam is about two-thirds of the way down the Gwembe Trough, a short distance below where the Sanyati River joins the Zambezi. Kariba Lake, therefore, backs up into the trough, its capacity 4 times greater than that of Lake Mead on the Colorado River, until now the world's largest reservoir. High tension wires normally carry power 275 miles north to Kitwe, the main power transformer station in the Zambian copper belt; southwards, 660 miles of power lines carry electricity to transformer stations at Norton and Umniati in Rhodesia, and thence to Bulawayo and Salisbury.

About 50,000 people inhabited the area that now forms the reservoir. Water now covers the lands that were formerly cultivated, so these tribes had to be resettled. Since this was previously a famine area, precautions are being taken to carry out careful planning along with the resettlement so that famines will not recur.

Construction on a second dam is scheduled to begin in 1968 on the Kafue River, a tributary of the Zambezi. Although the Kafue is a smaller stream, the flow is swifter and the dam is expected to generate more power than Kariba.[9]

[9] According to F. W. Bruce of the Federal Power Board, Salisbury, in an interview with the writer.

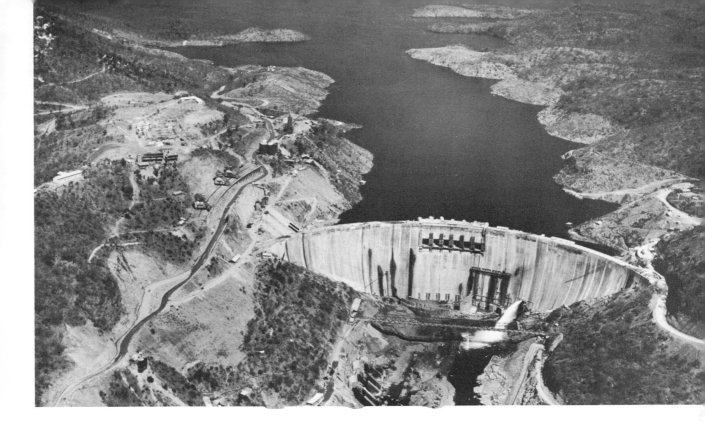

(a)

(b)

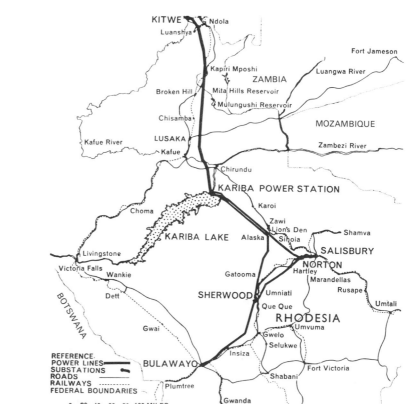

FIGURE 16.7 Kariba Dam (a, above) with
lake forming in the background; (b, right)
power transmission from the Kariba installations. (a courtesy Federal Information Department, Salisbury, Rhodesia; b courtesy
Federal Power Board, Salisbury, Rhodesia.)

## MARGINS AND COASTS OF THE CONTINENT

*The Eastern Coasts.* The Zambezi River flows out to the Indian Ocean across the Mozambique plain, the most homogeneous surface in southern Africa, except the Kalahari. The present plain is due to marine deposition. It rises gradually from sea level inland to the slopes of the Lebombo in the south and the Niassa uplands in the north; much of the once sea level plain now stands at about 1,000 feet elevation, the result of simple uplift. The coastal zone is relatively uneven because of dune formations that in places are over 600 feet high. Dunes have blocked some of the smaller rivers, causing great lagoons to form back of them, such as Lake Poelela, on which Inharrime is situated. The shore dunes are backed by wide expanses of sand ridges, whose crests rise up to 200 feet, ranged about ½ mile apart and trending north-northwest. A dense bush and grass vegetation covers the dunes.

The river floodplains, large sectors of which are covered with alluvial and swamp soils, are the most fertile parts of the Mozambique lowland; of these, the most intensively cultivated are those of the Incomati and Limpopo rivers in the south, the Buzi in central Mozambique, and the Zambezi farther north. The plain is malarial, however, and, in places, the tsetse fly also prevails, causing some regions to remain almost uninhabited. Rainfall is highest along the coast, decreasing inland; the valley of the Zambezi is the driest part of Mozambique. Here, agriculture is not possible without irrigation.

The coastal belt, wide in Mozambique, narrows to the south in Natal where the plain is backed by the relatively abrupt slopes of the Drakensberg. In northern Natal, the coastal areas of Zululand are like those of Mozambique, the floor being one of marine deposition recently exposed, and dipping toward the sea; generally flat, in places great dunes have been thrown up. Because the rise to the escarpment is

**FIGURE 16.8** The fertile Hex River valley where grapes are produced for both domestic and export markets. *(Courtesy Public Relations Section, South African Railways.)*

sharp from the plains of Natal, any distance inland from the shore brings one into very rugged hill country—mountainous, in fact, owing to the dissection of the plateau edge by rivers; the slopes are covered but thinly with soil and are rocky.

*The Southern Cape Belt.* The southern Cape region breaks into three physiographic divisions: (1) the Cape folds, fronted by (2) the coastal foreland, and backed by (3) the basin of the Great Karroo. The folded formations of sandstone, and sand and marine deposits dominate the region. They divide into two sectors, the eastern belt of folded ranges trending east-west, and the western region where the folded formations describe a great arc, concave to the west and with a general north-south trend. The meeting of the axes of the two lines of folding lies along the Hex River between Worcester and Hexburg; the river flows within a northeast-trending syncline, the Hex River Mountains forming the anticline on the northwest, and the Kwadouw on the southeast. (See Figure 16.8.)

In the eastern section of the Cape folds, valleys cover a much larger part of the region than in the western zone. The valleys comprise two groups: the Karroos (Little and Great), and the eastern lowlands. The Little Karroo are the lowlands found between the Langeberge on the south and the Swartberge on the north. They are fertile but dry valleys, dry because they lie in the rain shadow of the range mountains. The Great Karroo lies at the base of the Great Escarpment, between it and the folded mountains. Physiographically it is a great basin, or series of basins formed by stream erosion, and was likely a part of the plateau itself originally. Structurally the Great Karroo is simple, in the north tipping slightly toward the interior, in the south abutting against the Cape folds. In general, soils are immature because aridity has not permitted their development; however, in river valleys some alluvial soils are to be found and where not brackish, they can be cultivated.

The pressing need of the Great Karroo is water; it is an arid region, and one of the most sparsely inhabited regions in the Republic. Winter grazing is about the only economic pursuit carried on here; on the whole, it is a pastoral rather than an arable region.

One large dam, the Kendrew, has been erected in the Great Karroo for purposes of irrigation; this is on the Sundays River to the north of Graaff Reinet. It irrigates a small area of quite good alluviums. Such small schemes are workable; but in the main, uncertainty of precipitation, a small rainfall, and restricted stream flow make farming very hazardous.

The coastal forelands along the Cape folds are varied; outcrops and even ranges occur to break up the continuity of the plain. In front of the Langeberge ranges, the coast rises from the sea in precipitous cliffs and extends inland as a coastal shelf that grows higher toward the mountains, to reach elevations of 800 to 900 feet at the mountain base. Through this coastal plateau rivers have eroded great gorges, and the region is one of scenic beauty; however, except for forests, the area, although well watered, is economically unimportant because of the great depth and constricted nature of the valleys. The Gamtoos and Sundays rivers, however, have wide floodplains in their lower courses, and land is intensively cultivated; farther east, the plains south of Grahamstown and in the Great Fish River valley are likewise wide and fertile.

*The Western Coasts.* The lowlands along the west side of Africa are generally narrower than in the east. They consist, in the main, of a desert coast from the Olifants River northward to beyond Moçâmedes, and from there extend as a narrowing zone of moving sand dunes, sand, or bare rock surfaces to about 12°S. Vegetation in this northern sector is a sparse grass, and the region semiarid. The Namib Desert covers the remainder. Since no desert is completely without rain, rain does at times fall in the Namib, but it is a region marked by its barren character, and portions of it are covered with sand that has accumulated to greater or lesser depths; the rest is bare rock or gravelly. Aridity is greatest in the central portion between Walvis Bay and Luderitz Bay, where the desert extends farther inland than elsewhere, about 100 miles. Rainfall increases with elevation, and the 2,000-foot contour perhaps marks the approximate zone of separation between desert and semidesert conditions. Desert conditions along the shore are accentuated by the cold Benguela Current that flows up along the coast from the polar seas.

**FIGURE 16.9** Flat lying strata of the Table Mountain formations. *(Photograph by writer.)*

## Approaches to the Realm

Although the coasts of southern Africa have some magnificent natural harbors, Delagoa Bay, Baia de Fernão Veloso, Durban and Table bays and others, these were not always so accessible or protective as they are now. Human skill, working with the physical advantages, created the ample, sheltered anchorages that we know. Most of the harbors were merely potential, many closed from the sea behind barrier bars or shallow entrances that blocked passage, as up and down the east and west coasts; others, large with broad openings, required the construction of breakwaters to make them safe, as at Cape Town and Port Elizabeth (Figure 16.10); "false" bays, that gave promise but not fulfillment of haven, were twice so-named along this shore. Just east of Cape Peninsula, and between it and Cape Hangklip, is the best known

of the two "false" bays—a great inlet, wide open to the seas; the second is the inner "bay" of Lake St. Lucia on the Zululand coast, completely closed and without access. At most of the ports, goods and people had to be lightered in to the shore.

Table Bay was chosen as the site of Cape Colony for three reasons. It lay about midway along the route from the Orient to West Europe and was well situated for fueling and victualing, the purpose for which the colony was settled; the Portuguese were active along the East African coast; Table Bay was the best natural harbor thus strategically situated, offering some protection from the buffeting seas despite the 6-mile-wide entry, and it was accessible. Interestingly, except for the Portuguese and German lands, most of southern Africa, even Natal, was filled in by Europeans from this initial entry point at the Cape.

The approaches to southern Africa, as along much of the coast of the continent, were not easy nor the harbors ready-made. The west coast is remarkably smooth, owing in part to the fact that structure tends to run with the coast rather than transverse to it, in part to the constancy and strength of coastal currents, and in part to climate; much of the west coastal zone is characterized by arid to semiarid conditions. These same factors, however, also favored the development of sheltered bays: Sandspits, built by the inshore Benguela Current flowing north from southern waters, act like breakwaters to form protected inlets. Thus, the bay at Lobito, over 100 feet in depth, is sheltered by a 3-mile northeast trending spit of sand, as is Walvis Bay where the spit (called Pelican Point) is 5 miles long. Sandbars block most of the river mouths most of the time, even that of the Cunene, which flows into the sea as a very small stream because of the low rainfall, high evaporation, and seepage in its lower course; only at flood periods does it carry enough water to its mouth to wash out the bar. Lagoons occur, enclosed behind the bars; some of the lakes are drying out and filling with deposited materials.

In more detail, from Lobito south to near Luderitz the coast tends to be sandy and much smoothed by the action of the current; the southern half of this sector comprises the shore of the Namib Desert, a

FIGURE 16.10 The harbor at Port Elizabeth on the south coast is entirely artificial. (Courtesy South African Railways.)

belt of moving dunes, unvegetated and barren. Around Luderitz and for about 100 miles south, the coast becomes rugged and often clifflike as the rock structure changes; inlets still face north, and harbors are associated with the inlets, as at Luderitz Bay. The next 300 miles of coast change again; as in the north the shoreline is smooth, but raised beaches, 20 to 30 miles in width and covered to great depths by sand, are characteristic. This "sandveld" of Cape Province is covered with a scrub vegetation, so the sands are anchored, contrary to what is true in the Namib Desert. It is in these raised beaches that the diamondiferous gravels, so highly productive along the coast of South-West Africa, occur.

The east side of southern Africa, from Algoa Bay north to beyond Durban, also has an unusually smooth coast. Physiographically most of the shore changes from a sand beach that inland swells into sand dunes that are backed in turn by the plateau edge, the latter rising gently or steeply depending upon the character of the rock. Sandbars and spits obstruct the river mouths completely during the dry season; during seasons of greater flow, the larger rivers break channels through the barriers to the sea. It was for this reason that the Durban harbor lay unused for over 3 centuries. The Dessimian Collection of Manuscripts in the Cape Town Public Library record that the East India Company would most likely "have taken possession of this fertile land years past but for seeing at the mouth of the Port a reef or sandbank that no galliot without touching could get over without danger."

From northern Natal to beyond the mouth of the Zambezi the coast is raised, and the shore zone is therefore quite level except where the sand has piled up into dunes because of the action of wind; in places, these dunes mount to 400 feet, and are generally covered with a dense scrub vegetation. Deep estuaries occur at the mouths of some of the rivers, and at such places an inshore, north-flowing current has tended to cause the formation of sandspits across the river mouths, as at Delagoa Bay, Inhambane, and off Cape Sebastian, where the visible portions of the spit occur as islands. A sandbar has formed across the mouth of the Pungwe River, site of the port of Beira; here a riptide and a strong, scouring tidal flow of water in the spring keep a channel open through the barrier. Sand accumulations at the mouths of each of the distributaries of the Zambezi make navigation of the river difficult, and at times a shallow bar even forms near the head of the delta where the Chinde distributary turns off.

To the north of the Zambezi, coral reefs become characteristic, fringing both the coast and islands, and adding another hazard to coastal navigation. Despite this, one of the two best East African harbors occurs along this part of the shore, namely, Baia de Fernão Veloso; the other is Delagoa Bay, on which the port of Lourenço Marques is situated, the finest natural shelter along the east side of the continent.

# 17 INTERIOR STATES OF THE SOUTH: RHODESIA, ZAMBIA, AND MALAWI

*The immense and brooding spirit*
  *shall quicken and control.*
*Living he was the land and dead*
  *his soul shall be her soul.*

RUDYARD KIPLING

## The Opening of the Southern
## Interior by Europeans

Early events in southern Africa knit the histories of the Portuguese lands and the interior countries of the south, and economic ties bind them to each other today, for the Portuguese lands of Angola and Mozambique are the doorways to the world for those of the interior.

As noted before, it was a Portuguese explorer Diôgo Cão, who discovered the Congo River (see Chapter 13). He sailed south from the river mouth, along the full length of the Angolan coast, formally annexing the territory for Portugal's rulers in 1483 by erecting a stone cross near the site of what became Porto Alexandre. Other Portuguese came in his wake, such as Bartholomew Diaz, who rounded the Cape, and Vasco da Gama, who made the initial voyage by Europeans across the Indian Ocean to the Indies. During the course of the trip he landed briefly on the shores of Mozambique (1498).

The Portuguese were quick to recognize the advantages of holding points along the East African coast, convenient as victualing and, later, fueling stops for ships passing to and from the East. And so despite the fierce resistance of the already established Arabs, they set up a string of fortified colonies all along the coast from Kenya southward. Thus in 1505 Sofala, a very old Arab settlement, was occupied by the intrepid Portuguese.

The lands inland from the West coast of Africa had lain, and were destined to lie for some centuries shrouded in mystery. Not so with the hinterland behind the eastern littoral. From very early times there had been contacts between the East coast and southern Asia, and Arab traders and slavers had penetrated into the African interior from the eastern coasts. They had gone far into the upper tributaries of the Zambezi, to Lake Tanganyika, into Uganda and the upper Nile country, and had even reached regions tributary to the Congo.

Hence, the way in from the east was already opened up, in a sense, for the Portuguese: they followed the Arabs into the interior. The first Christian missionary to reach what is now Rhodesia was a Portuguese priest (Gonzales Silveira, martyred in

March, 1561). Eight years later a Portuguese expedition attempted explorations into Rhodesia, only to be driven back by tropical diseases. In 1798 Dr. de Lacerda, Portuguese governor of Sena (city in Mozambique), made a journey into Zambia. He died near Lake Mweru, but the record of his trip was saved because his diaries were carried out by a missionary. Despite these penetrations, the central south long remained almost unknown to most Europeans; too many hardships stood in the way of the early exploration and settlement of these lands, especially those territories that became known as Southern and Northern Rhodesia, and Nyasaland, now Rhodesia, Zambia, and Malawi.

In the 1830s, the Boers from Cape Colony made their migrations into the veld, territory not in but adjacent to the Rhodesias and Mozambique. And beginning in 1851, David Livingstone began his "missionary travels," expeditions of exploration that did much to clarify the map of south-central Africa. The first English traders arrived in Barotseland (Zambia) in 1872, and three years later a mission was established in southern Nyasaland. From that time on, invasion of the interior lands of the south by Europeans took place rapidly—traders, missionaries, planters, and empire builders—and by one means or another, land and mineral rights were soon acquired.

Cecil John Rhodes entered the area in 1888. Immediately he became a dominating influence. In 1889 he went to London to accomplish two things: first, to deal with opposition by rival syndicates to his growing power in southern Africa; second, "to persuade the British Government and public to entrust the administration and exploitation of the interior of Africa to a chartered company formed by himself."[1] On October 29 of that year, a royal charter was granted to the British South Africa Company giving it the right to administer and develop the territories of Southern and Northern Rhodesia.

By 1900, there were about 10,000 Europeans in the area; by 1910, the present system of Rhodesian Railways had been completed. The British South

[1] Basil Williams, *Cecil Rhodes*, New York: Holt, Rinehart and Winston, Inc., 1921, p. 130.

**FIGURE 17.2** Transport within the interior states and to the outside. (Courtesy W. P. Watson.)

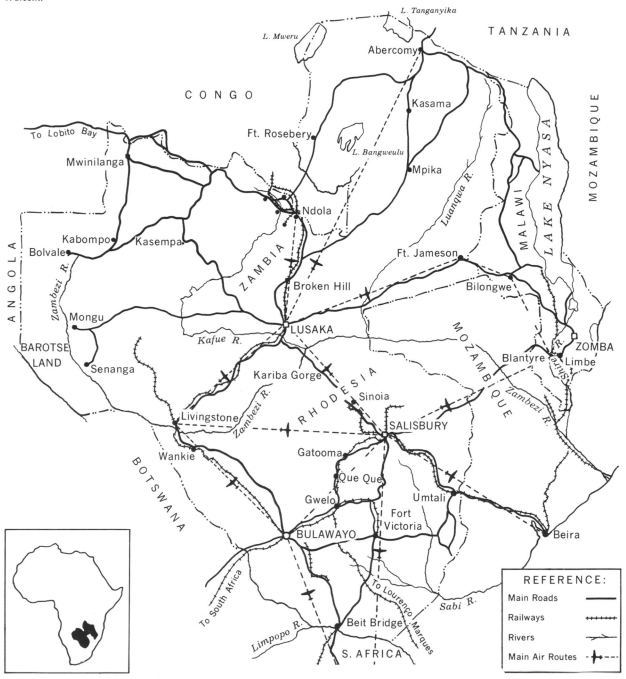

Africa Company still held great economic advantages in Rhodesia as late as 1960, but it ceased to administer the territories in 1923, when the government of the United Kingdom took over from the Company the administration of Northern Rhodesia, and made Southern Rhodesia a self-governing colony under the Devonshire Agreement.

Nyasaland came under British influence with the discovery of Lake Nyasa by David Livingstone in 1859, and later with the establishment of missions and trading posts. In 1889, a British protectorate was declared over the country. After the abolition of slavery in 1896, the protectorate developed quite peacefully.

## The Federation of Rhodesia and Nyasaland

As noted, the Federation broke up on January 1, 1964. It had come into being in 1953, superseding the Central African Council, which had been a nebulous body constituted for joint cooperation but without any real power. Before federation, Nyasaland and Northern Rhodesia were British protectorates, and Southern Rhodesia was a self-governing British colony.

The Federation covered a large territory (Figure 17.2), extending across nearly 1,000 miles north and south, and embracing an area of over 486,900 square miles, making it larger than the Republic of South Africa, and larger that the combined area of Texas, California, and New York. The region was, however, sparsely populated for only about 9.5 million people lived there. Of these, over 9,140,000 were Africans, some 309,400 were of European descent, and the remaining were Coloured (see Glossary) and Asian; 96.3 percent of the population was African (a proportion fairly typical in black Africa). The Africans spread in not too disparate numbers but very unequal densities over the three countries; most of the European population was (and is) concentrated in Rhodesia, over 223,000 in the southern territory, as against about 77,000 in Zambia and 9,400 in Malawi.[2]

[2] 1962 statistics as issued by the Central Statistical Office, Federation of Rhodesia and Nyasaland.

The Federation was formed largely for economic reasons, the purposes being: to combine the resources of the three areas, which vary greatly in size, economic potential, and development; to coordinate the copper industry of Northern Rhodesia with the mining and secondary industries and the agriculture of Southern Rhodesia (Figure 17.3); to make readily available to the Rhodesias the excess of African labor in Nyasaland (that country's greatest contribution to this coordinated effort); and to coordinate the communication and transport systems, a major advantage to all three territories. Southern Rhodesia was handicapped by a shortage of labor, which Nyasaland was able in large measure to supply. Nyasaland benefited greatly from federation; what prosperity it has can be traced to these economic associations with the Rhodesias. Yet Nyasaland was the country most opposed to federation, and was always an unwilling constituent largely because paternal European elements, particularly in the Rhodesias, opposed eventual independence for Nyasaland.

The Federation was never strong, and early began to show signs of breaking up. Europeans in Northern Rhodesia felt that their territory was bearing the weight of financial support at the same time that Southern Rhodesia, with nearly three times as many Europeans as the larger northern state, held the control of government; thus, the white populations were at odds. In Nyasaland, Europeans were few in number, and mostly British in the employ of the colonial government. Realizing the benefits of federation for themselves, they were against secession at the same time that they desired more territorial responsibility and a relaxation of Colonial Office control. (Although Nyasaland was a protectorate with a British Governor, in practice the government had been directed by the leader of the powerful African Malawi Congress party, Dr. Hastings K. Banda.)

Racial tension between Africans and Europeans was pronounced in the Federation, and most bitter in Southern Rhodesia, where white settlement on the land was more important than in the other two territories. The Africans in Nyasaland wanted an independent black state; Africans in the Rhodesias demanded equal representation in government—one person, one vote, equal opportunity economically, and

FIGURE 17.3 Minerals of the central interior south. (Courtesy Federal Information Department, Salisbury, Rhodesia.)

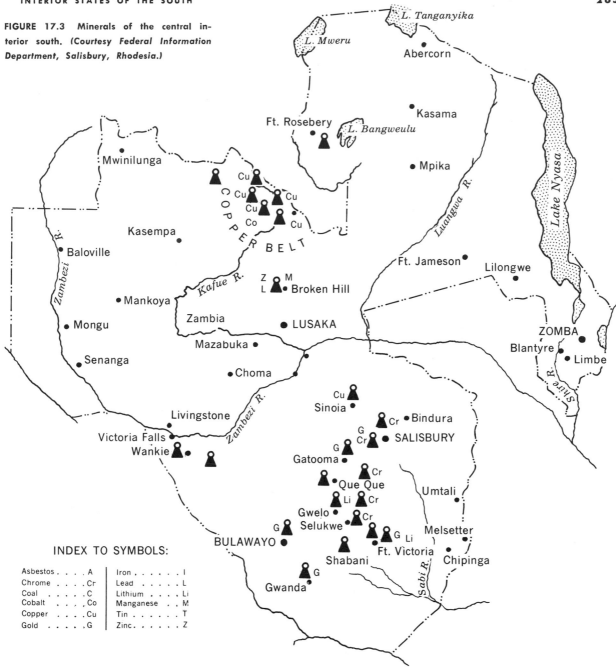

INDEX TO SYMBOLS:

| | | | |
|---|---|---|---|
| Asbestos . . . . A | | Iron . . . . . . I | |
| Chrome . . . . Cr | | Lead . . . . . L | |
| Coal . . . . . C | | Lithium . . . . Li | |
| Cobalt . . . Co | | Manganese . . M | |
| Copper . . . Cu | | Tin . . . . . . T | |
| Gold . . . . G | | Zinc . . . . . Z | |

equal social status with Europeans; the Europeans, representing a small minority in the population, desired to retain political control, as they feared a minority status among the majority blacks under conditions of political equality.

Of the three countries that formed the union, only Southern Rhodesia really desired the tie to continue. The breaking up of the Federation took place without upheaval, something few would have dared forecast a year previous to the event. The transference of sovereignty to Nyasaland and Northern Rhodesia began with the collapse of the Federation, but Southern Rhodesia was denied independence; Nyasaland, as Malawi, became a sovereign black state in July, 1964, and Northern Rhodesia, as Zambia, in October of the same year; Southern Rhodesia, as simply Rhodesia, remained a self-governing colony. Independence is being denied this territory by the British Government until some form of representation, satisfactory to the majority Africans, has been worked out. However, in November, 1965, Rhodesia declared itself an independent nation.

## The Land

The central interior straddles the high plateaus of southern Africa, embracing as well a part of the great rift valley and the rift mountains. Most of the area is high plateau across which rivers have eroded deep trenches—the Zambezi and its affluents, the Sabi (tributary to the Sava River) and the Limpopo. Whereas the plateaus are healthful, "subtemperate" in climate, the engorged valleys of these rivers are tropical and enervating.

The highveld extends centrally through the compact, semicircular domain of Rhodesia, roughly in the form of an inverted T, the long axis running southwest-northeast between Matabeleland and Mashonaland; the cross at the north runs northwest-southeast from west of Salisbury to the Mozambique border at Inyanga. Elevations are highest around Inyanga, where heights of over 8,000 feet are reached. All of the highveld lies above 3,500 feet elevation but, from there, elevations fall away along the south and southeast to the Limpopo and the Sabi rivers; in the west-southwest, into lowveld which, in turn, blends into the Kalahari basin; and, along the north, northwest, and northeast toward the Zambezi, across which lies Malawi.

Zambia is shaped like a bow. From the knot, the Muchinga Mountains extend northeastward centrally across the eastern lobe. The watershed of this central highland axis separates the Luangwa trench on the east from the depression occupied largely by the Bangweulu swamps and Chambezi valley in the northwest; at the southwest end of this saddle, the

low "knot" is essentially the water divide between Luangwa and Kafue (Zambezi) drainage.

The western lobe of Zambia is a great, monotonous upland plain, averaging about 3,500 feet in elevation, but so level that great shallow pools of water extensively cover the area during the rainy season, waterlogging the land. This is especially true in Barotseland, the lowest sector of the western lobe, which is crossed by the upper Zambezi and some of its headwaters. Drainage becomes somewhat better in the southeast sector of the lobe, where the land rises to the Batoka plateau, and in the north where it rises to the higher lands of the Congo-Zambezi water parting.

Long, angular Malawi is a rugged, mountainous country for the most part, bordered along the east by the rift lake, Nyasa, and encompassing the southern end of the lake and a portion of the rift trench, south of the lake, through which the Shiré river flows. Lake Nyasa, about 360 miles long, is part of the boundary between Malawi to the west and Mozambique and Tanganyika to the east. It is the southernmost of the rift lakes; south of the lake, the rift continues as a broad trench with a flat floor, disappearing off the continent at the coast of Mozambique, but extending offshore under the ocean. The Shiré River did not erode this trench; the stream flows on the floor of the rift valley, joining the Zambezi shortly before it flows into the Indian Ocean. One-fifth of the area of Malawi is covered by the waters of Lake Nyasa.

Along portions of the west shore of the lake narrow plains occur. They are backed by the abrupt escarpments of the rift edges, which average over 5,000 feet above sea level and in the north near Livingstonia, rise to above 8,000 feet. South of the lake, in southeastern Malawi, rift mountains are represented in the Shiré highlands and Mount Mlanje; eastnortheast of the Shiré highlands is Lake Chilwa, occupying part of a swampy depression.

Whereas certain stretches of the rivers of the central interior are navigable and extensively used, there are no streams that provide an unimpeded outlet to the ocean. Falls occur along the Zambezi (not only Victoria Falls, but also Kebrabasa Falls in Mozambique) and the Shiré (Murchison Falls about midway along the river in Malawi), while the seasonal character of the flow of the Limpopo makes it unsuitable for navigation.

Location makes the central interior states tropical, for they extend from 8 to 22°S. Broadly, the climate is tropical wet and dry matching that of the Sudan north of the Equator, although local variations and moderation of the tropicality occur because of the range of latitude and the altitude of the plateau. In the lower lands and particularly within the trenched valleys, temperatures and humidity are consistently high, rendering those sectors more difficult to live in and creating an environment where disease germs and insects flourish. Cattle rearing is confined to the uplands because of the prevalence of the tsetse fly in the valley bottoms, as along the Limpopo, the Zambezi-Shiré, the Loangwa, and the Sabi rivers. Most of central interior south is plateau, however, with altitudes averaging between 3,000 and 5,000 feet. For this reason, Europeans have found the interior states of the south attractive and healthful places to live.

Throughout the territory the wet and dry regime is characterized by a single period of maximum precipitation that begins lightly in October and rises to maximum amounts in December and January, taper-ing off to May when the dry season might be said to begin. Rarely are there any months that register no rainfall, particularly on the plateaus; in the western-most portions of Rhodesia and in southeast Zambia, the dry season is more pronounced than elsewhere.

Diurnal temperature ranges are greatest during the dry season; in the lowlands, which are humid most of the time, daytime shade temperatures approach 120° and drop as low as 85°F at night, whereas during the period of rains, midday temperatures average around 100°F and drop to between 85 and 90°F. On the plateaus the same patterns are to be observed except that temperature levels are several degrees lower because of altitude. On the plateaus of Rhodesia and higher uplands of Malawi, frost occurs rather frequently during the dry season.

Precipitation varies between about 20 and 50 inches, being generally higher in the north and east and decreasing toward the south and west; it is con-centrated during the higher sun period, the dry season showing either no rain or only traces of it for periods lasting from 5 to 7 months. The wet and dry regime, and the decreasing amount of precipitation from north to south is due to latitude; the decrease from east to west is explained in the facts that rain-bearing

**FIGURE 17.4** Mammoth boabab tree in the Victoria Falls vicinity. (Courtesy H. F. Donner.)

winds blow in from the east, and that the highest lands are in the east. Exposure causes local variations within the generalized pattern. Over 30 percent of the area receives less than 30 inches of precipitation, slight for the tropics, which makes these lands precarious for farming. Another limiting factor is the torrential character of the rainfall, most of it coming in heavy thundershowers so that runoff is excessive. This limits not only the amount of moisture that sinks into the earth, but also causes serious erosion and washing away of the topsoil.

Vegetation is largely savanna grasslands or grasslands with trees (Figure 17.4). To ride by train across the central south, from Ndola to Livingstone via Lusaka and thence southward to Johannesburg, is very monotonous; mile after mile of flat terrain passes by with almost no change in vegetation except for more or fewer trees. Forests occur in the uplands of Malawi and in the eastern part of Rhodesia, and some of the rivers are bordered by dense growths of tropical forest. The forests, although somewhat depleted as compared with their extent a century ago, are extensive. More than half of Zambia still has woods containing trees fine for construction, and these timbered areas continue to provide material for sawmilling, one of Zambia's oldest industries. In parts of Rhodesia and Malawi there are sectors, ill suited to anything else, that could profitably be planted to eucalyptus and Mexican pine; the interior states import wood pulp and timber, when they could supply the demand for these products from their own lands without difficulty.

The savannas are rich in game, sharing with the rest of the African savannas this wildlife resource that is incomparably more varied and numerous than anywhere else on the earth (Figure 17.5). Tourism is a developing industry in all three states. There are many other features to attract travelers as well, among them the magnificent Victoria Falls and the Zambezi River, the Zimbabwe ruins, game reserves, and many sports such as boating, swimming, fishing (especially in lakes Kariba and Nyasa), and hunting.

**FIGURE 17.5** Buffalo in the Wankie Game Reserve. Note the savanna. (Courtesy Federal Information Department, Salisbury, Rhodesia.)

# Wealth of the Land

## SUBSURFACE RESOURCES

But the lands of the central interior south are best known for their minerals, which are also varied and rich. Centuries before Europeans occupied these territories, the interior south had been extensively explored and mined for gold, iron, and copper by primitives whose identity has not been established. More than 700 of their mines, known as ancient workings, have been found. The early miners had no means of dewatering their mines, however, so when the groundwater level was reached, the mines had to be abandoned. The ancients took their ores from the richest pockets within the mines, and it is assumed that they exported the gold ore because no treasury of gold has been discovered. A number of dry-masonry ruins in Rhodesia, of which the largest are the Zimbabwe ruins (obscure as to age and origin), have given rise to the legend that these were King Solomon's mines. However that may be, Rhodesia, during its European era, has produced gold to a value of more than 218 million pounds.

The Africans, however, were not working the mines just previous to the coming of the Europeans. They were "rediscovered" in 1865 by an elephant hunter, Henry Hartley, and a German geologist, Kark Mauch. Publication of the travels and discoveries of these men in their book, *Road to Ophir*, led to British negotiations with the African king, Lobengula, and to the securing of the Rudd concession in 1888, which gave the holders a monopoly on minerals in Lobengula's kingdom. Following this came the occupation of Rhodesia and in 1890 the founding of the Colony of Southern Rhodesia.

*Rhodesia.* North and south, through the middle of Rhodesia for 350 miles, extends the "geologically mysterious" Great Dyke, outwardly simply a range of hills, apparent and distinct from the air; but within, a storehouse of mineral ores, especially chrome, vast in quantity and of the highest quality, occurring in thin layers or bands. This is one of the world's largest deposits of chromite; additionally, it lends itself to large-scale mining that is low in cost; just west of the Great Dyke, at Selukwe, are other chrome deposits. Figure 17.6 shows the division of minerals.

The Great Dyke also holds platinum and nickel, but since no economic means of recovering these ores has been developed, they remain resources for the future. Asbestos also occurs within this geologic phenomenon, and Rhodesia is the third largest producer of this commodity in the world; in fact, in 1955 asbestos surpassed gold in value of output, and it has held first place ever since, lengthening its lead margin year after year. Most of the increase has come from major mines at Shabani and Mashaha, where fibers of good length (spinning grade) are mined.

Along both sides of the Great Dyke lie goldfields, richer on the west side (but less regular in form) than in the east, and extending eastward as far as Umtali. Gold is the mineral second in value in Rhodesia. Most of the ore bodies are small, however, and mining costs are becoming so high that operators have been forced to close down. Despite this, the gold output has not declined. Most of the mines are on the highveld, and are quite widely distributed, the major producing districts being at Gwelo, Hartley, Bulawayo, Salisbury, Umtali, Fort Victoria, and Gwanda. The gold produced comes largely from lode mines, and the proportion of lode ore is expected to increase because, although it is necessary to go deeper to dig gold from lodes, it is cheaper than mining vein or reef ore since the ore bodies in lodes are larger.

Coal is fourth in value of output among the subsurface resources of Rhodesia. Rhodesia is, in fact, the largest producer of coal in tropical Africa, and its Wankie field one of the largest on the continent. The Wankie mines supply most of the Rhodesian coal output; they are strategically situated on the railway connecting Bulawayo with Livingstone and the copper belts of Zambia and Katanga. Their proven reserves of coking coal exceed 800 million metric tons, and even larger amounts of noncoking coal, suitable as fuel for steam engines and the generation of electricity, occur in association with the coking coal. Rhodesia has other coalfields, the two largest being in the Sabi River valley. However, they lie farther away from centers of demand than those at Wankie, and have no rail connections leading into them. Their development, nonetheless, is expected in not too long a time. Iron ore also occurs.

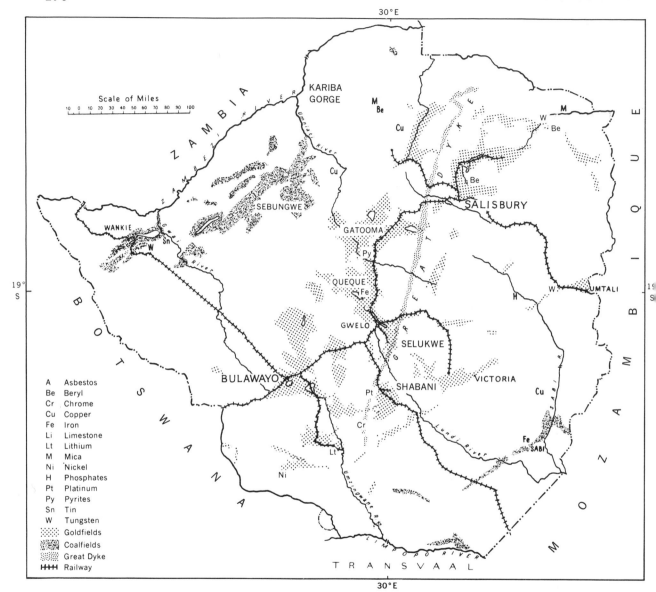

**FIGURE 17.6   Rhodesia's minerals. (Courtesy Geologic Survey Office, Salisbury, Rhodesia.)**

*Zambia.*   Important as mineral production is in Rhodesia, the value of ore output is small when compared to that of Zambia, where the value of copper alone exceeds that of all ores and fuels produced in Rhodesia by about 5 times (Figure 17.7). Seventeen ores are mined in the northern state, but only four—copper, zinc, cobalt, and lead—are economically of great value.

The story of modern mining in Zambia began with lead smelting at Broken Hill in 1915. Six years later some preliminary work was done with copper at Nkana, but falling copper prices on the world market caused these developments to proceed slowly. The value of mined copper had reached only 1.5 million pounds by 1932. Smelting began in 1937 at Mufulira, and at Nchanga in 1939.

The enormous price rise in World War II caused copper to boom, so that by 1953 Northern Rhodesia had become one of the world's largest copper producers. Almost all of the output comes from the six mines of Mufulira, Nchanga, Roan Antelope, Rhokana, Chibuluma, and Bancroft. Zambia may in time exceed Chile because all six mines working to capacity have a potential annual production of over 500,000 metric tons. Chibuluma and Bancroft came into production only in 1956 and 1957.

Lead and zinc come from a single reserve, that at Broken Hill where, as noted, nearly 50 years ago mining operations in the territory had their beginning. This ore body is nearly exhausted and output has dropped, but mining can continue for some years yet if tailings are worked over. Zambian cobalt production, while much smaller than in The Congo, is nonetheless the fourth largest in the world; nearly all of this is produced at the Nkana mine. Until 1952 the cobalt was exported in the form of a "high-grade cobalt-copper-iron alloy," but since that time an increasing proportion of this metal has been marketed in the form of a high-quality electrolytic cobalt. The electrolytic technique of treating the ore has been very successful and will undoubtedly supersede the method whereby the alloy was produced.[3]

[3] George H. T. Kimble, *Tropical Africa*, New York: The Twentieth Century Fund, 1960, p. 302; *Minerals Yearbooks*, U.S. Bureau of Mines.

FIGURE 17.7 Zambia's copperbelt. (From Kenneth Bradley, Copper Venture, London: Max Parrish and Company, Ltd., Printers, 1952. Courtesy Mufulira Copper Mines Ltd., and Roan Antelope Copper Mines Ltd.)

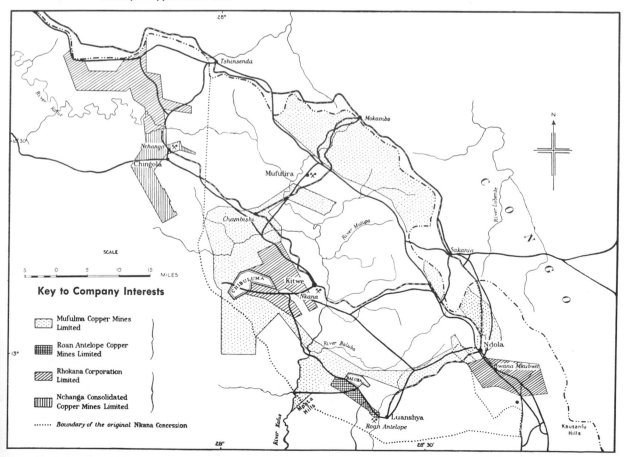

SCALE

Key to Company Interests

Mufulma Copper Mines Limited

Roan Antelope Copper Mines Limited

Rhokana Corporation Limited

Nchanga Consolidated Copper Mines Limited

······· Boundary of the original Nkana Concession

*Malawi.* Mineral production in Malawi is almost nonexistent, although the country has known deposits of coal, iron ore, gold, bauxite, and pyrochlore; small amounts of alluvial gold are taken, but Malawi is not an important producer. The country needs development. Labor has found its greatest outlet across national borders.

A project has been suggested for impounding the Shiré River at Liwonde. This would have several important effects. Navigation is obstructed along the Shiré by the Murchison Falls; fluctuation in volume also limits its navigational value so that only in its lower course, below Port Herald, is the river constantly in use. The dam would raise the level of the upper Shiré making it navigable, could equalize the level of Lake Nyasa which now fluctuates considerably, and would make possible the generation of hydroelectricity.

## PRODUCTION FROM THE SOIL

*Preindependence Land Policies.* British policies of land tenure differed among the three territories, determined in part by the number of Europeans residing in the several lands, and in part by the suitability of the area to European colonization. The original constitution of Southern Rhodesia provided for native reserves, and the Land Apportionment Act of 1941 provided additional native areas which are termed "special areas." There are also "native purchase areas" in which Africans can purchase land up to 1,000 acres with security of freehold tenure. Forested belts were also set aside, reserved for forestry purposes and not to be alienated for anything else. Besides these categories of land use, there are "European areas," national parks, and unassigned lands.

All of the land of Rhodesia has been alienated (categorized) in one way or another: 49 percent is alienated to one type or another of the native areas, 4 percent to forest areas, and 47 percent is classified for European use. The reserves and special areas are those where the Africans in the past followed their traditional mode of life until the Native Land Husbandry Act of 1951. Since then, steps have been taken to advance the Africans progressively from the traditional conditions of tribal land tenure toward individual allocation of land and farming rights.

A "centralization plan" has also been implemented whereby a farming area is developed as a community, the families supposedly living in a planned village. Only a few such planned communities have been set up, and they are experimental. Generally speaking, centralization calls for a village of some sort, and individual farms extending outward from the village. No shifting cultivation is practiced under this system; basic rotations usually are prescribed.

The Land Husbandry Act, which applies only in reserves and special areas, is now established throughout the country, and gives each cultivator (1) the right to an allocation of land if he is a farmer; (2) the right to a certain number of cattle; and (3) the right to graze his animals if he is a cattle owner. These rights (to a specific piece of land) are registered, but are not actually the same as ownership. It is rather the "right to use" the land.[4]

In Northern Rhodesia most of the territory was allocated by the British for Africans, although a considerable area was set aside as "Government land" already alienated, or available for leasing to Europeans; most of Nyasaland was designated African "reserve" land, the remainder being either public land or land held in freehold almost exclusively by Europeans. Privately owned land in Nyasaland made up less than 4 percent of the total area.

*Agriculture and Ranching.* Although in dollar value less important than mining in the economies of the central interior states, agriculture supports more people than any other activity. These countries do not, however, produce enough food to meet their requirements. Maize is the leading subsistence crop, and since 1953 has also been exported; wheat and rice are grown, but not in quantities sufficient to fill the demand; fruit and vegetable production also must be supplemented by imports, usually from South Africa; peanuts are an important crop, almost entirely

[4] Symbolically the chief is always present at any land allocation. Although land is allocated by government officials, the chief still speaks for the people. For a European or Indian to go into a native area, he must prove to the chief that his activities will benefit the Africans; a missionary, educator, or, in some cases, a storekeeper can operate until an African can take over.

FIGURE 17.8 Ranching in the Eastern District, Rhodesia. (Courtesy Federal Information Department, Salisbury, Rhodesia.)

locally or nationally consumed. Tobacco, cotton grown for seed, and tea are the major commercial crops, and among these tobacco ranks first.

Tobacco has had a checkered history but it is Rhodesia's crop par excellence, and since the end of World War II production has quite steadily mounted. How important tobacco is to Rhodesia is indicated in the fact that Salisbury is the largest individual tobacco market in the world; in 1963 it ranked seventh in the world in tobacco production. Most of the commercial tobacco grown in Rhodesia and Zambia comes from European farms, whereas in Malawi Africans also cultivate tobacco for sale. Flue-cured Virginia-type tobacco is the dominant variety raised, but since the cultivation of this type requires constant care, considerable experience, and a rather large outlay in capital for curing barns and other buildings, flue-cured tobacco is entirely a European enterprise; fire-cured varieties are raised by Africans, who produce only about a seventh as much as Europeans.

Malawi is the largest producer of tea, and most of this is exported. Production in the small country has gradually, but not spectacularly, mounted until in 1961 there were over 14,300 tons produced. Compared to India's production, around 345,000 tons, this is slight. Malawi, however, ranks eighth[5] in the world as a producer. Rhodesia also raises small amounts.

An important side of agriculture in the central south is the livestock industry, because many parts of the area that are not suitable for cultivation make good pastureland. Europeans usually practice integrated farming, and beef cattle, hogs, and poultry are all raised. Dairying is important around urban centers; Rhodesia is self-sufficient in milk production, and all three of the states make enough cheese to meet demands. However, beef must be imported de-

[5] *Statistical Yearbook*, New York: United Nations, 1964.

spite the fact that large cattle ranches are a feature of the economy of Rhodesia (Figure 17.8). These ranches stretch across most of Matebeleland, the lowveld, and parts of the eastern districts; ranching is less important in Zambia and Malawi because of the prevalence of the tsetse fly.

## PROBLEMS OF EXPORT

By value of output, minerals rank as follows in the central interior states—copper, asbestos, gold, chrome, zinc, lead, coal, and cobalt; two-thirds of the total export revenue comes from minerals; tobacco and tobacco products bring in a little over one-fifth, and the remainder comes from a great variety of items among which textiles lead.

But these products must get to the coast, and the interior states are landlocked, entirely dependent upon the seaboard states that lie around them for access to the oceans. This accounts for the strong economic ties that have developed between the interior south and the Portuguese lands. Beira, in Mozambique, has long been the major outlet for Rhodesian ores, although Lobito (Angola), which is about the same distance as Biera from the copper belt, is 3,000 miles closer to the major ore markets; an early agreement with the Rhodesian Railways tied the copper companies to Beira until 1956. Since then, however, the mining regions have had a choice among three gateways, Beira, Lobito, and Lourenço Marques in Mozambique, the latter opened to this transit trade by the completion of the Limpopo Railway in 1955. This port is more favorably situated to serve as an outlet for the minefields of South Africa than of the southern interior states, however.

One railroad only serves as an outlet for Malawi. It runs inland from Beira to Salima, via Limbe and Blantyre. Tea and tobacco, especially, are exported from here, not minerals.

## *Cities*

To the person unfamiliar with Africa, it is somewhat surprising that there are sizable cities and impressive industrial developments in black Africa. Although the population of the interior states is largely rural, there

are cities. Salisbury, capital of the former Federation and now of Rhodesia, is one of these, and one of the fastest growing towns in all of Africa. Its population numbers about 300,000 people.

Situated at over 4,800 feet elevation, it is a healthful city, European in character. It has a bright, new look—almost as if it had not been used—but it also has the appearance of the provincial pioneer town that it actually is (see Figure 17.9). It was founded in 1890 when the pioneer column sent into Mashonaland by Cecil Rhodes to select a townsite, ended its march at the locale of the present city. It is a trading and industrial center, for a number of industries have grown up; and here also are the headquarters of the Rhodesia Tobacco Association.

Bulawayo (population about 200,000) is the trading center of western Rhodesia, and the headquarters of the Rhodesian Railways. Although founded 4 years later than Salisbury, the city has an older look. It is built on the site where Lobengula, last king of the Matabele, had established his kraal; Government House, in fact, now rises above the exact spot where the kraal stood. The name means "Place of Slaughter," referring to incidents in Matabele history.

Lusaka, capital of Zambia, is also a market center and crossroads town. It lies at the junction of the Great North Road leading from Rhodesia to Tanganyika, Kenya, and the Congo, and the Great East Road leading to the Luangwa valley, Malawi, and Mozambique; it is likewise on the main line railway between Congo and Bulawayo. It is not so large as the main centers of Rhodesia, however.

Livingstone might be mentioned. Situated on the north bank of the Zambezi River a few miles from Victoria Falls, it is a tourist center from which people take off for "The Falls," the Wankie Game Reserve, and Kafue Game Park. Although best known for this, it is as well a major trading point for agricultural and timber products. The other towns of importance in Rhodesia and Zambia tend to be associated with mining areas; their function is the extraction and reduction of ores.

Blantyre-Limbe is the largest urban center in Malawi, formerly two towns but constituted into one municipality in 1956. The twin cities, 5 miles apart and across the Shiré River from each other, together comprise a nucleus of about 90,000 people. Blantyre

FIGURE 17.9  A section of Salisbury, Rhodesia. (Courtesy Federal Information Department, Salisbury, Rhodesia.)

is the air terminal for all of Malawi, and planes from Fort Jameson, Salisbury, and Dar es Salaam come into the airport; Limbe grew up, somewhat later than Blantyre, around the headquarters of the Nyasaland Railways. Tobacco grading and auctioning, and tobacco manufacture are among the most important activities of the center; plants also process cottonseed; and furniture, cement, lumber, and mineral water are produced in quantities necessary to meet the needs of the country.

Zomba is the present capital of Malawi, but a new capital is being built at Lilongwe, the focal point of Malawi's grain belt and a former center of tribal civilization known as Maravi. Malawi's main purpose in building the new capital, like Brazil's in building Brasilia hundreds of miles from the seacoast of that South American country, is to develop the interior. In Malawi, this interior sector produces grain, vegetables, and other products that help to feed the country. Roads are being built into the Lilongwe area to help open up the region.

It is planned to make Zomba a university town, and buildings formerly used for government will be converted to university uses. The Malawi University held its first semester of classes in Blantyre in September, 1965.

# 18 THE PORTUGUESE LANDS OF SOUTHERN AFRICA

*I have tasted command,*
*and I cannot give it up.*

NAPOLEON BONAPARTE

FIGURE 18.2 Two views of Luanda today. (Courtesy Casa de Portugal.)

## Geographical History

Angola and Mozambique are the largest possessions left to Portugal of the far-flung lands won by bold ventures during the fifteenth and sixteenth centuries. At one time the Portuguese held practically all of the African East coast, and chartered companies made attempts to penetrate the interior, via the Zambezi, to find the gold of Monomotapa that legends recounted was there. By the end of the seventeenth century, however, Portuguese control had been pushed south to Cape Delgado near the northern tip of Mozambique.

During the eighteenth century, Mozambique itself did not prosper; the attention of Portugal was centered on a search for gold and diamonds, and the colony was not strong enough to sustain itself; British, French, Dutch, and even Austrians harried the land; and "half-caste dynasties to whom lands had been granted by the Crown rebelled against governor-generals."[1] Then, in the middle of the nineteenth century the powerful Zulus swept in, in wave after wave, overwhelming the settlements.

On the west coast almost a century elapsed from the time that Diôgo Cão set up his cross until settlements began to be established. In 1575 Luanda (then São Paulo de Luanda) was founded, and for 300 years slaves poured out from there to supply labor for the sugar plantations in Brazil, the West Indies,

[1] Irene S. van Dongen, "Mozambique," *Focus*, vol. IX, no. 1, p. 1, September, 1958.

and North America. (See Figure 18.2.) It was a trade that made Brazil and Angola mutually dependent, and when the Dutch attempted to unsettle the Portuguese in South America they attempted to do the same thing in Portuguese West Africa, actually occupying Angola for 7 years (1641 to 1648).

The political and economic interdependence of the two colonies, one in the New World and the other in Africa, did not cease until Brazil broke away from Portugal in 1822 and became independent. After that, with much of its slave market gone, the Portuguese in Angola began to look about for resources other than human to exploit. Between 1840 and 1870 explorers began to probe inland; four of them succeeded

FIGURE 18.3 View of Benguela, one of the oldest cities of Angola. (Courtesy Portuguese Embassy.)

in traveling across the continent to Mozambique on the East coast. Thus began a Portuguese dream of an African empire extending across southern Africa, connecting the colonies on the Atlantic and Indian Oceans.

Between the two Portuguese colonies, however, British interests were laying hold on land and resources. At the Berlin Conference of 1884 to 1885, British interests came into direct conflict with Portuguese ambitions to consolidate their African holdings, and by 1890 a block of British-owned colonies formed a wedge that permanently separated Portuguese East and West Africa.

## Bridgeways to the Oceans

Since then, the economic efforts of the Portuguese have been heavily centered in developing their lands as outlets for the interior, particularly Mozambique. To the landlocked British territories this was all to the good; in fact, much British capital has gone into the development of the Portuguese ports.

## ANGOLAN GATEWAYS

Angola developed internally to a greater degree than did Mozambique. Shortly after the Berlin Conference, the first railroad was begun, the intention in the beginning being to build a transcontinental line that would connect Atlantic and Indian Ocean ports. It began at Luanda, but the farthest this northern line extended inland from the West coast was to Malange. Benguela, centrally situated, and Moçâmedes, farther south, also became ocean termini for railroads. Benguela (Figure 18.3) was an old trading post, and Moçâmedes a center in which immigrants from Brazil had located.

The bay at Benguela is shallow, however, and this resulted in the shift of the port to Lobito, situated on the best natural harbor along the West coast. It is Angola's only international port; through Lobito, Katanga copper, cobalt, and manganese go out in large amounts, transported to the coast along the railroad that still bears the name "Benguela" Railroad. Lobita handles about 62 percent of the exports and 23 percent of the imports of Katanga.

Lobito, Moçâmedes, and Luanda in the north are the three major ports serving Angola. Each marks the terminus of one of three major railroads that give access to and outlet from interior Angola; only the line from Lobito goes beyond the bounds of the country. The rail lines of these three ports lead into the three principal "tiers of the country. Between and beyond them are a score of minor shipping points of incontestable regional utility, whose progress, however, has been impeded by the deficiencies of maritime site, the lack of adequate ties with the interior, or the unproductive character of their hinterlands."[2] A few short rail spurs dip a few miles into the regions that lie between the tiers. Two such spurs project from Luanda; one arcs northeastward and then recurves back to the main line; the other connects with Caxito to the northeast. There are plans to extend this line across the northern frontier to connect with the Kinshasa-Matadi Railway. Another spur runs from Porto Amboim to Gabela; and from Sá da Bendeira, on the line from Moçâmedes, a longer branch runs southeast. Minor ports, important as coffee and fish ports, connect with the rest of the country only by roads.

Although growth and developments at Lobito, because of its international character, have far surpassed those at the other two principal ports, this does not mean that either Luanda or Moçâmedes has receded. Quite to the contrary, as the economy of Angola has developed these two ports have expanded both their facilities and functions, and it is expected that they will by 1970 become international by the extension of their railroads into The Congo, Zambia, and Rhodesia.

Luanda is not only a major ocean gateway for Angola (see Figure 18.2), but is also the biggest city (over 220,000 in size) and the political, financial, industrial, and commercial capital. It is, in fact, the largest city in metropolitan Portugal outside of Portugal itself, and among the cities in the Overseas Provinces, it most closely resembles Lisbon. Luanda has more European residents than any city along the West African coast, and one of the largest urban concentrations of black Africans. The hinterland of Luanda is large, the port acting as the trade focus for 4 of the 13 administrative districts of the province; north and northwest Angola also feel the pull of this important urban center. Through coastwise shipping, Luanda likewise serves smaller centers along the Angolan littoral.

## GATEWAYS THROUGH MOZAMBIQUE

Two rail corridors run from the interior lands and South Africa across Mozambique to the Indian Ocean. They terminate at Beira and Lourenço Marques, the major ports of Mozambique, the latter especially significant as a gateway for the Johannesburg district; Beira is most important for Rhodesia, Zambia, and Malawi, but serves as well the eastern parts of The Congo. Not only the ports but Mozambique as well have benefited from the near monopoly of ocean trade to and from the extranational territories inland from Portuguese lands. Industrial developments in Mozambique have been drawn to these ports, also, and most of the European population is centered here.

The site of Beira is only moderately good. The city lies 15 miles upstream from the mouth of the Pungue River, at its confluence with the Buzi. The oldest portion of the city spreads along the shore, northeast of the river, over a low marshy flat that is silted and bordered with mangrove; the offshore waters are shallow, and only far off the coast are depths of 30 feet reached. Sandbars lie across the river mouth, and entrance to the harbor is regulated "by the changing water depths over the entrance bar . . . : a high tidal range of 18–23 feet allows entry of all ocean-going vessels drawing up to 30 feet." The channel should be deepened, however, and the harbor regularly dredged because large amounts of silt are constantly carried down by the Pungue. All vessels must be piloted through the entry, where at low tide the shallow passages are treacherous because "strong currents" at times "surge in the estuary."[3] Previous to the development of Lourenço Marques and its access

---

[2] Irene S. van Dongen, "The Port of Luanda in the Economy of Angola," *Separata do Boletim da Sociedade de Geografia de Lisboa*, p. 3, January–March, 1960.

[3] William A. Hance and Irene S. van Dongen, "Beira, Gateway to Central Africa," *Annals of the Association of American Geography*, vol. XLVII, no. 4, p. 311, December, 1957.

FIGURE 18.4 Along the wharves of Beira, Mozambique. (Courtesy Portuguese Embassy.)

railways, Beira handled 80 percent of the overseas trade for the interior lands of the south (Figure 18.4). In the early post-World War II years, congestion on the railways leading to Beira greatly overtaxed the port facilities; the opening of Lourenço Marques, and "an agreement releasing some traffic to move via Lobito have greatly relieved the port."[4]

[4] William A. Hance, *African Economic Development*, New York: Harper & Row, Publishers, Incorporated, 1958, pp. 101–102.

Lourenço Marques has served as an outlet for southern Mozambique and the South African Transvaal for a long time, ever since the completion in 1895 of the railway linking Johannesburg and the Witwatersrand with the Mozambique port. However, after 1955, when the Limpopo Railway was opened to provide a rail link with the landlocked but rapidly developing Federation and Katanga, the importance of Lourenço Marques greatly increased; from then on, it became an alternate route to the overworked facilities at Beira. It is a beautiful city, and one of the most pleasant in Africa in which to live.

As already noted, the harbor at Lourenço Marques (Delagoa Bay) provides the finest shelter along the entire African coast between Suez and the Cape of Good Hope. It is protected from the trade winds of the Indian Ocean by Inhaca (Inyack) Peninsula and Inhaca Island, and three entrances give access to the inner harbor through Polana Canal, which is dredged to a minimum depth of 27 feet. Pilotage is necessary, but maneuvering of the entrance is not difficult. Ships that draw more than 31 feet of water generally enter at high tide.

The city lies 25 miles inland from the open sea. It was one of the earliest of the major African ports to build a wharf for ocean shipping; this was done in 1903, one year ahead of Durban. By 1914 the port area along the north shore had been developed almost to the point that it is today, although the original quay was extended somewhat in 1930 and again in 1951. Fifteen ocean-going vessels can be accommodated at its berths at one time. The port actively competes with South African ports for Transvaal traffic, handling more than three-fifths of the Transvaal's imports, and nearly two-thirds of all of the exports from the Republic of South Africa. The transit trade along its railways and through its port provides an outstanding source of income for Mozambique; and coastal vessels carry goods and passengers between Lourenço Marques and all the other ports along the Mozambique coast, way up to Cape Delgado.

Lourenço Marques is not only a major port of Mozambique but also the capital of the province (Figure 18.5). The city, which had a population of well over 100,000 when the 1955 census was taken, is growing spectacularly and the population is expected to reach 200,000 by 1975; in 1962 it was about

184,000; Delagoa Bay will allow for almost unlimited port developments. The city is one of the very important centers of the East coast and southern Africa, and its significance as a city and port will increase.

Because Lourenço Marques and Beira are international gateways, the invisible earnings of the transit trade shipping and African emigrant labor have largely overcome the unfavorable balance of trade that Mozambique shows because of the large volume of imports. The principal products that come in through the ports are cotton textiles, motor vehicles, wines and spirits, machinery, and petroleum; aside from revenue deriving from transit trade, the largest sources of export income are products of the soil, i.e., cotton, sugar, copra, sisal, cashew nuts, tea, and vegetable oils.

Neither Beira nor Lourenço Marques is situated on either of the two big rivers that flow into the Indian Ocean through Mozambique territory, namely, the Zambezi and Limpopo. Both lie slightly south of these major streams.

A number of smaller ports serve limited hinterlands back of the coast, each usually associated with a particular development. They include Inhambane, Quelimane, Moçambique, Porto Amélia, Nova Mambone, Vila de João Belo, and others. It will be noted that several of these lie at river mouths.

## Mozambique

Mozambique (Portuguese East Africa), an Overseas Province of Portugal, is strategically situated along the East coast of Africa between Tanganyika and South Africa, and east of Rhodesia, Zambia, Malawi, and the Transvaal. This position, coastward from landlocked states, has accounted for most of the prosperity of the province.

About half of Mozambique is a broad coastal lowland less than 600 feet in elevation, deepest in central Mozambique where the lowland projects westward like a tongue along the Zambezi to the Luangwa trench. Along the inland sides, the plain rises to uplands that become the plateau that is shared with the countries among which Mozambique lies. Flowing through the plateau in the depths of the gorge, the Zambezi continues on into Mozambique to the coastal plain, across which it takes a broader, more shallow course that is bordered by swamps of its own making, especially along the south. From the north out of Lake Nyasa and across the border flows the Shiré River, its course running through the lower end of the great rift valley (which grows nearly indistinguishable beyond the plateau edge).

Although latitudinally the southern part of Mozambique lies in what are considered subtropical zones,

**FIGURE 18.5** Airview of Lourenço Marques. *(Courtesy Portuguese Embassy.)*

the whole of the country has a wet and dry tropical climate because of the influence of warm Mozambique Current which makes southern Mozambique very mild; inland, the country becomes quite arid along the river valleys and lowlands; one region, Tete, is called "the hell of the Zambezi." Vegetation of the country is grass savanna with trees; only in the highland areas and the humid section behind Beira, which are better-watered regions than most of the lowlands, do trees grow in dense stands.

## LIVELIHOOD AND THE RESOURCES OF THE LAND

Mozambique is agricultural. But although the cultivation of the land is the major occupation, several things handicap farming, among them seasonal extremes of moisture, which bring excess water and flooding during the wet season, and parching drought during the dry; another is the lack of adequate drainage and flood control. Every year rivers, at flood stage, inundate fields and wash away crops almost ready for the harvest; on the other hand, during the dry months that follow, "plants wither on parched land for want of irrigation." A third handicap is a chronic labor shortage.

Although one-third of Mozambique is suitable for agriculture, only about 1 percent of the total land area is under cultivation. Conditions vary widely. Abundant rainfall, untapped rivers, and virgin soil favor cropping in some areas, whereas uncertain weather conditions, periodic floods, and tropical cyclones in the south and in some parts of the north have hindered agricultural development in these areas. The lack of an adequate rural credit system has also stood in the way of the extension of farming.

Conditions are most favorable in the north, and this is Mozambique's outstanding agricultural sector. For a long time it was undeveloped except for some European owned sisal plantations near the coast and the production of copra outside of Quelimane, but in the 1940s cotton cultivation began to take hold, and today, cotton grown by Africans is the outstanding territorial export; 75 percent of it comes from the four northern provinces. Rice, cashew nuts, and groundnuts are also exported.

In central and southern Mozambique, where soils are rather poor and sandy, maize is the leading crop,

FIGURE 18.6    Flour mill, Matola, Mozambique. (Courtesy Casa de Portugal.)

grown for subsistence. Along major rivers, however, where valleys are rich with alluvial soil, large company-owned plantations grow sugar, especially in the lower Zambezi and Buzi valleys and along the Incomati, and citrus and bananas in the Incomati valley; successful subsistence farming is carried on in "the black marshes" (machongos) that have been reclaimed outside Inharrime and Inhambane.

Much of Mozambique is menaced with the tsetse fly, and hence the number of livestock is somewhat limited. Only in the southern and northwestern parts of the country are animals raised, and these are almost entirely owned by Africans. Cattle are the most numerous, goats rank next, and some hogs and sheep are raised; both Europeans and Africans keep poultry. The coastal waters of Mozambique are rich in fish, but fishing is almost entirely for local consumption, although shrimp are exported in small quantities to South Africa.

Mozambique has proven deposits of a number of ores, the more important being copper, tin, bauxite, beryl, mica, rutile, graphite, corundum, and coal. They remain almost untouched, however, and coal is the only subsurface resource that is mined for industrial use. This comes from Moatize and is used by the Beira Railway, on sugar plantations, and for bunkering ships. Some years ago, Portugal engaged an American company to prospect for minerals to determine the actual extent of ore reserves, but no report has been issued. The most promising mineral fields appear to be located in the Tete area and in the Manica and Sofala region near the Rhodesian frontier. Portuguese and foreign companies have shown some interest in mining in Mozambique in recent years. However, inadequate inland transportation is one of the major hindrances confronting any mining venture, and so far many mining reserves have been considered uneconomic to develop owing to transport difficulties.

Industry in Mozambique, just beginning to be developed and therefore largely concerned with the processing of the products of agriculture, is concentrated in two areas: the major center is in and around Beira and along the railroad into Rhodesia, the second in the vicinity of Lourenço Marques. Near Beira large hydroelectric installations on the Revue River supply cities and some of the growing industries with power, and some power is sold across the border to the Umtali district of Rhodesia. The first manufacturing had developed in and around Lourenço Marques, drawing on Transvaal coal for fuel; the Beira hydroelectric plant has the effect of decentralizing industry, a wholesome development for the country.

The established industry includes a cotton mill at Villa Pery, which is inland from Beira and on the railroad; this is the first and only one in Mozambique. The country also has a jute mill, and at Dondo, in from Beira at the junction of the railroad from the north with the rail line to Beira, a fiber-cement plant. Cement, flour, tobacco products, vegetable oils, industrial alcohol, pulp and paper, and brewed stuffs also are produced around Beira. A number of the same products are produced at Lourenço Marques; in addition, an aluminum ware factory and the province's only iron foundry are located here.

## Angola

Angola (Portuguese West Africa), like Mozambique, is an Overseas Province of Portugal "with corresponding judicial and social status." It is larger in area than the East coast province but smaller in population; included as a part of the provincial domain is the exclave Cabinda, separated from Angola proper by the mouth of the Congo River and the surrounding

Congolese territory, a small bit of land lying between the Republic of The Congo and Congo. (See Figure 18.7.)

Varied in relief, Angola rises from a coastal lowland that, at its broadest, is only 100 miles wide up the edge of the Great Escarpment and on to the broad tableland of the Angolan plateau. The ascent from the west is made in a series of broad steps that are in the nature of "subplateaus," the first at about 1,000 feet altitude, the second at approximately the 3,500-

FIGURE 18.7  Rain forests of Cabinda. (Courtesy Portuguese Embassy.)

foot level, and so on upward, interruptedly, until the 4,000 to 7,000-foot heights of the central upland are attained. In the south and central portions, the rise is difficult and abrupt; in the north, it is more gentle. Along the east the upland again falls away, this time toward the interior of the continent.

The central Angolan uplands, highest in the Bihé plateau, form the water divide between Congo (Kasai) and Zambezi drainage. Here average elevations attain 6,000 feet, and heights rise to over 8,500 feet. From the Bihé plateau, the remainder of the tablelands grow lower—strikingly in the west, as the terraces (noted above) form giant steps to the coast. The Kasai River and its tributaries drain most of the north, in places forming the Angola-Congo boundary. The Zambezi and its affluents drain southeast Angola, while the south-central sector is drained by streams that disappear across the southern border into the sands of the Kalahari; through parts of their courses they flow ephemerally. Several short streams and two major rivers flow westward to the Atlantic: the Cuanza in the north, flowing into the sea somewhat south of Luanda; and the Cunene in the extreme south, where it forms part of the boundary between

Angola and South-West Africa. Both rivers rise in the high parts of the central uplands, and take circuitous courses to the sea. (A good drainage map, therefore, will show a threefold water divide.)

Rainfall varies with relief and latitude. On the plateaus, it averages between 25 and 60 inches, higher in the north and on the lofty central areas, and decreasing southward. The wet and dry regime obtains throughout; the extreme north shows a double maximum of rainfall at some stations; southward, rainfall not only decreases but the dry period becomes longer.

Mean temperatures on the plateau are about 69°F, a pleasant climate favored by both Europeans and Africans. Because of elevation, temperatures are lower than they otherwise would be at these latitudes; during the dry period, frosts are not uncommon at higher elevations. Here, on the several high plateaus where a savanna vegetation is interspersed with light forest, is found the heaviest concentration of African farmers and many Europeans, the latter cultivating fruits and vegetables that are normally associated with the mid-latitudes.

The plateau is productive farming country. Nine-tenths of the maize, grown by Africans and by bulk

**FIGURE 18.8** "Planned" village for Africans in southern Angola. (Courtesy Portuguese Embassy.)

the largest export from Angola, is produced in these high uplands, and beans, peanuts, cassava, castor seed, rice, and other crops are raised for subsistence and sale; surpluses are bought by Portuguese traders, who transport the products to the coast for export abroad. This is also cattle country, especially the southern half of the plateau. Cities that are not ports tend to be found on the high tableland, like Nova Lisboa, which is destined one day to become the capital, Sá da Bandeira, the chief urban center of the south, and Silva Porto.

Much of the rest of Angola is haunted by a water problem, either seasonally or perennially. (See Figure 18.8.) In the southeast and along the valley of the Cunene, rainfall does not exceed 15 inches and is often far less; these parts of Angola are very barren. So also is much of the coast; Luanda (8°49′S) averages about 13.5 inches of rain annually, small for a latitude where evaporation tends to be high; Luanda marks the approximate boundary between the arid and semiarid sectors of the coast.

The coast is cool for its latitude. The moderation of temperature and the aridity (in part) are due to the cool current that flows close to the shore from Antarctic waters, namely, the Benguela Current: onshore winds are cooled as they blow across the cold current, and hence reach the coast chilled and with a drying effect, because as they move across the land they warm and tend to pick up rather than release moisture. Fog, characteristic of desert coasts brushed by a cold current, occurs all along this shore. It dissipates quickly with distance inland, however, as the moisture evaporates. Any easterly winds also accentuate coastal aridity, for they descend from the plateau to the shore, compressing and warming in the process.

North of about 8°S the coast becomes moister, and in the warmth and greater humidity oil and coconut palms, and sugarcane grow; along river valleys the vegetation becomes quite luxuriant; but sugarcane grown on European estates along the Catumbela River and outside of Porto Amboim must be irrigated to live through the dry season. Sisal, which is drought resistant, grows without irrigation at some locations along the coast. The hinterland east of Luanda (the Libolo region) and the area around Benguela are the most favored of the lowland zones for this crop.

## USE OF THE LAND

There has been little planned development of Angola until recently. The economy is based on the growing and export of cultivated products, particularly coffee, and to a lesser degree, on the transfer of imported goods. With the exception of diamonds, minerals are not yet an important contributor to the gross national product, although an expansion of iron ore and manganese production is expected. Coffee, diamonds, sisal, and fish products make up over two-thirds of the value of exports.

*Agriculture.* Angolan agriculture is beset with problems. Among the most critical is that of converting the African farmer from the traditional but wasteful practice of migratory cultivation and to attachment to the land; destruction of the vegetation and soil erosion are concomitants of the former method of land use. This problem is common throughout most of black Africa.

Angolan farmers can be classified into about three broad groups: (1) the African population, which concentrates on subsistence farming, the collection of forest products and beeswax, and the commercial cultivation (in some regions) of coffee, cotton, and maize; (2) Portuguese colonists on the plateaus, who cultivate subtropical and midlatitude crops, such as wheat, other cereals, and fruits; and (3) plantation growers, both medium and large, and some farm colonists, who raise coffee, sugar, and sisal on the plateau, tobacco and cotton in the central plains, and tropical tree crops such as the oil palm in the northern part of the province and in Cabinda.

Coffee is Angola's great commercial crop, producing over a third of the total export revenue. Angola is the third largest coffee producer in Africa, ranking after Ivory Coast and Uganda. The coffee, largely *robusta*, is grown mostly at elevations that range between 1,300 and 3,300 feet although some *robusta* is found below these levels, and a few coffee plantations are located as high as 4,290 feet; but these are in the minority. Two regions are outstanding. The most important lies north of the Cuanza River, very heavy in a semicircular area back of Luanda but spreading north to include even a large portion of the Congo district: 78 percent of Angolan coffee acreage and 79.9 percent of the production comes from this northern belt.[5] The second region is south of the Cuanza. Here production has tended to remain about the same, in contrast to the northern belt where output multiplied 3 times within a decade.[6] This growth in coffee production is helping the country's economy, and has induced as well port and urban developments. Luanda might be called the São Paulo of Angola because, like the Brazilian city, it has become a bustling metropolis because of coffee. Demands by the coffee industry for machinery, trucks, and the like have led to an expansion in imports.

The production of cotton is of particular interest to the textile industry in metropolitan Portugal, and efforts have been directed toward gearing its cultivation in overseas territories to the needs of Portugal. In Angola, some 55,000 to 60,000 Africans do small-scale cotton cultivation on farms of a hectare or so. Legislation has been passed that is designed to stabilize the market, regulate the sale of cotton by the Africans, and maintain (or increase) the acreage planted to the fiber.

Maize, beans, and cassava are staples of the African diet in many sectors while millet and sorghum, also staple foods, are important especially among Africans living in south central and southern Angola. Oil seeds, mainly palm oil, peanuts, and castor beans, are grown, the type raised depending upon the climate.

Although the plateau of Angola offers a suitable environment and interesting investment possibilities for raising cattle, both dairy and beef, the number of animals is relatively small, and most are African owned. Attitudes toward and methods of rearing cattle have changed little from the old, traditional ways; most are kept as an indication of wealth by migratory Africans living in the south; poor care, droughts, and epidemics cause many to die annually.

Certain Portuguese regulations have discouraged Europeans from raising cattle, especially the single price controls which do not take quality into account.

[5] Irene S. van Dongen, "Coffee Trade, Coffee Regions, and Coffee Ports in Angola," *Economic Geography*, vol. 37, no. 4, p. 326, October, 1961.
[6] For a discussion and mapping of the coffee industry of Angola see van Dongen, *ibid*.

Despite this, some small but significant beginnings have been made. In 1959, 200 Danish cattle were imported to Cela to serve as a nucleus for the beginning of a dairy industry there, and later 1,700 more head were brought in; Cela now has a small pasteurization plant. A number of farm and cattle-raising cooperatives that have been formed in central and southern Angola are increasing the economic strength of these units.

*Minerals and Industry.* Although the mineral potentialities of Angola have not been thoroughly explored, they are believed to be considerable. Diamonds, iron, copper, manganese, mica, and asphalt are being produced in small quantities, and phosphates, marble, wolfram, titanium, and other minerals are known to be present though not yet developed. Diamonds and iron ore are the only significant mineral exports with diamonds accounting for about four-fifths of the value of mineral production, and over one-sixth of the total exports. The diamond fields, alluvial in nature, are an extension of the vast diamond deposits of the Kasai in The Congo and like them occur in the gravels of an ancient river that no longer flows. Although more hand labor is used in recovering the diamonds in Angola, they nevertheless compete in price with those from Congo.

Iron ore was first produced and exported in 1957. It occurs in a number of regions, but most of them are so far from transport facilities as to make mining uneconomic. However, in 1961 plans to connect the port of Moçâmedes with iron reserves at Cassinga and Cuima were announced.

Manganese deposits are worked on the Luanda-Malange railway at Malange, and manganiferous ore is of some significance and is expected to be of growing importance. The gauge on the Luanda railroad was widened and additional gondolas were purchased in 1960 to facilitate movement of the manganese. Large phosphate deposits north of Luanda are not yet developed, but if the ores could be converted into fertilizer they would be invaluable to the overworked soils of Portugal as well as to the leached soils of Angola.

In 1955 oil was discovered near Luanda at Benfica. The deposits proved to be economic to develop, and the work of sinking wells began immediately; at the same time, construction on an oil refinery was started at Luanda. Angola has high hopes of supplying not only its own needs of liquid fuel but also those of The Congo from this reserve.

To people living in the villages along the coast, especially in southern Angola, the sea has offered a bounty that the land has not. Small fleets of fishing boats go out daily from the many ports and villages—Moçâmedes, Benguela, Porto Alexandre, Baía Farta, Baía dos Tigres and many others—and mackerel, sardines, and tuna are brought back in the holds to the canneries, to be canned or processed into fish meal, fish manure, and fish oil; some are dried in the sun and shipped inland to help supply protein for the Africans' protein-deficient diets.

The fishermen of Angola, mostly Europeans, are well trained to take marine products, for traditionally Portuguese have been fishermen and sailors, long exploiting oceans. Thus, as also in Portugal, salt is obtained by evaporating seawater from briny pans closed off along the shore behind embankments.

A development of the forest resources has taken place in recent years and exports of wood, usually in log form, have increased. The Republic of South Africa has proven a good market for railway ties. The Cabinda exclave has extensive reserves of both hard and softwoods, as yet largely unexploited but potential for development. (See Figure 18.7.) In Angola proper, although some areas have good forests, and conservation and replacement practices have been put into operation, many sectors are lacking in such reserves, and the forests have been badly depleted. Especially in the district around Moçâmedes and along the Moçâmedes Railway is there a great need for forestry conservation practices to be adopted; here the trees have been indiscriminately cut to furnish fuel, and this region has so low a rainfall that replacement will be difficult. Along the Benguela Railroad, especially near Nova Lisboa, eucalyptus is cultivated for use as fuel on trains.

## Portuguese Policy

It was long after most other parts of Africa had achieved independence that the Portuguese territories began to show signs of political unrest. These lands had appeared uniquely peaceful, politically and socially, and racial troubles did not seem to exist; however, unrest began in the early part of 1961.

Angola and Mozambique became Overseas Provinces of Portugal when that European state politically reorganized its extra-European possessions after World War II. Associated with this was a 6-Year Plan (initiated in 1953) under which economic development was to take place.. Most of the money allocated to Mozambique was channeled into improving communications, transport lines, and roads. Under the plan, the Limpopo Railway was completed, a new seaport was opened at Nacala to serve the far north, a large airport was constructed at Lourenço Marques, and air service expanded greatly.

Still another feature was the movement of landless Portuguese peasants from Portugal to the lower Limpopo valley in Mozambique, where a colony was established. Some of the poorer residents of Portugal's cities were also relocated here in an effort to relieve the great overcrowding in metropolitan areas in the European state. The project, known as the lower Limpopo valley scheme, included the construction of a barrage for the irrigation of some 240,000 acres of land to be cultivated or used for grazing, and the settlement of 10,000 families who should work their own land without the assistance of African labor. In time it is planned that Africans also will be settled here, in the upstream areas, as small freeholders. Schemes similar to this are anticipated for the uninhabited uplands that lie along the borders of Lake Nyasa and the Zambezi valley.

Included in the plans for Angola are a number of "colonization projects" similar to those being carried out in Mozambique but in harmony with the needs and realities of the western province.

### POLICY REVISIONS

Portugal has been criticized for failing to develop her African territories and raise the standards of living and education of Africans living within the colonies. Although the charges are true, a balance must be kept in viewing these things. It should be noted that in Portugal itself, wages are low and literacy rates are below the European norm; on the positive side, the Portuguese have shown little color discrimination, and have perhaps achieved a higher degree of integration with the Africans than have any Europeans in Africa, as they have also in Brazil with Indian peoples and cultures.

In late July, 1961, the Portuguese government began the move to grant constitutional equality with whites to Africans in Angola, Mozambique, and Portuguese Guinea, giving all inhabitants the same constitutional privileges to vote and hold office. These rights are conferred on the basis of educational standards, however, as is now the case in metropolitan Portugal and some of the other overseas territories. No longer will 95 percent of the Africans automatically be disenfranchised because they are legally "uncivilized." Until these reforms were introduced, the ruling minority of "civilized" whites, mulattoes, and Africans were the only persons with these rights; tribal Africans were classed as "uncivilized." The constitutional reforms also do away with the system of *indigenato*, a system of paternalism which was introduced in the 1920s to protect Africans from being exploited; however, it also denied them nearly all legal rights.

Further reforms made in September, 1963, to meet some of the bitter criticism from Africa and abroad, modified the laws concerning overseas territories, namely, the Organic Law for Overseas Territories established in 1953, which specified the political relationship of the overseas lands to Portugal. The declared objective was: "to provide broad decentralization of the overseas 'provinces' without 'endangering the political unity of the Portuguese nation.' "

The revision permits a larger number of Africans to vote for members of the provincial legislative councils and national counsels, at the same time that provincial authorities are given increased powers under the general administrative decentralization. Much power hitherto held by the Ministry of Overseas Territories was, by the reform of the laws, transferred to governors and the elected legislative councils.

For the further decentralization of the provinces, new district boards with deliberative and advisory powers were established, and the reform provides for representation of the overseas provinces in the corporative chamber and other advisory bodies at the national level. The overseas provinces were already sending deputies to the National Assembly, and their quota was increased.

Portugal does not consider its African lands "colonies," but an integral part of the Portuguese nation. How long Angola and Mozambique will remain attached to Portugal cannot be forecast. Since many of the terrorist activities have been carried out by persons who have slipped from neighboring countries across the borders into Portuguese lands, it cannot even be reliably stated just what the attitude of the Africans is toward independence, or continued association within the nation of Portugal.

# 19 THE REPUBLIC OF SOUTH AFRICA

*Then answered cunning Dives: "Do not gold
and hate abide
"At the heart of every Magic, yea, and,
senseless fear beside?"*

RUDYARD KIPLING

## A Plural Society

The Union of South Africa broke all ties with the Commonwealth of Nations on May 31, 1961, and declared itself an independent republic. It had been a member of the Commonwealth since 1910, when Cape Province, Natal, Orange Free State, and Transvaal were welded into a Union by Great Britain.

It is a big country with a relatively small population—without South-West Africa, some 472,700 square miles in area inhabited by about 17 million people.

However, whatever South Africa lacks in numbers of people, it makes up in complexity of population composition; it has been called a "plural" society. Four groups, that show distinctive racial and/or ethnic characteristics, comprise the South Africans: the African Bantu, making up about two-thirds of the people; Europeans, totaling over 3,000,000 but divided into two groups, each of which is quite homogeneous on the basis of the nationality of the motherland, namely, those of English derivation as against the Afrikaners, who are, in most part, Dutch and French Huguenot, with some mixture of German and Scandinavian; Asians, numbering about ½ million and mostly Indians; and the Coloureds, somewhat more than 1½ million in number, a nonhomogeneous group of purebloods and mixtures of various sorts. Counted among the Coloureds are all those who do not fall within any of the other three categories—pureblood Bushmen, Hottentots, and Malays, and mixtures of these three

**FIGURE 19.2  Bantu areas. The enclaves are the British high commission territories of Bechuanaland, Basutoland, and Swaziland. Bechuanaland and Basutoland are now the independent states of Botswana and Lesotho; Swaziland remains a dependency of Britain.**

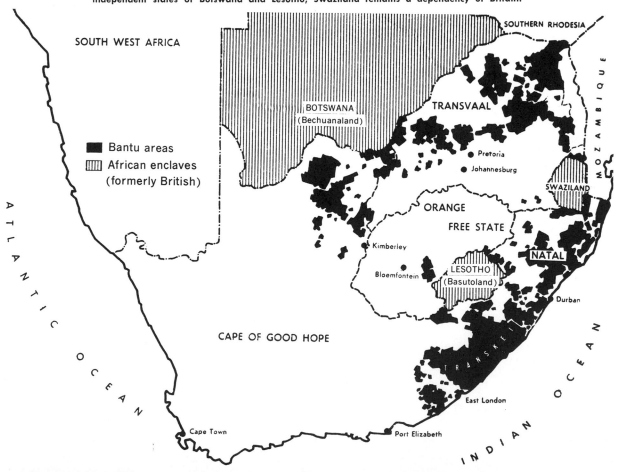

with each other and with Europeans, Bantus who are descendants of former slaves largely imported from Madagascar and West Africa, and sailors from all over the world. Slaves and sailors contributed heavily to the mixtures.

The distribution of the groups was pretty well set when the Union was formed, a distribution that reflects not only the economic capabilities of the various areas to support a large or small population, but also the historic occupation of the land by the racial groups involved. This pattern has tended to be perpetuated by the way in which land was allocated among the racial groups, and by laws that have controlled the movement and employment of all who were not of European blood. (See Figure 19.2.) Thus, the Coloureds are found almost exclusively in Cape Province, the English heavily in Cape Province and Natal, Afrikaners in greatest numbers in the Transvaal and Orange Free State, and Indians in the Durban area of Natal, spreading up into the Transvaal. Two other features of population distribution are worth emphasizing, namely, the relatively dense population found in the east as contrasted with the sparse numbers of people in the west, and the heavy concentration of people in urban areas.

(a)

FIGURE 19.3  Faces of South Africa: (a, above) Bantuane children; (b, left below) Indians leaving their place of worship, Durban; (c, below) Bushman, one of the heterogeneous group called "Coloureds." (Courtesy South African Information Service.)

(b)

(c)

No other country in the world presents an example of a plural society in so classic a form as does South Africa. All the groups—the majority blacks, and the minority European, Indian, and Coloured South Africans—hold justifiable claims to this land, through history and through the parts they have taken in developing the state and the economy. Although of foreign ancestry, Europeans and Indians feel as akin to the soil of this country as do the black Africans, as much a part of Africa as Americans feel a part of the United States. They regard themselves as South African, and even African.

The Republic is a diverse land: From its rockbound Cape coast, across the heather-covered hills of Cape Province to the palm belt of Natal and the stupendous, brown hills of Zululand, to the flat-to-rolling savannas of the veld, South Africa is vast and impressive. The Europeans have placed their strong cultural imprint upon their portion of the land, and the African has left his mark upon that part that remained to him; even the Indian has created his own sectors and scene.

But although the four groups share the space, they do not live together as a society. Each lives to itself; apartheid or "apartness," which means complete social, physical, and geographical separation of the European-derived South Africans from the other three groups and these three from one another, is the policy that is attempting to regulate the ways of the society and the apportionment of the land.

## Separate Development: Apartheid

Apartheid is not so much race against race as it is each group in its own place. In fact, in August, 1961, the Nationalist government officially dropped the term "apartheid," and substituted the phrase "separate development."

The strongest supporters of this idea favor the establishment of "separate territorial entities" for Africans, the Bantustans, the first of which came into being in late 1963. By this means, the Nationalist government not only would set up separate black states but would also reinstate tribalism among Africans who have long been detribalized (namely, most of those who live in cities) because the Bantustans are

tribally expressed. Indian and Coloured communities also are to be relatively self-sufficient and live apart.

As they have in the case of the Portuguese lands, African countries and other so-called anticolonial states have put pressure on the United Nations to take action against the Republic of South Africa; and at the Addis Ababa Conference there was almost unanimous backing of resolutions "to 'liberate' Portuguese possessions and the African subjects of white supremacy governments in southern Africa."[1] The Nationalist government, however, stands firm in its position, as the words of South African Premier Verwoerd made clear: "I believe in the divergence of the nations of South Africa and in the friendship created by neighbors."[2]

Certain questions naturally have been raised for many years, and are still raised: Why does the Nationalist government cling to separate development as the only policy acceptable? Is the goal of full territorial partitioning attainable, and will it provide a solution to the problem of South Africa, the most technically advanced African nations?

### THE IMPLEMENTATION OF SEPARATE DEVELOPMENT

As the policy of separate development is being carried out since 1960, the country is being divided into a white area and eight autonomous African homelands, called Bantustans. For a transition period, direction of the African sectors will come from the South African government; but ultimately administration will pass to the Africans. The "white" sector comprises about 85 percent of the total area of South Africa, but out of this the Indian and Coloured sectors also come; the Republic's black Africans will be settled in the remaining territories. These appear to be overpopulated in terms of population density to resources and the level of technology on the reserves, although some of these lands are among the best watered and were possibly at one time the most fertile sectors of the Republic.

[1] John K. Cooley, "Africa Unity Put into Focus," *The Christian Science Monitor*, May 31, 1963.
[2] Spoken when he moved the second reading of the Constitution Amendment Bill in late June, 1963 (as quoted in *South African Digest*, p. 1, July 3, 1963).

(a)

FIGURE 19.4 African suburb of Pretoria. (a) The slums in the foreground are being abandoned for the new housing development in upper portion of picture. (b) An African home in the redevelopment suburb called Meadowlands, near Johannesburg. (a, courtesy P. G. Higgins, municipal photographer, Johannesburg; b, courtesy South African Information Service, Bantu Administration Department.)

(b)

Neither the millions of Africans living in cities (Figure 19.4) or in European rural areas outside of the native reserves nor the Coloureds or Asians have political rights within South Africa as a whole; and Africans have no right of freehold, and no right of residence in white sectors unless currently employed by Europeans. However, political franchise will return to Africans upon their repatriation to the tribal homelands, i.e., to the Bantustans, and to Indians and Coloureds within their localized communities.

*The National Indian Council.* The plan under which the Indians will receive the local franchise and control of certain affairs of the Indian community in South Africa (i.e., such affairs "as may be delegated to it from time to time by Parliament") has already been accepted by leaders of the Indian community. It calls for the establishment of a National Indian Council that will pave the way for an eventual democratically elected council which would, as noted above, control such of the Indian affairs as were delegated to it from time to time by the South African parliament including "legislative and administrative powers in respect of all matters directly affecting the Indian community, such as social services, education and local government." The plan does not call for the establishment of "homelands," as in the case of the Bantus, but for segregated communities, in both rural and urban areas, that will function as self-contained units.

*Schemes for the Coloured.* The plan for the Coloureds is much the same, although with undertones of the Bantustans. In intensive farming areas of Cape Province, the scheme designates the establishment of small towns—villages to be established at "suitable places to be indicated by the Department of Community Development, in collaboration with the Divisional Councils concerned"—within an area demarcated by a line from Humansdorp to Colesburg and from there along the Orange River, a line that coincides with the limits of the region traditionally and currently occupied by the Coloured peoples.

Labourers on adjacent farms would be housed there, and villages would have a school designed in such a manner that it could also be used as a community hall,

health center and a crèche (day nursery). The arrangement would counteract migration to the cities and insure a permanent and efficient labour force.

Divisional Councils could acquire land for the undertaking. . . . The scheme's advantages, among others, were that farmers [White] would not have to use valuable land for housing their labourers, and that squatting would be ended or reduced.

"Coloureds will be employed progressively in these areas as the Bantu return to their own areas."[3]

*The Bantustans.* A Constitution Amendment Bill passed in June, 1963, provided for the establishment of the Bantu "homelands." It cleared the way for the introduction of the Transkei Constitution Bill, which later accorded self-government to the Transkei.[4] However, "the Transkei will remain a part of the Republic." The first amendment bill included a language clause, which provided that: the equality of English and Afrikaans will be retained; the "Bantu languages will be recognized in the Constitution, and it will become a part of national policy that they shall be recognized and used. It amounts to the recognition of the right of every group to have their own language in their own territory and among their own people." The bill is only an "enabling measure," and every time the Government wants to use it, it will have to pass legislation. In practice, therefore, it will only be used when self-government is given to a Bantu territory.

The first Bantu state to be set up was the Transkei, traditional tribal lands of the Xhosa peoples. It came into being in the fall of 1963; during November, 1963, much of the administration was turned over to African civil servants, and state elections were held; and in December it was constituted a self-governing state.

In area 64,000 square miles, the Transkei is 4 times larger than Switzerland and, like that European state, a mountain country. It is situated along the east coast between Durban and East London; Umtata is the capital. Its population is something over 3 million people of whom about 17,000 are whites and 13,000 Coloureds; the rest of the people belong to the Xhosa "nation." It has a legislature elected by universal

[3] "Scheme to Meet Needs of Coloureds in Farming Areas," *South African Digest,* p. 3, Nov. 4, 1963.
[4] Act no. 48, 1963.

African adult suffrage; whites and Coloureds have no political representation. Foreign affairs are in the hands of the South African government. Critics of the policy adopted for the establishment of "homelands" for the Bantu point out that the most productive farm lands, the industrial centers, the major mines, and the ports all lie within the European sector and that the ethics of partitioning a country are debatable. Apartheid is defined by them as "a policy of despair," because it emphasizes the problems of racial difference rather than solves them—the history of India and Pakistan since partition is given as evidence.

To make up for the lack of industrial development in the native area, and to relieve the pressure of high population densities, there are plans for Europeans to site new industries on the edges of the Bantustans, "border industries" that will allow a daily migration of African labor across the frontiers to factories, but will avoid the social and political consequences of a multiracial community. A number of border industries have been and are being established, and the Nationalist government is optimistic about this plan as an outlet for Bantustan labor.

Around some of the major cities, such as Johannesburg, a complex of "Bantu townships" is being established. Whether these are interim measures to take care of urban labor needs or will constitute permanent arrangements is not clear. Undoubtedly they will eventually disappear if a white labor force can replace the black Africans.

Some observers feel that "there is just a chance that the Bantustan policy, if carried out to the full, could provide a blueprint for other racially-mixed communities." In South Africa, the key is whether it is economically practical or not. Can the policy provide a permanent solution?

This latest development in apartheid—that is, the plan to create one white and eight black nations—makes no land allowance for the other two groups, the Indian and the Coloured, even though as early as 1959 moves were implemented to have Indians live in separate, economically self-sufficient villages and to curtail the privileges of the Coloured. With nine separate states already projected, the government is becoming increasingly vulnerable to the charge that it is fragmenting the country. According to some, the Coloureds and Asians appear "to be doomed to commute restlessly between the two major groups." However, the Indians live largely in urban areas. A period of adjustment lies ahead, its duration depending upon the "tempo of industrial development in the border areas and the amount of cooperation from Whites in regard to the surplus labour at their disposal." They have been advised that the best way of meeting the latter problem is "to investigate and implement mechanization and other labour saving techniques including efficient organization of management, production, manpower, and, last but not the least, self employment."[5]

Basically two solutions were offered to the racial problem, integration or segregation. According to Mr. Verwoerd,

> One could not rely on constitutional blocks at one stage or another—in the end, the majority must rule in a mixed society.
>
> "The lesson of Africa is clear: A constitution is set aside sooner than a boot that grows old. I am not prepared to give away our heritage. I am prepared to fight to the death for my right and that of the nation to exist"—[but also] to grant other racial groups similar rights. The ultimate object of the policies of the Government in respect to the various racial groups in South Africa—is to [live] "together in equality and friendship."[6]

## Historical Background of the Plural Society

Cape Town was founded for the purpose of supplying fresh fruits and vegetables to ships rounding the Cape on the route between Holland and the Indies. It was to replace St. Helena as the supply base. During the first 3 years the settlement was communal in nature. But in 1655, the company (the Council of Seventeen, in Holland, that had sponsored the expedition) began to permit settlers to cultivate private gardens, and 2 years later, to "release" families for farming. Hence,

[5] M. C. Botha, "Prepare for Withdrawal of Bantu Labour," *South African Digest*, p. 5, May 2, 1963.
[6] "Multi-national Co-existence Sought," *South African Digest*, p. 5, Sept. 5, 1963.

7 years after the establishment of Cape Town, Dutch began to occupy the hinterland; and two small farming centers, Groeneveldt and Hollandsche Tuin, grew up along the Liesbeek River.

The outward movement could not be stopped. Colonists took over more and more land, advancing across the legal boundaries. Within two generations, the eastern frontier had been pushed from the Breede River (Breë), a bit north and east of Cape Agulhas, to the Fish River, nearly 100 miles east of what is now Port Elizabeth. At this frontier they faced the Bantu for the first time; in the north, they had encountered the Bushmen.

The isolated character of the white occupation outside of the Cape area was such as to encourage predatory raids for cattle, especially by the Bushmen. Frequently, Boers (farmers) were killed, and the government in Cape Town could not meet all of the demands for protection. Boer commandos were organized to deal with the natives, and scores of the Bushmen were taken as prisoners and used as servants; scores were killed. Slavery had been introduced in 1658, and soon, by official company policy, it was decided that only black, rather than white, labor should be brought in.

Huguenots, who were Protestants fleeing the persecutions of sixteenth- and seventeenth-century Catholic France, joined the Dutch colony, and soon these Europeans were moving up the beautiful and fertile valleys of the Cape, establishing vineyards. By 1756 the free burgher population of the colony had reached 5,123, and that of the slaves over 6,500, outnumbering the whites by about 1,200. By the middle of the eighteenth century, three groups made up the slaves: Africans imported from other parts, Malays, and half-castes. The latter group were mixtures of Europeans with slaves or Hottentots; today these people of miscegenation are a part of the Cape Coloured.

The frontier life, the freedom from performing grinding labor themselves, the nomadism that associated itself with the cattle industry and the search for pastures and water, troubles with the natives, the separation of the trekboers from close political and judicial ties with Cape Town, all acted to breed within the frontiersmen strong feelings of independence and self-reliance, and a reluctance to accept the imposition of the law of the outside (Cape Town).

Trekking was a part of their life and tradition by now. Climatic conditions were such that what with a series of good years followed by a series of drought and bad years, they had to be ready to move when the necessity arose; and at least along the eastern frontier, the more arid lands were those occupied by the whites; across the frontier, the lands of the black Bantu were better watered.

## BRITISH–FRENCH RIVALRY FOR THE CAPE

In Cape Colony the Dutch held the most strategic bit of land on the long route to the East. Both Britain and France envied the Netherlands this holding and sought in divers fashion to acquire it. A long and complicated history of rivalry among French, British, and Dutch for this strategic holding eventuated at last (January, 1806) in the capitulation of Cape Colony to the British; the Congress of Vienna confirmed Britain's rights to the Colony under the terms of a treaty in 1814.

By this time, border disputes with natives had become more frequent and had gained in intensity, especially along the eastern frontiers where the Xhosas had actually moved in and occupied some of the Colony territories. To help create a populated frontier that could be a buffer against native attacks, the British colonial authority tried to induce Britishers to settle in South Africa, the only alternative to the maintenance of an expensive military force to protect the frontier. The plan for settlement was successful, for in 1820 some 4,000 Britishers left the islands for South Africa.

The new colonists doubled the settlers of British nationality, who now made up about one-seventh of the total population of 47,000; the eastern frontier became predominantly British; some also settled in Natal (1824). From this time on the status of the Colony, which had begun changing very early under the Dutch from a way station to a settled colony, became very apparent. It was a colony in its own right.

*The Great Trek.* What caused the Great Trek that began in the early 1830s and resulted in the establishment of the independent states of Transvaal and the Orange Free State?

There were a number of causes, not one. In a sense, the Great Trek was simply a phenomenon of the moving frontier—a moving out, a migration, from the first center of settlement around Table Bay toward and across the peripheries. The risky character of the frontier itself might have been cause enough to start the Boers into the great migration; this did not spark the outward drive of the ox teams, however, although it was one of the influencing elements.

The trekkers did not migrate by chance. Before any group set out, at least three exploratory parties had investigated the practicability of trekking as far eastward as Natal, northeastward to the Zoutpansberg (mountains, continuing the Drakensberg escarpment, in northern Transvaal), and, along the west, north to beyond the present location of Windhoek. The trek was organized, and the number of people involved was large; *the move was made by a group that was resisting change.* The shuffling of control of the colony between the Dutch and British, the abolition of slavery and the inadequacy of compensation to the slave owners for the slaves (accompanied by the difficulty of obtaining payment from the government offices in London), plus the feeling among the cattle farmers that the government was increasingly interfering in personal affairs (Ordinance 50) and not enough in those realms that were really governmental such as border protection, caused much bitterness against the authorities in Cape Town, who were now British. These especially contributed to set the trek in motion. "Actually," states de Kiewiet, "its striving was to maintain itself unchanged. There was little room for the development of liberal ideas about the status of a servile population."[7]

Why the Boers migrated is not an easy question to answer, and prejudice colors most interpretations of the Great Trek. The events of the migration, however, are now legend. In part, this is so because of the scanty documentation left by the trekboers. Outside of Pretoria, on a mountain facing the city, is a huge monument erected to the *Voortrekkers.* On a frieze inside the monument are portrayed the storied incidents of the Great Trek as the tales passed down,

mainly by word of mouth, from past generations to the present one. Accented are: the battles of Vegkop (1836) and Kapain (1837)—during the battle of Kapain the Matabele were thrust northward to beyond the Limpopo, and the Transvaal thus made safe for colonization; the trek of the Boers, led by Retief and Maritz, across the Drakensberg escarpment and into Natal; the palavers of Retief with the Zulu chief, Dingaan, and the ensuing death of the Boer leader through Dingaan's treachery; the massacre of the Boers by the Zulus at Weenen (Place of Weeping); the Boer Vow, taken under Retief's successor, Pretorius, before the engagement at Blood River (1838), where Dingaan was defeated, and the erection of the Church of the Vow at Pietermaritzburg; the killing of Dingaan by the Swazis; Boer women doing the work of their men while the latter were in battle; the occupation of Natal by the British, and the emigration from Natal and recrossing of the Drakensberg by the trekboers; the Sand River Convention (1852) under which the British withdrew from the territory, and acknowledged the independence of the colony beyond the Vaal River. In 1854, under the Bloemfontein Convention, the independence of the Orange Free State was recognized.

## THE SCHISM BETWEEN THE WHITES

Cape Province expanded from Cape Colony, established along Table Bay, into its present large proportions. First settled in 1652, people of European descent have continuously lived here nearly as long as Europeans have inhabited New England. The indigenous people found in this area by the first Dutch settlers were Bushmen and Hottentots; the Bantu are as much newcomers into most of South Africa as are Europeans because they were moving south along the coast, and from there pushing west, at the same time that the Cape colonists were pushing east and north. The two racial groups reached the Great Fish River about the same time, approximately 1775.

When the British began to come in (about 1820), and British authority began to replace that of the Dutch, discontent caused many Dutch frontier farmers (*boeren*) to migrate outside British jurisdiction, and thus the Orange Free State and the Transvaal were set up, established as independent states by the

[7] C. W. de Kiewiet, *The Imperial Factor in South Africa,* London: Cambridge University Press, 1937, p. 3.

Boers. The new countries remained fairly free of any British pressure until the discovery of diamonds and gold in these territories. Then floods of prospectors, including many British, moved up to the new mining districts, and as trouble developed between the governments of the Boer states and the "foreign" colonists, the British stepped in and proclaimed the Transvaal to be British territory (1877). The Transvaal temporarily regained its independence (under British suzerainty) in 1881, but lost it again in 1902 when both the Transvaal and the Orange Free State were annexed as British colonies.

The Boer War was fought between 1899 and 1902, the climax of a series of events that were set in motion when the Cape settlement was ceded to the British in 1814. Although the aftermath of the Boer War was the establishment of the "Union" in 1910, it did nothing to bring the two white groups more closely together: the country remained divided into the two mutually suspicious groups as deeply as was the United States after the Civil War. On one hand were the Afrikaners, descendants of the original Dutch and French Huguenot settlers, essentially a rural, conservative people reared in Calvinism; on the other side of the divided white society were the descendants of the later British settlers, who for years have controlled the majority of the wealth of the nation—the gold and the diamonds, and the financial, business, and industrial establishments. Afrikaners hold only 1 percent of the mining interests, 6 percent of the manufacturing, 12 percent of the finance, and 25 percent of the commerce of South Africa.[8] Most of the tensions of the present Republic had their beginnings back in this turbulent history.

It is only within the context of this history that the present policy of separate development can be seen and understood.

## People and Population

The first official census made in South Africa was carried out in Cape Colony in 1865, but not until 1904 was a census taken simultaneously in all four provinces of the territory. In that year population totalled 5,174,827. In 1960, according to figures of the census of September of that year released in late 1963, population was 16,002,797; of these 3,088,492 were whites, 1,509,258 Coloureds, 477,125 Asians, and 10,927,922 Bantus; 1962 figures showed over 17,000,000 people living in South Africa. In percentage, there has been little change in racial composition during the century since 1865: Europeans decreased from 21.6 to 19.3 percent of the total; Bantu increased from 67.5 to 68.3 percent; Asians from 2.4 to 3.0 percent, Coloureds from 8.6 to 9.4 percent.

The Coloured make up the third largest racial group in the Union: 90 percent live in Cape Province, 5 percent on the Witwatersrand. They are, as noted, a mixed people who run the color gamut from dark to such light-hued skins that they are often mistaken for Europeans. They are not distinctive in race, language, or culture, and until they were removed from the European voting roll to a separate one of their own in 1956 by the National Party, they were officially classified as a subordinate part of the white race. They range the economic scale from farm laborers to artisans and professional people; socially, their position is more difficult than that of any other group, "being caught between the exclusiveness of the whites, with whom they would like to associate themselves, and the rising power of the Africans with whom they feel little in common."[9]

The Bantu of South Africa belong to four main tribes: Nguni which include the Zulu and Xhosa subgroups; Sotha; Venda; and Shangana-Tsonga. (See Figure 19.5a and b.) Some West African blood was introduced in the earliest days of slavery, but the majority of slaves in the Union came from Madagascar, and were racially black with an infiltration of Indonesian blood; linguistically they were Malagasy, and had only a smattering of Bantu words in their language.

Asians are largely of Indian origin because, according to official definition, the Cape Malays are Coloureds.

---

[8] *State of the Union Yearbook for South Africa, 1959–60,* Johannesburg: Da Gama Publications, 1961.

[9] Gwendolen M. Carter, *The Politics of Inequality,* London: Thames and Hudson, 1958, p. 19.

(a)

(b)

FIGURE 19.5  (a) Zulu kraal; (b) Pediland landscape: hoeing. (Courtesy South African Information Service, Bantu Administration Department.)

## PROVINCIAL DISTRIBUTION

The Coloured problem belongs to Cape Province despite the fact that two-thirds of the nonwhites are now Bantu, and less than one-third Coloured. Natal has an overwhelming nonwhite majority, nonwhites outnumbering whites 7 times; Bantu make up 83 percent of this majority. In no other province is the proportion of nonwhite to white so pronounced as in Natal. Natal also has the largest Asian population; out of some 487,000 Asians residing in the Republic, over 360,000 live in Natal. The Indian problem is, and has been, almost entirely Natal's, although soon after their arrival the Indians began to spread to other provinces. The Transvaal attempted to prohibit Indian immigration into its territories, but the London Convention of 1884 prevented this. The story of the Indian in the Transvaal parallels on a smaller scale that in Natal. In religion, the Indians are 72.7 percent Hindu, 19.4 percent Moslem, 4.9 percent Christian, and 0.8 percent Buddhist. They have remained an unassimilated group, racially and culturally pure.

Because it is the most heavily industrial, the Transvaal attracts many African laborers. Population here increased by 4½ times in the nearly 60 years of which there are records; four-fifths of these are nonwhite; and of the nonwhite majority, nearly 96 percent are Bantu. Bantu make up over 71 percent of the total population. Of the Bantu labor force of the Republic 98 percent are tribal Bantu, natives who come in from the "bush" to work under contract for a period of time. About one-third of these are South Africans; large numbers have come from Portuguese East Africa, and the rest are from the high commission territories and other nearby areas, such as Malawi. At present as much as one-fifth of the male labor force of Botswana and 43 percent of that of Lesotho are working in the South African mines and industries at any one time. Swaziland also sends large numbers of its men into the Republic as migratory laborers, under contract, generally, from 9 to 18 months, after which term they return to their homelands. About 70 percent of this Bantu force works underground in the mines.

The Free State with some 1,200,000 inhabitants has the smallest population; three-fourths are Bantu.

The European population is divided into English- and Afrikaans-speaking groups, the latter descendants of the original Dutch settlers mixing with French Huguenots, Germans, and some Scandinavians. About 45 percent speak English, and might be regarded as British, for they are largely of English, Scottish, and Irish descent; about 50 percent or more consider themselves Afrikaners.

## The Habitat

South Africa is one of the few parts of the continent that lies outside of the tropics, and climatically is healthful and invigorating. Like the coastal sections of the Atlas countries, the Cape is Mediterranean in climate, with mild but predominantly sunny winters with rain, and dry, warm, bright summers. Brilliant blue skies are typical; vegetation consists of moderately dense brush, similar to the chaparral of California, which is thoroughly adjusted to drought. Around the Cape the waters of two seas incessantly pound, and the coast stands out to meet the oceans in stark bold outlines.

On the opposite side of the country, Natal is humid subtropical, a softly rounded land whose hills are covered over large sections with jade green sugarcane fields; in the foothills of the Drakensberg a lush tropicallike vegetation belies the subtropical location. In general, Natal has year-round rainfall with a summer maximum, the winter months averaging about one-fourth to one-third as much rainfall as the months of summer.

Upon the plateau and into the interior, the climate becomes temperate with chilly winters and warm summers. All of this area is semiarid to arid, with most of the rain falling during the summer season, and winter months having almost no rain. Some parts, the deserts, have no predictable rain.

Scarcity of water is South Africa's greatest physical problem: over 85 percent of the country is semiarid; one-third receives less than 25 inches of rain a year, the minimum amount for cultivation in most parts of South Africa. No great lakes or large perennial rivers lie within its bounds, and even the Vaal-Orange system, largest of its stream systems, usually becomes low during the dry period. There is a saying in South Africa that "if you fall in a stream in the Orange Free State, get up and dust yourself off." On the other hand, rains, when they do occur, are likely to be torrential, and therefore very erosive in this semidry land, so that deep gullies (called dongas) scar the landscape, slopes are washed bare of soil, and the rivers at their mouths can be traced into the sea because of the loads of silt they carry off the land.

How large the Republic is may better be comprehended when we say that it is over 5 times the size of Great Britain, and larger than Germany, France, Italy, and Portugal put together. Of the four provinces that combine to form the state, Cape Province is the largest and southernmost, alone covering an area one-fifth greater than France; Transvaal, covering 110,450 square miles in the north, is nearly as large as all of the Philippines; Orange Free State is larger than the state of Louisiana; Natal, along the East coast, is the smallest, 33,578 square miles in size. South-West Africa, an arid territory in the west, to the north of the Cape by some distance, is twice as large as California. It is administered by the Republic as an integral part of the state, although the United Nations regards it as a trust territory. Formerly a German colony, it was mandated to Great Britain after World War I, and then transferred by Great Britain to the Union of South Africa. In October, 1966, the United Nations General Assembly voted the termination of the South African trusteeship over South-West Africa, declaring the territory to be "a direct responsibility of the United Nations." As of this writing South Africa does not recognize this decision.

## Economy

### AGRICULTURE

History and the resources and environment have influenced the way in which the provinces developed. In the Mediterranean region of Cape Province, in typical Mediterranean pattern, wheat is the main crop, grown on winter rain, as are also barley and oats for animal feed. Grapes and citrus grow in the fertile irrigated valleys in the western part of the province, again reflecting climatic influence, but also the historic. Although the first vine was planted by Commander Jan van Riebeeck himself in 1655, 3 years

(a)

FIGURE 19.6 Vine-wine culture in Cape Province: (a) vineyards along the Hottentot, Holland; (b) winery at Paarl; (c) grape
harvest in the Cape. (a and c courtesy South African Information Service; b photograph by writer.)

(b)

(c)

after the colony was founded, and the first wine pressed from South African grapes in 1659, it was the French Huguenots, who brought the vine-wine culture with them when they fled from France to South Africa, who extended the industry and made it an important one. The vineyards are limited to the southwestern districts of the Cape where the cool, rainy winters ensure a period of full dormancy for the plants, and where warm dry summers permit the grapes to grow and ripen into rich flavorful fruit. The coastal belt and irrigable valleys in the Little Karroo are the centers of vine-wine culture. The vine-wine culture is what particularly distinguishes agriculture in the Cape from that of all other areas in the Republic (see Figure 19.6).

In addition to grapes and citrus fruits, apples, plums, and other deciduous fruits are also grown. Some of these are dried or canned, others go into the making of brandies, juices, and marmalades; many are packed and shipped to the fresh fruit markets of Europe, particularly Britain, whose fruit season is at the opposite time of year to that of South Africa. Some tobacco is raised in the irrigated valleys of the dry southwest, most of it of Turkish variety. Grazing is unimportant except for sheep. However, cattle are produced on fodder for dairy purposes and for meat, and the number could be increased if more land were put into feed crops.

In the southern coastal region of Cape Province, the winter rains of the Cape begin to blend with the summer rains of Natal, and here, where moisture is greater, wheat becomes less important and oats and potatoes increase. In places, as around George, fruit growing is carried on, especially apples. Natural pastures are improved here over those of the southwest, and both cattle and sheep (for wool) increase in number—sheep on the drier slopes, both beef and dairy cattle in the better watered districts.

In the arid lands of the Great and Little Karroo, most of the streams are intermittent in their flow, and only where large dams have been constructed can the land be intensively cultivated. Such valleys as those of the Sundays, Dwyka, and Olifants rivers are very productive; here lucerne (alfalfa) and citrus fruits are the outstanding crops. Near the base of the Great Escarpment, tobacco, grapes, and lucerne (or wheat, sometimes) are grown under irrigation,

but this cannot be so intensive as where dams have assured a continuous supply of water. Grazing is important in the Karroos because, although the carrying power of the land is low, the vegetation is nutritive. Land holdings of those who graze animals are large, ranging between 4,000 and 10,000 acres. On the upper Karroo, pasture is very meager, and rainfall not only slight but uncertain. Here farm sizes average between 4,000 and 20,000 acres, and farmers depend upon underground water to supply their animals; sheep are the main resource. In a few spots along rivers, cultivation is carried on usually by a system of inundation basin irrigation, as in the Zak valley.

On the highveld of the Orange Free State and southern Transvaal is found the "maize triangle" of the Republic. Maize is the single most important crop cultivated in South Africa. Of the 115,000 white farmers of the Republic, approximately one-third commercially produce corn, part of which is exported. Since its introduction into South Africa, it has also replaced kaffir corn, a type of sorghum, as the main subsistence food of the Africans, who know it as "mealies"; Europeans, however, rarely eat maize although at first it was grown as a food; today, almost all of the European produced maize that is not exported is used as cattle feed. About 45 percent of the maize produced is grown in the "maize triangle" by European farmers, and from here also comes all that is exported; over 70 percent of the land cultivated in South Africa is sown to maize.

Along the edges of the maize belt, the land becomes wheat and sheep pasture country. The native grasses are not very nutritive for grazing however; according to plant scientists, they apparently lack some diet requirement of the animals; locusts are at times a plague. Only about one-fourth of the wool produced in South Africa comes from the Transvaal and Orange Free State. Wool is the biggest agricultural export commodity, and after gold the single biggest item on the list of South African exports; 85 percent is merino wool, and of very high quality. The Karroo is the main center of the sheep raising industry. About 65 percent of the annual wool clip is produced in Cape Province, 20 percent in the Orange Free State, and 6 percent in the Transvaal; the balance comes from South-West Africa.

Despite the difficulties imposed by climate the veld is spotted with farms, and buildings are often sheltered by orchards of trees that have been planted—gum, pine, apples, or even Australian wattle. However, the windmill is an almost invariable feature, used for pumping water to the surface. Despite the problems that beset the farmers, the "triangle" is a very important agricultural region; and about 75 percent of all of the land cultivated in the Republic is found here. The difficulties that harass the veld sound very similar to those that plague the Great Plains region of the United States: good years are followed by bad ones, when drought, hail, or excess rain may destroy or harm crops. Bloemfontein is the market center for the highveld, situated on the drier margins of the region in the sheep-wheat country rather than in the central maize area.

Sugar, like maize, holds a major place in the agricultural economy of South Africa. It was introduced into Natal in 1851, into an area near Umhlali some 30 miles out of Durban, and from here it has spread south and north, even into Zululand. Natal is possibly unique in the world in having developed a system of raising cane on hillslopes. At present, ½ million acres of land are planted to sugar, and although continuously cultivated, fertility of the soil is maintained and erosion checked even on the steepest slopes. The rolling hills of Natal behind the coast are covered with cane in various stages of growth. Cane takes about 2 years to mature in this subtropical region.

The most pressing problem faced by the sugar industry in the years of its earliest development was a labor shortage, and to alleviate the need for workers in the sugar fields and mills, Indians were brought in as indentured labor. Now, however, Indians have been replaced on the plantations and in the factories by Bantu labor, Indians having gone into other lines of work.

Perhaps the greatest impetus to the expansion of sugar in Natal was the opening of the many rich mining fields in South Africa, providing a market outlet for the sugar. Natal takes care of the sugar needs of the entire country and even exports some. By 1958 to 1959 it had become one of the eight cane growers of the world that produce more than 1 million tons of sugar; it ranked seventh in cane sugar production in 1963–1964. See Figure 19.7.

### Problems and Possibilities in Agriculture.

South African agriculture is confronted with difficulties, both natural and man-made, that raise problems for cultivation. Rainfall is erratic and generally low, arable soil is scarce, and there are numerous pests to combat; overcropping during the pioneer period exhausted and caused erosion over much of the land. However, for a number of years, farmers and government have worked together to restore fertility and halt erosion through conservation measures. An intensive research program is in progress to combat plant and animal diseases and pests, to introduce suitable varieties of plants and improve seed, and to bring in new animal breeds; the improvement of old breeds is a part of the program. New peach, apricot, strawberry, wheat, and kaffir corn varieties, hybrid maize, and new strains of cattle and sheep like Bonsmara, the Dorper, and the Dohne merino have contributed greatly to higher production. Cotton is illustrative of the improvement and expansion that is being made in most phases of agricultural and animal production in South Africa.

Cotton has been grown in South Africa since American Civil War days, when it was introduced to help fill the import vacuum of English mills cut off from cotton supplied by the Southern States. New methods of combatting insect pests, prospects for more water for irrigation, better adapted varieties, guaranteed prices by cotton mills for all cotton produced, and the overproduction of certain other crops in the cotton areas have stimulated cotton production so that it is now increasing strongly in the Republic, as is cotton consumption.

The area planted to cotton has risen to over 40,000 acres a year, dry land area in Natal and Transvaal accounting for about two-thirds of this, irrigated land on the lower Orange River for the rest; most of the latter is centered around Upington. Much land is available in the dry land regions for the extension of cotton growing; expansion is expected to take place in the irrigated sectors also. "It is claimed that insect control methods alone can step up cotton production fourfold in the near future."

Agriculture in South Africa presents a variety and vigor exceeded by few countries. In the last decade the volume of agricultural produce has doubled, and South Africa is becoming self-sufficient in an increas-

FIGURE 19.7  Scenes in the humid coastal belt of Natal, up and down from Durban: (a, above) irrigated sugar fields; the irrigation channel follows the contours above the narrow-gauge rail line; (b, below) cutting the cane, done by hand in Natal; (c, right) cane-growing areas of Natal (a and b courtesy South African Information Service; c from Owen Williams, "Sugar Growing and Processing in the Union of South Africa," Economic Geography, vol. 35, no. 4, October, 1959. Courtesy Economic Geography.)

(b)

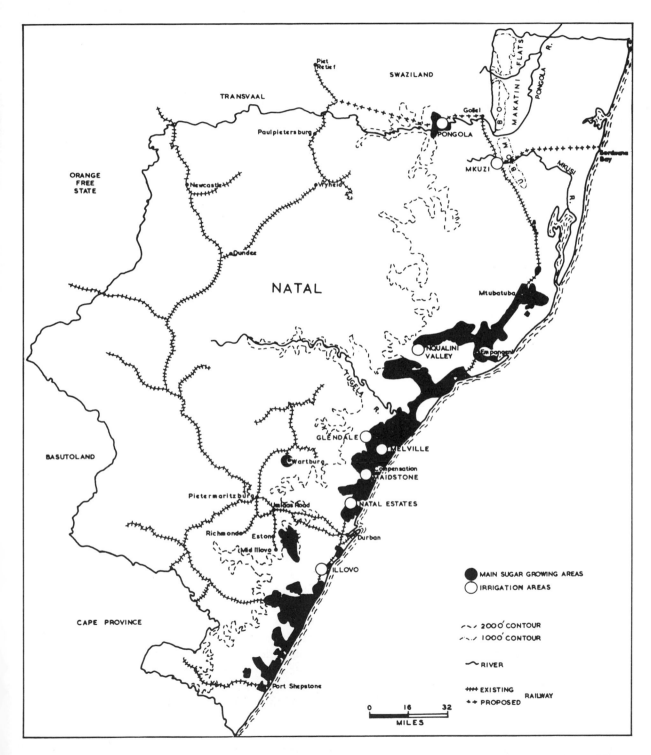

MAIN SUGAR GROWING AREAS

IRRIGATION AREAS

2000' CONTOUR

1000' CONTOUR

RIVER

EXISTING RAILWAY

PROPOSED

0   16   32

MILES

(c)

ing measure; the value of food imports is less than one-tenth of the total value of the food consumed. This has been an aim of the government in the face of the mounting opposition from the outside to its policy of separate development.

*Summary.* Because of the low carrying capacity of the land, pastoralism is the most important side of the agricultural scene, nearly 90 percent of the area of South Africa being devoted to grazing. The sheep are raised mainly for wool, 85 percent being wool producers; over four-fifths are merinos; wool ranks after gold among South African exports. Two-thirds of the country's sheep are grazed in Cape Province; the drought-ridden Great Karroo produces the merino sheep. Mohair goats are also raised. The industry is centered in Cape Province, and South Africa ranks third in the world in mohair production.

Cattle do not rank in numbers or importance with sheep, and South Africa does not meet its meat needs. The indigenous Afrikander cattle are the dominant breed, and over 40 percent are Bantu owned. A number of European-bred dairy cattle have been introduced, and dairying has greatly increased in recent years both on intensive dairy farms and on farms where multipurpose cattle are grazed on natural pastures.

The cultivation phase of the rural economy has experienced a near revolution in methods and production in recent years: mechanization has greatly increased and the value of output from farms has risen by one-half since World War II. The importance of maize and sugar among tilled crops has been noted. Fruits also are highly significant. The citrus are widely scattered from western Cape Province and coastal sectors in the eastern parts of the Cape, to subtropical Natal around Durban, to several areas in the Transvaal (north, west, and east). The largest citrus farm in the world is said to be at Zebediela in the northern Transvaal; in 1961, nearly 1 million citrus trees were set out here. Citrus fruits rank after maize in value of crop exports. In the Natal and eastern Cape Province, subtropical in location but near tropical in climate, tropical fruits grow—bananas, pineapples, and even papayas and mangoes; papaya production has reached an annual value of about ½ million dollars.

The "controlled marketing" of animal and cropped products is a characteristic of South African agriculture. "Some 17 control boards regulate approximately 70 percent of the total value of" all such produce sold. Exclusive of wool, most of the farm products exported "are sold at a loss, sometimes at a substantial cost to the government" in subsidies to the farmers. Certain crops, however (like citrus), have the advantage of producing for their European markets at the European off-seasons, winter in the Northern Hemisphere coinciding with summer in the Southern.

Cooperatives are another feature of the rural economy. The citrus and vine-wine industries are highly organized on this basis; in fact, the Cooperative Winegrowers Association (KWV), with headquarters at Paarl, "regulates the supply of wine" for the home market, and has done much to increase the foreign market.[10]

Long distances, high temperatures, and vast areas that are sparsely populated make transport of perishable products expensive and inconvenient. In spite of these handicaps, South Africa has established an exceptionally efficient distribution system, and marketing costs compare favorably with those in even more industrialized Western nations.

## MINING AND INDUSTRY

Most minerals of South Africa are concentrated in the northeastern part of the country. Although the Republic has a great variety of both metallic and nonmetallic minerals, gold overshadows them all in the commercial life of the country. South Africa yearly produces more than one-half of the world's gold.

The story of gold in South Africa (Figure 19.8*a* to *c*) began when the world was very young—when forces at work on the surface of the earth deposited a deep band of sediments (later compressed into rocks), varying in thickness from 14,000 to 27,000 feet, in the present Transvaal-Orange Free State goldfield. This series of rocks is known as the Witwatersrand system. It occurs as a large synclinal structure roughly similar in shape to an elongated saucer that measures more than 200 miles along the arc of its northern

[10] William A. Hance, *The Geography of Modern Africa,* New York: Columbia University Press, 1964, pp. 544–548.

(a)

(b)

FIGURE 19.8  (a, above) Overburden from the gold mines in Johannesburg rises like flattened pyramids; (b, below) gold bars; (c, next page) the Witwatersrand. (a and b, courtesy South African Information Service.)

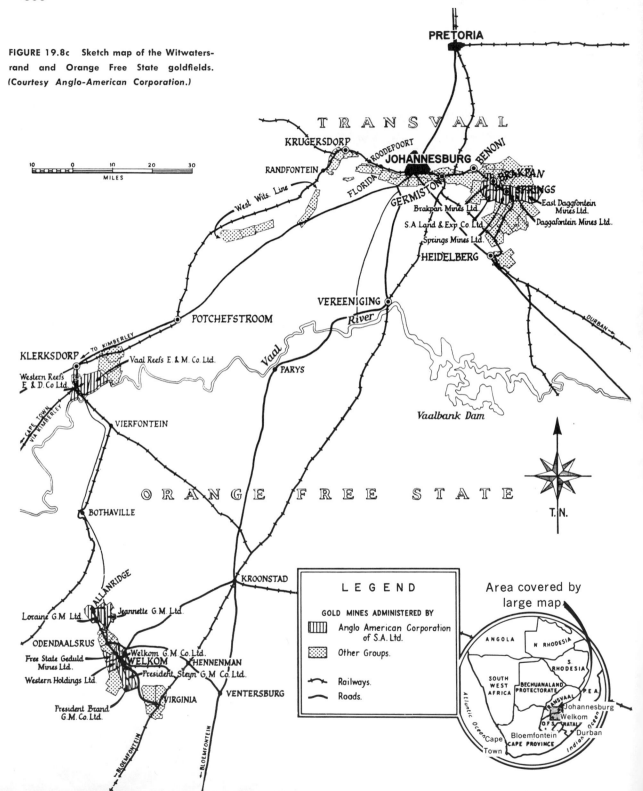

FIGURE 19.8c   Sketch map of the Witwaters-rand and Orange Free State goldfields. (Courtesy Anglo-American Corporation.)

edge. In the course of the centuries, younger rocks covered the earlier sedimentary beds, and later, pressures on the earth's crust tilted the rocks, pushing them again toward the surface; as more centuries passed, erosion helped them to become exposed. The Witwatersrand extends across the grasslands of Transvaal and the plains of Orange Free State: 57 large mines produce an average of 16.5 million ounces of gold a year, and towns and mines dot all of the 200-mile rim of this ancient sedimentary system. The Witwatersrand is the world's largest goldfield.

Shaft mining is necessary to obtain the gold, and several hundred holes bore into the formations, the deepest to 11,000 feet. For a long time the economy of South Africa was supported by gold. This is no longer true, although gold is the single most valuable product produced and exported. All the gold from South Africa's mines is sent for refining to one central plant, located at Germiston near Johannesburg; it is the largest plant of its kind in the world, and from here the bricks of pure, refined gold go out to all corners of the earth.

Already the world's largest single source of gold, South Africa is also now the world's third largest producer of uranium; and the Republic has some of the world's largest proven reserves of uranium-bearing ores. Although production began only in 1952, the ore had been identified in the conglomerate formations of the Witwatersrand many years before. With the discovery that the nucleus of uranium was fissionable the early scientific reports, some of which were gathered as early as 1915 and 1923, were useful in making further explorations. The uranium is found in association with the gold, but although it occurs wherever gold occurs, only 23 mines produce uranium, because elsewhere the ore bodies do not contain sufficient uranium to make extraction worthwhile.

Three factors contribute to the strong position of the Republic in the uranium industry. First, there is the advantage of the resources of the established and highly-organized gold mining industry in making production economic; second, the ore bodies are regular and consistent; and third, the consistency of the South African ore bodies in the existing goldfields makes possible the accurate assessment of ore reserves in the same way that gold ore reserves are calculated.

However, it was the discovery of diamonds in 1867,

and the subsequent mining of them, that set South Africa on the road to industrialization. Today, with gold and uranium, diamonds are one of the chief sources of national income and foreign exchange. The combined diamond output of South Africa and South-West Africa is worth more than that of any country in the world—this, despite the fact that The Congo produces the greatest quantity: the diamonds from The Congo are mainly of the industrial variety; most of the world's gem diamonds come from the mines of South and South-West Africa. The average annual value of the gem diamonds produced in South Africa is about 53 percent of the total value of diamonds of gem variety recovered in the world.

In South Africa most of the diamonds occur in the famous kimberlite pipes (Figure 19.9a to c); in South-West Africa, they are alluvial, found in gravel beds far removed from the locale of their formation by the denudation of pipes. Three pipe mines operate at Kimberley, the Dutoitspan, Bultfontein, and Wesselton; others are the New Jagersfontein mine at Jagersfontein in the Orange Free State, and the Premier mine at Cullinan, near Pretoria, in the Transvaal. Alluvial deposits are found sporadically along the banks of the Vaal River, at Kleinzee on the Namaqualand coast of Cape Province, and at Alexander Bay where the State alluvial diggings are situated. But the main alluvial diamond area is at Oranjemund in South-West Africa, and northward along the coast for more than 50 miles. Here the marine beach deposits of Consolidated Diamond Mines of South-West Africa yielded 980,000 carats in 1957, of which 95 to 98 percent were of the gem variety.

Considerable resources of coal lie beneath the surface of South Africa's soil,[11] and proven deposits of

---

[11] Although the Republic has large reserves of coal, only a limited number of the beds are developed; South Africa has no shortage of fuel for transportation. However, where long distance passenger train services and heavy freight trains are operated over difficult terrain, electric traction has been found both more economical and more efficient than coal-burning locomotives. About 6 percent of the rail service is electrified (including suburban trains) and it is being extended. In 1963, 46,798,000 metric tons of marketable coal (bituminous and anthracite) were produced (*Minerals Yearbook*, U.S. Bureau of Mines, 1963; *Statistical Yearbook*, New York: United Nations, 1964).

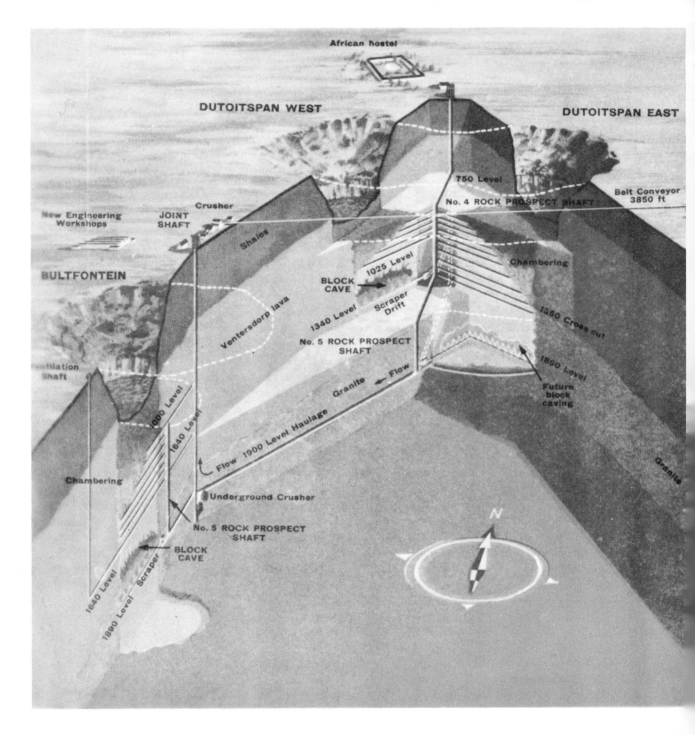

**FIGURE 19.9a** Aerial perspective and cutaway section of three operating mines at Kimberley showing Bultfontein, Dutoitspan, and Wesselton mines in relation to the new treament plant. The surface is cut away in the foreground to show the interconnecting underground haulage between Dutoitspan and Bultfontein.

All ground at Dutoitspan and Bultfontein is hoisted up the joint shaft at Bultfontein and is then transported to the new treatment plant by means of a covered conveyor on the surface.

Bultfontein mine came into partial production again during April, 1958, with ground from block caving. The western half of Dutoitspan is mined by block caving and the eastern section by the chambering method. This system is envisaged for the next drop-down on the eastern section of Dutoitspan.

Wesselton mine operates separately and only chambering is being done. The 2160 development is being transported to the new treament plant by an endless rope haulage, but will be replaced by a 10,500-foot conveyor. (*Courtesy South African Information Service.*)

(b)

FIGURE 19.9  (b, above) Diamond selection, Premier mines; (c, below) scraping diamonds off the grease table, Premier mines. (Courtesy South African Information Service.)

(c)

iron ore compare very favorably in quantity and quality with some of the world's greatest producers. Only the United States, India, Brazil, and France are greater. The main ore fields occur in the Rustenburg district in the Transvaal, the Postmasburg arc of Cape Province, and around Dundee in northern Natal. Production is still small, however, only slightly above 3 million long tons annually.

Since the Republic also has deposits of manganese, it has all the most basic raw materials for a steel industry. Including the relatively small production of manganese from South-West Africa, South Africa accounts for over 9 percent of the world's manganese production; the combined output makes it the third highest producer; about two-thirds of this is exported. The deposits found in the Postmasburg area are among the finest in the world, superior for the hardness of the ores, which means a minimum of loss during transport.

The Republic is the world's third largest producer of asbestos; and it has probably the world's largest deposit of titaniferous magnetite. This latter ore contains about 10 to 15 percent titanium, and 1.5 percent vanadium. If an economic method of treating the ore is found, South Africa could become the world's leading producer of titanium. Other minerals occur, but they do not have the importance of the ores listed.

*Industry.* In addition to the industries associated with mining, such as diamond cutting and polishing, gold refining, the processing of uranium, and the like, and the processing of agricultural, fish, and meat products, South Africa also has a small iron and steel industry that produces over 2 million metric tons of steel a year, a tire plant at Port Elizabeth owned by Firestone, a General Motors automobile assembly plant at East London, great shipbuilding and repair yards, and many factories that produce consumer goods, such as shoes, clothing, and the like. Industry is expanding rapidly, and foreign capital is being encouraged to invest.

Among recent developments in the mining and industrial fields are both power and factory projects. The vast scheme on the Orange River, set up in mid-1963, is one of these. The first phase calls for two huge water-storage dams and power control stations, a 50-mile tunnel connecting the Fish and Orange rivers, and a 100-mile pipeline from the eastern Cape Province to Bloemfontein, the latter a water and irrigation pipeline. The construction of a pipeline for the transport of petroleum products between Durban and the Witwatersrand has been approved. Another very complex operation, the transfer of a section of the Lancashire cotton industry of England, was set in motion in May, 1963: new factories, being built near East London, will hold the looms and other machinery being shipped from the cotton district in England; trained workers and their families are transferring from the historic factory area to the new one in South Africa. In other words, an industry is being moved, complete with labor.

A submarine pipeline to pump diesel oil and petrol from ship to shore was completed in early 1963 off the South-West African coast at Oranjemund, to supply the Consolidated Diamond Mines of South-West Africa with its fuel needs. It replaced the expensive and slow system of overland deliveries from Port Nolloth, 60 miles south of Oranjemund. The largest petroleum refinery in Africa south of the Sahara, Shell and BP South African Refineries' plant at Reunion near Durban, went into production in October, 1963. It produces a complete range of petroleum products, and represents more than 60 percent of the existing petroleum refining capacity in the Republic, and 15 percent of that of the entire African continent.

The historic De Beers diamond mine in the center of Kimberley, "the biggest man-made hole in the world," was reopened in mid-1963 after having been closed down for 55 years. It reached full scale production again in 1965. New methods of mining and of treating diamond-bearing blue ground influenced the decision to recommence production. Alcan Aluminium of South Africa began construction of an aluminum sheet mill at Pietermaritzburg in June, 1963, that will increase that company's output by 2.5 times.

Construction work preparatory to mining copper on an unprecedented scale in South Africa began in mid-1963 at Phalaborwa. When in full production, approximately one-third of the copper taken will supply the entire needs of the Republic; the remainder will be exported. It is estimated that 300 million tons of ore will eventually be removed from this mine, which will be worked by open-pit methods. The copper content of the ore is relatively low, but the scale of operations is expected to make the project economic. Vermiculite and phosphate rock already are mined as large scale projects at Phalaborwa. The phosphate rock is likewise taken by open-pit methods.

The timber industry, including the construction of sawmills and wood products factories, is expanding. This industry faces many challenges and difficulties, however, because scarcely any of the South African forests are natural, and the timber holdings are relatively young; as yet, the Republic does not produce timber in lengths much beyond 20 feet; competition from plastics and steel also adds problems.

Despite the attempts at sanctions against South Africa, foreign trade has increased.

## Cities South of Capricorn

### JOHANNESBURG, "CITY OF GOLD"

Johannesburg on the "Rand" is the industrial and business giant of the Republic, the most modern city on the African continent, and with a population of more than 1 million people, the largest city south of Cairo. It was built *on* gold, *of* gold, and *for* gold; it is the focal city for all of the gold mining centers that arc outward from it east to southeastward to Heidelberg, and southwest, south, and then southeastward to Welkom. Here are located the head offices of the Anglo-American Corporation of South Africa, one of the greatest corporate entities in the world, of which De Beers is a subsidiary.

Only a little more than 75 years ago there was nothing on this patch of veld of the Transvaal highveld: the Witwatersrand, the Ridge of White Waters, curled along the breadth of the great plain, the potentially richest plain in the world because the Ridge of White Waters is the famous gold reef that sweeps in a vast semicircle over the Transvaal. Johannesburg now stands on "the reef," approximately centering it.

The city was founded almost immediately after the spectacular gold strikes were made in the Rand in 1886, because the government in Pretoria sent representatives to the area, in the mid-1886s, to "proclaim"

**FIGURE 19.10** Looking at Johannesburg across railway tracks and station. *(Courtesy South African Information Service.)*

the fields and choose a likely place for a town. The location chosen was that now occupied by Johannesburg. The industrial empire controlled from this city and Zambia reaches northward across Rhodesia and from ocean to ocean across southern Africa.

Undoubtedly Johannesburg will continue to be the industrial center of the Republic even after the gold in the Witwatersrand is exhausted. Uranium will likely carry on the mining, and further, the city lies within the rich agricultural heart of the maize triangle, and is a natural market center for all of the area. It is the hub of South Africa's transport system because when the gold mines were developed, all routes were focused on the Witwatersrand in deference to the importance of the precious metal.

## THE CAPITAL CITIES: CAPE TOWN AND PRETORIA

South Africa has two capitals, a recognition of the place of the historical in the present. Pretoria, 34 miles north of Johannesburg and capital of one of the former Dutch republics (Transvaal) is the administrative capital of the Republic; Cape Town, on Table Bay in Cape Province, first white settlement in Cape Colony and capital of the early Colony, is the parliamentary capital. Consulates and embassies are distributed between the two centers. Bloemfontein is sometimes regarded as a third capital city, for the Supreme Court sits in session there.

Pretoria, "City of the Blue Jacaranda," has a population of over 415,000 inhabitants. The city is one of great dignity and beauty, steeped in the traditions of Boer history. It is largely governmental.

Cape Town is more than governmental, for it is a port as well; its population numbers three-quarters of a million people. The situation of Cape Town is remarkably beautiful—facing Table Bay, and couched within the rugged arc of Devil's Peak, Table Mountain, and Lion's Head. With over 300 years of unbroken history since its founding by Jan van Riebeeck, the city reflects its age, and its mixed traditions and cultures: Dutch and Cape-Dutch architecture blend with modern buildings to give the city architectural individuality; the jumble of its streets gives it a quaint character, and the variety of its population has evolved tricks of speech that are colorful. Malay and Coloured are found here in greater numbers than elsewhere in the Republic. In fact, the Malay-Coloured problem is scarcely even a problem of Cape Province, but rather of Cape Town itself.

Table Bay is a vast semisheltered inlet, within which a commodious artificial harbor has been built through the construction of breakwaters. Cape Town is not the leading port of South Africa, but it handles about one-fourth of the Republic's overseas trade, both imports and exports; general cargo, maize, and fruits are its main exports. It is an important refueling port, about half of the oil imported going out as fuel for ships; coal is shipped as bunker cargo.

## DURBAN: PORT OF SOUTH AFRICA

Durban, being nearest to the Witwatersrand and the Free State gold fields, is the major port of the Republic. General cargo, maize, wattle bark and extract used in tanning leather, sugar, coal, ore, and minerals are shipped out; it has a big oil port. It is also a large industrial, commercial, and fishing center, including among its industries a sizable whaling fleet, sugar manufacturing, and some of the biggest textile, soap, rubber, cigarette, fertilizer, and paint factories in the country. In addition, Durban is one of the foremost resort cities in Africa; its waterfront, offside from the harbor, is lined with luxury resort hotels; a bracing climate the year around draws people from the more tropical lands, seeking relief from the constant heat and humidity; the large Indian community, with its colorful markets, also attracts tourists. Much of the prosperity of Durban derives from its function as a port, however, because over half of South Africa's ship cargo passes through here.

The early history of Durban is largely the history of Natal. Vasco da Gama, who pioneered the sea route to India, passed along this coast on Christmas Day, 1498, and, because of the day, christened the land "Terra Natalis." However, it was 325 years before any attempts were made to settle Natal. There was little to attract explorers along this coast: the plain fronting the sea is rarely more than 12 miles deep; there are no broad, deep rivers leading into the interior; and the only practicable harbor—Natal harbor —is obstructed by shifting sandbars. However, in 1824 the first landing was made, and a settlement began. It was called Port Natal, a name which the city retained until 1835 when it was renamed Durban, in honor

of the Governor of the Cape, Sir Benjamin D'Urban.

The port of Durban is situated on a landlocked lagoon, separated from the Indian Ocean by a barrier bar through which a passageway has been dredged to give access to the port. It is the third largest city in the Republic, very mixed in population, but with the highest proportion of Indians of any center in the Republic.

## LESSER PORTS

Port Elizabeth, East London, Mossel Bay, and Walvis Bay (South-West Africa) are also important outlets for the country. Port Elizabeth, second largest city in Cape Province and third port of the Republic, extends for 7 miles along the shores of Algoa Bay. Wool and citrus fruit are its main exports, followed by general cargo, minerals, and ores. East London is an export port for maize and wool; as noted, it is also becoming a major center of cotton manufacture. Walvis Bay handles largely minerals and ores.

## HARBOR IMPROVEMENTS

Port improvements have been major among the developments designed to strengthen the South African economy. An ore loading installation at Port Elizabeth came into operation in April, 1963; it makes Port Elizabeth one of the modern ore harbors of the world. A widening of the entrance to Cape Town harbor, from 200 to 600 feet, was commenced in late 1961; and construction of a tanker berth, the first in Table Bay harbor, which was initiated in the last quarter of 1963, was completed before mid-1966. A new ocean terminal at Durban was used for the first time in July, 1962. All South African harbors are also being improved to meet the expanding demands of "coaster traffic," including plans to provide for all additional berths, cranes, and shed space, and enlarged ship repair facilities.

The number of ships and the amount of cargo handled by ports are growing, and railway and pipeline developments are keeping pace with increased cargo and with harbor improvements: the oil pipeline between the terminal at the port of Durban and Johannesburg has been mentioned; the electrification of railways for greater efficiency is being stepped up.

(a)

(b)

(c)

**FIGURE 19.11**  Durban (a, at left, top) at night; (b, at left, bottom) harbor and entry to it; (c, above) the Esplanade. (Courtesy South African Information Service.)

## African Enclaves of South Africa

Swaziland, Botswana, and Lesotho, enclaves within South Africa, have been administered by Great Britain under a High Commissioner of the British Crown, Swaziland and Botswana as protectorates and Lesotho as a colony. They had a varied history before they became high commission lands. (See Figure 19.2.)

Lesotho is that lofty, nearly impregnable country that sits atop the highest portion of the Great Escarpment. Its people, the Basutos, were warred on by the Zulus and Matabele, had many quarrels with the Boers, and in 1843 were taken under British "protection," to be annexed by the British in 1868 and made a part of Cape Colony 3 years later. In 1884 they were brought under direct control of the British government.

Lesotho is an African territory, without European settlers or landowners. The total population is probably over 800,000 of whom fewer than 2,000 are Europeans (government officials, traders, missionaries, artisans), about 250 Asians, and less than 650 mixed-bloods. The country comprises an area of over 11,500 square miles, of which no more than one-fourth is below 6,000 feet elevation—ranging upward from sea level; the high country is a formidable but picturesque plateau with elevations to 11,000 feet. Maseru, the capital and about 5,000 in population, is the only town of any size; it is connected by a railroad, 16 miles long, with the Bloemfontein-Natal line at Marseilles.

The Lesotho economy is one of subsistence agriculture and pastoralism, with wheat, corn, and sorghum grown as the main crops; sheep and cattle the most numerous animals. Soil erosion is a grave problem. To counter this the British have attempted to introduce such conservation practices as terracing, training banks, and grass strips where the land is cultivated, and attempts are being made to instruct the Africans in the practices of rotation grazing in the mountains, where livestock is important. The economy is closely tied to South Africa. Mohair and wool, the country's only major exports, are shipped through South Africa's markets; as much as a fourth of its people work in South African mines or industries, or on farms.

Lesotho became independent in 1966.

Botswana was occupied by the British in 1884, at the suggestion of Cecil Rhodes, and when organized as a British protectorate the following year, was divided into the Bechuanaland Protectorate and British Bechuanaland. The latter was attached to the Cape in 1895, but the Bechuanaland Protectorate north of the Molopo River remained British; it has been administered by the High Commissioner since 1891.

Botswana is a vast tableland of some 275,000 square miles, not yet entirely surveyed. The Kalahari Desert covers a large part of the southwestern part of the territory, merging gradually into the bushveld in the north and east. The 1957 census recorded fewer than 300,000 persons living here, of whom some 292,750 were indigenous Africans. This is essentially pastoral country, any cultivation depending directly upon rainfall or waters for irrigation. Livestock, hides, and so forth are exported, mainly to the Republic of South Africa, and such exported products reach a value of about 2.5 million pounds. There is some small production of minerals, namely, gold, manganese, and asbestos.

This sprawling, sandy protectorate in southern Africa became an independent country in September, 1966. For the occasion the new and modern city of Gaberones was established as the capital. Like Lilongwe and Beida, it is a deliberately chosen and planned capital. The site, in mid-1964 still a virgin land of thorny shrubs, small trees, and poor red soil, was dictated largely by water supplies; the large Gaberones Dam, recently completed, will meet the needs of the city for many years. Botswana is a resource-poor, underdeveloped country whose ties are very close to South Africa. It is land-locked, its capital lying 450 miles from the nearest coastline. Gaberones, although at an altitude of 3,329 feet, has the reputation of being one of the hottest centers in this hot, arid land; temperatures of 108°F are not uncommon. Independence will not be easy.

Swaziland became a high commission territory of the British in 1906. It is a small land, 6,704 square miles in area—approximately 120 miles north and south, and 90 east and west. Traveling the territory from west to east there are three successive belts longitudinally defined. The first, a spur of the Drakensberg Ranges, is a region of mountainous veld with average elevations of 3,500 feet, and heights rising above 6,000. The rugged terrain is cut through by river gorges whose steep, boulder-strewn slopes often defy cultivation but create scenes of great pictur-

esqueness. Sheep grazing is a winter occupation; forests have been planted, "believed to be the largest man-made forests in the world." Mbabane (population about 3,300 of whom some 1,090 are Europeans), the capital, is set near the eastern edge of this mountain belt of highveld; it looks eastward also to the second belt of middle veld, which lies about 2,000 feet lower than the highveld.

The middle veld is a region of rolling grasslands given over to mixed farming and dairying. Such subtropical and tropical crops as citrus, pineapples, bananas, cotton, rice, and tobacco are raised. Around Bremersdorp and Goedgegun are concentrations of Europeans practicing plantation agriculture and mixed farming. Both the high and middle veld are very well watered, and many small rivers unite with larger ones to drain the country generally from west to east. Only the lowveld, with elevation ranging from 500 to 1,500 feet, is not well watered. It reaches to the eastern border. Heat during the summer period becomes excessive, and yet this area also holds some small but important concentrations of European population, as at Stegi. In the northeast is the Swaziland irrigation scheme, a large scale undertaking of the Colonial Development Corporation, using water drawn from the Komati and Black Mouluzi rivers. In the central eastern area is the Big Bend irrigation project, expected to become an important center for growing sugarcane. Rice, cotton, citrus and other tropical fruits, and vegetables are raised on the irrigated lands of the lowveld.

Some of the best land in Swaziland has been taken up by Europeans.

# 20 THE EAST AFRICAN REALM

*They came to the Delectable Mountains.*

JOHN BUNYAN, *Pilgrim's Progress*

## The Realm

East Africa reaches from the northern bounds of Mozambique, Zambia, and Malawi to the Red Sea and the Gulf of Aden, and from the eastern borders of The Congo and Sudan to the Indian Ocean. Ethiopia and the Horn, the East African plateau and the neighboring ocean littoral, and the offshore islands of Zanzibar, Pemba, and Madagascar are included. The western borders of the region toward the north are marked by the abrupt edge of the Ethiopian plateau as it drops to Sudan; along the north, the East African plateau also falls to Sudan; between The Congo and the Lake plateau, rift lakes and mountains outline the limits; in the east it falls to the sea. There are a number of reasons why it is practicable to consider this whole territory as a realm: the plateau character of the East and the linking of the series of faults, in the enormous depression that is known as the great rift valley, across the entirety of this plateau area make it geologically and physiographically a unit; and the cultural and commercial associations of the eastern littoral and the offshore islands tie these sectors closely to the Great Lakes plateau.

East Africa is cut through by the Equator, and all sectors lie well within the tropics: it extends from beyond 10°S to nearly 20°N. However, within the tropical similarity of location there are some extremes of climate, induced both by latitude and altitude. The temperature contrasts tend to be altitudinally determined, because except for differences in elevation, all of these lands would be hot all of the year. The large differences in altitude induce dissimilarities not only in temperature, however, but in precipitation as well. Lands with tropical and equatorial locations are moderated in temperature, while summer reigns forever and winter never comes; high plateaus that have their roots in deserts are drenched with rain and rise like lofty islands of green from sterile, arid lands; plateaus that straddle the Equator have eternal snow on some of their mountains and are not equatorial, as might be expected, but tropical—wet and dry, similar in temperature, rainfall regime, and vegetation to the lands that lie next to the equatorial zones rather than in them.

The Lakes plateau and the adjacent littoral and Ethiopia are lands of mixed and varied peoples and cultures; Somalia, although closer to the lines of world movement than many parts of Africa, has a relatively unmixed population, and both Ethiopia and Somalia are little known; in these countries nature is forbidding, the approaches make them relatively inaccessible, and man himself has not welcomed intruders.

It is in East Africa that the White Nile has its birth, and also the Blue Nile and the Atbara; through here flow the Juba River and the Webbe Shibeli, streams that struggle toward the sea across the dry wastes of Somalia, sometimes disappearing in the sands and not reaching the shore—in contrast to the Nile, which springing from the well watered equatorial and monsoon drenched uplands, survives across the thousands of miles of arid wastes to the distant Mediterranean.

East Africa is an area rich in history, but it is also one of the places that has suffered most bitterly from racial strife, because in all of the continent, there are few parts that compare to the Lakes plateau as an agreeable and healthful place to live.

The political units whose territories spread over East Africa include Tanzania, Kenya, Rwanda, Burundi, Uganda, Ethiopia, Somalia, French Somaliland, and the Malagasy Republic.

FIGURE 20.2 (Right) Physiography and rail approaches to the East African plateaus. (Base map Physiographic Diagram of Africa, copyright A. K. Lobeck; reproduced with permission of the publisher, The Geographical Press, a division of C. S. Hammond & Company, Maplewood, N.J.)

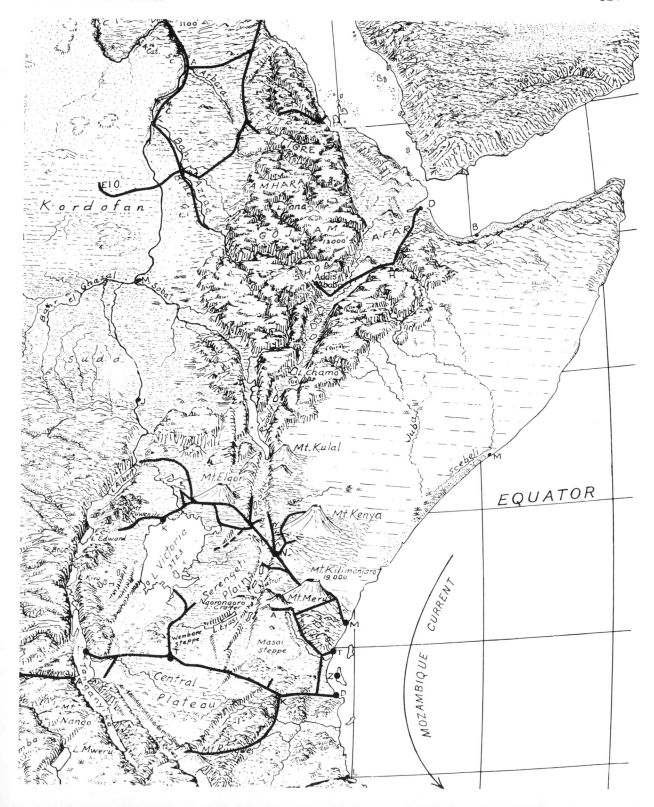

## The Natural Habitat

### PATTERNS OF RELIEF

The two great plateaus that occupy much of East Africa—the Lakes plateau, averaging above 3,000 feet elevation, and the loftier Ethiopian plateau, whose elevations rise to above 13,000 feet in places— are separated by two basin depressions that average not more than 1,500 to 2,000 feet in altitude (Figure 20.2). A bridge of higher land, seemingly forming a connection of a sort between the plateaus, stretches about centrally through the basins and causes them to drain in opposite directions. One of the depressions is a portion of the basin of the Bahr-el-Jebel of Sudan and looks inward toward that country and inner Africa; the other, occupying the northern part of Kenya and draining eastward, reaches its greatest depth in Lake Rudolf. It merges into the low, arid, and sparsely populated lands of Somalia.

The ethnography of the two plateaus indicates that the lowlands mark an important break also, because the lowland separates quite different peoples and dissimilar cultures. The Ethiopian plateau has tended to hold her own people to herself and to ward off invaders, not only because of the abruptness with which the escarpment rises along all sides of the massif, but also because of the aridity that characterizes the lower lands all around it: drought laps along the edges of the entirety of Ethiopia, and is an effective barrier.

The Ethiopians were themselves invaders of the area. They were members of an ancient Semitic people, akin to the Sabaeans, who came over to Africa from Arabia before the beginning of the Christian era, settling at first along the Red Sea coast to the south of Egypt. Reference to Figure 2.4 indicates that the people of the Ethiopian Plateau and the Horn are linguistically Afro-Asian.

The ethnographic structure of Ethiopia is extremely complex, nonetheless; and yet, in all of the peoples, "there is a common Ethiopic denominator—, [and] an undoubted close link between the Somalis and the Ethiopians taken as a whole."[1]

[1] Czesław Jeśman, *The Ethiopian Paradox*, London: Institute of Race Relations, Oxford University Press, 1963, p. 3.

On the other hand, the East African plateau has been the route of access to the very heart of the continent: all of inner Africa, including the entire Congo basin, unfolded to explorers and traders who entered from the coast opposite Zanzibar. Arabs, Malays, Greeks, and Portuguese entered these lands early. The Bantu invaded the East African plateau, but never penetrated even the margins of Ethiopia. The East African plateau, therefore, evolved varied and mixed populations and cultures that are, nevertheless, basically black African.

The physical aloofness of the Ethiopian plateau is especially pronounced along the west and south, and because of this, Ethiopia has been and is more detached from Egypt and Sudan than from other Arab lands; south of Ethiopia the depression has promoted isolation of the peoples of one plateau from the other. Hence, on the whole, Ethiopia and the Horn have remained ethnically fairly distinct from the lands around them.

### CLIMATE AND VEGETATION

Seasons in East Africa are based on rainfall, not temperature, but after that statement has been made, few other generalizations on climate are possible because dissimilarities are very marked. However, climatic changes are more pronounced altitudinally than latitudinally in terms of temperature; expressed in rainfall, both altitude and latitude induce differences in amount and seasonality.

Temperature changes induced by altitude are most pronounced in Ethiopia, where three zones are generally recognized: the *quolla*, hot lowlands of desert and semidesert; the *woina dega*, the cooler plateau country; and the *dega*, mountains where elevations are above 8,000 feet. In the Lakes plateau increasing altitude brings the same moderation of temperature, but we find, generally speaking, only two zones— warm lowlands and cool plateaus.

As to rainfall, Figures 20.3 and 20.4 show a moist coast in Tanzania and on the islands of Zanzibar and Pemba, with rainfall averaging 40 to 60 inches and higher. This whole region, except on islands, has a short dry season during the low sun period when rainfall averages less than 1 inch monthly for 2 or 3

**FIGURE 20.3 (Right)** Annual average rainfall, Lake Plateau. *(After Philips' Modern College Atlas of Africa, p. 50. Base map copyright George Philip & Son, Ltd., London. Used by permission. United States distributor, Denoyer-Geppert Company.)*

**FIGURE 20.4 (Below)** Seasons of annual rainfall of the Horn. *(After Philips' Modern College Atlas of Africa, p. 57. Base map copyright George Philip & Son, Ltd., London. Used by permission. United States distributor, Denoyer-Geppert Company.)*

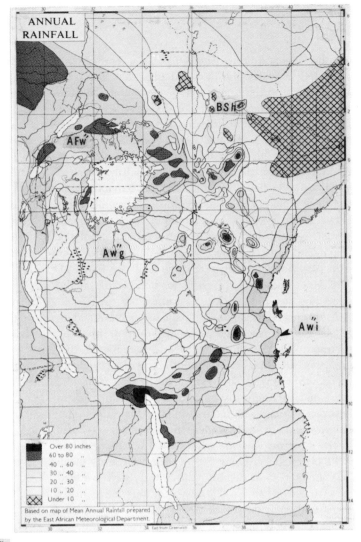

ANNUAL RAINFALL

Over 80 inches
60 to 80 ,,
40 .. 60 ,,
30 .. 40 ,,
20 .. 30 ,,
10 .. 20 ,,
Under 10 ,,

Based on map of Mean Annual Rainfall prepared by the East African Meteorological Department.

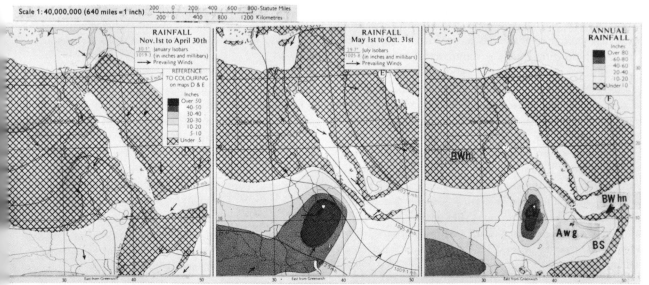

Scale 1:40,000,000 (640 miles = 1 inch)

months. Beyond the Kenya-Tanzania border this moist belt narrows abruptly and plays out along the northern half of the Kenya coast, where rainfall lessens to 30 or 40 inches a year, the dry season lengthens slightly, and drought, during the latter season, is more pronounced. As the Kenya-Somalia frontier is passed the 30- to 40-inch average declines to 30 to 20 to 10, to less than 10 inches. Mogadishu receives less than 16 inches of rainfall, and has 6 months with less than 1 inch of rain. As moisture lessens, distances between the isohyets broaden, and from not much beyond Mogadishu, desert country extends from the Somaliland coasts almost up to the base of the Ethiopian highlands; at best, these lands are semiarid. The water balance becomes more unfavorable in the same direction and at about the same rate.

Ascending the Ethiopian plateau, however, rainfall averages grow larger, as moisture is dropped by the monsoons that move in twice a year. Figure 20.4 indicates that the same rainfall pattern prevails to the south: on the southern third of the Tanzania coast and for some distance inland, rainfall averages between 30 and 40 inches; inland, the rainfall increases regularly as elevations rise, reaching a climax in the Rungwe volcanic mass at the northern end of Lake Nyasa, where over 80 inches a year are typical. The isohyet that delimits the rather well watered area receiving 40 to 60 inches of rain also nearly delimits the abrupt rise of central plateau of southern Tanzania. Spots of higher rainfall mark places of increased elevation, as on Mounts Kilimanjaro and Meru.

In contrast to the moisture pattern of increasing rainfall inland along the 10°S line, from about 8°S and north to the Equator the pattern is one of a moist littoral and decreasing rainfall, as the eastern slope of the plateau is mounted, to well beyond the eastern rift valley where the rainfall again increases toward Lake Victoria. The eastern slope of the plateau is, therefore, semiarid. Interruptions to this occur only where mountain projections wring out more moisture by forcing the winds to rise and cool orographically. This area is characterized generally by two rainy and two less rainy seasons. No month is rainless, and the two rainier periods are not equal; the "long rains" fall from April to June, and at higher elevations even to August, the "short rains" between October and December.

Except for the desert stations along the Red Sea coast and the lowland of the northern half of Somalia, where aridity reigns throughout the year, Somalia and Ethiopia show single seasons of wet and dry almost invariably; in places, the dry season is interrupted briefly by the "little rains" that generally occur in February or March; the "big rains" fall from mid-June through September.

The detail of vegetation in East Africa is remarkable (Figure 20.5). Savannas vary from solely tropical grasslands to parklike grasslands embellished with trees mostly of the acacia genus, to a brush and grass type, to thorn forests. They merge, usually imperceptibly, into each other although often thorn forests, or patches of thorn or of nearly bare ground stand out abruptly. The term savanna covers a great variety of vegetation.

Forests range from evergreen rain forests and dry (or mist) forests on the slopes of mountains to subtropical forests of deciduous trees that may be anything from acacia woodlands to arid thorn and scrub and bushlands. Scrub and bush are well represented in East Africa. Aubréville describes this as follows:

These formations of low, generally dense, and in some places almost impenetrable forest are frequent in East Africa, especially in central Tanganyika. Here they appear as thickets from two to six meters high, usually dense but sometimes open, composed of bushes and small trees that tend to be spiny, twisted and exceedingly branchy, and that have deciduous leaves. A few taller trees, irregularly spaced, may dominate these thickets, and the ground may be covered with a herbaceous carpet of Acanthaceae. Lianas are common.[2]

Scrub and bushland occur in semiarid regions of the tropics, where rainfall averages perhaps 25 to 30 inches, and seasons are characterized by a long dry spell of about 8 months, and a short rainy period lasting 3 or 4 months. Thorn forests occur where rainfall is less than 25 inches in a period of 5 or 6 months with a dry season that is 6 or 7 months long. Under such conditions of drought trees fight for sur-

[2] André M. A. Aubréville, "Tropical Africa," in Stephen Haden-Guest, John K. Wright, and Eileen M. Tetclaff (eds.), *World Geography of Forest Resources*, New York: The Ronald Press Company, 1956, p. 381.

FIGURE 20.5 Vegetation. (After Philips'
Modern College Atlas of Africa, p. 58. Base
copyright George Philip & Son, Ltd., London.
Used by permission. United States distributor,
Denoyer-Geppert Company.)

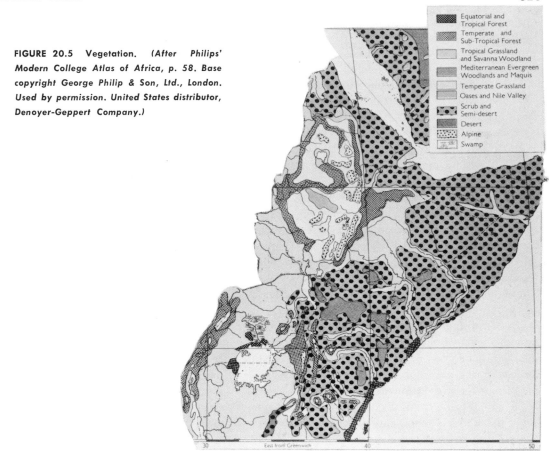

survival and only a few species, mostly acacias, outlive
the rigorous conditions of heat and drought; those
that do survive do so because they possess heat-
resistant and water-conserving devices such as spines,
thorns, thick bark, and deep roots. In places where
moisture conditions are

least unfavorable, . . . these trees may either form very
open forests about 50 feet in height above a grassy floor
or may crowd together in jungle-like thickets of about
the same height. More generally they are stunted,
gnarled and misshapen, and rise from an uncompro-
misingly thorny ground. They are nothing if not hardy;
some of them manage to survive on the desert's very
edge.[3]

[3] George H. T. Kimble, Tropical Africa, New York: The
Twentieth Century Fund, vol. 1, p. 71.

Rain forests cover only small areas of the East and
are less dense than elsewhere on the continent. They
are found, generally, inland at mountainous elevations,
or along the coasts of the Indian Ocean, as in the
hinterland of Tanga and on the islands of Zanzibar
and Pemba. Even at best the trees do not compare
with those of the equatorial forests to the west; at
their poorest they can scarcely be distinguished from
the dry forests. However, where they occur along the
coast they are storied forests, always green, and
floristically luxuriant, resembling the forests near the
West coast, even to containing some of the same
species. Coniferous forests occur in places above 7,500
feet elevation; Kenya, alone, has over 2 million acres
of such forests. Between the rain forests and the
thorn woodlands, many types and combinations of
vegetation occur, usually one type gradually blending
into another.

Even terminology is difficult because terms do not always stand for the same thing to everyone: "dry forest," for example, is used to denote forests that grow under conditions of rainfall that vary from 25 to 55 inches, with a dry season of not more than 4 or 5 months; at times, the mist forests are also classed as dry woodlands. Rainfall requirements for the dry forest are not everywhere the same. Dry forests occur on and along the edges of the Ethiopian plateau in places; mist forests cover some upper portions of the Ruwenzori slopes. Grassland and savanna woodlands, and bush and scrub, or thorn, are more prevalent in East Africa than any other type of vegetation. These generally merge up the slopes of mountains into subtropical and temperate forests, which include the conifers. Although showing some detail, vegetation maps are still generalized.

Much of the vegetation found in East Africa is man induced, that is, the use of the land under various types of human occupance induces destruction or modification of the primeval climax vegetation, as when brush or grass fires are set for hunting, or for clearing of the land for cultivation, or when grasslands are overgrazed. Zanzibar, for example, which would naturally be tropical rain forest, has a vegetation complex that is almost entirely man induced.

## The Human Factor in the Realm

Population distribution is very uneven throughout East Africa. Generally speaking, the hot-humid and hot-dry coasts are not so densely peopled as are the highlands. Not only the availability of fertile land and adequate rainfall account for the uneven distribution of population; equally important are the seasonal patterns of rainfall distribution, and the prevalence or absence of the tsetse fly.

People have congregated in the areas that favor settlement without much regard to the availability of transportation. As time has gone on, this has enhanced the need to develop communication and transport lines, and the necessity of specializing in high value crops if exports are to be sent out from the densely populated but remote areas. The population distribution has, therefore, largely dictated the communication pattern that has evolved.

## PATTERNS OF TRANSPORTATION AND COMMUNICATION

Communications, that is, railways, harbors, posts, telegraphs, civil aviation, and customs of the East African plateau states are under one system, amalgamated by the British administration between 1947 and 1949 when the East Africa High Commission was established. The purpose of the Commission was to coordinate efforts in the solution of problems common to all three territories.

As independence came to the first of the states (Tanzania, in December, 1961), Tanzania voiced its desire to maintain the close economic ties with Uganda and Kenya that had been initiated by the British. Earlier in the same year, leaders in the three countries had begun to feel that union, not only economic but political as well, might be desirable. With this in mind a conference was held in London in 1961, in which representatives from the three East African plateau states took part; in addition, Zanzibar sent observers, and there were British representatives present. Out of this conference came the establishment of the East African Common Services Organization (the EACSA, locally sometimes called the Common Market), which became effective immediately following the independence of Tanzania, replacing the East Africa High Commission.

The Commission had been composed of the governors of the three territories assisted by advisory and executive personnel; the prime ministers of the three states form the core of authority in the Organization, making the general policy; ministerial committees are in charge of the several services involved in the coordinated effort. For example, the combined rail system of the three countries is administered by the East African Railways and Harbours; posts and telegraphs were transferred to the East African Posts and Telecommunications Administration.

There are varying degrees of advantage and disadvantage to the individual states of East Africa in this economic union, but as a whole it has been beneficial and has made the services less costly to each country than would otherwise have been the case. The customs union practically broke the barriers to the movement of goods and people among the three countries, whether the goods arrived from inside or outside the plateau: once the goods entered the Organization's territory, as at the ports of Dar es Salaam or Mombasa, and began movement to its final destination in some other part of the region, there was no customs stopping or checking along the way, even at border points. Each country uses those facilities that are most convenient. For instance, the Arusha-Moshi hinterland of Tanzania tends to ship out through Kenya's harbor at Mombasa rather than through Tanga or Dar es Salaam.

Since the customs union eliminated the collection of import duties on goods arriving in any of the three states from either of the others, and since resources, and industrial and agricultural development are unequal among the three states, Uganda and Tanzania were disadvantaged at finding sources of tax revenue to replace the income formerly received from the imposition of import duties, because these two countries are less advanced industrially than Kenya; Uganda is also less developed agriculturally.

Over 3,335 miles of meter-gauge railways serve the East African plateau (see Figure 20.2). A considerable program of expansion, not only of railroads but also of lake transport and harbors, has been undertaken by the East African Railways and Harbours Administration. One important rail extension was constructed in Uganda connecting Tororo, on the main Mombasa-Kampala line, with Pakwach on the Albert Nile. It was laid over the 3-year period between 1962 and February 1964, and provides a rail outlet for the area that lies north of Lake Kyoga; it is particularly important to the cotton-growing district around Lira (see map). Since this line reaches, at Gulu, to within 90 miles of the Sudan border, it is expected to promote closer relations between that country and Uganda. Pakwach is close to The Congo border. Another short but important Uganda rail extension is the Bukonte cutoff which shortens the distance from Jinja to Kampala, and hence also to Tororo and Kenya, by about 45 miles. This cutoff was expensive and difficult to construct because of the swampy character of some of the terrain it covers.

The most important rail extension in Tanzania is a north-south line that connects Mnyusi, on the Arusha-Moshi-Tanga line, with Ruvu on the Central line of Tanzania terminating at the port of Dar es Salaam. The Tanga line already connected with the Kenya-Uganda line that terminates at Mombasa. The main benefit that has accrued from this new connection is that it allows a choice of either the Central or the Kenya-Uganda lines at peak seasons, thereby relieving congestion at critical periods; peak seasons arrive at different times on the two railways. The new connection also will permit the transport of perishable goods from the Mount Kilimanjaro area to the capital more easily. The Mnyusi-Ruvu connection is expected to cause Tanga to decline somewhat as a port in favor of Dar es Salaam; Tanga is a lighterage port, and is not furnished with such modern mechanized equipment as is the harbor at Dar es Salaam.

Another extension of the Central line, shorter and more limited in its significance than that from Mnyusi to Ruvu, is a branch 44 miles long that runs from Kilosa to Mikumi, opened in 1960. Because of this short line Mikumi, formerly a small village on a main road, has become a railhead of much importance for much of the southern highlands; it is also a bulk oil depot. This branch is being extended for 20 miles beyond Mikumi in order to open up an outlet for the important sugar-growing lands in the large Kilombero valley.

The Kenya-Uganda line has always been the most important in East Africa (see Table 7). It extends

TABLE 7 Ton-mileage in 1961 (million ton-miles)

| | |
|---|---|
| Kenya-Uganda line | 1,271 |
| Tanga line | 22 |
| Central line | 328 |
| Southern Province line | 2.6 |

from Mombasa to Nairobi, and from there to Nakuru where it branches two ways, west to Kisumu on Lake Victoria and northwestward across the Uganda border to Tororo; from there, as already noted, connections reach northwestward to Gulu and Pakwach as well as westward, via Jinja and Kampala, to Kasese just east of Mount Ruwenzori near The Congo border. Numerous branch lines dip out from the main Kenya-Uganda line. The most important areas of agricultural and industrial developments in Kenya are served by this system of railroads. The busiest sector of the Kenya-Uganda line lies between Nairobi and Mombasa, and Mombasa is the busiest port in all of the

**TABLE 8**   Tonnage Handled by Ports in 1962

| Mombasa | 2,619,000 |
|---|---|
| Tanga | 218,000 |
| Dar es Salaam | 804,000 |
| Mtwara | 120,000 |

Source: A. Long, "Internal Transport Developments in East Africa," *Geography*, vol. 1, part I, p. 81, January, 1965.

East African plateau region. Traffic through these ports is given in Table 8.

Other rail extensions are under consideration in all three countries, and existing rail facilities are being improved.[4] On the other hand, some of the existing lines have been closed down or removed, as those that were put in to serve as outlets for the produce when the British initiated their great peanut project. Neither the Kongwa branch, which was opened in 1928 and torn up a number of years ago, nor the 131-mile Southern Province line from Mtwara to Nachingwea ever paid out. The latter rail line was very recently closed down (see Table 8).

Despite the rise in railroad building, the proportion of the East African plateau that is actually served by rail lines is small, and most places lie miles away from a railroad. The importance of good road connections is therefore apparent. The roadnet varies in density in about the same ratio as population densities vary; it has a cobweb structure with focal centers where the threads of communication and transport are close and intricate, holding together long single strands traversing regions that are sparsely peopled.

Like the railway system, the roadnet interconnects between the plateau states. Not all roads are all-weather routes, however, and interconnections easily break down under the stress of heavy rains or floods, or from season to season. The miles of first class roads with a stone base and bituminous surfacing are few; these generally converge on important urban centers, playing out into gravel and eventually dirt roads in rural areas. Not many new roads have been built in recent years; rather, money has been used to improve the surfaces of existing roads, and this has proven to be a wise course.

Although rivers provide practically no inland waterways, the Great Lakes do, and regular steamer service operates on Lakes Victoria, Tanganyika, Albert, Kyoga, and Nyasa between ports within and between states under the Railways and Harbour Authority. In 1961, "6311 miles of river and lake services—handled 331,000 tons, 71 percent on Lake Victoria, 16 percent on Lake Kyoga, 11 percent on Lake Albert and the Nile River, and 2 percent on Lake Tanganyika."[5] Kisumu, Kenya is the leading port on Lake Victoria although Mwanza has become more competitive since that port was improved by the construction of a new passenger port 4 miles from the existent one. The new port will handle all passenger boats. A new rail terminal at Kisumu improved the facilities at that lake port.

The leading changes in lake traffic have been improvements in the passenger service on Lake Victoria. This was begun in 1961 when a new vessel, the *RMS Victoria*, was introduced into service on the lake. The ship's parts were built at Clydeside in Scotland and transported to Kisumu for assembling. This ship is said to be the largest vessel ever so handled.

Train ferry service was initiated on Lake Victoria in the latter part of 1965. For this, two wagon ferries were constructed at Clydeside and, like the *RMS Victoria*, transported in parts to Kisumu to be assembled on the shore of the lake. The ferries are used for regular ferry traffic and, additionally, to meet traffic demands at peak seasons by the interchange of rolling stock between the Kenya-Uganda and Tanzania sections of the rail system.

As in many parts of the world where land communication is difficult and population spotty, transport by air is important. The East African plateau is very well served by airplanes. Nairobi is the major air terminal in East Africa although Kampala, as a jumping-off place for Khartoum and Cairo, Dar es Salaam, and Tabora (to a lesser extent) are also important.

The independent state of Somalia has no railroads. A few miles of roads are paved, but most roads are not; the greatest number of routes on which traffic

---

[4] See A. Long, "Internal Transport Developments in East Africa," *Geography*, vol. 1, part I, pp. 80–82, January, 1965.

[5] William A. Hance, *The Geography of Modern Africa*, New York: Columbia University Press, 1964, p. 386.

moves are merely trails or tracks. Camel caravans and migrants with their animals follow the trails.

Transportation and carriers exist in extremes and contrasts in Ethiopia, from the ubiquitous donkeys to modern airplanes with all degrees of transport in between. Ethiopia has its own airline, Ethiopian Airways. In some of the more picturesque parts of this rugged land the mule, which was bred first in Ethiopia, is the most effective means of getting about. Distances are great, and roads are few and poor, generally extending out only a short way from some of the larger cities. Only two railroads serve Ethiopia. One is the French-built line that extends from Djibouti, French Somaliland, to Addis Ababa; the other is the short Eritrean line that extends inland from Massawa to Asmara and Agordat. Airplanes, that can transport people in a few hours between places which might otherwise require weeks and even months by other means, are therefore important when speed is a consideration.

## POLITICAL CHANGE IN EAST AFRICA

Modern Ethiopia has had a checkered history. Wars and two annexations of Ethiopian territory by Italy have characterized the modern era which began in the latter half of the nineteenth century; the second annexation, in 1935, followed invasion and conquest by the European state. Independence was restored to the Kingdom after its liberation in 1941 by the British.

Somalia was declared a free republic on July 1, 1960. On this date Italian Somaliland, a trust territory, was given independence by the United Nations, and simultaneously with independence was united with former British Somaliland, the small country north and west of the trusteeship, which had attained sovereignty 4 days previously from Britain; it had been a protectorate. These combined lands give Somalia an area of 246,137 square miles (slightly smaller than Texas) and a population of about 2,150,-000. One more Somaliland remains unincorporated with the independent state, namely, French Somaliland, 8,492 square miles in area, 69,300 in population, and an Overseas Territory of the French Union. Although most of the Somali people live in the countries designated as "the Somalilands," they spill over into Ethiopia and Kenya: the Ogaden region of Ethiopia is largely inhabited by Somalis, as is also northeast Kenya. Along these frontiers, border troubles have been recurrent ever since independence was granted to Somalia; Somalia wants these lands, and the Somali people living as minority peoples in Ethiopia and Kenya desire unification with the rest of the Somalis.

The British lands of East Africa are among the latest to be accorded independence. Tanganyikan independence came first, in December, 1961. It had been mandated to the British by the League of Nations on January 10, 1920, becoming a trust territory of the United Nations, still under British protection, in 1946. Previous to this the territory, a colony of Germany, was known as German East Africa and included Ruanda and Urundi, the latter states separated from Tanganyika and mandated to the Belgians at the same time that Tanganyika was made a mandate of the British. Uganda, proclaimed a British protectorate in 1894, became sovereign in October, 1962; Kenya Colony and Protectorate received independence on December 12, 1963. All three of the formerly British states remained within the Commonwealth.

The sultanate of Zanzibar, a British protectorate which embraced the islands of Zanzibar and Pemba and islets within their territorial waters, plus a strip of Kenya coast 10 miles deep and 52 miles in length, attained independence on December 10, 1963. The new sultanate was made up only of the islands. A month after independence, the government changed hands and form when a *coup d'état* overthrew the sultan and set up a "republic." In late April, 1964, the Republic merged with Tanganyika, and the united country took the name, Tanzania. Madagascar, a French colony, became the independent Malagasy Republic within the French Community in June, 1960.

In July, 1962, Ruanda-Urundi attained independence as the two self-governing African states of Rwanda and Burundi. A tragic struggle between the former rulers, the minority Watusi, and the majority Bahutu ensued in Rwanda, during which many Watusi either fled the country or were killed as the Bahutu sought revenge for the long years of near slavery they had endured under the quasi-feudal system that the Watusi had maintained.

## EAST AFRICAN FEDERATION

For more than 6 decades, various men for varied reasons have attempted to shape a single political unit out of the territories of East Africa that occupy the Lakes plateau. This region, that lies between the rift lakes and the Indian Ocean on one hand, and the deserts of Ethiopia and the humid lands of Mozambique on the other, encompasses an area equal to that of Western Europe, and nearly one-fourth the size of the 48 contiguous states of the United States.

On July 5, 1963, just a few days after elections had brought internal self-government to Kenya, leaders of the three largest plateau states, all formerly British —Prime Ministers Milton Obote of Uganda and Jomo Kenyatta of Kenya, and President Julius Nyerere of Tanganyika—met to declare their intention of federating before the end of the year. Economic integration was already well begun; the intended political federation announced in mid-1963 would carry that economic integration further.

Economic union had been at least partially accomplished despite the inequalities resulting from disparate development and resources, and the heads of government of the three states pledged to try to form a political union within 7 months. In the months that followed, the inherent weaknesses of integration, and the hostilities among the states showed themselves. Had Kenya, Tanganyika, and Uganda been given independence simultaneously so that, as Julius Nyerere of Tanganyika had wanted, they could have federated on the same day that they became sovereign, political union might have been accomplished. But for several reasons Britain did not do this; instead, it delayed independence to Uganda for about 1 year and to Kenya for 2 years. "Thus was the first opportunity for federation lost."[6] By 1963, when the three

[6] Clyde Sanger, "Some Reflections on Leaving East Africa," *Africa Report*, p. 29, October, 1965.

heads of government met, "it was already too late." Hostilities were revealed at the conference itself, one instance being when Ugandans asserted that on no account would they accept Nairobi as the federation capital; it had to be at Entebbe. A lack of public debate on the issue of federation did not permit grievances to be brought out into the open. The result has been that by mid-1965 Kenya, Tanzania, and Uganda were farther from federation than at any time since the formation of the Common Market;[7] even some aspects of the economic integration that the British and Africans worked so hard to accomplish are now dissolving. The customs union is disintegrating, for Kenya and Tanzania are imposing trade restrictions on each other;[8] in June 1965, Tanzania announced that one year later it would establish a separate currency.[9] "Their situation is worse than an engagement that broke up in a quarrel: the three East African states have to continue to live next door to each other and are economically dependent one on the other to a great extent."[10]

Federation in East Africa, for the time being at least, has collapsed, and unity is unlikely to come in the foreseeable future. Nonetheless, Nyerere in mid-1965 again restated the hope that the three states would federate: "We do not want to quarrel with our colleagues. We said long ago that we wanted East African unity. When Tanganyika and Zanzibar were ready, we had a union of Tanzania. . . . If Kenya is ready, we are ready."[11]

[7] *Ibid.*
[8] "Interstate," *Africa Report*, p. 59, October, 1965.
[9] "News in Brief," *Africa Report*, p. 34, July, 1965.
[10] Sanger, *op. cit.*, p. 29.
[11] Stated on July 7, 1965, as quoted in *Africa Report*, p. 33, August, 1965.

# 21 STATES OF THE EAST AFRICAN PLATEAU

*We have the world before us.*

DAVID LIVINGSTONE

## Physical Character

The East African plateau rises as an elliptical uplift stretching about 700 miles north and south, and 500 miles in an east-west direction, to elevations of between 3,000 and 6,000 feet. Marginal faults, comprising between one-half to two-thirds of the 3,000-mile circumference of the plateau, mark the places where the rock crust was strained until it broke "by the uplifting force . . . ; elsewhere it has apparently been flexed or, if faulted, faulted so intimately that the displacements are not conspicuous."[1]

On the southeast, the (Tanzania) plateau is bounded by the abrupt walls of the Fufu fault which runs almost straight southwest for over 200 miles; along the southwest is the Rukwa fault, also a sheer, nearly vertical plane that trends northwest for about the same distance as the Fufu fault. These faults define branches of the great rift graben, and at the same time mark the edges of the East African plateau in the south. The Rukwa fault dies out in the north in an elevated peneplain. About 40 miles to the west lies Lake Tanganyika, occupying a trough that, in the southern half, runs parallel to the Rukwa graben.

The approaches to the central portion of the plateau from the coast are, in general, across a series of step faults. Along the railway from Dar es Salaam, the ascent goes from sea level to a general altitude of perhaps 3,500 feet in interior Tanzania; Kenya rises from the edge of the continent, which is marked by the Ruvu fault and submerged in shallow water off Mombasa, to the heights of the Aberdare Range, an ascent of about 12,000 feet in approximately 300 miles; here the Aberdare, a part of the eastern rift valley escarpment, are cut off along the western edge by a long series of upthrust step faults that drop to the rift valley. The character of the plateau slope differs to the north and south of the Pangani River; on the north the domelike rise is more apparent.

The Pangani River itself runs along a faulted valley which is overlooked from the east by the Usambara and Pare ranges. Facing the southwest with a bold but irregular front, these mountains taper off on their back slopes as a series of long spurs, evidently a fault block, although their character has not been geologically determined. The Pangani valley is an "apparent downthrow, . . . the lower edge of the tilted slope from the Masai Steppe." This fault extends northwestward for about 200 miles, and then becomes lost beneath the lavas of Kilimanjaro, apparently ending there because it does not appear again northwest of the volcano. The fault of the main rift trough replaces it, and trending east-west across the line of juncture of these two faults, there occurs a line of eruptive centers.

A region of mesas and plains typifies the coastal sector south of the Pangani; and this coastal zone widens rapidly as the shore bends southeast and the plateau edge diverges toward the southwest. The plains and low mesas rise gradually inland in a series of steps to the Masai steppe, which stands about 3,300 feet above sea level. This plateau might be described as a gently undulating surface, interrupted here and there by residuals, but over wide stretches very flat, resembling a monotonous high plain. The undulations are a series of alternating low swells and broad hollows several miles in diameter. Wind erosion is active and the hollows, which contain water during the wet season but are as dry as evaporation vats during the dry period, are usually bordered along the edges with encrusted salts. On its northwestern edge, the Kilimatinde-Ufiome flexure and escarpment mark the first of a series of rises that lift the plateau to the heights of the Serengeti plains, at their highest about 5,000 feet above sea level.

North from the uplands of southern and central Tanzania (sometimes called the central plateau) the Nyanza plateau, of which the Serengeti plains are a part, stretches away almost without any interruptions to mar the continuity of the plateau surface.

FIGURE 21.2 (Right) Western rift zone Albert-Edward Downwarps, Ruwenzori Upwarp, and basin of Lake Kivu. (*Bailey Willis, East African Plateaus and Rift Valleys, Washington, D.C.: Carnegie Institution Publication no. 470, Studies in Comparative Seismology, 1936, plate IX. Courtesy Carnegie Institution of Washington.*)

[1] Bailey Willis, *East African Plateaus and Rift Valleys*, Washington, D.C.: Carnegie Institution of Washington, 1936, p. 38.

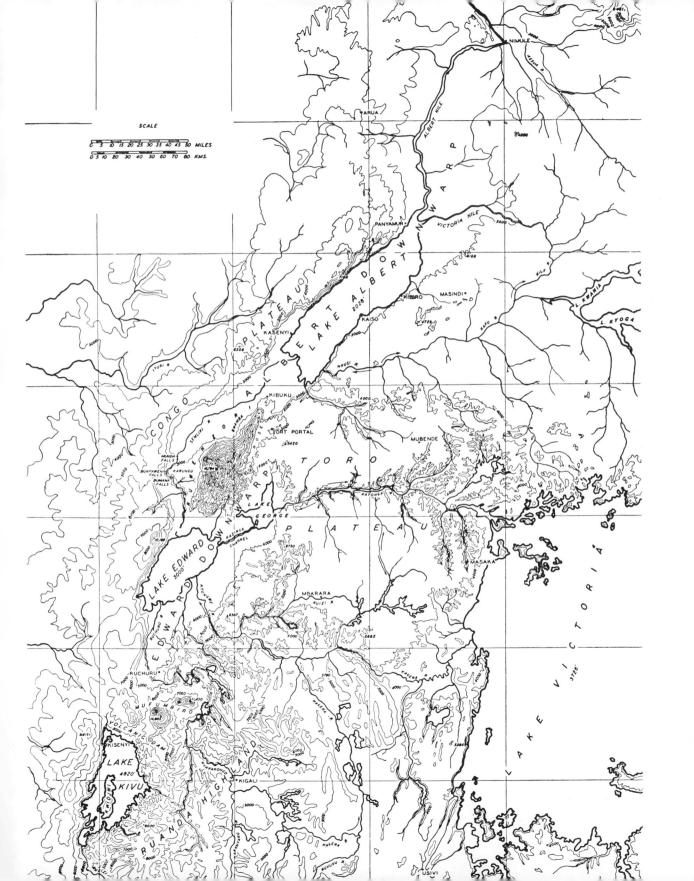

SCALE

0 5 10 15 20 25 30 35 40 45 50 MILES
0 5 10 20 30 40 50 60 70 80 KMS.

The distinction between the Tanzania and Nyanza plateaus is merely one of convenience, although there is this difference; whereas the plateau of Tanzania is a mild arch, the Nyanza plateau is slightly depressed in the center, and the saucerlike dip more or less filled with the waters of Victoria Nyanza. The western bounds of the Nyanza plateau are readily followed because they are aligned along the arc of the rift trough (Figure 21.2) that is occupied in part by lakes Tanganyika, Kivu, Edward, and Albert; beyond the limits of Lake Albert, the Nile valley may serve to mark the northwest limits although this valley is actually neither a structural nor a physiographic boundary, as the East African plateau merges imperceptibly into the Sahara in the northwest.

Generally speaking, the surface of the Nyanza plateau resembles that of the plateau of Tanzania; it is a high plain interrupted by monadnocks (see Glossary) and other residuals, hillocks, and the like, covered with a thorn or grass, or forest or marsh growth, depending on conditions of soil and climate. Essentially the physiography is similar throughout. Lake Victoria is the central feature of the Nyanza plateau. The area of the water surface varies considerably because of the shallowness of the basin, the lake showing quickly any changes in volume.

North of Lake Tanganyika rises the domelike upland of Burundi and Rwanda with a diameter of about 300 miles. Its base lies at about the 5,000-foot contour of the plateau, and from that elevation, it rises upward to about 6,500 feet above sea level in the center. Roughly 120,000 square miles in area, it "approaches" lakes Tanganyika, Victoria, and George, and stretches beyond Lake Kivu westward to the watershed of the Congo. In contrast to most of the plateau surface, the Rwanda dome, the highest upland (but not mountain) surface on the Great Lakes plateau, is greatly eroded for it is the water divide between Congo and Nile drainage: from here flow the Kagera River and the Ruvuvu, affluent of the Kagera, farthest source of the Nile since the Kagera flows into Lake Victoria, out of which the Nile emerges; other drainage flows generally south into Lake Tanganyika, as the Ruzizi; Lake Tanganyika is the source of the Lukuga, tributary to the Lualaba, which is the headstream of the Congo.

On the north, the Rwanda dome slopes into the Toro plateau of Uganda, just east of the Ruwenzori Mountains, to connect with the plateau southeast of Lake Albert. On its northern slope "the great East African uplift . . . descends very gradually to the sink of the Sudd . . ."[2]

For about 100 miles inland from the southwest shore of Lake Rudolf, a high divide separates the watersheds of the lake and the Nile. This is a winding escarpment, irregular and broken, but it extends from about 4°N almost to the Equator, terminating southward in the prominent, east-facing, lava-covered Elgeyo escarpment.

Volcanic activity occurred in three major areas of the Lakes plateau, the individual occurrences seemingly unrelated except through the fact that they are all situated along the periphery of the plateau and are associated with the zones of faulting. One, the Mufumbiro chain of volcanoes, extends east-west across the lakes Edward-Kivu downwarp in the western rift, and forms the water divide between Congo and Nile drainage. Rungwe, at the northern end of Lake Nyasa, comprises the second area; it fills the trough between the Livingstone (on the east) and Rhodesian plateaus (on the west).

The third large area of eruptions and volcanoes occurs along fissures in the northeastern half of the East African plateau, largely in Kenya but extending into the adjacent regions of Uganda and Tanzania. This is an ill-defined zone of about 50,000 square miles; both fissure flows and central extrusions are found here. The region is traversed by the eastern arm of the great rift valley, and includes some of the most magnificent volcanoes in the world. On the south is the volcanic district of Kilimanjaro and the Giant Craters; on the north, Mounts Kenya and Elgon are the most impressive. Two great centers of eruption, joined by minor cones, comprise the southern district. The western center of eruption is known as the Giant Craters, embracing a triangle of great cones including Ngorongoro; far to the east is Kilimanjaro, whose crest mounts 19,455 feet above the sea. The northern volcanic region differs from the other two in that previous to the building of the great cones of Mounts

2 *Ibid.*, pp. 36–37.

**FIGURE 21.3** Mount Kenya, although almost on the Equator, is always capped with snow. *(Courtesy Kenya Information Services.)*

Kenya and Elgon, earlier lava flows, issuing from fissures, spread deposits over an area of some 30,000 square miles. During this phase of activity only minor cones were formed; later the great cones were constructed. Kilimanjaro, it has been noted, is situated at the end of a well-defined fissure along the edge of the plateau. Although the foundations of Elgon and Kenya (Figure 21.3) are concealed, it is assumed that they were built up by the eruption of volcanic materials through comparable fractures. Mounts Kenya and Elgon rise 17,058 and 14,178 feet above sea level respectively. The volcanic deposits on the plateau are responsible for the rich soils that characterize East Africa in places.

Ruwenzori—one mountain and not several despite the distinctive names of its highest peaks—is a mountain of striking individuality, superior altitude, and isolated location. It is not a volcano in origin but a dome, the main arc of which measures 30 to 40 miles in width. This dome carries pinnacles that exceed 16,000 feet in elevation: so high does the central mass tower that the top of the mountain is usually wrapped in a cloud cover, making Ruwenzori "a phantom mountain," sometimes seen, frequently obscured from the view. This is the highest nonvolcanic mass in Africa.

The flora of the Great Lakes plateau, and of the coast and islands reflects the variety of climate and relief that is found. The tropical species of grass and trees give way to mangrove swamps along the shores, and to grasslands, parklike savanna, and thorn forests inland; up mountain slopes the vegetation merges from open forests to canopied evergreen forests to mountain meadows. Along the coast of northern Kenya semidesert scrub is typical. In this northeastern sector of Kenya (east of the uplands), the country has a "drought-dormant listlessness" from which it is released but briefly "during and after the fugitive rains. For the rest of the year the ground is parched, the thornbushes lifeless, and the most characteristic color is the red of the bare earth."[3]

[3] George H. T. Kimble, "Kenya," *Focus*, vol. III, no. 10, p. 2, June, 1953.

## Early Immigrants to East African Shores

East Africa had trade connections with Arabia and the Orient before the beginning of the Christian era. Active colonization by Arabs from Oman appears to have started in the eighth century of the Christian era when Shi'ite refugees fled religious persecution in Oman, and settled along the East African coast; in the ninth century, orthodox Sunnis from Shiraz in Persia founded colonies in East Africa. Mogadishu and Brava, on the coast of present-day Somalia, were thus established, and the town of Kilwa in southeast Tanzania was colonized by tenth-century descendants of these Persians as a port for the gold trade of the Zambezi region.[4] It is possible that settlers from both Arabia and Persia arrived many centuries earlier. The Chinese, attracted by the ivory, gold, tortoiseshell, ambergris, and slaves exported from these shores, sent fleets on several occasions to East Africa.

Undoubtedly the first foreigners seen by many of the peoples of East Africa were the Arabs. In spite of the nefarious slave trade in which the Arabs engaged, the Moslem creed with its emphasis on "the dignity of men, courage, and the public worship of Allah" held a great appeal for Africans, and the Islamic religion took a firm hold along the coast and in plateau centers where Arabs had settled, such as Tabora. Linguistically also the Arab influence is apparent because the lingua franca of East Africa, Swahili, has borrowed heavily from Arabic. So important were the Arabs in East Africa that in 1832, the Sayid of Muscat moved his capital from the Arabian Peninsula to Zanzibar, where he extended his rule across portions of the African mainland as well as over the offshore islands.

In parts of East Africa the Arab influence (Figure 21.4) is still dominant; in Tanganyika, however, the Arabs received such a setback from the Germans after the suppression of the rebellion of Bushiri bin Salim that they did not become so prominent economically or numerically in this territory as they did in Kenya. In 1961, out of a total population of over 9,400,000 in Tanganyika, 27,600 were of Arab descent; in Kenya,

[4] Roland Oliver and J. D. Fage, *A Short History of Africa*, New York: New York University Press, 1963, pp. 97–98.

FIGURE 21.4  It is not uncommon for turbaned Arabs of East Africa to wear scabbards and daggers. (*Courtesy Public Relations Department, Tanzania.*)

there were 39,000 Arabs in a population of somewhat less than 7,300,000.

Indian influence may be as old as that of the Arab, but not until the beginning of the nineteenth century did it begin to be comparable in importance. Nevertheless, a great part of the ocean shipping that carried goods to and from Africa was owned and manned by Indians; it is probable that the Indians were also influential in financial matters, acting as bankers, money changers, and lenders. They were highly valued as colonists. At the time that Zanzibar was made an Arab capital, there were already over 1,000 Indians residing on the island; they were to be found, as well, in every sizable town along the east coast of the continent. They were all called "banyans" (also spelled banian) without discrimination although, strictly speaking, banyans are a Hindu caste of merchants and traders; most of the Indian immigrants professed the Islamic faith. Indians were used by the

Zanzibar Sultan, Seyyid Said, as customs collectors and some of these "were well known to all the early explorers who fitted their expeditions in Zanzibar . . . it was the 'banyans' of Zanzibar who financed the Arab slave caravans." [5]

Indians have played an important part in both the history and the economic development of the East: the petty Indian trader has penetrated to every part, and is actually the one who introduced money economy to the East Africans. Indians are found in high positions in every phase of the economic and political life of the country.

## Commonwealth States of East Africa

### THE LAND AND ITS USE

*Tanzania.* Few people realize how large Tanganyika[6] really is. All of Texas, together with nearly two-thirds of California, could be fitted into it; 362,688 square miles in area, France, Netherlands, Switzerland, Belgium, and the German Federal Republic could be set upon it and there would still be a few thousand square miles of Tanganyika not covered; but it has only a relatively small population. Some 9¾ million people[7] live here. Within it are found a great variety of climates and soils that range from humid rain forests along the coast to the realm of ice and snow on Kilimanjaro, and from the barren scrub lands of portions of the Masai country to the highland regions of rich volcanic soils.

Zanzibar, the other constituent unit of Tanzania, is tiny. It comprises the islands of Zanzibar and Pemba, the islets within their territorial waters, and uninhabited Latham Island that is some 40 miles southeast of Zanzibar Island. It is situated just off the Tanganyika coast, separated by a channel that at its narrowest part separates Zanzibar Island from Africa

by 22.5 miles; from Zanzibar city to Dar es Salaam is 45 miles as the crow or airplane flies. Pemba Island lies 25 miles north of the island of Zanzibar. In area Zanzibar is only a little over 1,000 square miles; Zanzibar Island, the largest unit of the insular domain, is 640 square miles in size and, aside from Madagascar, the largest island off the East African coast; Pemba is 380 square miles in area.

Agriculture is the mainstay of Tanzania. As a tropical country with gradations of altitude going from sea level to great heights, the environment permits the cultivation of almost any kind of plant; the amount and distribution of rainfall are important in determining what is grown in any place. Parts of the country receive less than 20 inches of rain (see Figure 20.3 and 20.4), and where the rainfall averages only slightly more than 20 inches, or less than that amount, the region is likely to be comparatively arid. Since rainfall is torrential, much that falls on the plateau is relatively ineffective—the rains pound down upon the earth and run off rather than sink in. Fortunately, most of Tanganyika averages 30 to 40 inches or more of rain annually, enough so that crops can be raised in amounts sufficient to make the country self-sustaining, and also to produce a surplus for export.

Methods of working the land range from the primitive, purely subsistence migratory cultivation that is found in many other parts of Africa to a combination subsistence-commercial cultivation practiced by Africans, to the large scale commercial agriculture carried out on European estates. Among the staple subsistence crops grown by the Africans are millet, sorghum, cassava, maize, and bananas (plantains); these hardy crops grow with little effort on the part of the cultivator. Crops raised commercially by Africans include cotton, coffee, rice, tobacco, and peanuts, but since these require more care and labor than do most of those grown for subsistence, only the more ambitious farmers practice money cropping. The same commercial crops are raised also by non-African farmers, and in addition, there are some that are almost entirely European produced, namely, sisal (Figure 21.5*a* and *b*), citrus, coconuts, tea, cashew nuts, sugar, pyrethrum (a member of the chrysanthemum family whose flowers yield an insecticide), papain, found in the juice of the green fruit of the papaya and used as a digestive, seed beans, and sesame.

[5] Reginald Coupland, "East Africa and Its Invaders," *Handbook of Tanganyika,* Dar es Salaam: Government Printer, 1958, p. 299.

[6] "Tanganyika" is used in many portions of this section to distinguish this part of Tanzania from Zanzibar.

[7] *Statistical Yearbook,* New York: United Nations, 1964.

(a)

(b)

Sisal, coconuts, cashew nuts, cotton, sesame, rice, maize, sorghum, and citrus are grown in the tropical coastal belt; in the wide swamps along the coast, mangrove flourishes and is actually developed as a crop in the delta of the Rufiji River. On the plateau, at elevations of 3,000 and 4,000 feet, cotton, peanuts, and rice are the principal crops of trade. In northwestern Tanganyika (in what was the former Lake Province) to the south, southeast and east of Lake Victoria, cotton production has been increasing quite rapidly, so that this sector of the country accounts for four-fifths of the cotton cultivated. The yield is low, however, and the quality of the cotton could be improved by better handling and ginning.

Although mountains make up only a small portion of the country, the highland regions produce some important products: the eastern Usambara Mountains, receiving an annual rainfall of between 80 and 100 inches, are heavily forested and are well suited also to tea production; in the western Usambaras there is another tea growing area; coffee, cinchona, and fruit also grow, and pigs and poultry are kept. In Northern

FIGURE 21.5 The fiber of the sisal plant is in its spikelike leaf. (a, above) Cutting sisal; (b, left) after decortication, the sisal fiber hangs out to dry. (*Courtesy Public Relations Department, Tanzania.*)

Province, about 250 miles from Tanga, is a very important European and African coffee producing area on the slopes of Kilimanjaro; farther along, coffee culture becomes mixed with the cultivation of pyrethrum, papain, wheat, maize, and vegetable and flower seeds. The Masai country intervenes between here and the Mbulu highlands; in the latter area excellent coffee orchards are found, and mixed farming is practiced on the slopes of Oldeani, near Ngorongoro Crater. West of these centers there has been no European development, but 400 miles south, in the Iringa district, tobacco and cattle farms are found, and still farther south there are the tea plantations of Mufindi and Tukuyu, and the coffee farms and mixed farming regions of Mbozi. A variety of plants grow in the southeast and find an outlet via the railway at the port of Mtwara. African farmers contribute notably to the coffee, tobacco, and cotton exports; cooperative marketing is an important feature of African coffee production in the Moshi area of Tanzania. Sisal, coffee, and cotton are the three great commercial crops raised, and sisal is the major export from the country. Tanganyika produces nearly one-third of the world's sisal.[8]

Climate and vegetation make many parts of Tanganyika more suitable to pastoral than to farming activities. Even in areas where farming is well established, stock-raising in combination with cultivation is increasing, and simple cropping of the soil is being replaced with integrated farming. This is a healthy trend because livestock will be valuable in maintaining and restoring the fertility of the land. Improvement of the quality of the livestock is difficult, however, because, as in the rest of East Africa, most of the animals are owned by Africans, and are kept more for prestige than for economic reasons. Further, where communal pastures are used, it is usually difficult to show African herders the necessity of restricting the number of animals that graze on any particular area of pasture; as a result, the grasslands are overgrazed, leading to the destruction of the vegetative cover and soil erosion. This is true throughout East Africa where there are many groups of tribal Africans who are purely pastoral, or pastoral-agricultural. One of the purely pastoral groups are the Masai (Figure 21.6*a* and *b*). Their reserve, much of it thornbush country and greatly eroded, extends across the Tanganyika-Kenya border. It is much smaller than it was in the past, when the Masai were a powerful group claiming lands up to Mount Elgon straddling the Kenya-Uganda frontier. The number of cattle in Tanganyika nearly equals the human population.

Zanzibar and Pemba are tropical isles, with year-round high temperatures and plenty of rain. Maximum and minimum temperatures for Zanzibar town are 84.4 and 76.6°F; for Wete, the largest town on Pemba, 86.3 and 76.1°F; rainfall in Zanzibar town averages 61.9 inches, and at Wete, 76.9 inches. On both islands precipitation is heavier in the hilly regions than along the low eastern plains; both have a double period of maximum rainfall, the heavy rains falling in April and May, lesser rains in November and December; there are no months without rain, although in some years, during the months of January and February, and June, July, and August less than 1 inch of rain may fall; the total amount varies considerably from year to year.

Over much of the island domain the natural vegetation and the cultivated growth are luxuriant. Besides coconut palms, there are dark mango trees and trees producing other tropical fruits, shiny clove plants, and masses of brilliant shrubs. What impresses the traveler is the exuberance of the growth, and the great variety of agricultural conditions that obtain within so small a zone.

The principal feature of the islands' economy is the overwhelming dependence upon cloves and coconuts: on the average, up to 95 percent of the exports are supplied from these two crops; they are also the chief employers of labor and the principal sources of government revenue (through export duties). Industry is virtually confined to the processing of these and other products of cultivation. The growing of subsistence food crops is an important activity, but Zanzibar does not feed itself. Cassava and rice are the staple subsistence food crops.

As "spices" had been associated with wealth since the spice trade with the East had begun, Sultan Seyyid Said bin Sultan started the clove industry in the islands, introducing clove plants from the Moluccas, and establishing plantations. The clove was thus

_____

[8] *FAO Production Yearbook, 1964,* Rome: Food and Agriculture Organization of the United Nations, p. 151.

FIGURE 21.6 (a, left) Much of the pasture is poor in Masailand; (b, below) Masai village of its mud-constructed houses that somewhat resemble wasps' nests. (Courtesy Public Relations Department, Tanzania.)

(b)

not native to Zanzibar. The plant adapted so successfully, however, that the idea of specialization in the growth of this spice tree led to a feverish planting of the clove: rice and coconuts were abandoned over wide areas, and cloves put in instead. Within 20 or 30 years after the introduction of the plant in 1818, cloves had become the single most important element in the commercial economy of the islands.

It remains so today. Cloves alone make up 75 to 80 percent of the total value of exports. Despite this, these spice trees are relatively less important in the economy than they used to be; in the past, Zanzibar and Pemba resembled little island forests of clove trees; today cloves have declined on Zanzibar Island, and about 80 percent of the estimated 4 million clove plants are on Pemba Island.

The clove of commerce is the unopened bud of the clove flower. The wharves, the warehouses on the wharves, the very islands themselves smell of the fragrant scent of this spice. Clove trees, at all stages of flowering, spread across the islands. Cloves lie brown and open to the sun for drying, usually upon woven mats, sometimes upon hard concrete pavements between the warehouses and streets where dust from the passing traffic falls upon them, where trucks roll their great wheels across their drying floors, and even people tread upon the fragrant drying buds. They are shipped in burlap bags, graded by size and perfection of the flower bud. India and Indonesia are the chief customers, together taking from 50 to 60 percent of the exports. Since 1928 the Clove Growers Association has handled the marketing and export of the entire clove crop as well as distillation of clove oil. After cloves and clove products, coconut oil and copra are second in importance as money crops and exports; oil cake and fibres rank third.

Zanzibar and the Malagasy Republic, which together supply nearly 98 percent of the world's cloves and clove products, reached a quota agreement for the marketing of cloves in late 1963. It provided that Zanzibar will export 8,500 tons of cloves, Madagascar 3,250 tons. If the world market will absorb more, Zanzibar will export an additional 1,000 tons for every 250 tons exported by the Malagasy Republic. This gives the two republics about a 70 to 30 proportion of clove exports ("Economic Notes," *Africa Report*, p. 22, January, 1964).

Because of the heavy dependence on two export commodities, sharp fluctuations in export earnings result when world prices are low, when major importing countries impose import restrictions on cloves, or when the crop yield is poor. For this reason the British tried during their last years in the islands to bring diversification of cropping into the agriculture; chillies and coffee have been pushed; the former are exported, the latter may someday be exportable.

*Kenya.* Kenya is also a large country, only a little smaller than Texas, more than twice as large as West Germany; like Tanganyika, its population is small, somewhat over 8.8 million.[9] The small population within so large an area can be explained in part by the physical environment, for nearly all the northeastern portion of the territory is a region of deficient rainfall, making it of little value for anything but grazing, and even as pasture it is low grade; only in certain favored areas, as particularly in the hill districts, is cultivation practiced. The population density of the arid to semiarid sector averages about 2 per square mile.

The south and southwest are highly productive, however. If a diagonal line were drawn from the tip in the northwest (where the borders of Kenya, Uganda, and Sudan touch) down to an approximate midpoint on the Kenya coast, the country would divide rather significantly into two quite different sectors—the northeast half, generally low, semiarid, and sparsely vegetated; and the southwest half, generally high, with a mean elevation of over 5,000 feet except along the coast, and a mean rainfall that is nearly everywhere above 20 inches; across about half of the latter region, over 40 inches of rain can normally be expected.

Elevation gives the plateau of Kenya a healthful, invigorating climate. Although days are hot, nights are refreshingly cool; temperatures at Nairobi average 67.2°F; in contrast, at Mandera in the extreme northeast average temperatures are 84.3, at Garissa (0.29°S) 83.6, at Lamu on the northern coast 78.7, and at Mombasa on the south coast 80.1°F; Kisumu, plateau port on Lake Victoria, by contrast, averages

[9] *Statistical Yearbook,* New York: United Nations, 1964; estimate for 1963.

only 73.9°F. Elevation is responsible for these differences because Kenya has an equatorial location, being cut almost equally in half by the Equator. Frosts occur at times in the Aberdare Mountains; Mount Kenya, almost on the Equator, is capped with permanent glaciers.

The seasonal pattern of rainfall is not the same all over the humid southwestern sector of the country because some areas have one long season of rainfall (see Figures 20.3 and 20.4); others have two shorter seasons. Where the two seasons of rain are typical they usually occur as a longer and shorter season, the "long rains" and the "short rains," the former from April through June, although they may begin earlier and end later, the latter between October and December. The two-season rainfall pattern is more typical than the single-season pattern, especially near the Equator; with distance away from the Equator, as in the Tanganyika stations, the single seasons of wet and dry become more pronounced.

Vegetation reflects the wide ranges of rainfall and elevation. Mangrove swamps along the coast in the south give way northward, gradually, to scrub and even semidesert; inland the mangrove coasts yield to grass and parklike vegetation; here and there clumps of thornbush occur. Watercourses are bordered by trees or bushes, and stand out sharply from the rest of the landscape. The plateau itself is, generally, a savanna of grass and scattered trees; where highlands occur, and elevations wring out greater amounts of moisture, the park-savanna gives way to a thicker tree growth and even to close-canopied tropical forests, which with greater elevation may in turn disappear as they merge into highland meadows.

Forest starts at about 6,000 feet. The country upon which almost all of the economic production is centered lies between 5,000 and 8,000 feet. Mountains rise much higher; 1½ million acres of land in Kenya lie above 9,000 feet elevation. Mount Kenya, the highest mountain, rises majestically 17,040 feet, while the great rift valley runs like a vast jagged crack that splits the country from north to south.

As noted previously, the north and east, relatively low in relief and receiving less than 20 inches of rainfall, are semiarid to arid in places. The long period (or periods) of drought, interrupted only briefly by fleeting rains, keeps the vegetation in a state of dormancy most of the year, and the region has a desolate appearance; the earth becomes parched, and bare red ground shows through everywhere between the dull-colored plants. Only for a very short season does northeastern Kenya have anything but a lifeless character.

In the high rainfall areas that make up about 40 percent of the country's central and coastal regions, coffee, tea, sisal, pyrethrum, and fruits grow well, and are produced commercially (Figure 21.7a and b). Since Kenya's mineral wealth is small or unknown, the economy depends largely upon agriculture or the animal industries; water, soil, and livestock are Kenya's chief resources. In addition to the commercial products listed above, wattle bark, hides and skins, wheat, maize, cotton, wool, meat, and dairy products are also produced.

The cash crops were pioneered by the Europeans, and the better methods of European agriculture and the same cash crops are slowly replacing subsistence agriculture and primitive techniques among the Africans. Africans now cultivate about one-fourth of the acreage that is in coffee; in 1961, 23½ percent of Kenya's coffee was grown by Africans. Meru coffee, grown on the slopes of Mt. Kenya by Africans, is one of the best varieties of *arabica* coffee in the world, with a picking season that lasts for 9 months; profit-sharing cooperatives market the coffee for the Africans. European coffee estates tend to center around Nairobi. Sisal is largely European grown, some of the estates centering around Thika, and others on the coast and in Western Region. On some of the African reserves, sisal is grown as hedgerows and windbreaks but harvested; one tribe, the Wakamba in Machakos, operates a sisal-processing factory, using locally grown sisal and exporting the fibre.

Tea culture is centered near Kericho, in an area that lies about 2,000 feet above Lake Victoria. A good rainfall and cool climate provide ideal conditions for tea cultivation, and a number of large tea "factories" have been built by European companies. A program to encourage tea growing in African areas has been started by the government; tea factories and government farm supervisors give assistance to Africans on tree care, and the Tea Research Institute at Timbilil Forest near Kericho is carrying out scientific experiments on all aspects of the tea culture and industry.

In 1963, coffee ranked first by value among exports from Kenya, sisal and other agave fibres ranked second, and tea was third. Because of the program of tea culture that has been projected by the government, it is thought that tea may become the leading export by 1975.

Wattle bark, used for tanning, comes from higher regions, and has been both a European and an African enterprise; about equal amounts of wattle bark have been produced by Africans and Europeans. The Kikuyu have planted many acres of wattle on the slopes of the Aberdare Mountains and on the lower portions of Mount Kenya; exports of the extract are valued at about 2½ million pounds a year. Pyrethrum also grows at high elevations where for a long time European farms have produced important quantities. Kikuyu and other tribal groups who live at high altitudes, however, are engaging more and more in the cultivation of this plant, which is used in insect powders; most of that produced is shipped to the United States. The poison is extracted from the flowers, which are hand picked and dried for export.

European farms, generally found in the "scheduled areas"[10] at elevations of 4,000 to 9,000 feet, also grow and export pulses, maize, cashew nuts, dairy products, fruits, meat, bacon, and hides and skins. In some of the drier sectors, fine beef cattle are raised on ranches, as in the Laikipia cattle district north of the Aberdare Ranges, where rainfall at times drops to 14 inches; where this happens, 20 acres or more of land are required to graze each animal.

Much of the African-farmed land receives at least 30 inches of rainfall, enough for successful farming; however, the land holdings tend to be small and split up into uneconomic scattered units. For most efficient use of the land these small farms should be consolidated, and very large numbers have been. Some acute soil problems have resulted from the primitive methods of cultivation practiced by tribal groups, as among the Kiyuyu, Meru, and Embu tribes; although they live in good areas, where the soil is fertile and rainfall sufficient for cultivation, tradition and suspicion

[10] The lands leased or alienated to Europeans, of which the "White Highlands" formed over 90 percent. Alienated areas comprised about one-fourth of Kenya's total arable land.

of new methods retard progress. Nevertheless, African cultivation produces in significant amounts; Western Region, which has an African population of over 2 million, raises about 65 percent of Kenya's maize, and in normal years has a surplus for export; most of the sugar and cotton are also grown here.

FIGURE 21.7 (a, above) Coffee trees, Embu district, Kenya; (b, below) African family picking pyrethrum on their small holding. The flowers are used in making an insecticide. (Courtesy Kenya Information Services, Kenya.)

## UGANDA

Uganda, the third plateau state previously under the British, straddles the Equator. It lies north and west of Lake Victoria, incorporating a part of that lake and other lakes within its domain: about 13,700 square miles of the 93,981 square mile area are open water, because parts of lakes Albert and Edward, all of lakes Kyoga, Kwania, Salisbury, and George, plus numerous small lakes, swamps, and many broad rivers all lie within its bounds. The Victoria Nile has its birth near Jinja in Uganda, and the Albert Nile emerges out of the northern end of the lake of the same name and thus has its start also within the country.

The hydrography of Uganda is complex, significant in the amount of land water-covered, and interesting. The country, almost all plateau land with altitudes ranging between 3,500 and over 4,500 feet, is scarred by valley swamps through which the waters move sluggishly. Lakes Victoria and Kyoga occupy gentle downwarps, their basins so shallow that the lake edges fluctuate markedly with increase or decrease in rainfall.

The central parts of the country are relatively homogeneous; the peripheral sectors are more varied. Occupying a central position on the Lakes plateau, its western borders touch The Congo along the rift valley where, between lakes Albert and Edward, the mighty Ruwenzori tower. It shares some of the Mufumbiro volcanoes with Rwanda and The Congo; Mount Elgon straddles the Uganda-Kenya border in the east.

Between the volcanic mass of Elgon and snow-covered Ruwenzori, a rolling country, green as emerald, dotted with lakes and crosshatched by rivers, abounds with African wildlife, the elephant, buffalo, antelope, eland, gazelle, zebra, lion, and hippos. It is equatorial in location, but altitude gives Uganda an equable climate, with little variation in temperature, which averages between 70 and 75°F, and a rainfall generally of 40 to 50 inches or more; some of the finest agricultural lands in Africa are found here.

The population of nearly 7 million is and has been overwhelmingly African; foreigners include about 70,000 Asians and some 11,000 Europeans. About two-thirds of the Africans speak Benue-Congo languages, and most of the remainder are Eastern or Central Sudanic-speaking people (see Figure 2.4).

Although rich forests and fisheries and valuable mineral reserves are found, and water resources for the development of hydroelectricity abound, Uganda is a country of cultivators and pastoralists. At any one time, however, only about 13 percent of the land area is in crops, but there is plenty of land for the expansion of cultivation; forests and forest reserves cover about 7 percent; approximately 3 percent of the country has been set aside in parks; bush fallow and pasturage cover part of the rest. Uganda is more dependent upon agriculture than are Kenya and Tanzania: two-thirds of the gross national product and nine-tenths of the export revenue of Uganda derive from farm production. Over half of the land cultivated is worked by subsistence farmers, but despite this, the value of commercial crops is one-fourth greater than the value of those grown for subsistence.

Cotton and coffee are the major commercial crops. In fact, Uganda is the greatest exporter of these two crops within the Commonwealth. Cotton occupies the largest acreage and is entirely grown by Africans; its cultivation predates the advent of the European to that country, for when Speke and Grant traveled there, they found primitive species of cotton growing wild. Commercial cultivation began about 1903 to 1904. Coffee is outstanding in Buganda Province, but is not grown in the north, and only a slight production comes from Western Province; Eastern Province grows quite a bit. Coffee *Robusta* is the leading variety cultivated. Coffee, occupying only about one-fourth the acreage that is put into cotton, is also mainly grown by Africans, although some small amounts are raised on European estates. Tobacco is another commercial crop of the Africans; sugar tends to be grown by Asians, while sisal and tea are usually cultivated commercially by Europeans. The country is self-sufficient in food, millet, plantains, maize, sweet potatoes, beans, cassava, and peanuts being the outstanding subsistence crops.

Although in many parts of the country farmers keep animals, it is more usual for people either to cultivate the land or to lead a pastoral life. Integrated farming is rare, unfortunately, because better land-use practices depend in great part upon the integration of these two activities. About 35 percent of the country is infested with tsetse flies and little can be done to increase cattle keeping in these regions until the tsetse has been eradicated; in other parts of the country, however, there is much that can be done. The main sectors of tsetse fly infestation are found along or near the north and west borders of the state; outliers occur along Lake Victoria east of Jinja, and north of the frontier where Tanganyika and Rwanda border on Uganda.

The crescent of land bordering the northern edge of Lake Victoria is climatically and agriculturally the most favored part of the Uganda plateau; rainfall is dependable and plentiful, temperatures are moderated by elevation, and soils are generally more fertile than in most tropical regions. Peneplanation has reduced the plateau to a country of low, flat-topped hills that gradually decrease in height with distance northward; although elevations reach about 4,300 to 4,400 feet, the hills have a local relief of no more than about 500 feet.

The most important sector of the crescent is found in southern Buganda, the richest province of Uganda, whose people, the Ganda, are numerically, economically, socially, and politically the most important in the country. Over half of the population of Buganda are Ganda, Bangaruanda comprising the next most numerous people, and Barundi the third largest group; about 75 percent of the latter groups are migrant workers who come in from Rwanda and Burundi as farm laborers for the land-owning Banga.

Land use in the crescent reflects the necessity of adjusting to the realities of relief and hydrography. Swamps prevail along many valleys in Buganda, and these are generally in papyrus while the lower slopes of the hills, which are likely to have soils that are somewhat acid and sandy, are planted to sweet potatoes and grains; the hilltops are generally reserved for pasture, and the upper and middle slopes are cultivated for such subsistence crops as plantains, corn, cassava, sweet potatoes, and the cash crops of coffee and cotton.

North and east of the fertile crescent of land bordering the lake, conditions become less favorable for agriculture, and this is reflected in the crops that are raised. Plantains and corn are replaced by millet and sorghum, and coffee, the major cash crop of the crescent area, by cotton. The rearing of cattle is important, but as yet there are few outside of the crescent region who integrate cattle keeping with cultivation.

South and west of the crescent the terrain becomes higher and more rugged. Much of this sector is covered with grasslands and occasional trees and bushes and, along some of the rivers, forests. Millet, pulse, and potatoes are the main crops, grown for subsistence; cattle are not important except in parts of Ankole.

All the lakes are rich in fish. The fisheries are operated almost entirely by Africans, who with gill nets, beach seines, and long lines bring in about 40,000 tons of fish annually; basket traps are employed in the swamps. Of the commercial fishing craft employed on the lakes, most are hand operated plank canoes and dugouts; here and there, motorboats or motor powered canoes are used—to the envy of the rest of the 20,000 or so Africans who engage in fishing as a part or full time activity. The Europeans in the industry are few, and their main concern is with the research and development of fisheries, or with marketing, and the like; a few Asians also find employment here. In general, the fishermen of Uganda operate on a small scale and at low cost, using one or possibly two canoes and a bit of gear bought with a minimum of capital outlay.

Expansion and experimentation have characterized this industry in recent years. This has been carried out almost entirely through the efforts of the Uganda Fish Market Corporation (TUFMAC), incorporated in the fall of 1948. It is owned in part by individual Africans or African local governments, and by the Uganda Development Corporation Limited, which is government controlled. Fish farming, in the areas away from natural fishing grounds, is being encouraged by the government as a means of building a more balanced diet for the people.

**The Future of European Agriculture on the Plateau.** The name "White Highlands" signified the importance of the European farmer in East Africa. The name applied to uplands mainly in Kenya, where Europeans settled most heavily. What is the future for these people in the independent black states?

The answer is not clear. Since more Europeans settled in Kenya, the problem is more acute here than in the other plateau states. About one-third of the colonists left almost immediately upon independence; another third have declared they will not leave their homes; the rest appear to be waiting to see what happens; their ultimate action could swing one way or the other.

In January, 1961, a program to purchase European holdings for redistribution to Africans was initiated by the Kenya government. It has been regarded sceptically by both Africans and Europeans, and what success the land settlement program will have cannot be predicted. It rests on the willingness of Europeans to part with their land, on government policy and skill, and on the ability of African farmers.

> Certain predictions may be hazarded, . . . big tea and sisal plantations [likely] will be kept intact because of their great importance to exports and in providing agricultural employment. Pyrethrum production can probably be shifted to African farms with relative ease. Productive livestock activities depending upon exotic breeds and skilled management will be most severely affected. Pressure may develop to switch as much coffee production as possible from European producers to African producers; indeed such a move might go a long way to save the settlement and consolidation programs from failure.[11]

Less than 1 percent of the land in Tanganyika suitable to farming or grazing has been worked by non-Africans, and the role of these people, therefore, is less critical than in Kenya. Europeans dominate sisal and tea, however, and two-fifths of the value of farm exports are produced on European farms.[12]

## MINING, MINERALS, AND INDUSTRY

Although a variety of minerals is known to occur on the Lakes plateau, the actual potential is not known; mineral exploration is just in its beginnings.

Diamonds are the most spectacular of the minerals taken from beneath Tanganyika's surface. They were

[11] William A. Hance, *The Geography of Modern Africa*, New York: Columbia University Press, 1964, p. 402.
[12] *Ibid.*, p. 409.

mined, off and on, in small amounts between the two world wars but not until Dr. J. T. Williamson discovered the now well-known Mwadui kimberlite pipe in 1940, north and east of Shinyanga near the village of Luhombo, did diamond mining become a large enterprise; 95 percent of Tanganyika's diamonds come from the Williamson mines, now jointly owned by the government and DeBeers Consolidated Mines. All the diamonds produced so far have come from superimposed gravels, although the Mwadui is the largest pipe ever discovered, measuring about 3,500 by 5,000 feet across the oval; this diamond pipe is 3 times larger than that of South Africa's Premier mines. Tens of pipes have been discovered in Tanganyika, but only a few of the 40 or 50 that are known are producing any diamonds. The Mwadui kimberlite contains diamonds in quantities economic to mine, and cutting into the pipe has begun at one point.

Until 1938 gold exports were normally second in value only to those of sisal. Since that time production has generally declined, although about the middle of the 1950s it took an upturn; gold ranks second in value of mineral exports (1962 to 1963) and tenth among total exports. Both alluvial and hard rock gold deposits are worked. Silver is found, in varying combination, in association with gold in the hard rock deposits, and these two precious metals are found in combination, as primary occurrences, in four fields.

Tanganyika also has lead ores, of which the most important so far known are at Mpanda, where they occur in combination with copper, silver, and gold. This ore body is remotely situated 200 miles southwest of Tabora, and when planning for exploitation began was without a rail outlet. To promote mining, the Tanganyika government financed a branch line from Kaliua (on the Central Line) to the mine; it was completed in 1950. Since the region is highly mineralized, the railroad will likely pay out despite the fact that the lead ores already show signs of exhaustion.

Salt is produced, both along the coast and at Uvinza near Kigoma, in excess of national needs, and Tanganyika is looking for markets to absorb its increasing production of this chemical. Mica is obtained in the Uluguru Mountains, where two large African cooperatives work adjoining leases; meerschaum (clay) production is being expanded. Tin is mined, and the first tin concentrates were exported in 1958. A large phosphate deposit, discovered by New Consolidated Gold Fields when prospecting for other minerals in the Arusha area, may prove of major importance as a source of fertilizer.

Industrial development is negligible. Aside from industries associated with mining, such as the concentration of ores, washing and sorting of diamonds, etc., industries are based largely on the processing of agricultural products: the decortication of sisal; the pressing and distilling of volatile oils from certain plants such as the geranium, lemon grass, and citrus; butter churning, cotton ginning, rice packaging and polishing; the drying and pressing of pyrethrum; the extraction of tannin from wattle; and cigarettes and wheat flour manufacture. Many of these are new industries. Dar es Salaam is the major center of these industries. In 1959, the Bata Shoe Company of Czechoslovakia began the production of rubber and canvas footwear in this city.

Most industry in Kenya likewise involves the processing of agricultural or animal products, such as fruit, maize, coffee, tea, sisal, sugar, and rice, and preserving beef and fruits; dairy manufactures are expanding. Much of the industry has arisen in and around Nairobi, which is the major industrial center of East Africa.

Although Kenya has not been fully surveyed, the country produces a number of minerals. Soda ash, taken from Lake Magadi, is Kenya's leading mineral resource, and one of the country's major exports. Copper is mined in small amounts (about 200 long tons monthly) from the Macalder-Nyanza mines and exported as copper concentrate; lead occurs in several places in Coast Province. A small production of gold comes mainly as a by-product of the copper mining at the Macalder-Nyanza deposits; gold production is declining but there are supposed to be about 8,000 square miles of territory near the east shore of Lake Victoria that contain gold-bearing rock; silver is found in association with the gold. There are many deposits of ceramic clays in Central and Coast provinces; the production of mullite (see Glossary) from kyanite is well established and will increase as the processing techniques improve. Several kyanite ore bodies occur in Kenya. One of the more important deposits is outside Taveta, Coast Province,

and is accessible to both railway transportation and the port of Mombasa. Kenya expects to be one of the world's leading producers of kyanite. Deposits of a number of other minerals have been confirmed, and structures that are promising for oil have been identified. However, as yet, minerals (soda ash, copper, and gold) make up only a very small proportion of the value of Kenya's exports.

Extensive developments in hydroelectric and thermal power plants are anticipated to serve the country's domestic and industrial needs; a transmission line has already been run from the Owen Falls hydroelectric power complex in Uganda to add to the electricity produced in Kenya itself.

Minerals can play an important part in developing and broadening the basis of Uganda's economy. Even so, precedence is given to agriculture. According to official government policy, since the country "is predominantly agricultural it is most important that mining operations are conducted in a manner that will cause the minimum of interference with agricultural activities, . . ."[13] The result has been a retarded mineral development.

The mineral resources previous to World War II were either merely speculated upon, or regarded more or less as curiosities. During the war, however, tungsten began to be mined. Although the output of this mineral dropped sharply in 1958, it has been one of the leading ores produced. Tin is extracted from both placer and lode deposits, in the Ankole and Kigezi districts. Production has fluctuated since World War II, however, with a marked decline in the last few years. One company, the Kagera Mines Ltd., does most of the tin mining.[14]

Copper has been mined in Uganda only since 1956 despite the fact that deposits along the east flank of the Ruwenzori at Kilembe have been long known and mined by Africans. A production that began with 150 tons of blister copper in 1956 increased nearly 10 times in 3 years. The coming into production of the Kilembe mine has been the most notable feature

[13] "Mining," *Background to Uganda*, Kampala, Department of Information, no. 179, January, 1958.
[14] George H. T. Kimble, *Tropical Africa*, New York: The Twentieth Century Fund, 1960, vol. I, p. 320.

of mining development in Uganda in recent years; this mine also produces cobalt. Development awaited the opening of a railroad from Kampala to Kasese, without which exploitation would have been uneconomic.

Lead is taken in small quantities from small deposits near the edge of the rift valley, at Kitaka near the Ankole-Toro border. These are considered the most promising of the known lead reserves. There is a small but rising output of beryllium in Uganda at Kigezi, extracted by open-pit methods; however, when underground mining becomes necessary, the production of beryl is expected to drop sharply. Gold has been mined in varying quantities over many years. Most of this has been alluvial gold taken in the Toro district. The gold in this alluvium is nearly exhausted, however, and the mother lode from which the alluvial ore is derived has not been discovered. Gold mining in this region has all but stopped; most of the gold now produced comes from Busia near the Kenya border. Potentially the Busia deposit is regarded as important because it is structurally similar to rich deposits in Kenya and Tanganyika.

Although iron ore is only sporadically mined at present, large deposits of high grade magnetite are known to occur between Mount Elgon and Tororo. Hydroelectricity produced at Owen Falls may make possible the development of this iron. Phosphate rock production reaches about 3,000 tons annually. Other minerals, including tantalum, bismuth, mica, and asbestos are present but are not developed.

Since Uganda is incompletely surveyed, and since no great effort has been put into the development of the mineral resources, it is impossible to predict how important mining will be in the economy; further, before the development of mining can go very far, transportation facilities must be increased and improved.

The generation of electricity has risen sharply in Uganda since the first and subsequent stages of the Owen Falls power project have been completed. This dam, lying 2 miles downriver from the point where the Nile emerges from Lake Victoria, formerly Ripon Falls outside of the town of Jinja, dramatizes the change that Western technology is bringing about all over Africa; the dam erased "the falls," but opened up power possibilities for industrial development.

## URBAN DEVELOPMENT

The major cities of East Africa are either ports or administrative, market, or mining centers. Best known, perhaps, is Nairobi (Figure 21.8), capital of Kenya, a commercial, industrial, and tourist center of the first order; Nairobi was and is the outfitting point for many an East African safari, and a jumping-off place for tours of the plateau. It lies on the main railroad from the port of Mombasa inland to centers in Kenya and Uganda. Beginning as a railroad camp in the early 1900s, today it has a population well over 265,000. It is a modern city, the great industrial and commercial center of East Africa; air routes connect it with all parts of the continent.

Over half of all Europeans in Kenya live in Nairobi, which undoubtedly accounts for the important development of industry and commerce in the city. In 1957, 60.5 percent of the industrial workers and 58.5 percent of the factories of Kenya were in and around Nairobi. The climatic factor was important in the choice of Nairobi as a core of European settlement. In the environs around the town, Europeans took up land and began to farm so that the region became a wealthy and thriving center of agricultural development; European-owned sisal plantations are concentrated to a remarkable degree around Nairobi, although some were established along rail lines. The opportunity for employment both in industry and on European plantations and farms has drawn many Africans to this city; Nairobi also has a large Indian community.

Kenya's exports and imports pass through Mombasa, which handles 98 percent of the foreign trade of both Kenya and Uganda, and part of the overseas commerce for northern Tanganyika as well. Mombasa is Kenya's only port. Like many other African ports, Mombasa is congested, although the construction of new quays at Kilindini has relieved the situation somewhat. The town is situated on an island, and linked to the mainland by causeways that carry roads and a railroad. The island situation gives Mombasa two harbors. Kilindini (meaning the "Deep Water"), on the west, is the principal harbor, and its modern wharves and landlocked anchorage provide as fine a shelter as can be found on the East African coast. The Old Harbor on the east is the more picturesque

FIGURE 21.8 (Right) Airview of Nairobi, Kenya. (*Courtesy Kenya Information Services.*)

FIGURE 21.9 (Below) Dar es Salaam ("Dar," for short) curls around its beautiful bay. (*Courtesy Public Relations Department, Tanzania.*)

of the two because into it sail the dhows of the Indian Ocean, from Arabia and Iran, India, and other parts of East Africa. The city is over 1,000 years old, and the population reflects the long historical contact with foreigners—Arabs, Portuguese, Indians, and others. About 5 percent of Kenya's people of European extraction reside in Mombasa; large agglomerations of Indians live here also. Mombasa is East Africa's and Kenya's second industrial city, accounting for over 20 percent of the employed industrial labor and 22.5 percent of the manufacturing establishments in Kenya. From a city of about 85,000 in the decade of the 1940s, Mombasa has risen to a population of over 190,000.

Except for Tabora, Tanzania's major cities are all ports of which Tanganyika has three, Dar es Salaam, Tanga, and Mtwara. Dar es Salaam, capital and leading seaport (Figure 21.9), is situated on a sheltered, deep-water harbor that is well protected from the battering of the sea. The city was named Dar es Salaam, meaning "Haven of Peace," because of the safe anchorage that its harbor provided, one that is as protected as any that can be found in the world. Although less than a century old, and relatively young as a port, Dar es Salaam has during much of that time been an important outlet not only for Tanganyika but for eastern Congo, and Rwanda and Burundi as well, for which it serves as an accessory port. About 20 percent of all Europeans living in Tanganyika reside in Dar es Salaam.

Until the deepwater Princess Margaret Quay was opened in 1956, Dar es Salaam (called "Dar," for short) was only a lighterage port, and ships putting into the port had to anchor offshore in the harbor. Dhow traffic, both coastwise and foreign but largely carried on with Arabian ports, is important. Despite the protected nature of the inner harbor, access to the port is made somewhat difficult because entry must be made through an angular channel that runs narrowly between growth of coral reef, so all ships must be piloted in. Further hindering movements in and out are shoals and strong tidal currents that at times surge through the entrance.

Tanga, although Tanganyika's second seaport, is scarcely more than a roadstead with a limited, though important, function: it is the port through which most of the sisal crop is exported; a railroad

(a)

FIGURE 21.10 Sights and scenes in Zanzibar City: (a, above) dhows sway in the harbor. They come when the monsoons blow from India and return as the monsoons turn to blow toward Asia. (b, below) Coconut palms rear their fronds higher than buildings. (*Photographs by writer.*)

(b)

also connects the port with the rich coffee-growing regions around Mounts Kilimanjaro and Meru. Much of this coffee trade goes out through Kenya's port of Mombasa, however.

Mtwara is the newest and smallest of the ports of Tanganyika; plans are, however, that it will be the largest. Construction of Mtwara was begun in 1948 is association with the Tanganyikan peanut project of the British, for which there were high hopes at the outset. The Southern Province Railway was laid at this time between the peanut fields and the port. But the peanut project was not a success, and port developments lagged as this became apparent. Not until 1954 was the port officially opened.

The harbor at Mtwara is good, for it is almost completely enclosed, and deep enough to permit ships to enter and depart at any time; the facilities are modern, although restricted to a deepwater, general cargo quay equipped with mechanical loading gear and storage sheds. The port is not congested, and its capacity and the number of ships handled could markedly expand before congestion would occur. Although its hinterland is largely restricted to Southern Province, it could be enlarged by rail links into Rhodesia, Zambia, and Malawi. On the plateau, Tabora and Dodoma are leading market towns.

The most historic and colorful port of Tanzania, however, is Zanzibar on Zanzibar Island, for centuries the entrepôt of East Africa (Figure 21.10a and b). Zanzibar's position as a convenient point of entry to the African mainland, and its proximity to Asia and the monsoon seas meant that from ancient times to the present day it has had connections with peoples and civilizations over a wide area.

For 2 centuries following the arrival of the Portuguese off the African East coast, a struggle ensued between these Iberians and the various Arab principalities for control of the littoral and the offshore islands; and by the middle of the sixteenth century these lands had become tributary to the Portuguese crown. Eventually, however, in 1698, the Arabs of Oman captured the Portuguese fort of Mombasa, and thereafter the whole East African coast north of Cape Delgado, as well as the islands of Pemba and Zanzibar, rapidly passed from Portuguese domination to the suzerainty of the Omani sultan. Rule, however, was often actually in the hands of local non-Omani

Arab families who, far from Muscat, were virtually independent for great periods.

With the reestablishment of Arab influence along the east coast by the Iman of Oman, Arab settlement began again, at first slowly in the eighteenth century and then rapidly during the nineteenth century. During the 1830s Sultan Said of Muscat made Omani influence effective along the coast from Cape Delgado to Lamu, and because he was spending more and more time in his African territories, the sultan finally moved his capital to Zanzibar in 1832.

Perhaps it would be more accurate to say of Zanzibar that the destinies of East Africa were linked to the tiny island, because until near the beginning of the twentieth century, that is what happened; the power of the sultanate of Zanzibar was felt throughout most of the eastern sector of the continent. By the end of the reign of Sultan Said (Sultan Seyyid Said bin Sultan), Zanzibar had become politically and commercially the principal town in East Africa and had trade connections with India, Europe, and America, as well as in the East African hinterland; the port city was the slave emporium of the Indian Ocean; from here were launched the explorers of the eastern half and central interior of the "Dark Continent," with Zanzibar supplying the carriers, the provisions, and all of the needs that go into equipping such expeditions.

Thus Zanzibar has been in the midst of some of the most significant occurrences on the African continent since at least the early nineteenth century, and before that for several hundred years it had left its impress upon East Africa across and beyond the Lakes plateau, inland to the upper reaches of the Zambezi River, and down the Nile from its sources northward as far as Khartoum. Arabs, nominally tributary to Zanzibar but acting without restraint, exerted a powerful control across this vast African domain beyond the coastal strip because throughout all of this territory they were the traders and slavers. Great Britain opened a consulate in Zanzibar as early as 1841.

Today Zanzibar, capital city of the former sultanate, is more Oriental than African in appearance despite the predominance of African blood in its population. It is Arabic in style, with narrow, winding, cobbled streets and tall plain whitewashed houses embellished with balconies and magnificently carved wooden doors; its markets and the harbor where the tall-masted dhows from the Arabian Peninsula and the Persian Gulf lie swaying at anchor, add to the eastern flavor. Because of its charm, the city and island have attracted many tourists, and tourism has been quite an important industry on the isle.

Two shipping lines call regularly at the port, and scheduled air services operate between Zanzibar and Kenya and Tanganyika, and between Pemba and Zanzibar islands.

Kampala is Uganda's important city, the most rapidly growing and major commercial center; roads focus into it to give connections in all directions; a railroad links it with Nairobi. Entebbe, on a peninsula on the north shore of Lake Victoria, gave way to the growing power of Kampala when the capital of Uganda was moved from Entebbe to Kampala. A quiet and beautiful though somewhat isolated town, Entebbe nevertheless remains the major air terminal, internationally very important. Jinja, near the Nile outlet of Lake Victoria, is also growing fast and developing as a center of commerce and industry, deriving its power from developments on the Victoria Nile.

Some of the more important towns of the Lakes plateau are lake ports, because inland waterways are quite significant as connecting links among riparian states. Kisumu is the leading port for the traffic that moves on Lake Victoria, handling much of the flow of traffic between Kenya, Uganda, and Tanganyika; it is also the main market and trade center; Mwanza, a Lake Victoria port in Tanganyika, is of lesser importance although port improvements here are making the harbor more competitive with Kisumu than in the past. Kigoma in Tanganyika, Bujumbura in Burundi, and Albertville in The Congo are ports on Lake Tanganyika, which accounts for about 2 percent of the inland waterways traffic. These lake-river lines are especially important to Uganda and to Rwanda and Burundi, all small landlocked countries.

## Rwanda and Burundi

The former Belgian-administered trust territory of Ruanda-Urundi became the Kingdom of Burundi and the Rwanda Republic in July, 1962.

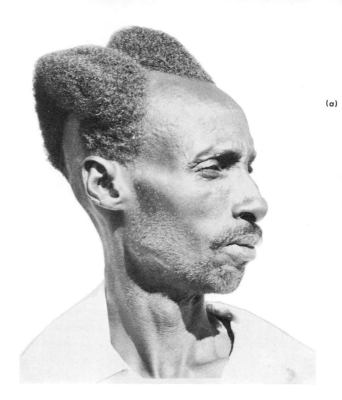

(a)

FIGURE 21.11 (a, above) Profile of the tall and haughty Watusi; (b, below) Bahutu of Rwanda. (*Photograph a by P. Laval; b, courtesy Service de l'Information, Leopoldville.*)

(b)

This was one of the last sectors of Africa to be penetrated by Europeans. In 1871 David Livingstone and Henry M. Stanley landed at Usumbura (now spelled Bujumbura), present capital and port of Burundi situated at the northern end of Lake Tanganyika, the lake which the two men were exploring in their attempt to determine the sources of the Nile. From 1894 to 1896 German explorers ranged over the lands of the small countries, and in 1899 these native territories were made a part of German East Africa (Tanganyika and Ruanda-Urundi). This remained the political status until the defeat of Germany in World War I, after which the territories were mandated to the Belgians by the League of Nations.

Both countries have essentially the same ethnic composition. Three groups make up the people. The tall Watusi (also spelled Watutsi or Batutsi, but popularly called Watusi), a pastoral people of Hamitic-Ethiopian background, were the rulers of the two kingdoms for about 400 years. Aristocratic and overbearing in demeanor (Figure 21.11a), they ruled their kingdoms under a quasi-feudal social system in which the second but majority group, the Bahutu, lived like serfs. The Watusi comprised 10 to 15 percent of the population. The Belgians knew Ruanda-Urundi as the "Land of the Shepherd Kings." It is rich cattle country, but the tall pastoralists keep their animals more for prestige than economic reasons; cattle with long, beautifully shaped horns are especially valued. Some of the Watusi farm the land, but generally it is the Bahutu who are the cultivators. The third group, the Batwa, are Pygmies, a minority people who live primitively and in a servile state. They are, however, skilled hunters. Pygmies comprise about 1 percent of the population.

The Bahutu, a Bantu-speaking people, were mountain peasants (Figure 21.11b). They performed all the servile tasks disdained by the Watusi including the cultivation of the land, which is generally looked upon as menial by primitive pastoralists. The preservation of the kingdom in Burundi likewise preserved the overlord status of the minority Watusi in that country; but the formation of a Republic in Rwanda established the rule of the majority Bahutu, and since independence, all the resentment of centuries of oppression has voiced itself in an unofficial expression of vengeance upon the Watusi. In Burundi, the Watusi had not ruled so autocratically as in Rwanda, and there had been less segregation between the Watusi and Bahutu and more intermarriage. The result was that no social or political revolution occurred in Burundi until considerably later; the predominantly Watusi party and government enjoyed considerable support from the Bahutu, and Burundi remained a kingdom. By early 1965, however, disturbances attributed to foreign influences had become pronounced, and in July, 1966, the Crown Prince suspended the constitution, dismissed the Prime Minister, and took over from the ailing King all powers as chief-of-state because, according to the Prince, state authority was losing hold. Whether the moves were made with or without the consent of the King is not known.

## THE LAND AND ITS USE

Rwanda and Burundi perch on the plateau above the sector of the western rift valley wherein lie Lake Kivu and the northern end of Lake Tanganyika. The plateau varies in height, but averages between 5,000 and 6,000 feet, higher in the west and south than in the central and eastern portions. The latter sector sags toward Lake Victoria and is drained by the Kagera River, but neither country touches the lake. Only the Ruzizi valley between lakes Kivu and Tanganyika and the Usumbura plain at the northern tip of Lake Tanganyika—the latter really a part of the lowland of the Ruzizi River—lie at lower elevations; even at Bujumbura altitudes reach 2,673 feet.

The land and resources of Rwanda and Burundi reflect the intensive and exploitive use of the people who occupy the land; and as a result, the little nations are faced with four staggering problems: overpopulation, subsistence economies, deforestation, and land erosion. Aggravating these problems are the tribal strife released by independence and the isolated, land-locked location of the two states, which is accentuated by the poor transport connections with other parts of Africa, even those just across the borders, and with places exterior to Africa.

These mountainous, eroded countries, averaging nearly 215 inhabitants per square mile, have a higher density of population than has any state of tropical Africa except Zanzibar. Rural density is far greater in the higher portions of the countries than on the

lowlands, with the result that the lofty hills, cultivated from the valley bottoms to the crests (Figure
21.12), are losing their soil by sheet erosion under
the continuous cropping, practiced without attention
to conservation practices; the torrential character of
the rains accentuates slope erosion where the natural
vegetation has been removed.

It is thought that Rwanda and Burundi were largely
covered with forest before the advent of the pastoral
Watusi, but by 1950 not even the requirements for
firewood could be met. Overgrazing has occurred
over large areas; and gullying, from minute to great,
gives evidence of the way in which the soil is washing away as vegetation disappears. Under the Belgians, a 10-year development program was initiated,
designed to implement conservation measures and improve agriculture. Included were three reforestation
projects: (1) forest enrichment in existing timbered
areas; (2) the planting of trees for firewood; and
(3) the reestablishment of the vegetative cover on
eroded slopes and overgrazed grasslands. Enrichment

was carried out in 10,000 acres of forest land and
136,000 acres of firewood have been planted. This
portion of the program was in part carried out by
asking the Africans themselves to plant "one hectare
of land for every 300 taxpayers and encouraging them
further to plant trees near their homes."[15] Since this
part of the afforestation had been worked at for a
long time, 81,000 acres of the 235,000 were already
planted when the 10-year program began. Restora-
tion of the vegetative mantle is the most difficult
task because it involves not only the planting of a
bush cover, but also the implementation of measures
to arrest "slippage and washouts" in areas where
erosion was most advanced.

Rwanda and Burundi have young populations.
Over 51 percent of the inhabitants are children 14
years old or younger, and the population is among

[15] *Plan decennal pour le developpement economique et
social du Ruanda-Urundi*, Brussels: Ministère des Colonies,
1951, p. 383.

FIGURE 21.12    The sculpturing of the hills reminds one of the Orient. (Photograph by writer.)

FIGURE 21.13 Long-horned cattle of a Watusi herdsman. (*Photograph by writer.*)

the most rapidly growing in the world. The increase is estimated at 2.5 percent per annum, a condition that makes the problems of soil erosion, deforestation, destruction of the pastures, and the like, the more critical.

Although a number of minerals occur, including tin, rare earths, phosphate rock, gold, mica, kaolin, bismuth, beryllium, tungsten, columbite, and others, production is minor for all of them and no great reserve of any one ore has been reported. A limiting factor in the development of minerals and trade is transportation. There are no railroads; roads are generally the thoroughfares of travel. Air service connects Bujumbura with Elizabethville and Bukavu, and boat transport on Lake Tanganyika links that capital with Albertville and Stanleyville in The Congo, Kigoma in Tanganyika, and other cities and towns. Some roads are paved, but most are not, and most roads are very narrow and winding. Of the approximately 5,400 miles of road in the two countries, two-thirds are characterized as local roads or merely tracks.

Rwanda and Burundi are agricultural in their economies. Because of the high density of population, most of the cultivation is subsistence; cassava, plantains, and yams lead as subsistence crops, followed by pulses and grain sorghums. Over one-fourth of the land is in field or tree crops, and over one-third is permanent pasture; about 6 percent is forested.

Although much of the agriculture is still subsistence, commercial cultivation was successfully introduced by the Belgians with the 10-year plan, under which the *paysannat* also was important. Since then coffee, rice, cotton, oil palms, and other oil producing plants have been introduced as cash crops, and varieties of food crops have been experimented with and improved; agricultural techniques include conservation methods for the retardation of soil and slope erosion, the introduction of such new crops as rice, the technique of fish farming, draining marshes in the lowlands or, in semiarid regions, irrigation of the land. The efforts to combat disaster seem small and late, because what has been done has merely scratched the surface of what must be done. Although the accomplishments are impressive, whether the work can progress fast enough to meet the need is still a question. Certainly it will require foreign assistance and guidance. The almost complete utilization of slopelands for farming, except in the most rugged and forested areas, reminds one of the intensively tilled slopes of the Orient. Coffee *Arabica* is the chief cash crop.

The highlands are free of the tsetse fly, a scourge over so many parts of humid tropical Africa. This makes the uplands safe for cattle rearing, a condition that has favored the accumulation of large herds by the Watusi: between the two countries, there are more than 1 million head of cattle (see Figure 21.13). Since the animals are kept, as noted previously, mainly for prestige purposes, this large animal industry plays only a minor part in the economy, and land used for pasturing the livestock could better be put to cultivation.

# 22 THE HORN OF AFRICA: SOMALIA AND ETHIOPIA

*Take thou also unto thee principal
spices, of pure myrrh five hundred shekels,
and of sweet cinnamon half so much, . . . ;
these sweet spices with pure frankincense:
of each shall there be a like weight. . . .*

EXODUS 30:23, 34

The people of Ethiopia and Somalia face each other across contiguous frontiers, at once related and opposed. Somalia lies bleached and thirsty along the northeast and east edges of the plateau country; it is Moslem in religion, a land culturally homogeneous yet divided by tribal allegiances. Ethiopia, although an Empire ruled over by a supreme head, is also strongly tribal; although officially Christian, most of the tribal groups hold to native religions, the Amhara comprising most of those who profess Christianity.

Both Ethiopians and Somalis are culturally and racially mixtures. The mixing of blood and cultures has gone on for so long in each country that the blending has become smoothed, each country having developed, even within its differences, a distinguishable people and culture. Both have adapted well to their contrasting environments, the Ethiopians to the rain-drenched mountain plateau habitat, the Somalis to the thornbush country most suitable to grazing.

FIGURE 22.2 Bounds of lands traditionally regarded by the Somali people as theirs. The former British lands, now a part of Somalia, are indicated. (*After The New Commonwealth, January, 1960.*)

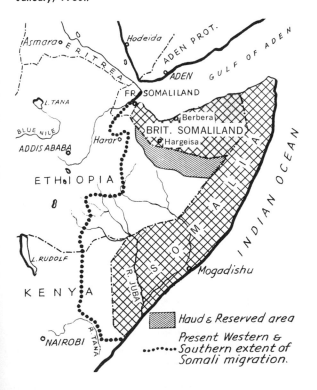

Haud & Reserved area

Present Western & Southern extent of Somali migration.

[They] are twice related: [first through language and a] common ancestry in Southern Arabia; [second, through their] intermarriage with Hamites whom they subjugated, absorbed, or decimated in the course of several centuries of successful raiding and expansion.

Much divides them, [however, especially a record of formidable wars, both in the present and in the past.] Even the ancient world was aware of the breakup of several empires in this part of Africa. In the thirteenth century, an Ethiopian hymn glorifying a victory identified the Somali as the defeated enemy. In the sixteenth century, the Iman of Harar and his multilingual troops were close to wiping out the Christian Ethiopians. When in the nineteenth century the Europeans came bearing gifts of ammunition to the kings of Ethiopia, the wheel of fortune turned again: Under Emperor Menelik II, the Amhara defeated all who stood in their way and added the large Somali province of Ogaden to the empire. The present emperor, Haile Selassie I, was bequeathed a long line of triumphs: over the Egyptians in the 1870's, over the Sudanese Mahdists, elsewhere so difficult to cope with; over the Emirate of Harar; and, most significantly, over the Italians at Adowa in 1896.

In the same period, the Somalis swept across the entire lowland area. They were no longer one among many but the only people identified with the arid zone, having driven out all competitors for grazing land and confined the Arabs to the coastal towns.[1]

Most clashes between Ethiopians and Somalis are over grazing rights because traditionally the nomadic and pastoral Somalis have regarded certain lands as theirs even when these lands straddle international boundaries. Such is the case in the frontier zone between Ethiopia and Somalia known as the Haud.

## Somalia

Independence came to Somalia, made up of the former Italian and British Somalilands, in 1960. This is a large country, over 246,000 square miles in size, with a smattering of people that total about 2 million. It curls around the edges of "the Horn," bordering on the Indian Ocean and the Gulf of Aden, and neighboring Kenya, Ethiopia, and French Somaliland.

[1] Leo Silberman, "Change and Conflict in the Horn of Africa," *Foreign Affairs,* vol. XXXVII, no. 4, pp. 649–651, July, 1959.

Mogadishu is its capital. French Somaliland, 8,492 square miles in size and with a population of about 70,000 people, lies just to the west along the shore, facing the Gulf of Aden and the Strait of Bab-el-Mandeb, which strategic narrows it partially controls. (See Figure 22.2.)

The Somalis did not constitute an independent and politically united nation previous to the partition of their pasturelands by Egypt, and later by France, Britain, Italy, and Ethiopia during the last quarter of the nineteenth century. They were a number of large and often hostile "clans," that were themselves further divided into many lesser subdivisions on the basis of blood kinship. There was, however, a common code of morality recognized by all Somalis, and a common tariff of damages and indemnities for wrongs. All disputes between rival groups could, when the parties were willing, be compounded by the payment of standard rates of compensation. There was thus as it were a common code of law; and courts of arbitration "could be set up to make judgments between contending factions." There was also a common sentiment of Somaliness, accompanied by a virtually uniform national Somali culture, which was reinforced by the strong adherence of all Somali to Islam.

"Thus the Somali have always constituted a nation, . . ." despite the fact that "political nationalism (has been) absent—largely because of the divisive forces within the nation;—only after imperial partition" took place was the way opened toward unification of the Somali tribes and formation of a Somali nation-state: the partition by non-Moslem, foreign colonial powers of the traditional grazing grounds of the Somali people into French, British, and Italian Somalilands, the Ethiopian Haud and Ogaden, and Northern Province of Kenya had the effect of reinforcing "Somali sentiments of national identity through Islam."[2]

Independent Somalia does not unite all Somalis living in the Horn, however; significant numbers live as minorities outside of the borders of the new state but contiguous to its frontiers in Kenya, Ethiopia, and French Somaliland; only political boundaries separate them.

[2] I. M. Lewis, "Pan-Africanism and Pan-Somalism," *Journal of Modern African Studies*, vol. I, no. 12, pp. 147–148, June, 1963.

Somalia is a republic. The constitution, in its final form and as accepted by the Assembly, reflects the ideal of Pan-Somalism, and also of that broader concept espoused by most African nations, Pan-Africanism. The objective of the unification of all Somali territories and peoples is to translate cultural nationalism into political nationalism, the basic platform of all major parties.

Because of the tribal organization of the Somalis and the degree of authority that has always rested in the tribe, one of the first needs of the national government was to attempt to lessen the power of the tribes, and to gain recognition for the national idea and allegiance to the national state. Political development has proceeded rapidly, much more rapidly than was expected, and more rapidly than economic and social changes have taken place. Although border tension has mounted and boundary disputes have multiplied since independence, these very difficulties have helped to strengthen the growth of the national concept, because they have united all Somalis in a common cause.

## THE LAND

Somalia is a long, narrow country varying in width from 95 to 250 miles in from the coast, which is about 2,000 miles long. The country lies on a structural block known as the Somali plateau or tableland, that is highest in the north along the Gulf of Aden, and tilts toward the Indian Ocean. The northern edge of the plateau is mountainous, the highest peak, Mount Bahai south of Candala, reaching about 7,200 feet. At Gardo, inland and on the border of what was British Somaliland, the elevation is 2,650 feet, and at places along the Ethiopian frontier it declines to 1,175. The southeast is an extensive flat region, less than 325 feet above sea level, veneered with alluvium, and eluvial material (rock material weathered and disintegrated) in places. From the Kenya frontier northward for over 785 miles, in other words for two-thirds of the length of the Indian shore, the coast is lined with dunes.

The largest Somalian rivers, the Webbe Shebeli and the Juba, rise in the high plateaus of central Ethiopia. The Webbe Shebeli, the smaller of the two streams, enters Somalia near Belet Uen and flows southeast directly toward the coast. Just north of

Mogadishu, however, instead of entering the ocean, it makes a sharp turn southward, and for the rest of its course runs parallel to the shore, finally losing itself in vast swamps formed by the deposit of alluvium, just below Merca. Two streams issue from these swamps, the Webbe Shebeli and Webbe Gofca, to unite some miles below their emergence and flow into the Juba as a single tributary, near the mouth of that river. Beginning at Mahaddei Uen the waters of the Webbe Shebeli are used to irrigate large areas of cultivated land; during the seasons of the spring and fall rains in Ethiopia, the waters reach a flood flow of from 5,250 to 5,650 cubic feet of water per second, but in February and March the river bed is normally dry.

The Juba is potentially more important than the Shebeli. It enters Somalia at Dolo, takes a southeastward course toward the shore, and empties into the Indian Ocean just north of Chisimaio (Kismayu). Normally water runs in its channel throughout all of the months of the year, although seasonal variations in volume are characteristic. Several other streams, which flow only seasonally at the periods of peak rains in the high country, take their courses across Somalian territory.

Southern Somalia is crossed by the Equator. Because of its tropical location, temperatures range between 60 and 110°F, and over the country as a whole average about 80°F. The highest temperatures and lowest precipitation occur along the northern coast, where less than 2 inches of rain are typical; rainfall increases generally with distance south, averaging in the moistest areas from 16 to 24 inches. Along the Gulf of Aden, on the other hand, years may pass with no measurable moisture falling.

Somalia has four seasons, based on moisture and related to the northeast and southwest monsoons and the shifting of these winds. In general, the seasons follow the quarters of the year. The first quarter, beginning about the first of January, is the period of the northeast monsoons. The weather is hot, dry, and frequently dusty; during this period the Juba River reaches its lowest flow, and the Webbe Shebeli is either dry or the water is merely standing in pools, without flowing much of the time. During the second quarter the wind has subsided and is shifting to the southwest. This is the rainiest season, during which about 60 percent of the rain falls; the weather is hot and humid. The season of the southwest monsoon, the third period, is the cool time of the year throughout most of Somalia; occasional light showers may bring some moisture; in the north, along the Gulf of Aden, this is the hottest period, and average temperatures soar above 95°F; daytime temperatures are excessively high. The fourth quarter is the period of the second or "smaller" rains, a wet season that is shorter than the first; the wind has again subsided, and is shifting toward the northeast; weather is hot and humid. The seasons of precipitation follow the spring and fall equinoxes, when the monsoons stop.

High daytime temperatures throughout the year accentuate evaporation and aridity. In the north an arid limestone plateau gives way to barren mountains inland. Neither the southwest summer monsoon nor the northeast winter monsoon bring rain to this area. Vegetation is drought resistant and scant throughout all but the southern parts of the country; the most prevalent varieties are acacia scrub and desert grass, the closeness of cover depending upon the extent of the rainfall or moisture and, in some cases, the salinity of the soil; myrrh and other incense-producing plants grow wild, and gums and resins are collected. Agricultural possibilities are limited, and most of the people depend upon herds of sheep and goats and the gathering of wild products from the bush for their livelihood.

In central Somalia north of the Webbe Shebeli, the country is a flat plateau and very arid. As in the north, about the only adjustment possible is that of nomadic pastoralism, with sheep or camels as the chief livestock. With luck, in certain seasons, durra and pulses may be grown, but this is an unusual rather than customary pattern.

Going south toward the Juba River climatic conditions improve, offering better possibilities for tilling the land and ameliorating somewhat the strict adherence to nomadism, which is necessary beyond the Webbe Shebeli. Along the rivers the farming of grains and cotton, and such tropical crops as sugarcane and bananas, is practiced quite successfully. This adjustment carries on into southern Somalia where the richest vegetation is found; trees that supply wood, especially the mangrove, grow here.

## LAND USE

When it is considered that according to estimates, only 17.5 percent of Somalia is cultivable, 43.5 percent suitable to some kind of grazing, and 39 percent unusable wasteland, it is not surprising that animal husbandry and agriculture are the bases of the Somalian economy. The land classified as "unusable" is mainly in the arid plateau in the north and in the coastal dune country that extends for such a great distance northward from the Kenya border; small scattered areas of highly saline soils also fall within this category.

The basic occupations of pastoralism and farming, the seasonal movements of people and herds, and the transport of goods are closely associated with climate. The interior of Somalia, like the coastal regions, has seasons of light precipitation after the spring and fall equinoxes when the monsoons do not prevail. During these periods upland tribes move south for grazing into the areas of rain; even the farmers living along the southern coast send their herds north to these interior pastures during the spring and fall seasons. Coastal tribes in the north, on the other hand, migrate to the highlands during the hot, arid summer. Camels, sheep, goats, and cattle are the principal livestock; animal husbandry is predominantly a Somali pursuit. The most important areas of animal husbandry, however, are between and along the two major rivers, in the southern half of the inland region west of the Juba, and northward near the coast as far as Obbia; goats and camels range outside of these areas; the transhumance of the north has been noted.

Major crops are durra, maize, sesame seed, cotton, bananas, sugarcane, and peanuts: durra, maize, sesame seed, and cotton are grown largely by Somalis while banana, peanut, and sugarcane production are mainly European enterprises, as is also sugar refining. Commercial cultivation is limited to the southern part of the country, where both inundation and perennial irrigation are practiced. Bananas are Somalia's leading export. Although modern techniques of agriculture, adapted to Somalia, are typical in European plantations, most of the native cultivation is done with the short handled, short bladed hoe so typical in all parts of black Africa, and here known as the *iambo*.

The migratory livestock industries produce few marketable products. Hides and skins are most important, but in general, except for black leopard, they are of poor quality owing to "their thinness" and the careless methods of skinning and tanning that are employed. Goat and kidskins find the most ready sale in foreign markets. A recent estimate of the number of livestock of Somalia placed it at a total of 6,720,300, classified as follows: goats, 3,800,000; camels, 1,300,000; cattle, 1,000,000; sheep, 600,000; donkeys, 20,000; horses, 300. The number of animals fluctuates greatly depending especially upon the amount of rainfall—with the fluctuations of which pastures will be fair or poor—and the availability of drinking water. If prolonged droughts occur, great numbers of animals perish, particularly cattle; but when pasture and water are relatively plentiful, the herds increase rather rapidly.

Water is the major problem of life in Somalia: it is scarce, and some of it relatively unpalatable even to animals; in the desert it is sold by the cupful. Locally, floods may occur but in the absence of any large dams or reservoirs, the precious water runs away as rapidly as it rushes in; a few hours after floodwaters have appeared, nothing but moist sand remains as evidence of their passage. Only here and there is irrigation practiced: the areas using flashflooding and inundation irrigation are along the rivers and the *desceks* (depressions) in the lower Juda; regions of perennially irrigated plantation agriculture are Villabruzzi, Afgoi, Genale, and the lower Juba (also spelled Giuba). Less than 1 percent of the potentially cultivable land in Somalia is irrigated, or about 250,000 acres only. Sedentary folk, who usually are both cultivators and pastoralists, live somewhat more securely than do the nomads; but bringing hazards to farmers are the locusts that generally invade the country twice a year, sometimes in disastrous numbers.

***Industry and Trade.*** Salt is the only mineral produced in the Somalilands. It is obtained by evaporating the moisture from diked-in basins along the sea. Some mineral deposits occur but none are developed.

Trade is negligible because cultivated products are not generally produced in surplus of the national needs, and fishing is merely a local occupation supplying demands among coastal settlements. By value of exports, bananas contribute not quite one-half of the export revenue;[3] animal products, especially hides and skins, and charcoal follow, comprising about 15.4 and 5 percent respectively; wood and wood products other than charcoal are among the exports following the three leaders. Most of this is fuel wood. The total income from products sold abroad is less than 10 million dollars annually; imports are valued at a little more than half again as much.

Two items of trade, however, are historically interesting. Since Biblical times Somalia has been a leading producer and supplier of incense, myrrh, and frankincense. Now, however, it makes up less than 1 percent of the value of exported products. Salt also has been important for a long time. Before World War II, Somalia was one of the world's leading producers of marine salt. During the war, however, Somalia lost her salt markets; in 1959, the country evaporated enough salt to meet all national needs, and exported 143 tons to foreign lands.

Mogadishu (Mogadiscio), capital of the country and an international air center, is also the leading port, especially for imports. Much of the industry of Somalia has grown up here or in the hinterland of the capital city. The large sugar mill owned by SAIS, that produces about half of the industrial output and employs about one-third of the industrial labor of Somalia, is located here; SAIS also operates plants that distill alcohol, gin cotton, extract oil, and make soap. Beef packing is an enterprise at Mogadishu and Merca, and tuna is canned at Candala and Abo; these beef and tuna plants do not operate up to capacity, however. Leather, shoes, and banana-fiber rope are also manufactured in Somalia. Most of the industry is owned by Italians.

## Approaches to the Horn

Somalia has one of the most inhospitable coasts in Africa: nearly all of it is arid or semiarid, making it difficult to supply fresh water and food to ships; and only one anchorage, Chisimaio near the mouth of the

Juba River, is naturally sheltered along a shore where shelter is desperately needed; little had been done to develop this natural advantage until the mid-1960s. Chisimaio also has its drawbacks, for during the summer monsoon, winds are onshore throughout the entire season and bad swells are frequent. Such shipping as there is has therefore tended to be seasonal. All ports other than Chisimaio and Mogadishu are open roadsteads, and goods and passengers must be lightered between ship and shore; the harbor at Mogadishu is an artificial one, completed only in 1965.

Mogadishu had the best developed port facilities in Somalia, however, and these were improved under a loan from the United States which permitted the development of the new deepwater port that has a capacity 20 times greater than the old port; facilities at Chisimaio also were improved; until these late installations at the two cities, no port in Somalia had had deepwater docking facilities, but Mogadishu and Chisimaio now have. Chisimaio and Merca, about 40 miles south of Mogadishu, ship out many of the bananas that are exported. (Until the new facilities were installed at Chisimaio, all bananas had to be loaded manually.) Berbera is the only port of consequence in the north. It has regular service with Aden by dhow, and occasionally small oceangoing vessels visit the port.

The best harbor within the Somalilands is in the French territory, Djibouti. The port is situated along the south side of the Gulf of Tadjoura, with ample space for accommodating many ships; except during the monsoon months of June, July, and August, entry and exit are easy at all times. The Djibouti harbor itself is artificial, constructed with jetties, but the port facilities have been little developed; there are no deepwater quays alongside which vessels may tie up; all ships must drop anchor offshore.

A rail line extends inland from Djibouti to Addis Ababa, in Ethiopia, and for many decades this French port served as the major outlet for that country. After Eritrea federated with Ethiopia, however, ports along the Eritrean coast were developed by Italy. Djibouti is therefore relatively less important to the plateau state than formerly, and the two Eritrean ports of Massawa and Assab are likely to compete increasingly with Djibouti, particularly Assab. Massawa was developed by Italy as a civil and naval port. It is roomy

[3] *Yearbook of International Trade Statistics*, New York: United Nations, 1963.

and able to accommodate large ships with ease; a rail line, likewise Italian built, extends from the port to Asmara and into the plateau giving Massawa an important advantage. Assab, near the Eritrean-French Somaliland border, is better situated than Massawa to become a rival of Djibouti for traffic because the hinterlands of Assab and Djibouti are more nearly coincident. Assab was converted from an open roadstead to a deepwater port during the 1930s by Italy as a part of its colonization program. It is not a first class harbor, but its improvement has high priority among Ethiopian development plans. A truck route connects Assab with Addis Ababa.

Loss of Ethiopian transit trade could lead to a decline of Djibouti were the city not so strategically situated. But because of its position near the Strait of Bab-el-Mandeb, as an outpost of the Middle East, and as an air junction between Europe, South Africa, and the Far East, it is unlikely that a decline will occur.

The Djibouti-Addis Ababa railway and the port are virtually the only assets of French Somaliland. Work on the railroad and at the port attracts labor even from neighboring Somalia. In an attempt to stave off the diversion of traffic from Ethiopia to Djibouti, in 1959 the French owners of the railroad sold a majority interest in the railway to the Ethiopian government. This transfer also strengthened French-Ethiopian opposition to the "Greater Somalia" movement: should Somalia absorb the French territory, the port and railway terminal would fall into the hands of an Islamic state, unlikely to be sympathetic to predominantly Coptic Christian Ethiopia. The antagonism would be reinforced by the fact that the advocates of a Greater Somalia have irredentist claims on parts of Ethiopia.

French Somaliland has almost no natural resources except this harbor. The coast, about 220 miles long and deeply indented by the Gulf of Tadjoura, is dry, bare, and desolate, punctuated with sharp cliffs and deep ravines, and covered with burning sands and sparse, thorny shrubs. Settlements all center around the Gulf of Tadjoura. Rainfall is infrequent and irregular except on Mount Dankali. The climate is torrid; Djibouti is one of the hottest spots on the face of the earth. Temperatures vary between 77 and 86°F from October to May when the northeast monsoon prevails, and reach 92°F between May and October,

soaring as high as 113°F when the sand-laden Khamsin wind blows from the northwest.

Two-thirds of the 70,000 inhabitants are nomadic pastoralists. More than one-half of the population are Danakils and about one-third Somali Issa; the remainder are immigrants from neighboring countries, including Arabs from Yemen.

Hides and salt are the leading exports, in addition to the transit trade from Ethiopia.

## Ethiopia

It is difficult to convey verbally just how isolated and inaccessible Ethiopia really is. The core of the country consists of two high, fantastically broken plateaus that project abruptly from their lowland base, lowlands that range from semiarid to arid deserts, desolate and wind whipped, where water is rare and the heat excessive. About half of the country is comprised of plateaus that average between 4,000 and 11,000 feet elevation, but rise higher on some of the peaks. The plateau extends as a formidable block from northern Kenya into Eritrea, bifurcated into two sectors by the rift valley.

On its plateau, this desert-surrounded nation was able to successfully fend off any would be conquerors for centuries. Not until its conquest by the Italians in 1935 did Ethiopia bow to invaders. Domination by the Latins was short lived, however—not long enough to bring changes in the feudalistic self-sufficient social and economic system that has characterized Ethiopia from the distant past, and still largely persists. The name Ethiopia goes back to Bible days. Ancient contacts were more frequent than modern ones, but Ethiopia has always tended to remain aloof and apart from the rest of the world, even from Africa and the Middle East, and much of the knowledge about the country was based on hearsay.

The first break into the isolation in modern times was made when the French, as part of their design for empire in Africa, obtained a concession to construct the 486-mile Djibouti-Addis Ababa railway in 1894. Menelik II was Emperor at this time.

European powers had attempted to make encroachments on Ethiopian soil before this. They became particularly interested in the Horn when the Suez Canal

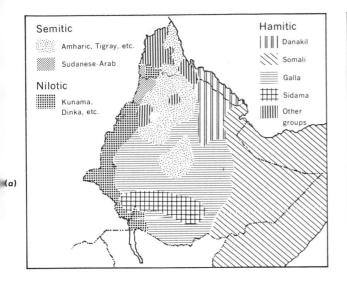

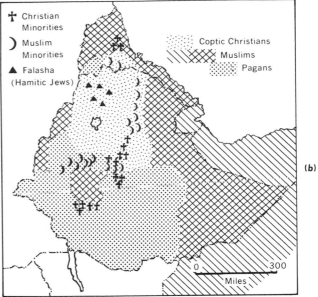

FIGURE 22.3 (*a, above*) Languages; (*b, above right*) religions; (*c, below*) detail of rainfall. (*After Leslie T. C. Kuo in Focus.*)

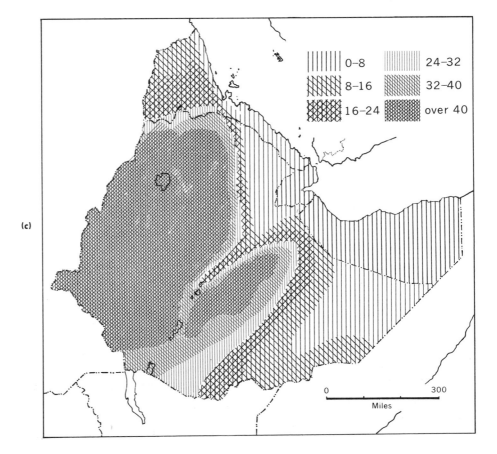

opened and the Red Sea-East African coast suddenly assumed an importance it had never had before, becoming strategic to the control of the trade route that passed through the canal. Egypt seized the Eritrean coast from Turkey; and private Italian interests bought the port of Assab from a local sultan in 1869. The port, in turn, was purchased from the private company by the Italian government in 1882, and three years later, Italy occupied Massawa, about 275 miles north of Assab. However, when the Italians sought to establish themselves inland, they suffered a defeat at Dogali.

For a time, Italy tried to strengthen her hold on Ethiopia by following the ancient Roman maxim of "divide and conquer," inciting two rival rulers against each other; but when Emperor John of the East was killed in 1888 in a battle with the Mahdi, the Italians turned to negotiation with the remaining ruler, Menelik II, and in 1889 the Treaty of Ucciali was signed.

This treaty was differently interpreted by the two signatories. The Italian text appeared to give Italy a virtual protectorate over Abyssinia. It read: Menelik "consents to avail himself of the Italian Government for any negotiations which he may enter into with other powers or governments"; and the Amharic text, the only one signed, stated—"or so it was claimed—simply that the Emperor might use the Italians if he so desired."[4]

In 1890 Italy consolidated her holdings along the coast, and formally named the area Eritrea. Further encroachments led to military action and the battle of Adowa in 1896, in which the Italians suffered a disastrous defeat. The victory by the African nation secured recognition of Ethiopian independence, and forced European powers to negotiate directly with Ethiopia as a sovereign state.[5] Despite the victory, at this time Ethiopia pressed no claims on Eritrea, as it did after World War II.

Menelik continued his military conquests, extending them south, southeast, and southwest, and as a result of his victories, established essentially the same boundaries that demarcate the state today. Menelik was the first ruler to attempt to modernize Ethiopia.

[4] Adapted from Ernest W. Luther, *Ethiopia Today*, Stanford, Calif.: Stanford University Press, 1958, pp. 16–17.
[5] *Ibid.*, p. 18.

Besides permitting the construction of the French railway which gave the country access to the sea, he had the first roads laid out, and introduced the first electricity, government schools, and postal service. He was very ill for many years, however, and as his health declined, European powers began to push their vested interests. In 1906, France, England, and Italy signed a tripartite treaty that confirmed the sovereignty of Ethiopia, but designated respective spheres of influence should the African state disintegrate upon the Emperor's death. England's sphere embraced the Lake Tana-Blue Nile River basin, the railway and right-of-way from Djibouti that of France; the Italian zone was a strip of Ethiopian territory connecting Italian Somaliland and Eritrea.

After the death of Menelik a struggle for power between Menelik's daughter, who became Empress in 1916, and Ras Tafari, who had been named regent and heir to the throne, eventuated in victory for the latter. Ras Tafari took the throne in 1930 under the name of Haile Selassie ("Power of the Trinity"), claiming to be a direct descendant of Menelik I, who was the son of King Solomon and the Queen of Sheba. The Ethiopian Emperor is an absolute monarch.

The reign of Haile Selassie was interrupted in 1935 by the conquest of Ethiopia by Italy. However, Italian hold over the country was broken when British troops entered from the Sudan in 1940 to 1941, wrested control from the Italians, and returned Ethiopia to its Emperor. Eritrea federated with Ethiopia 12 years later (September, 1953), after United Nations observers had ascertained that this was the wish of the Eritreans. Eritrea has an area of about 48,000 square miles and a population of slightly over 1 million.

## THE LAND AND ITS USE

The inhabited portion of the plateau divides into three regions in terms of elevation and climate: the *quolla*, *woina dega*, and *dega*, referring respectively to the hot, temperate, and cold zones, terms that are sometimes applied by the Ethiopians even to isolated pockets of climate having those particular characteristics of temperature. The middle zone of the plateau, the *woina dega* at elevations between 6,000 and 8,000 feet, is the most temperate and the largest in

FIGURE 22.4 High in the Ethiopian mountains, tribesmen guide their camels along the main road at Kombolchia. (*From The Lamp. Courtesy The Standard Oil Company of New Jersey.*)

area; temperatures here average between 61 and 68°F. Here, also, are found the densest population and most of the cultivation. Besides the subsistence grains, coffee, cotton, tobacco, grapes, and olives are grown. Above the *woina dega* lies the *dega,* more than 8,000 feet in elevation and colder, with temperatures that average from 50 to 61°F; beyond 11,500 feet lie the lands called the *wirch.* The *dega* is largely grassland, with scattered forests of alpine woods. Animals are raised on the mountain pastures, and wheat, barley, millet, pulses, flax, and fruits are cultivated. At elevations below 6,000 feet lies the zone known as the *quolla,* including not only the lower portions of the plateaus but also the plain of Danakil and the Awash valley, the lower portions of the Somali plateau in Ogaden, the Sidamo-Borana district, and the lower Sudanese slopes; the desert areas, included in the *quolla* are called the *bereha.* This is a pastoral zone inhabited by hardy people and equally hardy animals, camels and sheep, that subsist on the sparse thorn vegetation and savanna forests, and even penetrate

the deserts at certain seasons. The *quolla* is very sparsely inhabited; it is, in fact, almost empty as compared with the *woina dega* and *dega* zones. However, no part of Ethiopia is characterized by a dense population.

The Ethiopian federation is an agricultural country. More than nine-tenths of the people make their living by cultivating the soil or raising livestock: Ethiopians and Eritreans are bound to the soil, or to their herds. Land that can be cultivated is found throughout the country, but the region with the highest proportion of tillable soil is in the northern uplands, the traditional homelands of the Amhara.

Many crops on the plateau can be grown without irrigation, but on the slopes and in the lowlands cultivation depends more closely upon water availability and soils. In the western plains, where soils are black or brown clays known as cotton soils, tillage is limited only by the provision of irrigation water during the dry season; in the southern parts of the rift valley and on the southeastern Somalian slopes, where subhumid or semiarid conditions obtain and seasons alternate markedly between wet and dry, cultivation depends upon both water for irrigation and suitable soils; in desert regions, as along the Eritrean coast, the plain of Danakil, and the eastern Somalian slopes, water is still more scarce, and here only alluviums or the red desert soils can be cultivated, and then only provided water can be found to irrigate the land.

Wherever cultivation is practiced, soil erosion is pronounced, and no measures have been taken to arrest it. Agriculture is, in general, primitive and mostly subsistence; a possible one-fifth of the crops raised is sold. Yields are low, largely because of the crude methods that are still used. The Ethiopian plow is more of a digging implement than a plow, merely breaking and not turning the soil; to get an adequate seedbed, the soil must be reworked three or four times; seeds are scattered broadcast in the ancient way, and not planted in rows; this makes hoeing difficult.

Teff, a kind of millet, is by far the most widely grown subsistence food crop on the plateau, and one of the staple-foods in the diet of Ethiopians; little is exported because there is practically no demand for it outside Ethiopia. Wheat, maize, sorghum, and barley are also raised, the latter as feed for animals; oil seeds are important, and both locally consumed and exported; coffee is a leading agricultural export; ensete, the Abyssinian banana, is raised. Although cotton would appear to be highly suitable to the Ethiopian environment, little is grown despite the fact that it could help to fill the needs of the home market, which now requires imports.

So favorable for the raising of crops are temperatures and rainfall on the middle plateau (the *woina dega* zone) that almost any crop could be successfully cultivated if it were given the proper care. On the other hand, across great areas of Ethiopia water is one of the acute needs. Even where rainfall averages are high, precipitation is highly concentrated within a relatively short season, and in the absence of reservoirs and catchment basins, much of it is. allowed to run away and be lost. Once the rains cease, the earth becomes parched. Storage facilities are needed to correct this. They also would make domestic supplies of water, and drinking water for stock, easier

to obtain; during the dry season, water for domestic use must often be carried many miles from some distant pool or spring, and cattle may have to be driven equally long distances for water. Animals become emaciated, both from the distances walked and the lack of green pasturage. Poor practices of herding, and of selection of grazing areas worsen the problems imposed by the environment.

The foundation of the economy of Ethiopia lies in its livestock. Although the country divides broadly into two systems, agriculture and animal industries, and although the country areally divides roughly between these two adjustments, the activities merge because cultivation is mostly done with animal-drawn plows; between 4 and 5 million oxen are employed for this work. Livestock, therefore, are an integral part of all farming systems. Cattle, estimated at 23 million, are raised largely by pastoral peoples who depend solely on their animals for livelihood. Nomads who follow their flocks inhabit mostly the dry regions of the country, migrating long distances in search of grazing.[6]

Hides and skins are the leading exports from Ethiopia, of which cattle hides, and sheep and goatskins are the most important. The skins of wild animals, which include the leopard, lynx, otter, colobus monkey, and the like, also are shipped out. The skins are better handled than are the hides because of the easier processing involved; they therefore command higher prices. More than 100 weekly markets, scattered throughout the country, provide centers where hides and skins are bought and sold.

Since the economy of Ethiopia is practically self-contained, few exports are required to procure the modest import demands. The agricultural and animal products' surpluses take care of this.

*Mineral Resources.* The extent of the mineral and fuel reserves of Ethiopia has not been determined, but among the known resources is the potential of water power that resides in the rivers and lakes, the greatest of which is the Blue Nile-Lake Tana system. The river rises in Lake Tana, which lies at 6,000 feet above sea level, and enters Sudan at about 600 feet

[6] *Economic Handbook*, Addis Ababa: Ministry of Commerce and Industry, Imperial Ethiopian Government, 1958.

FIGURE 22.5 Sunshades shelter these Ethiopian women from the heat and glare as they walk toward the village of Kombulcha. The less conventional parasol is made of woven straw. (*From The Lamp. Courtesy The Standard Oil Company of New Jersey.*)

elevation; between its source and the Ethiopian border the Blue Nile drops about 5,500 feet. This steep descent, added to the great volume of water the river carries, gives it a high potential for power development. (See Figure 22.1.)

However, the first important Ethiopian hydroelectric scheme was not constructed on the Blue Nile, but on the Awash River at Koka, about 50 miles south of Addis Ababa. This project, now completed, will help to take care of some of the rapidly rising needs for electricity in the capital and at Dire Dawa. The United States has assisted in preliminary surveys of hydroelectric possibilities on the Blue Nile and elsewhere, and some small local power units, now in operation, were built with American financial and technical assistance. They consist only of small water wheels that turn small generators to produce energy for a limited use within individual villages, however.[7]

Oil explorations, carried out since 1945 along the coast of Eritrea, in the Dahlak Archipelago, and in the Ogaden region have struck no oil, but coal and iron deposits are known to exist. Deposits of potash,

cobalt, chromite, tungsten, manganese, tin, copper, asbestos, mica, vanadium, nickel, beryllium, mercury, and graphite also are known although their extent is not known; diamonds and garnets occur, as do platinum and gold. The mining of gold goes back beyond the recorded history of the country; some deposits have been worked since Old Testament times. The gold ore occurs in both alluviums and veins.

Salts are procured in the arid salt plain of Danakil as are also potassium-bearing minerals; kaolin, which occurs in several areas, is used locally in pottery making. Although the list of minerals is long, the value of the reserves is unknown, and mineral exports make up less than half of 1 percent of the export value of the country.

*Economic Change and Planning.* Like Menelik II, Haile Selassie has begun to modernize his country in his latter years, beginning on a national scale in the mid-1950s, when it was finally recognized that social and economic development could no longer be left to the traditional laissez-faire policy.

Priority has been given to investments that will accelerate economic development: agriculture is being expanded and modernized, with the aim of producing raw materials for industry, and commodities to export.

[7] *Ethiopia: General Background Information,* Addis Ababa: Press and Information Department, 1958, pp. 15–16, 60–64.

# 23 THE MALAGASY REPUBLIC: ISLAND OF MADAGASCAR

*Then I raised*
*My voice and cried, "Wide Afric, doth thy sun*
*Lighten thy hills enfold a city as fair*
*As those which starred the night o' the elder world?*
*Or is the rumor—*
*A dream as frail as those of ancient time?"*

ALFRED TENNYSON

Off Africa's East Coast lies a large island whose history and peoples, like Zanzibar's, have been linked to the history and peoples of Asia, namely, Madagascar with Malaysia; it did not, however, make the impress upon Africa that Zanzibar did. Contacts generally flowed the other way; Africans moved into the island, mingling with foreigners who were probably already there and had come from the Far East; the only countermovement, from island to continent, came as enslaved people from Madagascar were carried into South Africa. Madagascar remained the land apart that it is. It lay somewhat off the regular sea routes, and because of this marginal position, it was not an intermediary of trade for the continent of Africa, nor for countries north or east across the Indian Ocean.

A varied and mixed population was already inhabiting Madagascar when in A.D. 1500 Portuguese arrived at the island. Asian peoples from the East had come, possibly by chance, "Kon Tiki" style, and stayed; the black peoples were all likely of African origin. The populating of the island, however, is a matter of controversy.

Madagascar, domain of the Malagasy Republic, is the fourth largest island in the world. With an area of 227,736 square miles, it is larger than France, larger, in fact, than any European state except the U.S.S.R.; the population is about 5.8 million. A compact island, it has a seacoast that is shorter than that of Great Britain.

It is a diverse land with a varied topography, and climatic conditions that differ considerably from one part of the island to another despite its tropical location (from about 12 to 25°S) and compactness. It is situated off the southeast coast of Africa between 250 and 500 miles distant from the continent. A long, narrow block of land oriented north-northeast and south-southwest, Madagascar is approximately 1,000 miles long and about 360 miles wide at its greatest breadth.

They call it "the Great Isle" because Madagascar, in the contrasts of its vivid topographic outlines, its climates, vegetation, and peoples, is a world in itself. Descamps called it the "Continent of the Indian Ocean."[1] It is also a kind of paradox: geographically

close to Africa, it has remained relatively apart because of the isolating influences of the channel and its insular character; and the differences in cultural practices between Madagascar and the African mainland are widening. Despite the varied nature of its peoples and their sources of origin, which were the Malay Archipelago and Africa, culturally and linguistically the islanders are nevertheless relatively homogeneous because there has been much fusion of the races. Inbred minorities of both races do exist, but it is not really possible to discern where Malaya ends and Africa begins. Malgache, their language, is Malayo-Indonesian in its base.

Some islands of the world are situated near or within the paths of world trade routes, and their interests are broad and oriented toward the universe instead of to the confinements that insularity—size and position—often imposes. Such has been the case of Zanzibar for many past centuries. The situation of Madagascar, on the other hand, has tended to exclude the island from participation in either the economic or political affairs of the rest of the world. An inhospitable coast and the retreat of the most advanced group of Malgache peoples to the central parts of the island, where for a long time they purposely isolated themselves from surrounding peoples, likewise discouraged contact. Most vessels sailing the trade routes around the Cape of Good Hope, between Europe and the Orient, bypassed Madagascar, and with the opening of the Suez Canal in 1869, the large island became even more marginal relative to ocean shipping.

## THE LAND AND THE PEOPLE

Geologically Madagascar divides into two elongate zones that run generally north and south. The rocks in the central and east portions are of the same resistant strata that underlie the African plateau; the sedimentary formations of the west are open, clayey flats that rise terracelike to considerable elevations. These clays are hard and steppelike in the dry season, but during the period of rains are speedily transformed as vegetation turns green. The plains and low plateaus of the west form a belt of lowland that is from 60 to 120 miles in width.

[1] Herbert Descamps, *Madagascar*, Paris: Berger-Levrault, 1951, p. 6.

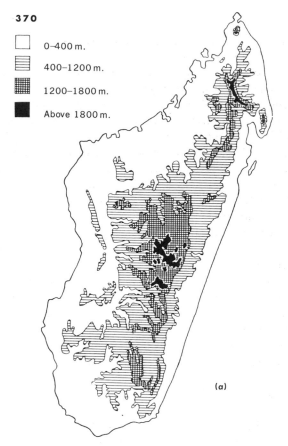

0–400 m.

400–1200 m.

1200–1800 m.

Above 1800 m.

(a)

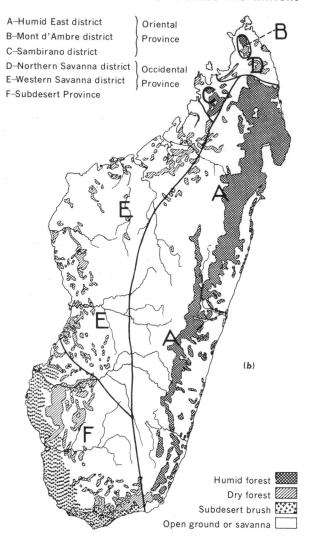

A—Humid East district ⎫ Oriental
B—Mont d'Ambre district ⎬ Province
C—Sambirano district ⎭
D—Northern Savanna district ⎫ Occidental
E—Western Savanna district ⎬ Province
F—Subdesert Province ⎭

Humid forest
Dry forest
Subdesert brush
Open ground or savanna

(b)

FIGURE 23.2 (a, above) Altitude; (b, above right) vegetation; (c, next page) physiography and railroads. (a and b from A. L. Rand, The Distribution and Habits of Madagascar Birds. Courtesy The American Museum of Natural History, New York. c from base map Physiographic Diagram of Africa, copyright A. K. Lobeck; reproduced with permission of the publisher, The Geographical Press, a division of C. S. Hammond & Company, Maplewood, N.J.)

Central Madagascar is an elevated mountain mass that extends nearly the length of the entire island, averaging 3,900 to 4,600 feet in elevation above sea level, and sloping away to the east and the west (Figure 23.2a to c). Although frequently referred to as a plateau, most of the surface is in slopes, hills, and even mountains, the highest eminences rising, in Mounts Tsaratanana, Ankaratra, and Andringtra, to over 9,400, 8,675, and 8,720 feet respectively. The eastern edge of the upland rises in a steep escarpment from a narrow coastal plain that varies from 10 to 25

to 50 miles in width, but plays out between Fénérive and the Bay of Antongil, where the highlands approach the water. The western side descends much more gradually, however, shelving off (as noted) in steplike drops to the plains along the Mozambique Channel.

Madagascar is a tropical isle, lying within the belt of the southeast trade winds—and athwart these winds, a circumstance that causes climatic belts to run north and south, and climatic differences to be expressed east and west. Four main climatic regions are to be

(c)

true throughout the island regardless of other differences in climate. Rainfall tends to be heavy, but varies east and west, and with exposure. Rain forest is the climax vegetation in this belt, and in some places along the east coast forestry is carried on.

In the central highlands elevation modifies temperatures, and the climate becomes tropical highland, comparable to that on the plateaus of East Africa. This is the second climatic belt. Vegetation (see Figure 23.2b) is a grassland savanna with mixed trees in places, or even bare ground. The third zone is along the west side and at the northern tip of the island where a truly tropical wet and dry savanna prevails; here the low-sun dry season is more pronounced than in the highlands; there is usually some rainfall in all months of the year, however. Savanna grass, parklike savanna, and in places, deciduous forests (deciduous because of the drought) comprise the vegetation; it resembles the savanna vegetation that lies adjacent to the rain forests of Congo and the Guinea coast. The fourth region is in the south. Conditions correspond to those of the dry savanna of the northern Sudan of Africa, the sahel: dry seasons are more prolonged than in the west, and precipitation is low and uncertain; vegetation is sparse. This part of the island is not an easy land in which to make a living because irregular rains produce poor pasture for animals and, at times, famines affecting both animals and human beings.

Because of the location of the island, hurricanes are a feature of the climate, especially along the eastern side where tropical cyclones typically strike once or several times every year; the western and central parts of the country are more protected from hurricanes, which move in from the east, but they are by no means free from them. Aside from the hurricanes, however, the east side of the island is characteristically a windy region—so windy that, as already noted, shipping is affected. Arab dhows are unable to put into the east coast ports; more than half of the time spent by vessels working or traveling through the waters off Madagascar is lost because of inclement weather and wave tossed seas.

The base of the Malgache economy is agriculture, in which 75 to 85 percent of the population is engaged. Over four-fifths of the people live in rural communities of less than 2,000 persons.

distinguished. The east and northwest coasts are rainy tropical, the east coast because of the effect of the trades as they strike the coast and rise against the escarpment, the northwest coast because of the "Mozambique monsoon," in the main. Heat and humidity prevail the year around, and there is little seasonal change in terms of temperature; rainfall, however, shows seasonal variations expressed in wet and less wet periods in the north and central areas, and two periods of greater rainfall at stations in the southern sector. This *patterning* of precipitation holds

FIGURE 23.3 Rural conveyance. (Photograph by Leavitt Morris, travel editor, The Christian Science Monitor. Courtesy The Christian Science Monitor.)

The systems of cultivation practiced on the island range from migratory agriculture in some parts of the eastern coastal zone, to irrigated rice (Figure 23.4) culture carried on throughout the country but heaviest in the central uplands, to animal industries which are sedentary in the west and associated with cultivation of the land to nomadic in the south, to European plantation agriculture; there are even a few forest groups, living in the eastern escarpments of the highlands, who are hunters and gatherers. Their number is exceedingly small, however.

In general, the subsistence cultivation of the Malgache peoples stands in considerable contrast to that of indigenous peoples throughout most of Africa; most of the cultivators raise wet rice in paddies,

Asian style. In the main the cultivated plots are small, although areas of large fields of wet rice occur on the uplands around Tananarive and in the Lake Alaotra basin, which lies at intermediate elevations in the east. Although rice is dominant, a considerable variety of other crops is grown by farmers for subsistence. These include cassava, yams, maize, bananas, and peanuts, all important on the continent as well.

Malgache farmers also produce a surprising number of items that they offer for sale, particularly in the local markets; the market at Tananarive (see Figure 23.1) is the most notable and one of the most striking even when compared with native markets in Africa south of the Sahara. Garden vegetables are among the cash crops raised in quantity for local market consumption, as well as a profusion of fruits, tropical, subtropical, and temperate, because the moderate tropical-oceanic climate permits the growing of a broad span of fruits and vegetables.

In terms of the amount of land devoted to the activity, livestock grazing ranks first among the pursuits by which the Malgache gain their livelihood. Madagascar is blessed by the fact that its lands are not infested with the tsetse fly, the killer insect that prohibits animal raising across millions of acres of savanna in Africa.

Madagascar has more cattle than it has people. It is estimated that the animal census of the island includes some 6,387,000 cattle, 346,000 pigs, 229,000 sheep, rabbits in unknown numbers, and poultry as follows: chickens, 13 million; ducks, 1.5 million; geese, 300,000; and turkeys, 150,000. Fowl, especially ducks, chickens, geese, and pigeons, meat from the larger livestock, and rabbits reach the markets of the country in large quantities at all times of the year.

Both Malgache and European farmers raise crops that are exported. The following are most important: coffee, which leads and makes up nearly one-third of the export value, and vanilla, sugar, rice, beans, raffia, and tobacco in that order.[2] Sixty percent of the world's vanilla comes from here. The variety of products raised on the land, both subsistence and cash crops, is greater than in most African states.

[2] Yearbook of International Trade Statistics, New York: United Nations, 1963.

**FIGURE 23.4** A checkerboard of paddy rice fields characterizes the Malagasy countryside on the way. to Lake Manlasoa. *(Photograph by Leavitt Morris, travel editor, The Christian Science Monitor. Courtesy The Christian Science Monitor.)*

Cattle are mostly zebu, and are thought to have been brought over from Africa about the ninth century. Selective breeding has been little practiced, and both on the plateau and in the south, where animals comprise the main wealth of the people, the animals are poor. Among the pastoralists in the south, as among the Bara, Antandroy, Antanosy, and Mahafaly, cattle are kept for prestige and ceremonial purposes, as is the case among many of the pastoral groups in East Africa.

Industrially, the Republic is one of the least developed African states. Industry accounts for less than 3 percent of the national income, and mining for about 1 percent.

## INTERNATIONAL ATTACHMENTS

The Malagasy Republic is an associate member of the European Economic Community. Politically, when independence came Madagascar retained ties with France, becoming a member of the French Community of Nations. As a member of the *Organisation commune africaine et malgache* (OCAM), it maintains close economic and cultural associations with the European nation and with other African states, now independent, that were a part of the French colonial empire.[3]

[3] For a good treatise on Madagascar's insular approach to regionalism, see Philip M. Allen, "Madagascar and OCAM," *Africa Report*, pp. 13–18, January, 1966.

# 24 AFTERTHOUGHTS: WINDS OF CHANGE

*. . . and God made a wind
to pass over the earth . . .*

GENESIS 8:1

Independence has come to most of Africa. By this pattern of political change—the granting of self-determination and, in some instances, the shivering of colonial territories into several pieces—the number of independent states in Africa has multiplied.

Problems of geographic size and economic structure have raised questions of a need for some form of integration. There have been many experiments with African unity, large and small blocs, bilateral, trilateral, and multilateral associations, and political, economic, cultural, and historic groupings, some overlapping one another. They form and dissolve, or form and weld; few have been very lasting. However, these attempts to integrate and to find solutions to Africa's staggering problems, the vigor of the experiments, and the vitality that they seem to instill in Africans are all important.

Among continental attempts at unity, the Organization of African Unity (OAU) appears to be one of the most viable. It emerged as a result of earlier attempts (the Pan-African congresses and the Conference of Independent African States), and has grown in strength and stature; its constitution has been hailed as an historic milestone. Its charter, adopted at Addis Ababa in 1963, set the pattern of African integration along the lines of that of the Organization of American States.

Among attempts at political unification was the federation of Senegal and Sudan (former French Soudan) to form the Mali Federation. This dissolved almost as soon as it was formed, but Sudan kept the federation name of Mali, a historic name in West Africa. The Ghana-Guinea-Mali union, announced in 1960, was not successful either, and in 1963 was declared dissolved. It was known as the Union of African States (UAS); "coolness" between the leaders of Ghana and Guinea lay at the base of this failure. Shortly after the overthrow of Nkrumah as head of Ghana by a coup early in 1966, this union was partially and one-sidedly revived when Touré, President of Guinea, declared Nkrumah the President of Guinea and Ghana, and the two countries united—an act rejected by the new government in Ghana which already had been recognized by a number of leading Western powers. The coup in Ghana followed a military coup in Nigeria by a few weeks. Twice Egypt has entered into unions with Middle East nations to form a greater United Arab Republic (UAR), and twice the federation has fallen apart.

However, some of the attempts at organic integration have succeeded, but all of these were accomplished at the hour of independence. The union of Gold Coast and the United Nations' trusteeship of British Togoland to form Ghana has endured, as has also the merger of British and Italian Somaliland into Somalia; the political affiliation of the British Northern Cameroon with Nigeria and of Southern Cameroon with the Cameroon Republic (former French Cameroun) have been lasting.

A number of broader but loose groupings have been attempted, usually on a regional or/and linguistic basis. Among them are the Pan-African Freedom Movement for East, Central, and Southern Africa (PAFMECSA), *Union Africaine et Malgache* (UAM) made up the territories of the former French empire in Africa and Rwanda, the Casablanca Group, the Inter-African and Malagasy States Organization (IAMO) or the Monrovia Group, the Associate Members of the European Common Market, and the *Organisation commune africaine et malgache* (OCAM), the economic counterpart of the UAM, which is political. Congo was admitted into OCAM in the spring of 1965. It should be noted that the two members not of the French Community are French speaking. A number of African customs unions also have evolved, as the West African Customs Union (former French West Africa), the Equatorial African Customs Union (former French Equatorial Africa), and the East African Common Services Organization (Kenya, Tanzania, and Uganda). Unification in East Africa has, in some form or other, been in existence since 1927, but in 1966 it seemingly began to fall apart.

The regional and linguistic groupings have caused debate and anxiety among the African nations not participating in them. But these integrative moves, historically and linguistically defined, have gathered strength, and as Africa began to seem to fall into "blocks," the word "Balkanization" began to be heard. Ghana while under Nkrumah was particularly forceful in its attack against the piecemealing of Africa. Egypt has been attacked for its attempt to unite with Middle Eastern states in a UAR, the feeling among black African states being that, by this act, Egypt turns its back on Africa and disclaims being African.

A sharp censure of the Arab League and Egypt by the *West African Pilot* (a newspaper owned by former President Azikiwe of Nigeria) is one among many indications of the delicate nature of the relations between Africa to the south and to the north of the Sahara. The Nigerian paper took strong exception to the League's announcement of its intention to open offices in certain West African states.

> Nigeria does not maintain relations of any sort with the [Arab] League, but we do with most individual members of the League, including its African members who never tire of selling us the political attitudes of the League. . . . it is a subtle device to involve us more directly with the frenetic politics of the Middle East. . . . African members of the League will have to decide soon where they stand. Are they in the Middle East or in Africa? They cannot honestly owe loyalties to two separate blocs on two separate continents.[1]

In the early days of his leadership in Egypt, Nasser stressed the great merit of Egypt's situation at the intersection of three circles—those encircling the African continent, the Arab world, and the Mediterranean world. The effort to function in all three worlds is, to an increasing degree, giving Egypt the appearance of being at best only peripherally African.[2] Nasser has stated that a North, East, West, and South Africa exist and that regional groupings should form along these lines. But he has also vaguely suggested, "Let there be an African League."

Is an African Commonwealth (the eventual ideal of the OAU) comprehending the entire continent possible? Diversity, which normally gives strength to a nation, in Africa is confounding the drive toward continental unity. It is not very likely that the great continent, second in size in the world and 4 times larger than the United States of America, can ever be united to form a single political state, advantageous though that might be.

There are first of all the two great divisions of the continent, Africa north and Africa south of the desert. This natural division is reinforced by the Moslem character of almost all of the peoples of the north, including the Sahara and down to a zone that runs irregularly from Senegal eastward and along the southern bounds of Nigeria's Northern Province, to Khartoum from where it bends north to the Red Sea following the Ethiopian border; Somalia is a large outlier of this Moslem world, Ethiopia a non-Moslem enclave. Language and race reinforce this line except along the southern side of the Sahara, where mixtures occur.

Verbal communication is another divider among Africans. In addition to an extraordinarily large number of African languages and dialects, there are Arabic and the Asian and European languages that prevail in various sections of the continent, the latter being the media employed at the conferences searching for unity; the only "African" languages widely known are Arabic (an import) and Swahili, the lingua franca of East Africa.

And where is the "heartland" that would link the extremities—north, south, east, and west—as do the great Central Plains of the United States? Where are "the master rivers, like our Columbia and Ohio, providing ready access through its mountains? Topographically, it is a maze—full of variety, but also of deadends."[3]

No infrastructure of transport exists. The colonial powers developed roads and railroads to serve their lands, outlets that ran straight to the shore and the sea. These spurs of communication each have their own integrity; while there may have been a sparse linkage of lines to serve a zone of colonial holdings, as British East and French West Africa, they all terminate abruptly toward the interior. The African "heartland" is void of transport connections except for such waterways as the Congo River, which curls along three edges of The Congo, and serves its river banks and the hinterlands that roads and railroads penetrate, and for such tenuous links as desert trails and roads; nor will it be simple to unify the transportation and communications systems that now exist along the edges by connecting them across that interior.

[1] Keith Kyle, "Arab League Criticized," *The Christian Science Monitor,* February, 1964.
[2] *Ibid.*

[3] George H. T. Kimble, "A 'U.S. of Africa'?—Not Very Likely," *The New York Times Magazine,* Mar. 29, 1964.

The problems of Africa indicate the need of working together. These problems have breadth and depth, are very diverse, and everywhere disregard boundaries, pointing out the need for "more than territorial if less than continental"[4] unity. Among the problems are also soil erosion, which is excessive across more than half of Africa; disease, which knows no bounds; and population increase and the widening economic differential. The solution of educational, social, and economic development problems would be more probable with cooperation.

The problems of stable government may be national, but the manifestations run across national bounds and many of them are common to many countries: one-party rule and the scramble for personal power and aggrandizement; strong tribal rivalries that surmount a "national" feeling; and military coups and the overthrow of constituted government. The coups, which after the first eruption have followed each other with growing momentum, reflect political instability and discontent, but more than this, they are perhaps signs of the changing times and growing political and national consciousness among Africans. At the height of the wave of independence in 1960, the accent was on the spirit of nationalism and anticolonialism. As time has passed, and as the concept of independence has evolved from the early excitement and glow of being free toward the realities of responsible nationhood, the trend has turned away from "isms," and the words "reconstruction" and "development" have taken their place. The "coup" appears to have moved like a contagion from country to country; it would seem that in like manner, African states can by suggestion help one another resolve their difficult and critical national-political problems.

## Africa: A "Brave New World"?

The catalog of African insolubles is of staggering length:

> True, there is another side to the picture. Here are delectable scenes to which only poetry can do justice:

scenes that stir the desire to return one day at all costs to recapture the emotion they evoke. John Dove would "give half my earthly possessions" to see once again a lovely landscape of the northern Transvaal. John Buchan found the same country "so enchanted" that he resolved "to go back in my old age, build a dwelling, and leave my bones there," . . . (But) Africa is still black indeed. The phrase 'Brightest Africa,' fashionable yesterday, is but euphemism. . . . Africa is one of the ultimate tests of . . . man's civilizing power. . . .[5]

These words of Isaiah Bowman, written in 1941, still characterize Africa, but with deeper and more varied meanings in this day of African independence than when they were written.

The whole story of modern Africa is contained within 60 or fewer years. By the last quarter of the nineteenth century, Africans still had had practically no contact with the outside world. They knew only the horrors of the slave raiders' caravans, the passing of the occasional explorer, and, in some areas, local exploitation of native labor and African resources by foreign enterprise. They had not evolved the plow or the wheel, there was no written language, no alphabet, no common tongue. The people, living in tribal groups in continual fear of their neighbors, were few in number in relation to the vast continent which they occupied. They were profoundly backward as "civilization" judges progress. They and their cattle were disease ridden, and in black Africa, the people lived primitive lives, ruled by tribal sanctions and customs based largely on ancestor worship and subject to the tyranny of the witch doctor and the authority of the spear.

They had not developed any of the necessities of a modern state: There were no roads or railroads—only trails or the waterways along which their dugouts moved; no stone buildings in the bush hinterland—only the picturesque huts that blended so indistinguishably with nature; no implements of agriculture or craft except the crudest forms produced in the Iron Age; no medical services, no hospitals, no schools had been evolved in black Africa other than the customs that were passed from parent, or headman to child, the ritualistic healing of the medicine men, the

---

[4] *Ibid.*

[5] Foreword in Richard Light, *Focus on Africa,* New York: American Geographical Society, 1941.

lessons taught for survival; and trade, where carried on, was barter. Commerce between Africans was most highly developed in the north and in West Africa, where trading expeditions for bartering products were carried out by some tribes. The heavy mass of peoples was either content, or oblivious to any other way of life, or was sunk in resignation and inertness. There were tribal village wars, but these were a part of life.

Western colonialism, with its energetic exploitation of natural and human resources, disturbed the tenor of living and the complacency of the tribes, and pricked Africa out of its somnolence. It took many decades of Western domination and exploitation, that wounded and destroyed bodies, disrupted tribal life, and broke morale, to effectively rouse the Africans; and it took many decades of European development within the continent, and contacts of Africans with European culture to bring effective changes. By now, however, Western culture has permeated more or less generally into all parts of Africa, although not equally all over.

## AFRICA: A VITAL EXPERIMENT

Africa is changing very rapidly. The old frontiers, that were staked out of bush and rain forest by the colonial powers, remain pretty much as they were then drawn. But within these bounds numerous new countries, new leaders and political parties, new governments, even new economies, have arisen.

Many of the problems that confront the people have been touched on. Formerly they were European problems; now they are African problems—or frontiers,

depending on the point of view. Rational nationalism, one-party rule and dictatorship, political coups, economics, sociological problems, and the issues of race, obsessive and haunting, are among the challenges. There is no place in the world where the living together of racial and ethnic groups must be worked out on so broad a scale as in Africa.

Here the world, in an age of instant communication, is able to observe at first hand a continent of people emerge swiftly and painfully from the confining shell of a primitive and colonial past; watch a continent shake itself awake and, in the same motion, begin to participate actively in the political, social, and economic activities of other men and other societies, all within the instant, so to speak. The telescoping of evolution into so short a period is unprecedented.

The evolution, which because of its speed is a revolution, bridges the space between the primitive cultures that are near counterparts of the Negro cultures prevalent 100 or 200 years ago, and the industrial and the political world in which all self-governing states must participate on the higher level of world government as expressed in the United Nations. There has been no time or place for a training period. The evolution that normally would develop gradually over centuries is condensed; a continent of people is trying to step out of localism and primitivism or, at the most, medievalism (in the north) into an international, ultramodern arena within a fraction of a generation's life.

# GLOSSARY

**alfa grass,** also known as esparto; a steppe grass that, in the Atlas, is exploited for paper stock.

**anticline,** arched strata that dip in opposite directions from a common axis.

**Arachnids,** large class of Arthropoda which includes scorpions, spiders, mites, and ticks.

*bidonville* (French), slum suburbs that have mushroomed along the edges of Maghrib cities; literally, "can" towns.

*bled* (Moroccan), rural backcountry.

**carrier,** normal person or one convalescing from an infectious disease who shows no signs or symptoms of disease, but who harbors and eliminates the microorganisms and so spreads the disease.

**Coloured,** in South Africa, a person of mixed European and Negroid ancestry or of Malaysian ancestry; by official definition, the Bushmen are also Coloured.

**condominium,** joint administration of a territory by two nations.

**cuesta,** a sloping plain which is terminated on one side by a steep slope.

**dolerite,** basaltic (igneous) rock.

**dolines,** natural funnel-form water tubes worn down vertically through limestone structures.

**dyke,** tabular body of igneous rock that cuts across the structure of adjacent rocks.

**East African plateau,** also known as the Lake plateau, the Lake Victoria plateau or the Nyanza plateau.

**ecumene,** the part of a country that has the closest transport net, the most industry, and the heaviest population density.

**entrepôt,** a port where goods are warehoused and from which they are again redistributed.

*erg,* term used in the Sahara, but applicable elsewhere, for sand desert.

**fellah,** Egyptian word for farmer.

**graben,** depression produced by subsidence of a strip between normal faults; downthrow along faults.

**groundnuts,** British word for peanuts.

**hammada,** desert with surface of bedrock.

**horst,** a block of the earth's crust that has been uplifted along faults relative to the rocks on either side.

**host,** the organic body upon or in which parasites live.

**isohyet,** line connecting places receiving equal amounts of rainfall.

**ITC,** Intertropical Convergence Zone.

**laccolith,** intrusive body that has domed the overlying rock strata.

**Lake Victoria,** sometimes called Victoria Nyanza.

**lopolith,** a large floored intrusive that is centrally sunken into the form of a basin.

**metric ton,** weight of 1,000 kilograms; for comparison, a long ton weighs 2,240 pounds or 1,016.06 kilograms, a short ton weighs 2,000 pounds or 907.20 kilograms.

**monadnock,** isolated hills (that stand above a plain formed by erosion) that escaped final destruction.

**mullite,** a mineral; most often observed as a synthetic mineral in ceramic products.

**netherlands,** the inland delta of the Niger; the lower Chad basin.

**orographic squeeze,** rainfall wrung out as a result of air cooling due to ascent over topographic barriers.

*palmeraie* (French), palm grove; more broadly used in North Africa to refer to luxurious irrigated garden.

**pan,** depression generally containing mud or water, but when dry (as often during a dry season) coated with a salt deposit.

**patina,** varnishlike film, red or black, that covers the surface of some hammadas.

**peneplain,** land surface worn down to almost a plain.

**plantain,** type of banana, larger, less sweet, and more starchy than the ordinary banana; never eaten raw.

**rainfall regime,** seasonal pattern of rainfall.

*reg,* gravel desert.

**ria coast,** long fjordlike bays that extend far inland.

**rift valley,** valley produced by subsidence of a strip bounded by two parallel rifts; an elongated valley formed by the depression of a block of the earth's crust between two faults or fault zones of approximately parallel strike, a graben.

**sebhka,** dry area or lake bed encrusted with salt.

**sensible temperature,** sensation of temperature that the body feels.

**shott,** closed basin occupied by shallow saline lakes.

**sill,** flat-bedded strata of hard rocks.

*souk,* market.

**subsequent valley,** valley formed by headward erosion.

**syncline,** rock fold in which strata dip inward from both sides toward axis.

**transhumance,** seasonal moving of livestock from or to the mountains.

**vadose water,** suspended water; subsurface water above the zone of saturation.

**vector,** an arthropod which carries microorganisms from a sick to a well person.

# SELECTED REFERENCES

## CHAPTERS 1 AND 2. AFRICAN LANDSCAPES AND AFRICANS

Alimen, H.: *The Prehistory of Africa,* translated by A. H. Brodrick, London: Hutchinson & Co. (Publishers), Ltd., 1957.

American African Institute, Inc. (The): *Africa Report.*

American Geographical Society (The): New York: *Geographical Review; Focus.*

American Society of Tropical Medicine and Hygiene: *American Journal of Tropical Medicine and Hygiene,* Baltimore, Md.

Association of American Geographers (The): *The Annals of the Association of American Geographers.* Lawrence, Kansas: Allen Press Inc.

Beer, George Louis: *African Questions at the Paris Peace Conference,* New York: The Macmillan Company, 1923.

Bohannon, Paul J., and George Dalton (eds.): *Markets in Africa,* Evanston, Ill.: Northwestern University Press, 1962.

Bovill, E. W.: *Golden Trade of the Moors,* Fair Lawn, N.J.: Oxford University Press, 1958.

*Bulletin de l'Institut Français d'Afrique Noire,* Dakar.

Butzer, Karl W.: *Environment and Archeology,* Chicago: Aldine Publishing Company, 1964.

*Christian Science Monitor (The),* Boston: The Christian Science Publishing Society.

Coon, Carleton S.: The *Origin of the Races,* New York: Alfred A. Knopf, Inc., 1963.

de Blij, Harm J.: *A Geography of Subsaharan Africa,* Chicago: Rand McNally & Company, 1964.

de Schlippe, Pierre: *Shifting Cultivation in Africa,* London: Routledge and Kegan Paul, Ltd., 1956.

*Economic Geography,* Worcester, Mass.: Department of Geography, Clark University.

*Encyclopédie Mensuelle d'Outre-Mer,* Paris: 3, rue Blaise-Desgoffe.

*Europe France Outremer.* Paris: 37, rue Marbeuf.

*France Outremer.* Paris: 37, rue Marbeuf.

*French Technical Bulletin.*

*Glossary of Geology and Related Sciences,* 2d ed., Washington, D.C.: American Geological Institute, 1960.

Goldschmidt, Walter (ed.): *The United States and Africa,* 2d ed., New York: Frederick A. Praeger, Inc., 1963.

Gourou, Pierre: *The Tropical World,* 3d ed., translated by E. D. Laborde, London: Longmans, Green & Co., Ltd., 1961.

Greenberg, Joseph H.: *The Languages of Africa,* Bloomington, Ind.: University of Indiana, Pub. 25 of the Indiana University Research Center in Anthropology, Folklore, and Linguistics, 1963.

———: "Studies in African Linguistic Classification," *Southwestern Journal of Anthropology* (Summer, 1947–Winter, 1954).

Haden-Guest, Stephen, John K. Wright, and Eileen M. Tetclaff: *A World Geography of Forest Resources,* New York: The Ronald Press Company, 1956.

Hailey, Lord: *An African Survey,* rev. ed., Fair Lawn, N.J.: Oxford University Press, 1957.

Hance, William A.: *African Economic Development,* New York: Harper & Row, Publishers, Incorporated, 1958.

———: *The Geography of Modern Africa,* New York: Columbia University Press, 1964.

Hanna, William John (ed.): *Independent Black Africa: The Politics of Freedom,* Chicago: Rand McNally & Company, 1964.

Hertslet, Sir E.: *Map of Africa by Treaty,* vol. II, London: H. M. Stationery Office, 1909.

Hodgkin, Thomas: *African Political Parties,* Baltimore: Penguin Books, Inc., 1961.

Hoerr, N. L., and Arthur Osol (eds.): *Blakiston's New Gould Medical Dictionary,* 2d ed., New York: McGraw-Hill Book Company, 1956.

Howell, F. Clark, and Francois Bourliere: *African Ecology and Human Evolution,* Chicago: Aldine Publishing Company, 1963.

*Industries et Travaux d'Outremer.* Paris: 37, rue Marbeuf.

International African Institute: *Africa,* London.

*International Conciliation,* New York: Carnegie Endowment for International Peace.

Jones, William O.: *The Food and Agricultural Economies of Tropical Africa,* Food Research Institute Study, Stanford, Calif.: Stanford University Press, 1961.

*Journal of Modern African Studies,* London: Cambridge University Press.

Kimble, George H. T.: *Tropical Africa,* vols. I and II, New York: The Twentieth Century Fund, 1960.

Langer, William L.: *Diplomacy of Imperialism,* New York: Alfred A. Knopf, Inc., 1951.

———: *European Alliances and Alignments,* New York: Alfred A. Knopf, Inc., 1952.

Lobeck, A. K.: *Physiographic Diagram of Africa,* Maplewood, N.J.: Hammond, Incorporated, 1946.

Lorimer, Frank: *Demographic Information on Tropical Africa,* Boston: Boston University Press, 1961.

Manson-Bahr, Sir Philip H.: *Manson's Tropical Diseases,* 13th ed., Baltimore: The Williams and Wilkins Company, 1950.

*Minerals Yearbook,* U.S. Bureau of Mines, U.S. Department of Interior.

Murdock, George Peter: *Africa: Its Peoples and Their Culture History,* New York: McGraw-Hill Book Company, 1959.

*New York Times (The),* New York: The New York Times Co.

Oliver, Roland, and J. D. Fage: *A Short History of Africa,* New York: New York University Press, 1963.

Ottenberg, Simon, and Phoebe Ottenberg (eds.): *Culture and Societies of Africa,* New York: Random House, Inc., 1960.

*Overseas Review,* London: Barclays Bank D.C.O.

*Réaliteés Africaines.*

Rensch, Bernhard: *Evolution above the Species Level,* New York: Columbia University Press, 1960.

Royal African Society: *African Affairs,* London.

Royal Geographical Society (The): *Geographical Journal,* London: Unilever House.

*Sabena Revue,* Brussels: Sabena.

Shattuck, George Cheever: *Diseases of the Tropics,* New York: Appleton-Century-Crofts, Inc., 1951.

Simmons, J. S., T. F. Whayne, G. W. Anderson, H. M. Horack, and Ruth A. Thomas (associate author): *Global Epidemiology,* vol. II: *Africa and the Adjacent Islands,* Philadelphia: J. B. Lippincott Company, 1951.

Stamp, L. Dudley: *Africa,* 2d ed., New York: John Wiley & Sons, Inc., 1963.

Trewartha, Glenn T., *The Earth's Problem Climates,* Madison, Wis.: The University of Wisconsin Press, 1961.

United Africa Company, Ltd. (The): *Statistical and Economic Review,* London: Unilever House.

United Nations: *Demographic Yearbook,* New York.

————: *Economic Survey of Africa since 1950,* New York, 1959.

————: *Economic Bulletin of Africa,* New York.

————: *Industrial Growth in Africa: A Survey and Outlook,* Addis Ababa, December, 1962.

————: *Production Yearbook,* Food and Agriculture Organization of the United Nations, Rome: FAO.

————: *Report on the Possibilities of African Rural Development in Relation to Economic and Social Growth,* Rome: FAO, 1961.

————: *Statistical Yearbook,* New York.

————: *Yearbook of International Trade Statistics,* New York.

U.S. Bureau of Mines: *Minerals Yearbook.*

U.S. Department of Commerce: World Trade Information, *Economic Reports.*

Wernstedt, Frederick L.: *World Climatic Data: Africa,* University Park, Pa.: Department of Geography, Pennsylvania State University, circa 1960.

Willis, Bailey: "Continental Genesis," Bulletin of the Geological Society of America, Washington, D.C., vol. XL, Mar. 30, 1929, pp. 281–336.

————: *East African Plateaus and Rift Valleys,* Washington, D.C.: Carnegie Institution of Washington, 1936.

*World Weather Records, 1941–1950,* U.S. Weather Bureau, 1959.

## CHAPTERS 3 TO 5. REALM OF THE MAGHRIB

Barbour, Nevill: *A Survey of North West Africa (The Maghrib),* Fair Lawn, N.J.: Oxford University Press, 1959.

Capot-Rey, Robert: *Le Sahara Français,* Paris: Presses universitaires de France, 1953.

Coindreau, Roger, and Charles Penz: *Le Maroc,* Paris: Société d'Editions Géographique, Maritimes, et Coloniales, 1949.

Despois, Jean: *La Tunisie Orientale,* Algiers: Faculté des Lettres, 1955.

————: *La Tunisie: Ses Régions,* Paris: Librarie Armand Colin, 1961.

Gautier, Émile-Felix: *Sahara, the Great Desert,* translated by Dorothy F. Mayhew, New York: Columbia University Press, 1935.

Lockwood, Agnese N.: "Libya: Building a Desert Economy," *International Conciliation,* no. 512, March, 1957.

Mikesell, Marvin W.: *Northern Morocco: A Cultural Geography,* Berkeley, Calif.: University of California Press, 1961.

*Oil and Gas Journal,* Tulsa, Okla.: The Petroleum Company.

Raymond, André: *La Tunisie,* Paris: Presses universitaires de France, 1961.

République Islamique de Mauritanie: *Mauritanie,* Paris: Éditions Diloutremer.

Secretariat of State for Information of the Tunisian Government: *Tunisia Works,* Tunis, 1960.

*The Lamp,* New York: Standard Oil Company (New Jersey).

Thomas, Benjamin: *Trade Routes of Algeria and the Sahara,* Berkeley, Calif.: University of California Press, 1957.

Villard, Henry S.: *Libya: The New Arab Kingdom in North Africa,* Ithaca, N.Y.: Cornell University Press, 1956.

von Grunebaum, Gustave E. (ed.): *Unity and Variety in Muslim Civilization,* Chicago: The University of Chicago Press, 1955.

White, Gilbert F.: *The Future of Arid Lands,* Washington, D.C., American Association for the Advancement of Science, 1956.

Zartman, I. William: *Problems of New Power, Morocco,* New York: Atherton Press, 1964.

———: "The Sahara: Bridge or Barrier," *International Conciliation,* no. 541, January, 1963.

## CHAPTERS 6 TO 8. LANDS OF THE NILE

Barbour, K. M.: *Republic of the Sudan,* London: University of London Press, Ltd., 1961.

Cressey, George B.: *Crossroads,* Philadelphia: J. B. Lippincott Company, 1960.

Eaton, Frank M.: "Irrigation Agriculture along the Nile and the Euphrates," *The Scientific Monthly,* vol. LXIX, pp. 34–42, July, 1949.

Gaitskell, Arthur: *Gezira: A Story of Development in the Sudan,* London: Faber & Faber, Ltd., 1959.

Harbison, Frederick, and Ibrahim Abdelkader Ibrahim: *Human Resources for Egyptian Enterprise,* New York: McGraw-Hill Book Company, 1959.

———: "Two Centers of Arab Power," *Foreign Affairs,* vol. XXVII, pp. 672–685, July, 1959.

Hurst, H. E.: *A Short Account of the Nile Basin,* Cairo: Government Press, 1944.

———: *The Nile,* London: Constable & Co., Ltd., 1952.

Krotki, Karol Josef: *First Population Census of Sudan, 1955/1956: 21 Facts about the Sudanese,* Khartoum: Ministry for Social Affairs, Population Census Office, 1958.

Kuper, Hilda: *Urbanization and Migration in West Africa,* Berkeley, Calif.: University of California Press, 1965.

Lebon, J. H. G.: "Control and Utilization of the Nile Waters: A Problem of Political Geography," *Review* of the Geographical Institute of the University of Istanbul (international edition), no. 6, Istanbul, 1960.

Moorehead, Alan: *The Blue Nile,* New York: Harper & Row, Publishers, Incorporated, 1962.

———: *The White Nile,* New York: Harper & Row, Publishers, Incorporated, 1960.

*Oxford Regional Economic Atlas, the Middle East and North Africa,* Fair Lawn, N.J.: Oxford University Press, 1960.

*Population of Sudan: Report on the Sixth Annual Conference,* Khartoum: Philosophical Society of Sudan (in conjunction with the Department of Statistics, Government of Sudan), January, 1958.

Platt, Raye R., and Mohammed B. Hefny: *Egypt: A Compendium,* New York: The American Geographical Society, 1958.

Schlippe, Pierre de: *Shifting Cultivation in Africa: the Zande System of Agriculture,* London: Routledge and Kegan Paul, Ltd., 1956.

*Sudan Almanac,* Khartoum: The Republic of the Sudan.

*Sudan Notes and Records,* Khartoum: Philosophical Society of the Sudan.

Sudan, Republic of, Department of Agriculture: *Agricultural Statistics.*

## CHAPTERS 9 TO 12. WEST AFRICAN REALM

Boateng, E. A.: *A Geography of Ghana,* London: Cambridge University Press, 1960.

Buchanan, Keith M., and John C. Pugh: *Land and People in Nigeria,* London: University of London Press, Ltd., 1955.

Church, R. J. Harrison: *West Africa,* 2d ed., London: Longmans, Green & Co., Ltd., 1961.

Cox-George, Noah A.: *Finance and Development in West Africa,* London: Dobson, 1961.

Fage, J. D.: *An Introduction to the History of West Africa,* London: Cambridge University Press, 1961.

Foltz, William J.: *From French West Africa to the Mali Federation,* New Haven, Conn.: Yale University Press, 1965.

Forde, Daryll, and Richenda Scott: *The Native Economies of Nigeria,* London: Faber & Faber, Ltd., 1946.

Galletti, R., et al.: *Nigerian Cocoa Farmers,* Fair Lawn, N.J.: Oxford University Press, 1955.

Galloy, Pierre, Yvon Vincent, and Maurice Forget: *Nomades et paysans d'Afrique noire occidentale,* Nancy: Faculté des Lettres et des Sciences humaines de l'Université de Nancy, 1963.

Hawkins, Edward K.: *Road Transport in Nigeria: A Study of African Enterprise.* Fair Lawn, N.J.: Oxford University Press, 1958.

Institut Français d'Afrique Noire (le), Dakar.

Johnston, Bruce F.: *The Staple Food Economies of Western Tropical Africa,* Stanford, Calif.: Stanford University Press, 1958.

Kup, Peter: *A History of Sierra Leone, 1400–1787,* London: Cambridge University Press, 1962.

*Nigeria Handbook of Commerce and Industry, 1960,*

Lagos: The Federal Ministry of Commerce and Industry, September, 1961.

*Nigeria Trade Journal,* Lagos: Federal Ministry of Information.

Petch, George A.: *Economic Development and Modern West Africa,* London: University of London Press, Ltd., 1961.

Taylor, Wayne Chatfield: *The Firestone Operations in Liberia.* Fifth Case Study in a National Planning Commission Series on *United States Business Performance Abroad,* Washington, D.C., 1956.

Thompson, Virginia, and Richard Adloff: *French West Africa,* Stanford, Calif.: Stanford University Press, 1957.

*Volta River Project,* Report of the Preparatory Commission, vols. I–III, London: H. M. Stationery Office, 1956.

Welland, James: *The Great Sahara,* New York: E. P. Dutton & Co., Inc., 1965.

## CHAPTERS 13 TO 15. EQUATORIAL AFRICA

Cahen, L.: *Geologie du Congo Belge,* Liège, Belgium: Imprimerie H. Vaillant-Carmanne, S.A., 1954.

Hance, William A., and Irene S. van Dongen, "Gabon and Its Main Gateways: Libreville and Port Gentil," *Tijdschrift voor Economie en Societie Geografie,* pp. 286–295, November, 1961.

"Mise en valeur de l'Afrique Equatoriale (la)," *Réalités Africaines,* July, 1956.

Merriam, Alan: *Congo: Background of Conflict,* Evanston, Ill.: Northwestern University Press, 1961.

Maurice, Robert: *Le Congo Physique,* Liège: H. Vaillant-Carmanne, S.A., Imprimerie de l'Académie, 1946.

"Plantations in Africa," *Statistical and Economic Review* of The United Africa Company, London: Unilever House, March, 1952.

Thompson, Virginia, and Richard Adloff: *The Emerging States of French Equatorial Africa,* Stanford, Calif.: Stanford University Press, 1960.

Trewartha, Glenn T.: *The Earth's Problem Climates,* Madison, Wis.: The University of Wisconsin Press, 1961.

——— and Wilber Zelinsky: "Population Patterns in Tropical Africa," *The Annals of the Association of American Geographers,* vol. XXIV, no. 2, pp. 135–162, June, 1954.

Veatch, A. C.: *Evolution of the Congo Basin,* Washington, D.C.: Geological Society of America, 1935.

## CHAPTERS 16 TO 19. SOUTHERN AFRICAN REALM

Carter, Gwendolyn M.: *The Politics of Inequality,* London: Thames and Hudson, 1958.

Cole, Monica M.: *South Africa,* New York: E. P. Dutton & Co., Inc., 1961.

de Kiewiet, C. W.: *Imperial Factor in South Africa,* London: Cambridge University Press, 1937.

———: "Loneliness in the Beloved Country," *Foreign Affairs,* pp. 413–427, April, 1964.

Duffy, James: *Portuguese Africa,* Cambridge, Mass.: Harvard University Press, 1959.

du Toit, Alex L.: *The Geology of South Africa,* 3d ed., Edinburgh: Oliver & Boyd, Ltd., 1954.

Hammond, Richard J.: *Portugal's African Problem: Some Economic Facets,* New York: Carnegie Endowment for International Peace, Occasional Paper no. 2, 1962.

*Modern Practices in Diamond Mining in Southern Africa,* Johannesburg: South African Institute of Mining and Metallurgy, 1961.

*Natal Official Yearbook,* Cape Town: R. Beerman.

*Optima,* Johannesburg: Anglo-American Corporation of South Africa, Ltd.

*South African Digest,* Pretoria: Department of Information.

*South African Railway News,* Johannesburg: Public Relations Section, South African Railways.

*South African Scope,* New York: Information Service of South Africa.

*South African Sugar Year Book,* Durban: The South African Sugar Journal.

*State of the Union Year Book for South Africa,* Johannesburg: Da Gama Publications.

*Summary of the Report of the Commission for the Socio-economic Development of the Bantu Areas within the Union of South Africa,* Pretoria: Government Printer, 1955.

*Survey of Wine Growing in South Africa, 1959–1960,* Paarl, South Africa: Public Relations Department, K.W.V., 1960.

*Swaziland, Report for the Year,* London: Commonwealth Relations Office.

Talbot, A. M., and W. J. Talbot (eds.): *Atlas of South Africa,* Pretoria: Government Printer, 1961.

Union of South Africa, Bureau of Census and Statistics: *Union Statistics for 50 Years,* Pretoria: Government Printer, 1960.

———, Department of Mines, Geological Survey: *Mineral Resources of the Union of South Africa,* Pretoria: Government Printer.

van Dongen, Irene S.: "Angola," *Focus,* vol. VII, no. 2, October, 1956.

———: "Cabinda Enclave, Angola: Its Economy and Shipping Points," Technical Report Cu 16-61-Nonr 266 (29) Geography, New York: Division of Economic Geography, Columbia University, 1961.

———: "The Port of Luanda in the Economy of Angola," Separata do Boletim da Sociedade de Geographia de Lisboa, pp. 3–43, January–March, 1960.

Wellington, John H.: *Southern Africa,* vols. I and II, London: Cambridge University Press, 1955.

Williams, Owen: "Sugar Growing and Processing in the Union of South Africa," *Economic Geography,* vol. XXXV, no. 4, pp. 356–366, October, 1959.

*Wine Grower in South Africa,* Paarl, South Africa: Cooperative Wine Growers Association of South Africa, Ltd.

Wohlgemuth, Patricia: "The Portuguese Territories and the United Nations," *International Conciliation,* no. 545, November, 1963.

Young, Bruce S.: "High Commission Territories of Southern Africa," *Focus,* vol. XIV, no. 4, December, 1963.

Yudelman, Montague: *Africans on the Land,* Cambridge, Mass.: Harvard University Press, 1964.

Lipsky, George A.: *Ethiopia,* New Haven, Conn.: Hraf Press, 1962.

Long, A.: "Internal Transport Developments in East Africa," *Geography,* vol. L, part I, pp. 78–82, January, 1965.

Luther, Ernest W.: *Ethiopia Today,* Stanford, Calif.: Stanford University Press, 1958.

Moffett, J. P.: *Handbook of Tanganyika,* 2d ed., Dar es Salaam: Government of Tanganyika, 1958.

Pankhurst, Sylvia: *Ethiopia, A Cultural History,* Woodford Green, Essex, England: Lalibela House, 1955.

Simoons, Frederick J.: *Northwest Ethiopia, Peoples and Economy,* Madison, Wis.: The University of Wisconsin Press, 1960.

*Tanganyika Notes and Records,* Dar es Salaam: Tanganyika Society.

Touval, Saadia: *Somali Nationalism,* Cambridge, Mass.: Harvard University Press, 1963.

van Dongen, Irene S.: "Sea Fisheries and Fish Ports in Angola," *Separata do Boletim da Sociedade de Geografia de Lisboa,* pp. 3–30, January–June, 1962.

White, F.: *The Abyssinian Dispute,* London: League of Nations Union, 1935.

Yudelman, Montague: *Africans on the Land,* Cambridge, Mass.: Harvard University Press, 1964.

## CHAPTERS 20 TO 23. THE EAST AFRICAN REALM

Beard, Peter H.: *The End of the Game,* New York: The Viking Press, Inc., 1963.

Bennett, Norman R.: *Studies in East African History,* Boston: Boston University Press, 1963.

Coupland, Reginald: *East Africa and Its Invaders,* Fair Lawn, N.J.: Oxford University Press, 1938.

———: *The Exploitation of East Africa, 1856–1890,* London: Faber & Faber, Ltd., 1939.

Freeman-Grenville, G. S. P.: *The East African Coast,* Fair Lawn, N.J.: Oxford University Press, 1962.

Fullard, Harold (ed.): *Philips' Modern College Atlas of Africa,* London: George Philip & Son, Ltd., 1959.

Jésman, Czeslaw: *The Ethiopian Paradox,* London: Institute of Race Relations, Oxford University Press, 1963.

## CHAPTER 24. WINDS OF CHANGE

Ashford, Douglas E.: *The Elusiveness of Power: The African Single Party State,* Ithaca, N.Y.: Center for International Studies, Cornell University, 1965.

Boutros-Ghali, Boutros: "The Addis Ababa Charter," *International Conciliation,* no. 546, January, 1964.

Currie, David P. (ed.): *Federalism and the New Nations of Africa,* Chicago: The University of Chicago Press, 1964.

*Foreign Affairs,* New York: Council on Foreign Relations, Inc.

Hodgkin, Thomas: *African Political Parties,* Baltimore: Penguin Books, Inc., 1961.

Williams, Chancellor: *The Rebirth of African Civilization,* Washington, D.C.: Public Affairs Press, 1961.

# INDEX

# DATE DUE

| DATE DUE | | | |
|---|---|---|---|
| MAY 1 '69 | | | |
| MAY 2 '69 | | | |
| MAY 8 | | | |
| MAY 13 | | | |
| JAN 28 '75 | | | |
| OCT 17 '78 | | | |
| OCT 17 '79 | | | |
| JUL 24 '79 | | | |
| DEC 27 1983 | | | |
| JAN 3 1984 | | | |
| JAN 24 '84 | | | |
| B 13 1984 | | | |
| MAR 11 '86 | | | |
| MAY 8 '91 | | | |
| MAY 2 '92 | | | |
| DEC 09 1997 | | | |
| GAYLORD | | | PRINTED IN U.S.A. |